ANNUAL REVIEW OF
NMR SPECTROSCOPY

Volume 2

ANNUAL REVIEW OF
NMR SPECTROSCOPY

Edited by

E. F. MOONEY

Department of Chemistry, The University, Birmingham, England

Volume 2

ACADEMIC PRESS
London and New York
1969

ACADEMIC PRESS INC. (LONDON) LTD.
Berkeley Square House
Berkeley Square,
London, W1X 6BA

U.S. Edition published by

ACADEMIC PRESS INC.
111 Fifth Avenue,
New York, New York 10003

Library of Congress Catalog Card Number: 68–17678

PRINTED IN GREAT BRITAIN BY
WILLIAM CLOWES & SONS, LIMITED,
LONDON AND BECCLES.

LIST OF CONTRIBUTORS

P. BLADON, *Department of Pure and Applied Chemistry, University of Strathclyde, Glasgow, Scotland*

R. A. DWEK, *Physical Chemistry Laboratory, University of Oxford, England*

W. G. HENDERSON, *Department of Chemistry, University of Birmingham, P.O. Box 363, Birmingham 15, England*

T. D. INCH, *Chemical Defence Experimental Establishment, Porton Down, Nr. Salisbury, Wiltshire, England*

E. F. MOONEY, *Department of Chemistry, University of Birmingham, P.O. Box 363, Birmingham 15, England*

J. F. NIXON, *The Chemical Laboratory, University of Sussex, Brighton, Sussex, England*

A. PIDCOCK, *The Chemical Laboratory, University of Sussex, Brighton, Sussex, England*

R. E. RICHARDS, F.R.S., *Physical Chemistry Laboratory, University of Oxford, England*

J. RONAYNE, *University Chemical Laboratory, Cambridge, England*

D. TAYLOR, *Physical Chemistry Laboratory, University of Oxford, England*

D. H. WILLIAMS, *University Chemical Laboratory, Cambridge, England*

P. H. WINSON, *Department of Chemistry, University of Birmingham, P.O. Box 363, Birmingham 15, England*

ACKNOWLEDGMENTS

For permission to reproduce, in whole or in part, certain figures and diagrams we are grateful to the following publishers—

American Chemical Society; American Institute of Physics; The Chemical Society; Elsevier Publishing Company; Gauthier-Villars; Masson et Cie; National Research Council of Canada; Pergamon Press Ltd; Redaktion der Zeitschrift für Naturforschung; The Royal Society; Société Chimique de France; Taylor and Francis Ltd.

Detailed acknowledgments are given in the legends to figures.

PREFACE

From the encouraging comments, that I have received from so many colleagues, I believe that *Annual Review of NMR Spectroscopy* has found a useful place in many laboratories. I hope therefore that these volumes will continue to assist chemists in keeping abreast with the ever increasing application of NMR Spectroscopy to chemical problems.

Any Editor, in deciding upon the special topics to be included in a Volume is liable to criticism. In this Volume the obvious bias to nuclei, other than proton, may possibly lead to such criticism. However, it will be clear from the content of the chapters that these subjects are not only receiving considerable attention but that the application of the study of these nuclei to the elucidation of structural problems is increasing.

Possibly one of the most difficult tasks each year is that of writing the General Review of Proton Magnetic Resonance because of the enormous number of papers dealing with such a wide variety of topics. However, I hope the more specialized chapters dealing with specific topics of proton NMR will help to broaden these aspects. The advent of sensitivity enhancement devices has clearly spurred the spectroscopist to make greater use of carbon-13 satellite spectra. The numerous references, to these satellite spectra, contained in this Volume will undoubtedly encourage chemists to make use of the information contained therein.

While the Nuclear Overhauser effect is not of general application in most laboratories, the authoritative article on this subject will clarify many misconceptions of ideas associated with this technique.

The tabulation of the phosphorus-31 data of co-ordination compounds and of boron-11 data of boron compounds, and their complexes, will be particularly useful to those working in these fields.

I must thank all the contributors to this present Volume for the care and attention given to preparing their manuscripts that has made my task such a pleasure. I would also like to thank the many authors of original papers for their kind permission to reproduce the figures included in this Volume. Finally I must express my sincere appreciation to all my friends and colleagues for their ever continuing encouragement.

ERIC F. MOONEY

Birmingham,
November, 1968

Errata for Volume 1

p. 26. The chemical shifts were omitted from structure **105** which should be as shown:

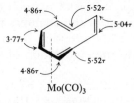

105

p. 98, column 2. For "[AA′]₂X" read "[[AA′]₂X]".

p. 107, lines 12, 16, 17. For "λ_ψ" read "$\lambda\psi$".

p. 111, penultimate line. For "Fig. 2" read "Fig. 4a".

p. 117, line 3. For "(Fig. 1c)" read "(see p. 114)".

p. 131, line 16. For "row" read "column".

p. 265, line 6. For "4*H*-pentafluoroterphenyl" read "4*H*-perfluoro-terphenyl".

p. 298, Table XXXIV. Part of the structures have been omitted. The first column should read from top to bottom:

$(CF_3)_2NF$, $(CF_3)_2NCl$, $(CF_3)_2NBr$ and $(CF_3)_2NI$.

CONTENTS

General Review of Proton Magnetic Resonance

PETER BLADON

Nuclear Magnetic Resonance Spectroscopy in the Study of Carbohydrates and Related Compounds

T. D. INCH

Solvent Effects in Proton Magnetic Resonance Spectroscopy

J. RONAYNE AND DUDLEY H. WILLIAMS

Nitrogen Magnetic Resonance Spectroscopy

E. F. MOONEY AND P. H. WINSON

Carbon-13 Nuclear Magnetic Resonance Spectroscopy:
Carbon-13 Chemical Shifts and Coupling Constants

E. F. MOONEY AND P. H. WINSON

Boron-11 Nuclear Magnetic Resonance Spectroscopy

W. G. HENDERSON AND E. F. MOONEY

Nuclear Electron Double Resonance in Liquids

R. A. DWEK, R. E. RICHARDS AND D. TAYLOR

Phosphorus-31 Nuclear Magnetic Resonance Spectra of Co-ordination Compounds

J. F. NIXON AND A. PIDCOCK

General Review of Proton Magnetic Resonance

PETER BLADON

Department of Pure and Applied Chemistry,
The University of Strathclyde, Glasgow, Scotland

I. INTRODUCTION

DURING the period under review (1967 and early 1968) the number of publications on the techniques and applications of high-resolution n.m.r. has continued to grow at an increased rate, and although work

1

on nuclei other than hydrogen occupies an increasing proportion of the total, proton n.m.r. is still pre-eminent. The impossible task of reviewing here all of this output will not be attempted; instead, salient new techniques and significant applications of established methods will be covered. Papers that, although not specifically concerned with p.m.r., describe generally applicable techniques and principles, and that are not dealt with elsewhere in this book, will be covered, but wide-line n.m.r. and "high-resolution" studies on solid-state materials are excluded.

II. NEW TECHNIQUES

In two papers[1,2] workers at Varian Associates Analytical Instrument Division, describe several methods for increasing the effective resolution of n.m.r. instruments (at the expense of decreased signal–noise ratio). All of the methods are illustrated by reference to the case of 3-bromo-thiophene-2-aldehyde (1) in which a small (0·05 c./sec.)

H_4 Br

H_5 S   CHO
1

coupling is present between the aldehyde proton and H_4. The first three methods[1] depend on manipulation of the normal output of the spectrometer by computer techniques (curve fitting, convolution, Fourier transform of transient response spectrum); subtraction of a proportion of the second derivative is the fourth method, which can be done by suitable networks attached to the spectrometer itself. The second paper[2] describes several double-resonance methods, which for their effect rely on the fact that although the n.m.r. sample as a whole is in an inhomogeneous field (the limitation of resolution), application of a weak second r.f. field to the sample may be used to enhance resolution provided it is weak enough only to excite that portion of the sample which is very close to the resonance condition.

The whole subject of signal enhancement and the related problem of resolution enhancement in magnetic resonance has been reviewed by Ernst[3] and Hall,[3a] and the subject of spectral line shapes in the context of magnetic resonance is discussed by Petrakis.[4] Double resonance employing strong decoupling fields, using vinyl acetate as an example,[5] and computer programmes for calculating double-resonance spectra[6] have been described.

A new and little understood technique that is worthy of attention is "chemically induced dynamic nuclear polarization" (CIDNP). A hexane–ether solution containing n-butyl-lithium, n-butyl bromide and diphenylacetylene, gives a transient spectrum resembling that of but-1-ene in which *some* of the lines are inverted. The authors ascribe the phenomena to the presence of free-radical intermediates, although the lines show no evidence of broadening due to paramagnetic induced relaxation.[7] See also ref. 7a.

A considerable interest in spectra of partially oriented molecules is evidenced by a spate of papers dealing with spectra in liquid crystal (nematic phase) solvents. Among molecules examined are: cyclopropane and cyclobutane;[8] s-trioxane;[9] cyclobutadiene iron tricarbonyl;[10] methyl fluoride;[11] and ethyl iodide.[12] Difficulties associated with reference compounds in this field are discussed,[13] and also the conventional ideas about magnetic equivalence which need to be modified when dealing with oriented molecules.[14] A closer understanding of the nature of the nematic phase and the cholesteric phase results from the observation that a liquid crystal mixture of 0·344 g of cholesteryl myristate and 0·655 g of cholesteryl chloride at 40°C used as a solvent allows the spectrum of oriented benzene to be obtained. Neither solvent alone behaves in this way. In the mixture, the opposed right-handed and left-handed spiral arrangements of the cholesteric phases cancel out and give a nematic phase.[15] The difficulties of elevated temperatures associated with working with the more usual nematic phases (e.g., p,p'-di-n-hexyloxyazoxybenzene) may be overcome by using a mixture of 36–42% sodium decylsulphonate, 4–7% decyl alcohol, and 4–7% sodium sulphate in deuterium oxide.[16] This gives a nematic phase between 10° and 75°C, and has been used to obtain a spectrum of oriented methanol.

The benefits of working with superconducting magnet n.m.r. instruments operating at a proton frequency of 220 Mc./sec. has been applied to work on proteins: differences in the spectra of native and denatured forms of ribonuclease, lysozyme, and cytochrome c have been detected,[17] and nearest-neighbour base frequency ratios have been determined in single stranded DNA.[18]

III. CHEMICAL-SHIFT EFFECTS

A. Anisotropy of bonds and systems (other than aromatic)

Evidence has been adduced[19] to show that the currently held views of the anisotropy associated with the carbonyl group (2) are incorrect, and that (3) is more correct (+ indicates shielding, − denotes

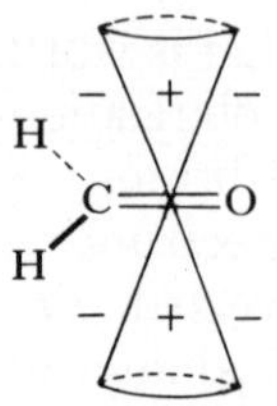

2 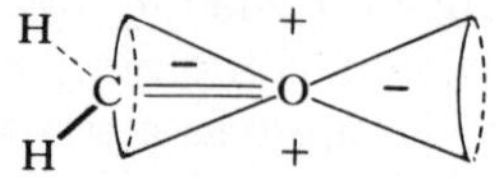   3

deshielding). This follows *inter alia* from comparisons of the chemical shifts of the α protons in (**4**, R = Me) and (**4**, R = t-Bu); in these compounds it is known[20] that the proportions of rotamers (**5A**) increases, and (**5B**) decreases as R goes from Me to t-Bu. The upfield shift of the α protons in going from (**4**, R = Me) to (**4**, R = t-Bu) can only be accommodated by the newer model.

$R \cdot CH_2 \cdot CHO$

4   **5A** 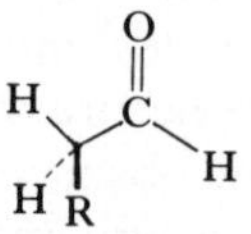   **5B**

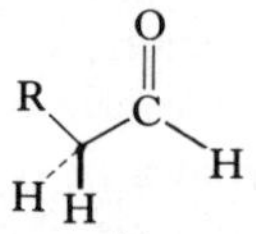

ApSimon and co-workers[21] have modified the McConnell equation[22] to allow the calculation of the screening effects of C—C and C—H bonds at nuclei relatively close to them; new values of the anisotropy constants for these bonds are given. A new treatment of the C═C bond by these workers[23] takes account of the complete anisotropy of this bond (i.e., three magnetic susceptibilities must be used). The idea usually adopted for shielding cones of C═C bonds is rejected; instead it is pointed out that deshielding of nuclei occurs only within a restricted region at the ends of the bonds, elsewhere nuclei either in or out of the plane of the double bond being shielded. Calculations based on these considerations[24] are applied in the diterpene series.

The anisotropy of the oximido-group has been studied;[25,26] the effect is due largely to the OH group causing a deshielding of neighbouring protons and not to the lone pair of electrons on the nitrogen atom (compare compounds (**6**), (**7**) and (**8**)). The anisotropy of cyclobutanes[27] (in pinane derivatives) and of heterocyclic nitrosoamines[28] has been reported.

A neighbouring-group effect of an acetyl group[29] has been cited: an equatorial proton adjacent to an axial tertiary OH group is shifted 1·1 p.p.m. downfield on acetylation of the latter. Shielding of the 3-*endo* proton in norbornene derivatives (**9**) due to the presence of a 2-*endo*-CH_2X substituent is reported:[30] the high-field shift (relative

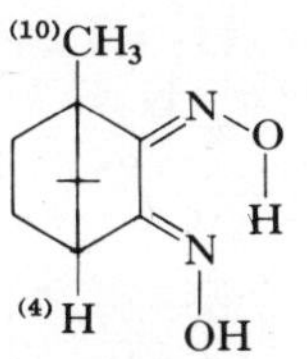

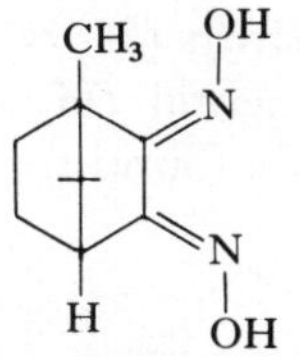

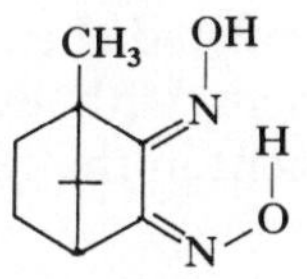

(10−CH_3)	9·01 τ	
(4−H)	6·93 τ	
6		

8·68 τ
7·01 τ
7

8·69 τ
7·62 τ
8

to 3-*endo*-H in norbornene) is correlated with the Pauling electro-negativity of X (SPh, Br, Cl, OH). A similar series of compounds was studied by Simon and co-workers,[31] who also give the following equation for the change (Δv) in chemical shift of a hydrogen atom when a hydrogen on an adjacent carbon atom is replaced by methyl (**10 → 11**)—

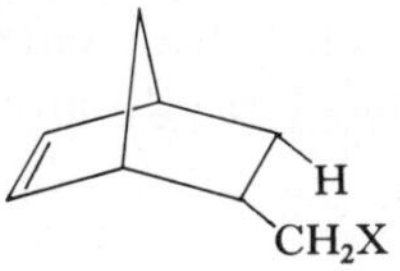

$$\Delta v(\text{c./sec.}) = v_H(\mathbf{11}) - v_H(\mathbf{10})$$
$$= 55\cdot92R \text{ (Angstroms)} - 173\cdot51$$

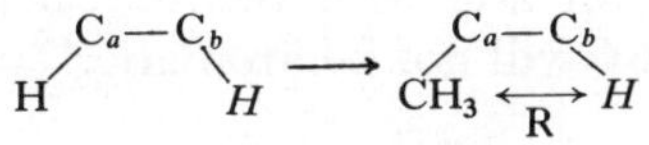

B. Anisotropy due to aromatic systems: aromaticity, anti-aromaticity, ring-current phenomena, etc.

During 1967 the proceedings of an international symposium on Aromaticity, held in 1966, were published.[32] The use of n.m.r. spectroscopy as one (if indeed not the best) method of establishing aromaticity is amply borne out by the articles in this collection, which will serve as a source book for much of the early work. Of particular interest are the articles by Sondheimer and his co-workers on the annulenes[33] and Longuet-Higgins on antiaromaticity and paramagnetic ring currents in [4n]-annulenes.[34] Experimental demonstration of antiaromaticity is provided by Sondheimer[33, 35] in the [12]- and [24]-annulenes. Calculations of the ring current based on the one-dimensional electron gas model for cyclic polyenes[36] of the non-Huckel type predict antiaromatic ring currents, and this has been confirmed for [16]-annulene.[36] LCAO-MO calculations[37] on biphenylene (**12**) and benzobiphenylene (**13**) predict relatively small diamagnetic ring currents (+0·563) and large paramagnetic ring currents (−1·028; benzene = +1) for the 6- and 4-membered rings, respectively. For (**12**), the calculated chemical shifts ($H_1 = 3\cdot338\ \tau$; $H_2 = 3\cdot244\ \tau$) are in good agreement with experimental ($H_1 = 3\cdot402\ \tau$; $H_2 = 3\cdot298\ \tau$). Similar agreement in the results is found for (13).

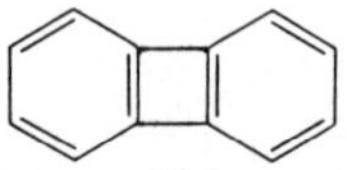

12 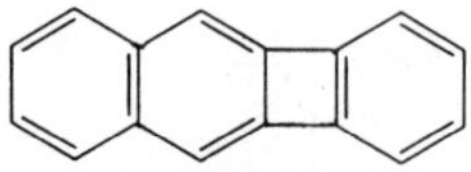   13

Dehydroannulenes reported by Sondheimer and co-workers include 1,3,7,9,13,15-hexadehydro-[18]-annulene (14), in which the protons (all "outside") resonate at low field, suggesting the presence of a dia-magnetic aromatic ring current.[38] In comparison, the protons of 1,5,9-tridehydro-[12]-annulene[39, 40] (15) resonate at high field and presumably (15) is antiaromatic. A tridehydro-[26]-annulene[41] of unknown structure and stereochemistry, even at $-60°C$, has only a very broad resonance in its n.m.r. spectrum ($\tau = 2\cdot0$–$4\cdot5$), resembling that of a linear polyene. This is taken to mean that no ring current is present, in line with theoretical predictions that $[4n+2]$-annulenes with $n \geqslant 6$ will not be aromatic.[42]

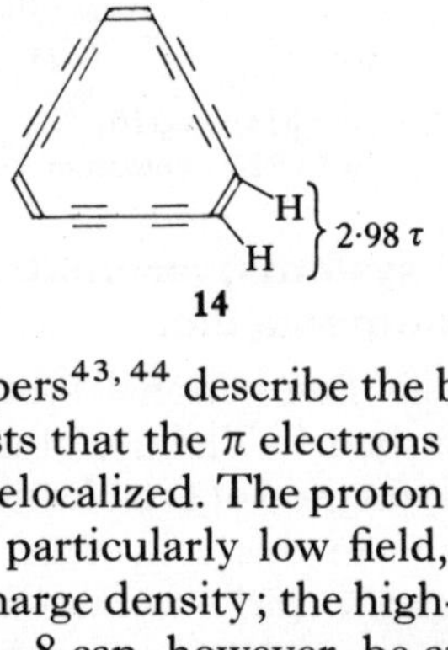

14 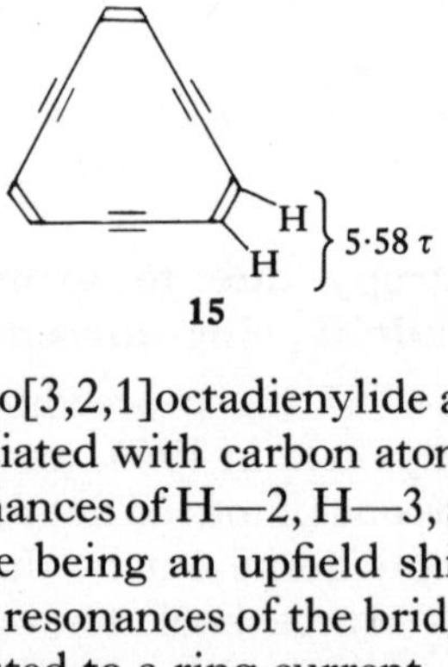   15

Two papers[43, 44] describe the bicyclo[3,2,1]octadienylide anion (16) and suggests that the π electrons associated with carbon atoms 2,3,4,6 and 7 are delocalized. The proton resonances of H—2, H—3, and H—6 are not at particularly low field, there being an upfield shift due to negative charge density; the high-field resonances of the bridge hydro-gens on C—8 can, however, be attributed to a ring current.

Other studies on systems claimed to be aromatic include calcula-tions on di- and triphenylcyclopropenium cations, in which modifi-cations of the conventional Johnson–Bovey–Waugh–Fessenden model

16   17

for the ring-current effect are discussed,[45] the 1,3,5-*tris*(cyclohepta-trienylium)benzene cation[46] and 3-phenyl-3-benzoborepin (17).[47] Details of the chemistry (including n.m.r. spectra) of *trans*-15,16-di-methyldihydropyrene (18) have appeared[48] as well as those of the corresponding diethyl derivative (19).[49]

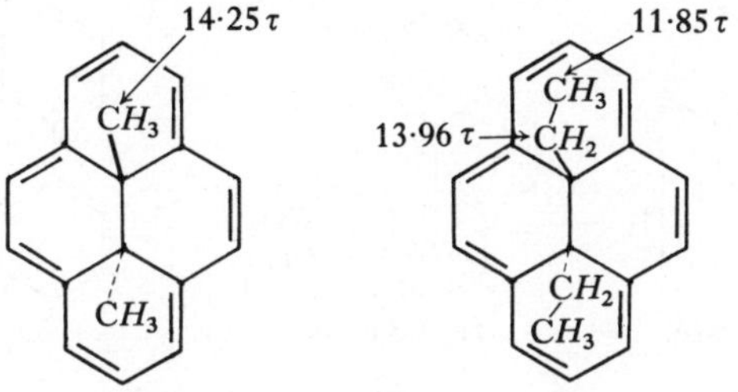

18   19

Annelation of benzene rings with one or more saturated rings results in progressive attenuation of the ring current, as judged by shift measurements on α-CH$_2$ groups. With 5-membered rings the effect is greater than with 6-membered saturated rings.[50]

The spectrum of 1,4,5,8-tetraphenyl-9,10-dimethylanthracene (20) shows methyl resonances shifted 1·3 p.p.m. upfield from the position in 9,10-dimethylanthracene (21). The calculated shift (Johnson–Bovey model) is much larger (4·7 p.p.m.) presumably because the ring

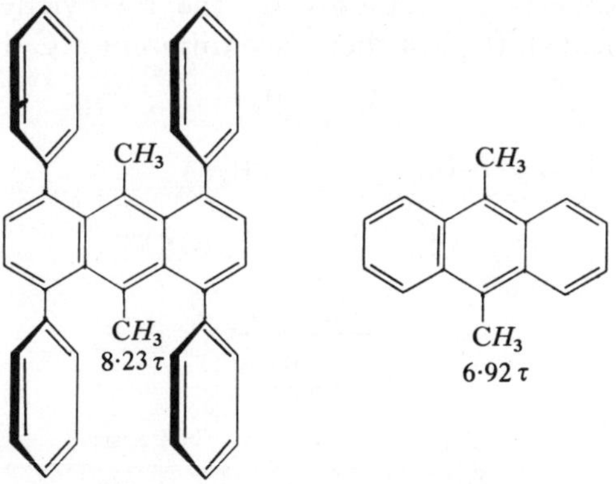

20   21

current is over-estimated.[51] Double-bond characters of the 9,10 bond in anthracene, the 1,2 and 6,7 bonds in pyrene, and the peripheral bonds in coronene have been estimated from consideration of long-range allylic coupling of methyl protons in the methyl derivatives (22), (23) and (24), respectively.[52] Other work on polycyclic aromatic systems includes theoretical and experimental studies on pentacyclic compounds (1,2,3,4-dibenzanthracene, 1,2-dibenzpyrene, picene, etc.),[53] non-alternant hydrocarbons (complete analyses of spectra of fluoranthrene and benzo[ghi]fluoranthrene[54]), azulene derivatives,[55, 56] triptycene[57] and heptahelicene.[58]

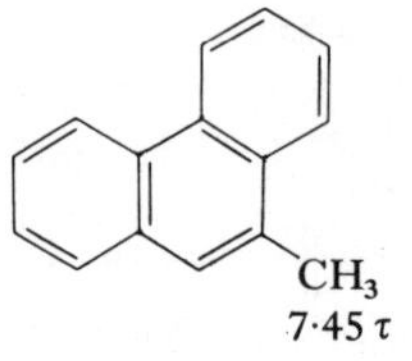

CH$_3$
7·45 τ

$\Delta v_{\frac{1}{2}}$ 1·1 c./sec.

22

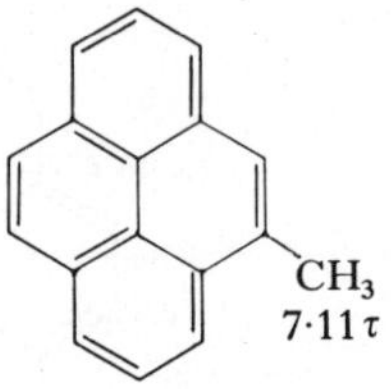

CH$_3$
7·11 τ

$\Delta v_{\frac{1}{2}}$ 1·3 c./sec.

23

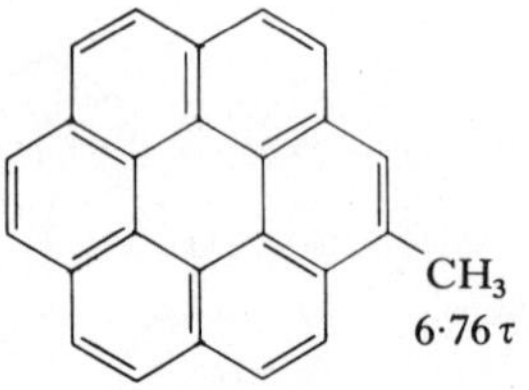

CH$_3$
6·76 τ

$\Delta v_{\frac{1}{2}}$ 0·9 c./sec.

24

C. Chemical shift non-equivalence of methylene and methyl protons, etc.

The presence of an asymmetric centre in the molecule gives conditions under which the methylene protons in an ethyl group or the methyl protons in an isopropyl group are potentially non-equivalent. One of the classic examples of this phenomenon, acetaldehyde diethyl acetal, (25), has been re-investigated recently;[59] a complete analysis of the ^{13}C satellite spectrum has confirmed the previous analysis of Kaplan and Roberts.[60] Not only do the methylene protons have different chemical shifts, but they have different ^{13}C–H couplings.

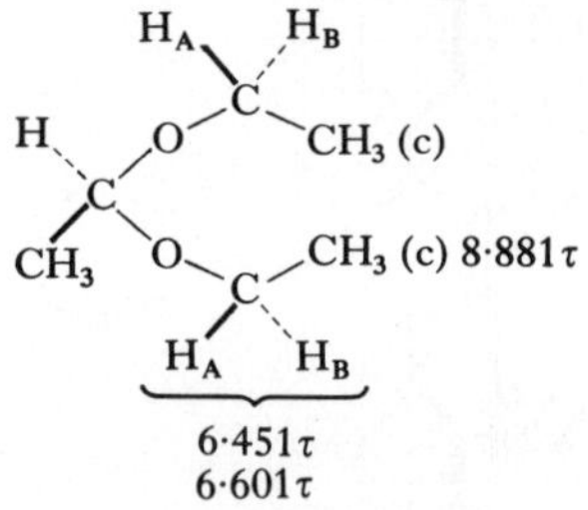

$J_{vic} = (J_{AC} + J_{BC})/2 = +7·04$ c./sec.
$J_{gem} = J_{AB} = -9·43$ c./sec.

$\left. \begin{matrix} J_{^{13}C-^1H_A} \\ J_{^{13}C-^1H_B} \end{matrix} \right\} = \begin{cases} 141·01 \text{ c./sec.} \\ 139·64 \text{ c./sec.} \end{cases}$ $J_{^{13}C-^1H_C} = 125·86$ c./sec.

25

A similar difference in coupling constants is shown by the non-equivalent methylene protons in the tetrahydropyranyl ether of trifluoroethanol (26).[61] Non-equivalent ethyl and benzyl methylene protons and isopropyl methyl protons have been reported in various sulphonium salts,[62] asymmetric ethyl ethers[63] and esters.[64]

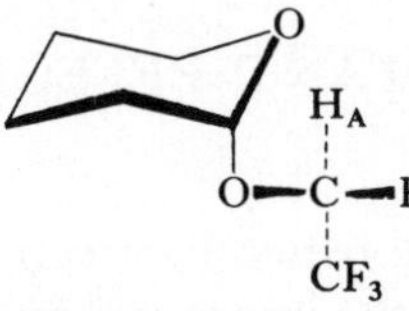

$(\Delta v)_{AB} = 8{\cdot}84$ c./sec.
$J_{A\dot{B}} = -12{\cdot}53$ c./sec.
$J_{AF} = 9{\cdot}13$ c./sec.
$J_{BF} = 8{\cdot}77$ c./sec.

26

Although asymmetry in a molecule is in general sufficient to account for non-equivalence of this type, non-equivalence is not always shown in such molecules. Conversely, in cases of isopropyl methyl non-equivalence, the large chemical-shift differences sometimes observed are only accounted for by assuming that steric preference for certain rotamers is enhancing the asymmetry effect, e.g., in N-alkyl-l-isopropylisoquinolinium salt,[65] in L-α-chloroacyl-L-valine derivatives[66] and in 3-isopropylcyclopentenes.[67] N-Nitroso-N-benzyl-o-chloroaniline exists in two stereoisomeric forms (**27**) and (**28**), of which (**27**) predominates. The *trans* isomer gives a single sharp line for the benzyl CH_2 resonance; in contrast, the *cis* isomer gives a broad line that at low temperature separates into an AB quartet.[68] Here there is no intrinsic asymmetry (except the amine nitrogen atom) in the molecules, and non-equivalence must result from steric factors.

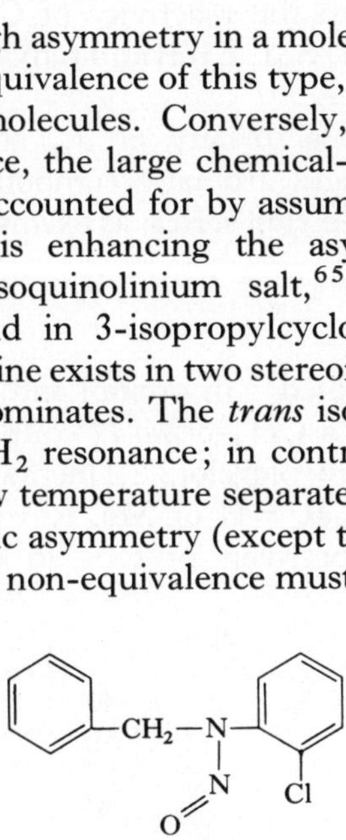

(*trans*)
27

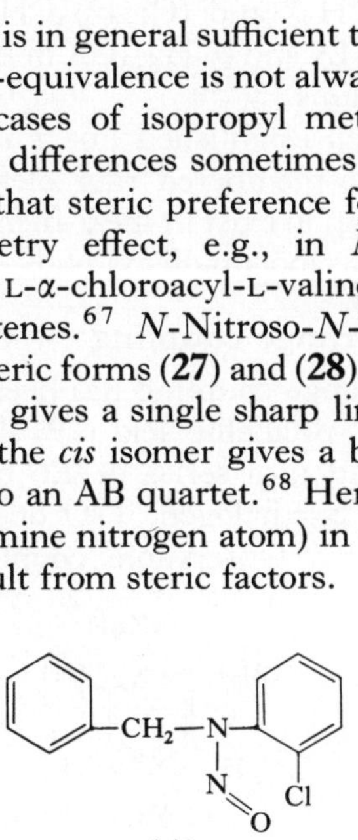

(*cis*)
28

In contrast to this, a study of the CH_2 resonance in several glycyl peptides has revealed a situation where (despite ample opportunity for steric effects to restrict rotamer populations) it is thought that non-equivalence (which does not occur universally) arises when the basic asymmetry of the molecules is reinforced by the presence of aromatic rings which provide large field gradients.[69]

A special type of chemical shift non-equivalence arises when a racemic mixture is dissolved in an optically active solvent. Solvent–solute interactions would be expected to be different for the enantiomers and should show up as non-equivalence of corresponding nuclei in the two forms. The effects so far detected,[70–74] are disappointingly small, but potentially useful; for proton work, optically active solvents containing no protons will be needed (see p. 116).

IV. COUPLING-CONSTANT EFFECTS

A. Vicinal coupling constants

An inverse correlation has been established between the magnitude of the vicinal coupling constant J_{AB} in the hydrocarbons $CH_3{}^A \cdot CH_3{}^B$, $(CH_3{}^A)_2CH_2{}^B$ and $(CH_3{}^A)_3CH^B$ with the reactivity of CH_3CH_2X, $(CH_3)_2CHX$ and $(CH_3)_3CX$ in E2, E1, S_N1, E1cB and radical-abstraction reactions.[75, 76]

The well-established linear relationship between J_{vic} and π bond order in 6-membered ring olefinic and aromatic compounds[77] has been shown to exist in the 5-membered ring series, as exemplified by a series of cyclopentadienyl ylids.[78]

B. Long-range coupling

Long-range coupling has been studied[79] in orcinol and its derivatives, e.g., orcinellic acid (29) shows a CH_3–ortho H coupling of 0·6 c./sec., and in a series of 2,6 bridged bicyclo[2,2,1]heptane derivatives (30, X=halogen, TsO or AcO, R′=H or Me, R″=R‴=H or =OH).[80, 81] Observable coupling between protons in chemically

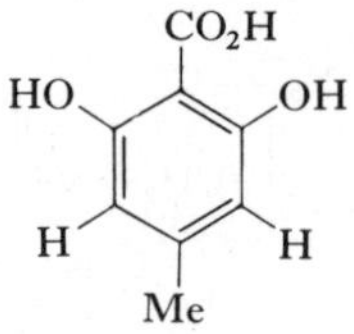

29

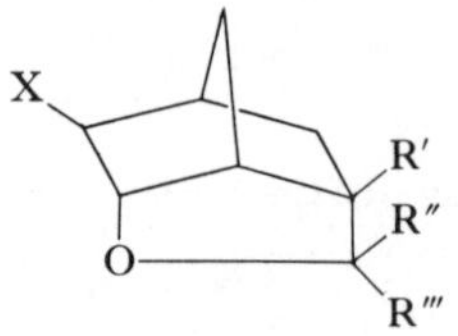

30

shifted non-equivalent gem-dimethyl groups depends critically on the presence of oxygen containing or other electron-withdrawing groups on the central carbon atom. Examples, additional to those discussed in last year's report,[82, 83] have now been found.[84]

The magnitude and signs of 4- and 5-bond couplings in formate esters have been determined (31).[85] The spectrum of methyl α-apopo-dophyllate[86] (32) shows several examples of homoallylic coupling.

Long-range proton–proton coupling in compounds of the type CH_3SMH_3 and H_3MSMH_3 is shown to increase as M is changed from C to Si and Ge. This type of coupling depends on the presence of sulphur as the central atom, since coupling is not detectable in the analogous oxygen compounds.[87]

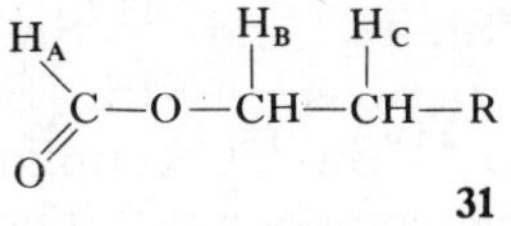

$$^4J \equiv J_{AB} \sim 0{\cdot}85 \text{ c./sec.}$$
$$^5J \equiv J_{AC} \sim 0{\cdot}50 \text{ c./sec.}$$

31

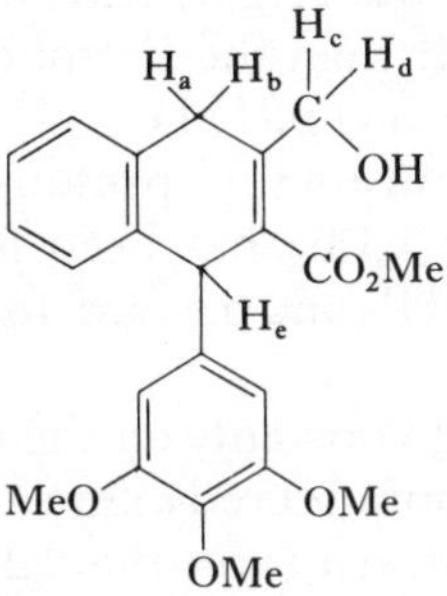

$$J_{ae} = J_{be} = J_{ce} = J_{de} = 6 \text{ c./sec.}$$

32

C. Coupling between protons and other nuclei

Couplings between protons and the other commonly studied magnetic nuclei (^{19}F, ^{31}P, ^{11}B) are continually being found and correlated. However a considerable interest attaches to the coupling that can be observed between protons and group IV elements. In all cases except germanium, isotopes having a spin of $\frac{1}{2}$ can be conveniently studied (^{13}C, ^{29}Si, ^{117}Sn, ^{119}Sn, ^{207}Pb) and if correlations of reduced coupling constants (J/product of gyromagnetic ratios of nuclei involved) are considered, meaningful trends in signs and magnitudes are possible. A detailed study of tetramethyl silane[88] is noteworthy. Carbon-13–proton coupling constants are reported for fluorobenzenes[89] and in cage compounds.[90] For a more detailed account of ^{13}C–^{1}H coupling constants see p. 176.

Silicon-29–proton coupling constants have been studied by Ebsworth and his co-workers[91–93] and directly bonded Si–H coupling constants were shown[94] to follow the relationship—

$$J = J'_{x,y} + J'_{y,z} + J'_{z,x}$$

where the J' values are associated with pairs of substituents on the central Si atom. A similar relationship has been found earlier for ^{13}C–H coupling.[95] Values of J' are: $J'_{HH} = 67{\cdot}6$; $J'_{HCl} = 84{\cdot}7$; $J'_{HMe} = 63{\cdot}5$; $J'_{HPh} = 66{\cdot}0$; $J'_{ClCl} = 120{\cdot}5$; $J'_{ClMe} = 79{\cdot}9$; $J'_{ClPh} = 84{\cdot}6$; $J'_{MeMe} = 63{\cdot}1$; $J'_{MePh} = 63{\cdot}4$; and $J'_{PhPh} = 66{\cdot}1$ c./sec.

In an extensive study of methyltin halides $[(CH_3)_x SnX_{4-x},$ X = Cl or Br, $x = 1$ to 4] by double-resonance techniques,[96] the ^{119}Sn–^{13}C coupling constants have been determined as well as the directly observable $^{13}C–H$, $^{119}Sn–H$, and $^{117}Sn–H$ couplings. Tin-119-proton coupling ranges between $+54.1$ $[Sn(CH_3)_4]$ and $+99.3$ c./sec. $[(CH_3)_2SnCl_2]$, and $^{119}Sn–^{13}C$ coupling ranges from -340 to -864 c./sec. for the same compounds.† The linear plot of J_{SnH} against J_{SnC} does not go through the origin, and this is taken as evidence of contribution of terms other than the Fermi contact interaction in the coupling mechanism (see also p. 181).

Long-range coupling of aromatic and methyl protons to ^{207}Pb in $(p\text{-}CH_3 \cdot C_6H_4)_4Pb$ and $(p\text{-}CH_3 \cdot C_6H_4)_6Pb_2$ has been found; values are 80 c./sec. for o-H's, 25 c./sec. for m-H's and 6 c./sec. for methyl protons.[97]

The dependance of $^{15}N–H$ coupling constants on the configuration of aldoximes has been observed.[98] In unhindered oximes both *syn* (33) and *anti* (34) forms are present. In the *syn* form the value of $J_{N–H}$ is between 2 and 4 c./sec., a higher (10–16 c./sec.) value being observed

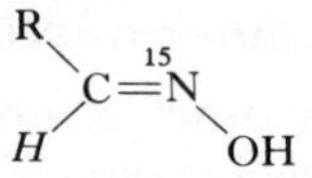

(*syn*)   (*trans*)
33   34

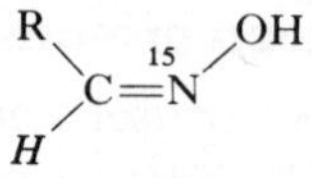

in the *anti* isomer. Hindered oximes (e.g., benzaldehyde and pivaldehyde oximes) exist only in the sterically favoured *syn* form. That the numerically higher coupling in the *anti* form is in some way connected with the lone electron pair on nitrogen is shown by the greatly reduced couplings observed in the protonated (conc. H_2SO_4) or quaternized forms. In heterocyclic compounds, e.g., isoxazole (35)[98] and quinoline (36),[99] $J_{N–Ha}$ (corresponding to the situation in the *anti* oximes) is

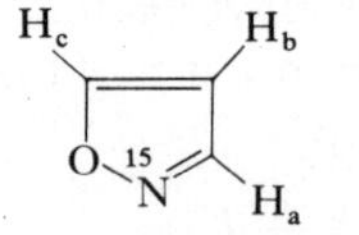

35 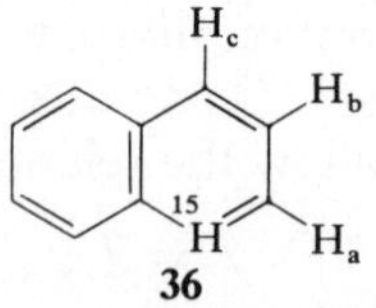   36

15 c./sec., and 11 c./sec., respectively, in aprotic solvents, and shows a numerical decrease on protonation or quaternization. The latter authors[99] infer that the sign of this coupling is negative and that the observed decrease is an algebraic increase.

Studies on $^{15}N–H$ coupling in a series of derivatives of urea and formamide, and in phenylhydrazones[100] has revealed a lineal correlation

† Reduced coupling constants have opposite signs to the J's since γ for Sn is negative.

between the germinal protons coupling in $\underset{H}{\overset{H}{>}}C{=}Z$ and the $^{15}N{-}H$

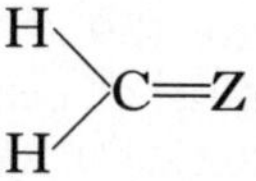

couplings in $\underset{H}{\overset{^{15}N}{>}}C{=}Z$ as Z is varied.

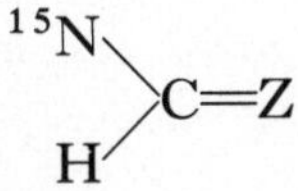

In 4-substituted N-ethylpyridinium cations, the observation of coupling between the ethyl CH_3 protons and nitrogen depends on the quadrupole relaxation of the nitrogen, which in turn depends on the nature of the 4-substituent. A roughly linear correlation of T_q (quadrupole relaxation time) with the Hammett σ function was observed[101] (see also p. 138).

V. SPECTRUM ANALYSIS: METHODS AND RESULTS

The methods of sub-spectral analysis[102] and the use of computers in spectral analysis[103] have been reviewed. An alternative representation of energy-level diagrams has been described.[104]

Among compounds whose spectra have been completely analysed are: allyl iodide (**37**, 100 Mc./sec. d.r.)[105] benzene (**38**, ^{13}C satel-

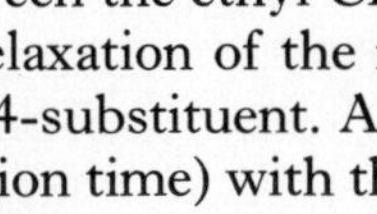

$\tau_A = 3.969$, $\tau_B = 4.785$, $\tau_C = 5.076$
$\tau_D = 6.168$ $J_{AB} = 16.6$ c./sec.
$J_{AC} = 9.8$ c./sec. $J_{AD} = 7.9$ c./sec.
$J_{BC} = 1.2$ c./sec. $J_{BD} = -1.1$ c/sec.
$J_{CD} = -0.4$ c./sec.

37

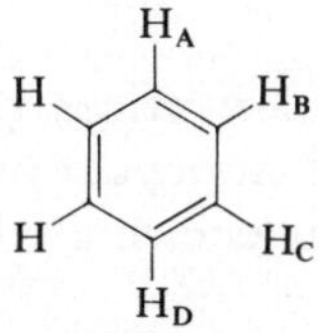

$J_o = J_{AB} = 7.54$ c./sec.
$J_m = J_{AC} = 1.37$ c./sec.
$J_p = J_{AD} = 0.69$ c./sec.
$J_{^{13}CH} = 158.34$ c./sec.

38

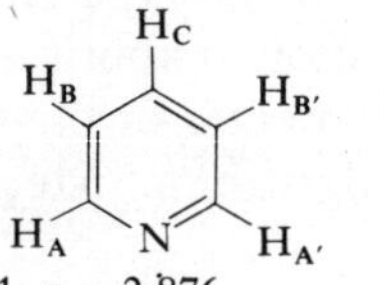

$\tau_A = 1.391$, $\tau_B = 2.876$
$\tau_C = 2.499$
$J_{AB} = 4.882$ c./sec. $J_{AC} = 1.842$ c./sec.
$J_{AB'} = 0.995$ c./sec. $J_{AA'} = -0.132$ c./sec.
$J_{BC} = 7.666$ c./sec. $J_{BB'} = 1.366$ c./sec.

39

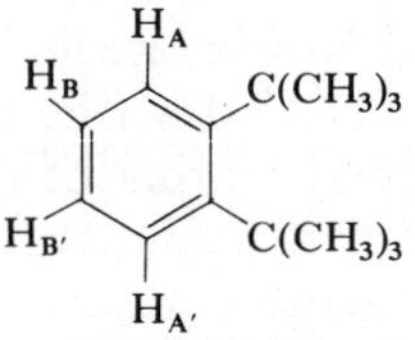

$J_{AB} = 8.1$ c./sec.
$J_{AB'} = 1.7$ c./sec.
$J_{AA'} = 0.2$ c./sec.
$J_{BB'} = 4.5$ c./sec.

40

lites),[106] pyridine (**39**, ^{14}N-decoupled, LAOCOON III)[107] *o*-di-t
butylbenzene (**40**),[108] cyclobutene (**41**, deuterated derivatives, [13]C-
satellites, LAOCOON II),[109] alicyclic protons of l-indanone (**42**,

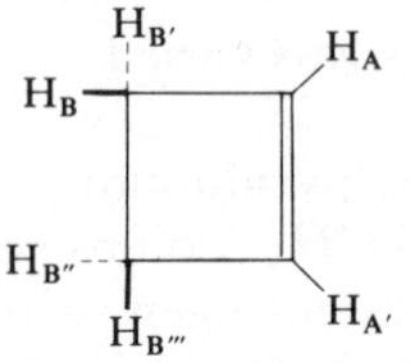

$\tau_A = 3.97$, $\tau_B = 7.43$
$J_{AA'} = +2.85$ c./sec., $J_{AB} = +1.00$ c./sec., $J_{AB''} = -0.35$ c./sec.
$J_{BB'} = -12.00$ c./sec., $J_{BB''} = +1.75$ c./sec., $J_{BB'''} = +4.65$ c./sec.,
$$J_{^{13}C-C-C-H_A} - J_{^{13}C-C-H_{A'}} = +4.0 \text{ c./sec.}$$
$$J_{^{13}C-C-C-H_B} - J_{^{13}C-C-H_{B'''}} = +7.0 \text{ c./sec.}$$

41

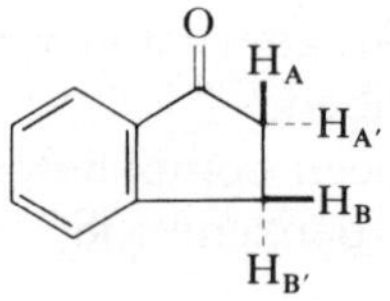

$\tau_A = 6.90$ $\tau_B = 7.40$

$\left.\begin{array}{l} J_{AA'} \\ J_{BB'} \end{array}\right\}$ $\left\{\begin{array}{ll} -14.32 \text{ c./sec.} & J_{AB} = +8.45 \text{ c./sec.} \\ -16.00 \text{ c./sec.} & J_{AB'} = +3.37 \text{ c./sec.} \end{array}\right.$

42

deuterated derivatives, d.r.),[110] cyclopropenone (**43**, ^{13}C-satellites),[111]
and *trans* 2-arylcyclo propanecarboxylic acids (**44**, Ar = various substituted benzene rings, LAOCOON II).[112]†

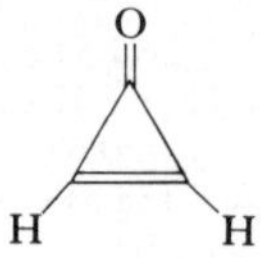

$\tau_H = 1.0$ (D$_2$O)
$J_{CH} = 230$ c./sec.
$J_{HH} = 3$ c./sec.

43

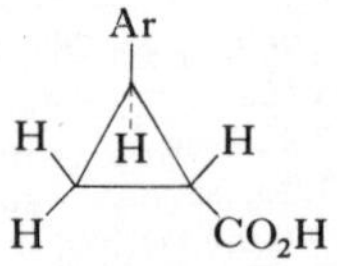

44

The spectra of several cyclobutanes of the type AA'BB' have been
analysed using weak double-irradiation experiments.[113] Several
papers[114–116] describe the analysis of spectra of the type X$_n$AA'X'$_n$,
exemplified by that of tetramethyldiphosphine, Me$_2$P·PMe$_2$, which
is a X$_6$AA'X'$_6$ spin system.

An extensive study of *NN*-dimethylaniline (**45**) involving use of
deuterium derivatives has yielded probably the first exact analysis of
a monosubstituted benzene derivative.[117] Other aromatic systems

---

† Significant techniques [e.g., double resonance (d.r.)] and computational methods
used are indicated in parentheses.

analysed include m-difluorbenzene (**46**)[118] and 1,3-difluoro-4,6-di-nitrobenzene in various solvents.[119]

N(CH$_3$)$_2$ 7·47 τ

H$_{A'}$ H$_A$ 3·484 τ

H$_{B'}$ H$_B$ 2·896 τ

H$_C$ 3·348 τ

$J_{AB} = 8\cdot37$ c./sec. $J_{AC} = 1\cdot02$ c./sec.
$J_{AB'} = 0\cdot48$ c./sec. $J_{AA'} = 2\cdot80$ c./sec.
$J_{BC} = 7\cdot29$ c./sec. $J_{BB'} = 1\cdot77$ c./sec.

45

H$_C$

H$_B$ H$_{B'}$

F$_D$ F$_{D'}$

H$_A$

$J_{AB} = 2\cdot2$ c./sec. $J_{AC} = 0\cdot4$ c./sec.
$J_{AD} = 9\cdot6$ c./sec. $J_{BB'} = 2\cdot0$ c./sec.
$J_{BC} = 8\cdot9$ c./sec. $J_{BD} = 9\cdot2$ c./sec.
$J_{BD'} = -1\cdot0$ c./sec. $J_{CD} = 5\cdot8$ c./sec.
$J_{DD'} = 3\cdot0$ c./sec.

46

Ph

H$_{X'}$ H$_X$

N

H$_{A'}$ H$_A$

$\tau_A = 8\cdot67$ $\tau_X = 7\cdot36$
$J_{AA} = 0\cdot65$ c./sec. $J_{XX} = 6\cdot25$ c./sec.
$J_{AX} = 2\cdot75$ c./sec. $J_{AX'} = 0\cdot0$ c./sec.
$J_{^{13}C-^1H_A} = 175\cdot0$ c./sec. $J_{^{13}C-^1H_X} = 166\cdot0$ c./sec.

47

The spectrum of 3-phenyl-1-azabicyclo[1,1,0]butane (**47**), analysed chiefly by studying the ^{13}C-satellites, and the spectrum of a deuterium derivative, proves the structure of the compound.[120]

VI. EQUILIBRIUM PROBLEMS STUDIED BY P.M.R.

A. Methods

Recently there have been critical re-appraisals of the n.m.r. methods for examining equilibrating systems,[121, 122] since results from different workers on the same systems tended to disagree.[123] One of the most frequently studied systems is the ring inversion of cyclohexane, since besides its central importance in the theory of conformational analysis, it is of sufficient simplicity to allow the various methods to be compared. In the detailed publication on cyclohexane-d_{11}, Anet and

Bourn[124] describe their use of the line shape method in the temperature range $-24°$ to $-82°$C (deuterium decoupling was used so that only the unperturbed single proton resonance was observed) and of a double-resonance method in the temperature range $-97°$ to $-116°$C. This involved the observation of recovery of magnetization of one of the two lines in the spectrum after a saturating r.f. field applied to the other line was removed. Consistent rates of inversion were found from both methods as evidenced by linearity of the Arrhenius plot. The results do not agree with the spin-echo results of Allerhand et al.[125] In this type of work, while fairly consistent results of rate constants may be obtained, there is dispute as to how the thermodynamic para-meters should be derived, even in the relatively simple case of cyclo-hexane.[126]

Another frequently used method for studying conformational equilibria particularly of acyclic compounds, e.g., substituted ethanes, is that of observation of variations of the averaged coupling constants and chemical shifts due to changes in the relative populations of the rotamers when the temperature is changed. A critical study on 1,1,2,2-tetrabromo-1-fluoroethane using both proton and fluorine resonances compares the results of this method (above $218°$K) with those obtained below $210°$K where separate fluorine resonances for the rotamers can be seen.[127] The authors conclude that there are serious limitations to the high-temperature-average method. The related method which studies changes in vicinal H–H couplings in ethanes (e.g., β-bromo-propionitrile) with changes in solvent is rather more reliable.[128]

A comparison of the line-shape method with an equilibration method[129] has shown good agreement in results (the Arrhenius plots for both methods are colinear). The example chosen was the intercon-version of rotamers in N-methyl-N-benzylformamide, which between $90°$ and $170°$C shows averaged spectra. One of the rotamers can be obtained substantially pure at low temperatures, and the return to equilibrium was studied in the range $-2·5°$ to $20°$C. A similar study using N-benzyl-N-2,4,6-tetramethylbenzamide and N,N-2,4,6-penta-methylbenzamide has also been made.[130]

For most purposes, organic chemists are satisfied with less rigorous treatments of equilibrium processes than those exemplified by the above. In the remainder of this Section are listed some of the many such treatments, some of which are more rigorous than others. They are classified according to the nature of the equilibrium involved. For convenience, those systems in which an equilibrium process was shown to be absent, and those, such as keto–enol systems, where equilibration is slow, are included here.

B. Rotational isomerism in open-chain compounds

The conformation isomerism in a wide range (31 examples) of 1-sub-stituted derivatives of 3,3-dimethylbutane has been examined. In some cases, the temperature variation of the vicinal coupling constants was studied.[131] In 1,1,2-trichloroethane the coupling constants of the *gauche* and *anti* isomers are deduced from solvent-dependent changes in the observed coupling constants.[132] In some similar systems (1,1,2-trichloro- and 1,1,2-tribromoethane in carbon tetrachloride and in benzene), a correlation of the dipole moments of the compounds and the vicinal coupling constants was found.[133] Rotational isomerism in the phenylalanine anion and dipolar ion has been studied in deuterium oxide solutions.[134]

C. Conformational equilibria in ring compounds

Conformational analysis of 6-membered rings dominates this field. Evidence that *cis*-1,4-dihalogenocyclohexanes (Br_2; Cl_2; Br, Cl) exist in chair conformations has been found.[135] Variable-temperature studies of the spectra of *cis, anti, cis-* and *cis, syn, cis-* 1,2,4,5-tetra-acetoxy[3,3,6,6-$^2H_4$]cyclohexanes (**48** and **49**, R=OAc) can yield estimates of 1,3-diaxial interactions.[136]

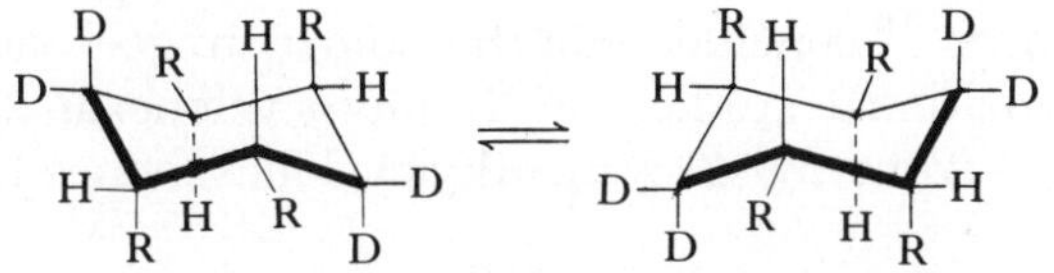

48

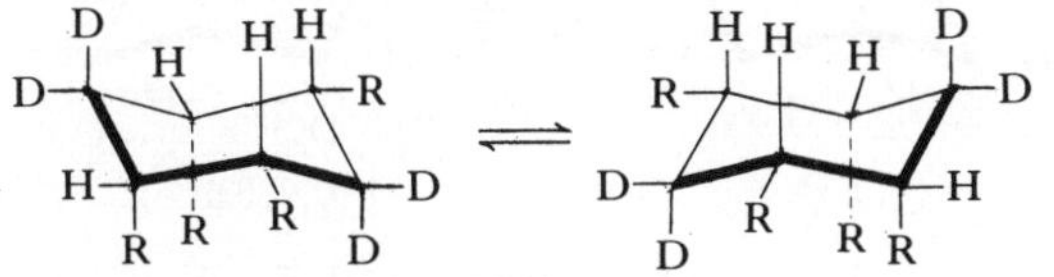

49

In 1,1,4,4-tetramethylcyclohexane (**50**) the rate of ring inversion has been studied by line shape analysis of the methyl resonance at various temperatures.[137] The results are compared with those obtained for the structurally similar acetone peroxide (**51**).[138] In these two systems (**50**) and (**51**), the equilibria are between two identical chair conformers and single coalescence temperatures are observed ($-61°C$ and $-66°C$ at 60 Mc./sec., respectively). In duplodithioacetone (**52**) the more stable twist-boat conformer enters into the equilibrium, and

no simple analysis is possible. At 0°C, the spectrum of (52) consists of
a peak at 8·32 τ due to the twist-boat form (52A) and two peaks of
equal area at 8·46 and 7·93 τ due to the chair conformer (52B). The
relative amounts of the two forms are 2·2:1·0.[139]

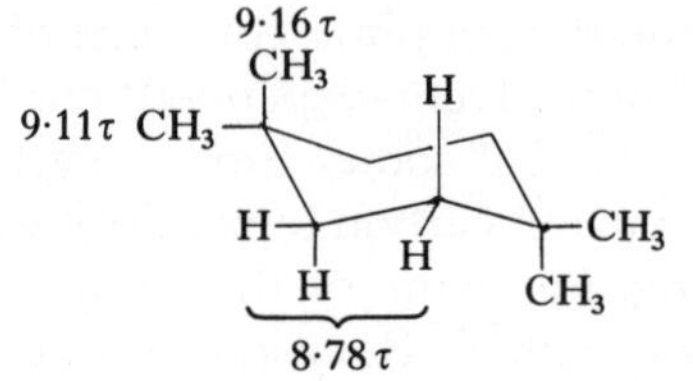

50

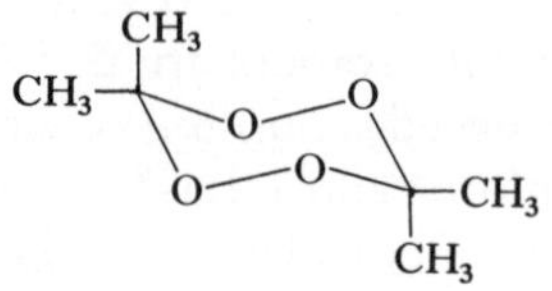

51

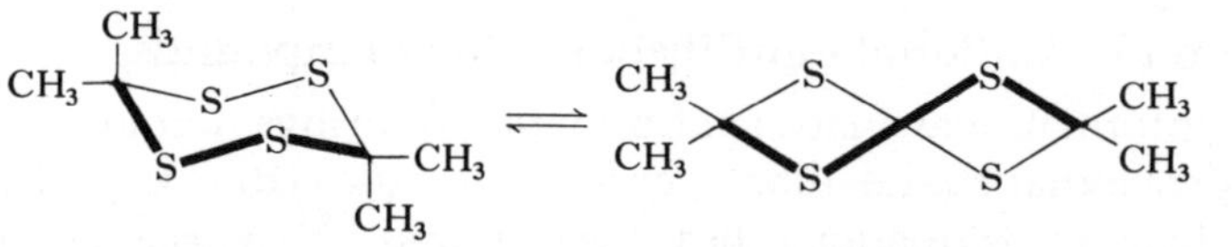

52A   **52B**

Spectra of *cis*-1,2-bismethoxycarbonyl-[3,3,4,5,6,6-^{2}H$_6$]cyclohex-
ane (53, R=CO$_2$Me), have been studied at various temperatures, two
coalescence temperatures being observed for the single inversion process. The authors[140] conclude that the isomerism goes via a half-chair
form. Conformational studies on 2-chlorocyclohexanols[141] and on
mono-, di- and trimethyl-β-cyanoethylcyclohexanones have been reported.[142]

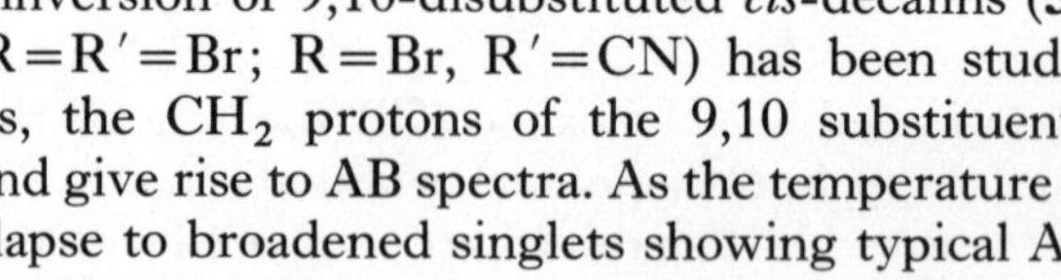

53A   **53B**

The ring inversion of 9,10-disubstituted *cis*-decalins (54, R=R′=
CO$_2$CH$_3$; R=R′=Br; R=Br, R′=CN) has been studied. At low
temperatures, the CH$_2$ protons of the 9,10 substituents are non-
equivalent and give rise to AB spectra. As the temperature is raised the
quartets collapse to broadened singlets showing typical AB exchange
patterns.[143]

Spectra of the furan analogue of metacyclophane (55) and the corresponding pyridine analogue (56) show variation with temperature, the
A$_2$B$_2$ patterns at low temperature collapsing to single line at 63° and
13·5°C, respectively.[144]

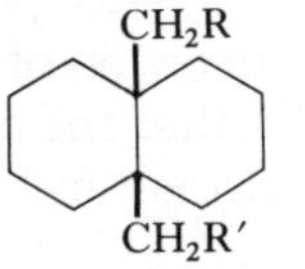

54 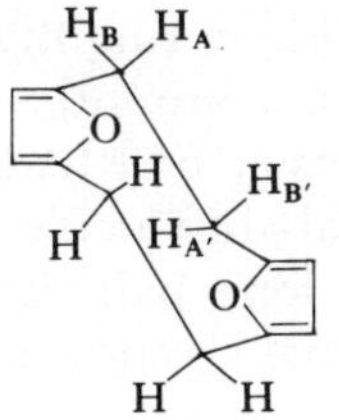   **55** 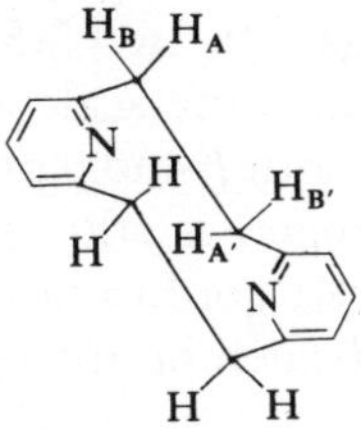   **56**

The energy barriers in the chair–chair inversion of hexahydro-1,3,5-trimethyl-1,3,5-triazine[145] and several other alkyl derivatives (**57**, R = Me, Et, i-Pr, t-Bu)[146] have been examined. The authors of the latter paper conclude that since ΔG is solvent independent, the observed effect is due to ring inversion and not inversion of the alkyl substituents on nitrogen. The former authors also examined hexamethyl-1,3,5-trithiane (**58**) and s-trioxane (**59**). Ring inversion of 1,3-dimethyl- (**60**, R = Me) and 1,3-diethylhexahydropyrimidines (**60**, R = Et) has been studied by line-shape analysis at low temperatures.[147]

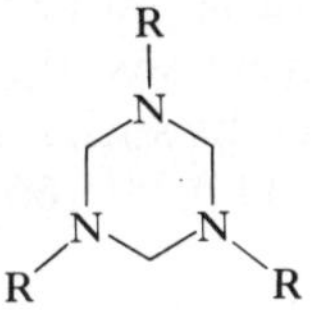

57 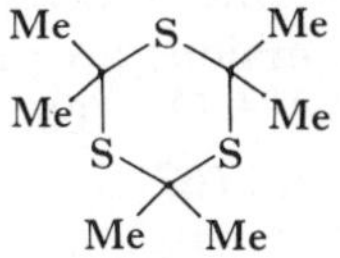   **58** 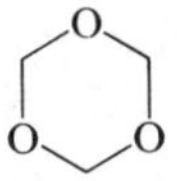   **59**    **60**

In the interconversion of conformers of *cis*-5,10-thianthrene dioxide (**61**) (and the *trans* isomer also) Purcell and Berschied[148] conclude that the rate is very high (>100 sec.$^{-1}$) even at low temperatures.

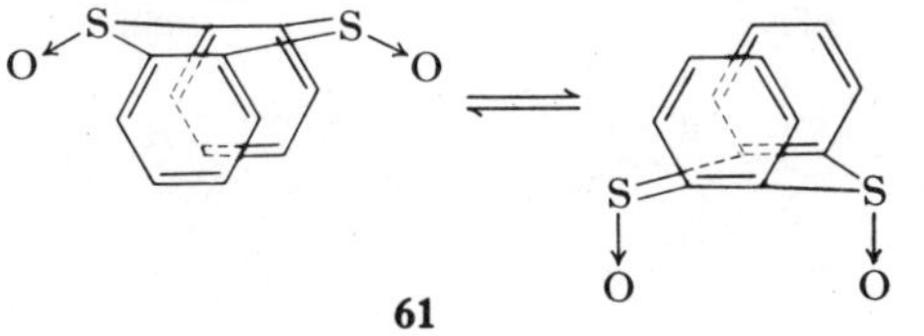

61

D. Inversions on nitrogen atoms

The conformation of piperidine has been examined in several deuterated derivatives.[149] In 4,4,-d_2-piperidine the spectrum of the ring protons analysed as an AA′BB′ system and gave a ratio of $^3J|_{trans}/^3J_{cis}$ of 2·09 (for 6-membered rings of type (**62**), such a ratio is close to the value (2·0) expected for perfect chair rings while a value of 1·2 is associated with flexible forms and 2·75 for distorted chair rings[150]). In 3,3,5,5-d_4-piperidine, ring flipping becomes slow on the n.m.r. time scale at temperatures around $-63\cdot5°C$ (coalescence point for both β and γ proton quartets at 60 Mc./sec.), while inversion of the nitrogen is still fast. Chemical-shift evidence indicates that the preferred conformation has the lone pair electrons equatorial and the hydrogen on nitrogen in an axial arrangement.

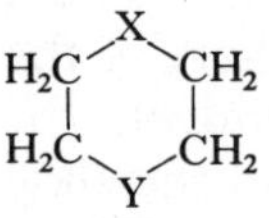

62 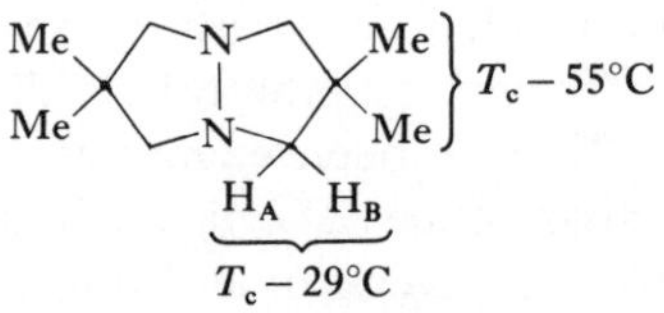   **63** 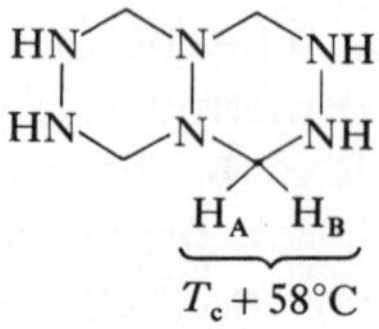   **64**

Ring compounds that have nitrogens at bridge-head positions have greater conformation mobility than their CH analogues. Examples are **(63)** and **(64)** which have coalescence temperatures as indicated at 60 Mc./sec.[151] Examples of double nitrogen inversions that are unusually slow (for this type of inversion) are provided by such systems as **(65, R=Me, CO$_2$Me, COEt),**[152, 153] **(66, R=CH$_3$),**[152] **(66, R= CO$_2$Et)**[154] **(67, R=CO$_2$Me)**[154] and **(67, R=CO$_2$Me).**[154]

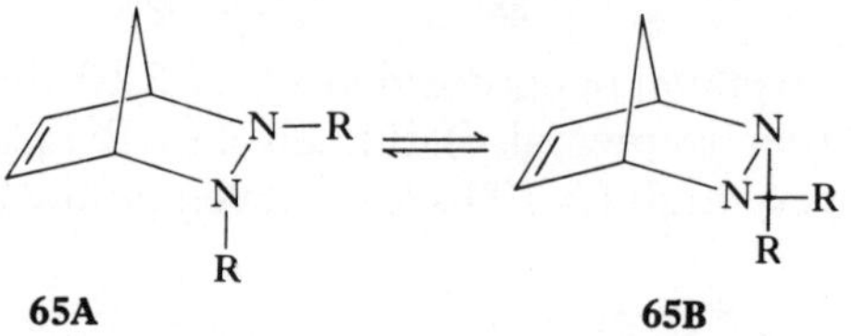

65A   **65B**

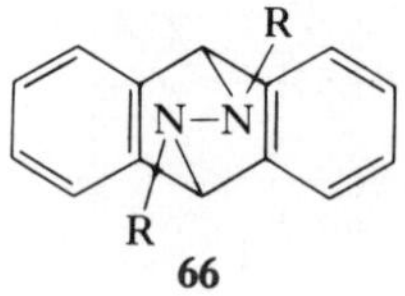

66 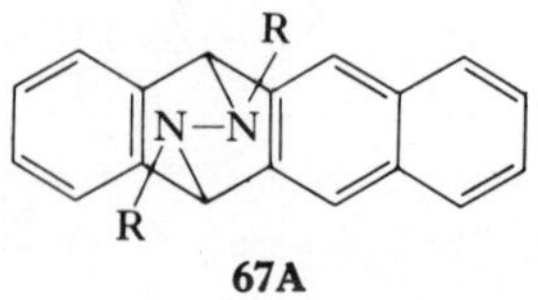   **67A**

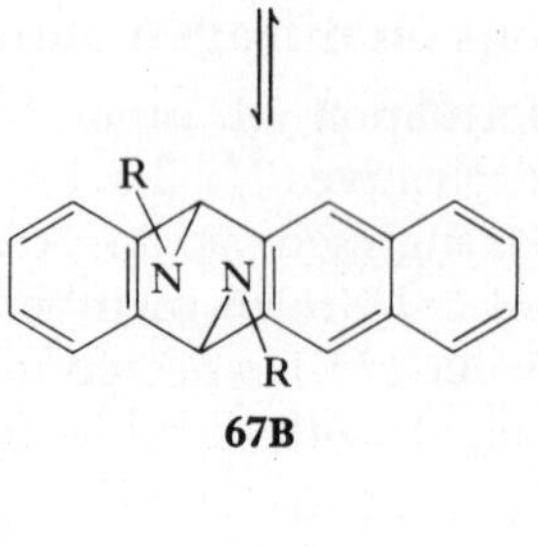

67B

E. Hindered rotation about formal single bonds

The classical case of dimethylformamide has been re-investigated using the techniques now available. The parameters E_a and ΔG have been re-determined.[155] The rotational barriers in other amides (and compounds that can be considered as amide derivatives) continue to occupy the attention of organic chemists; in some, e.g., 2-methyl-6-t-butyl-*N*-methylchloracetanilide, the two isomers have separate stable existence (**68A** and **68B**),[156] whereas rotamers are usually

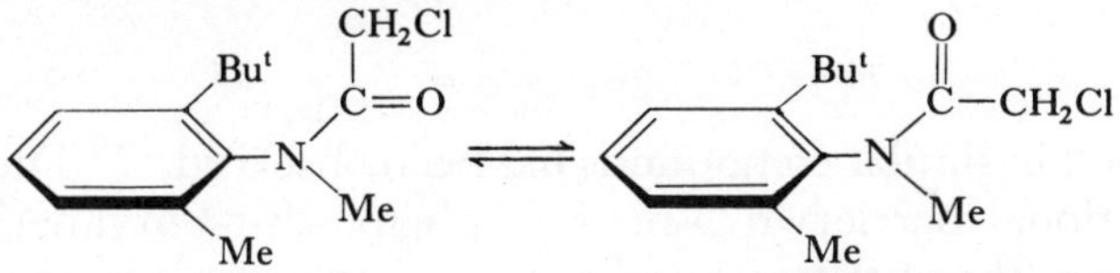

68A   **68B**

detectable by n.m.r. spectroscopy only. Examples of these are: *N*-methyl-*N*-(2-phenylisopropyl)-3,5-dinitrobenzamide (**69**),[157] *NN*-dimethylcarbamoyl chloride (**70**, R = Cl) (and the corresponding thio-amide),[158] *NN*-dimethylcarbamates (**70**, R = O-alkyl and O-aryl),[159]

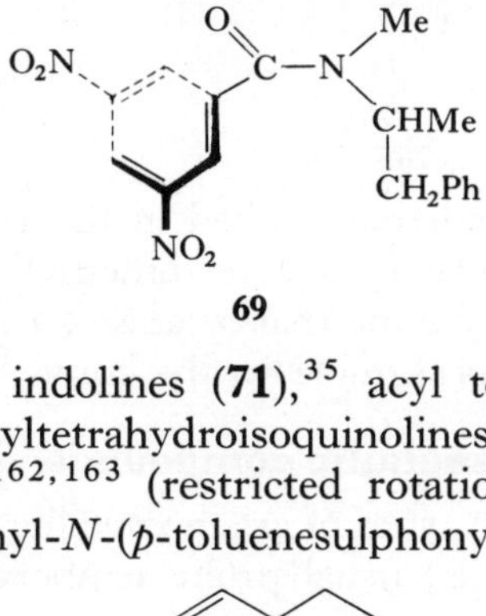

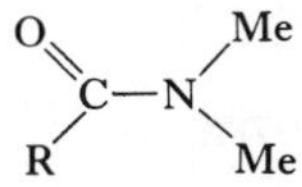

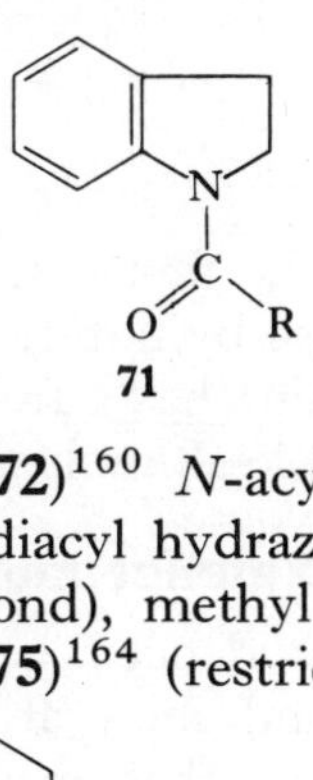

69   **70**   **71**

acyl indolines (**71**),[35] acyl tetrahydroquinolines (**72**)[160] *N*-acyl-1-benzyltetrahydroisoquinolines, e.g., (**73**),[161] *NN'*-diacyl hydrazines (**74**)[162,163] (restricted rotation about the N–N bond), methyl *N*-methyl-*N*-(p-toluenesulphonyl methyl)carbamate (**75**)[164] (restricted

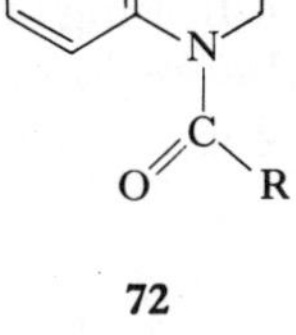

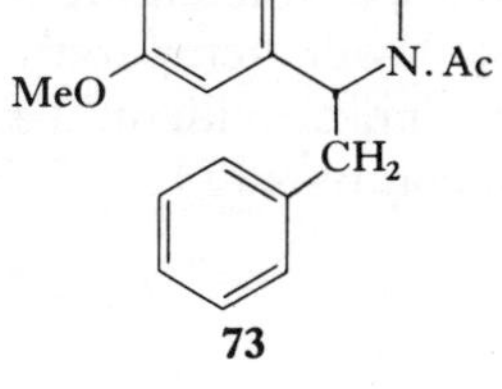

72   **73**

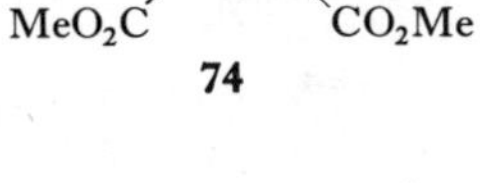

74   **75**

rotation about O—Me bond) and N'-aryl-N,N-dimethylformami-
dines (**76**).[165, 166] Restricted rotation can be detected about the N—C
bond in 6-dialkylaminofulvenes.[167] Cases of easy rotation about
formal double bonds have been studied in a series of enamines such as
(**77**) by variation of temperature.[168] Restricted rotation about the

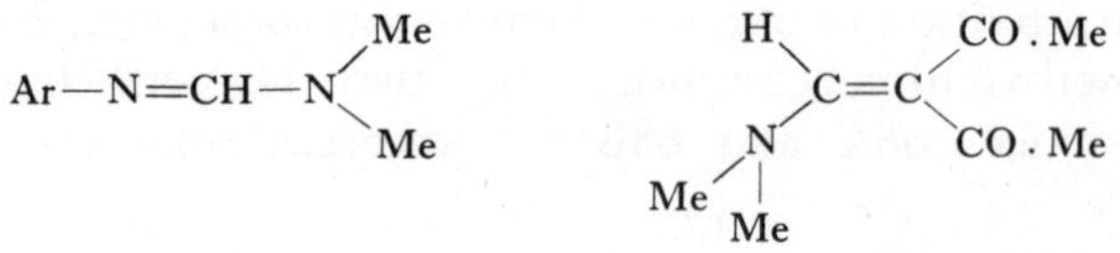

$$\text{Ar-N=CH-N}\begin{array}{c}\text{Me}\\\\\text{Me}\end{array} \qquad \begin{array}{c}\text{H}\\\\\text{Me}\end{array}\text{C=C}\begin{array}{c}\text{CO.Me}\\\\\text{CO.Me}\end{array}$$

76   **77**

C—N bond in similar compounds has been observed.[169] The existence
of a rotational barrier in p-methoxyphenyl-di-t-butylmethanol (**78**)
follows from the unsymmetrical nature of its n.m.r. spectrum at room
temperature.[170]

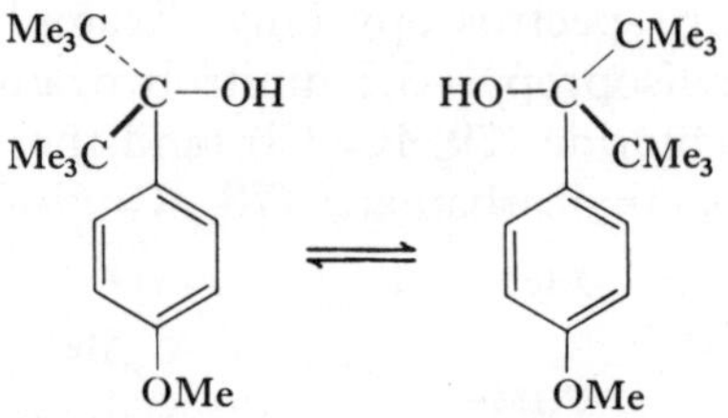

78A ⇌ **78B**

The first case of a rotational barrier being studied in the vapour
phase by n.m.r. methods has been reported: gaseous dimethylinitro-
samine has a free energy of activation for internal rotation (ΔG^*) of
$21 \cdot 1$ kcal./mole as compared with $23 \cdot 3$ kcal./mole for the liquid.[171]

F. Valence tautomerism in organometallic compounds

Evidence is accumulating that certain types of organometallic compound show at higher temperature (i.e., usual probe temperature)
spectra that are characteristic of the average environment of the ligands,
whereas at lower temperatures spectra indicating unsymmetrical
bonding becomes evident. Examples are the cyclo-octatetraeneiron
tricarbonyl complex (**79**) and the corresponding tungsten and molyb-

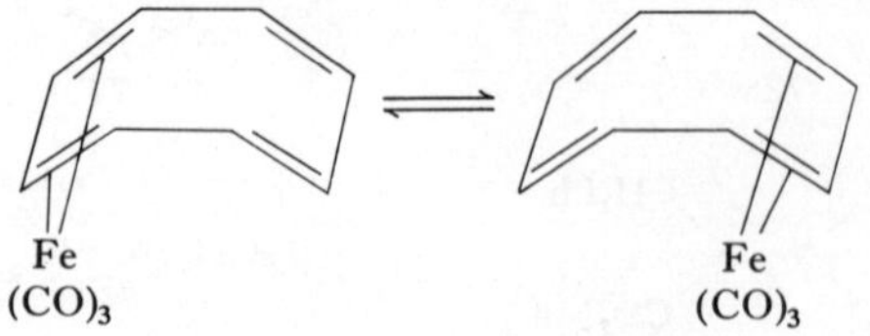

79A ⇌ **79B**

denum[172] and ruthenium[173] complexes and methylcyclo-octatetra-eneiron tricarbonyl.[174] A new type of complex is the tetramethyl-alleneiron tetracarbonyl (**80**).[175] At room temperature, in carbon disulphide, this complex shows a single resonance line at $8·16 \tau$, indicating that the four methyl groups are equivalent on a time-averaged basis. On cooling the solution down to $-60°C$, four bands at $7·97$,

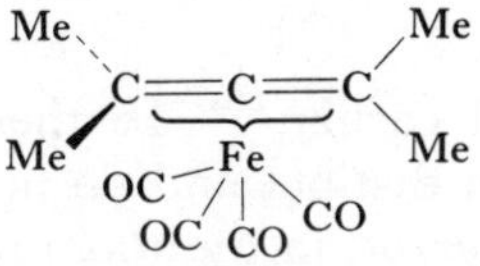

80 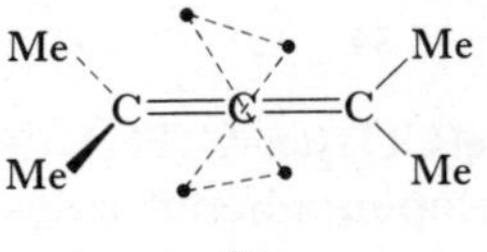 **81**

$8·02$, $8·23 \tau$ of relative area $1:1:2$ appear, consistent with a structure in which the iron atom is co-ordinated to one of the double bonds in the allene. At room temperature the iron is undergoing motion relative to the π electron systems of the allene, as indicated by the dotted lines in (**81**).

Equilibria of a different type are possible in some cases in π allyl complexes.[176] The authors of the last paper distinguish three types of σ and π allyl complexes and detail the types of n.m.r. spectra expected from each of them; these complexes are shown in the structures (**82–84**). In the last category falls tetra-allylzirconium. At $-10°C$, this compound shows a spectrum of the AX_4 type, with all four protons of the CH_2 groups in an allyl ligand equivalent on a time-average basis, and at $-74°C$ the spectrum is of the A_2M_2X type expected for one of the tautomers of the equilibrium (**84**). See also Cotton et al.[177]

In the case of the bisallylrhodium chloride dimer, which at $140°C$ has an AX_4 type spectrum, but has at $-20°C$ two pairs of dissimilar allyl groups [two σ bonded like (**82**) and two others, presumably π bonded like (**83**)] i.e., structure (**85**), it is suggested that the two types of allyl groups exchange their roles at high temperatures.[178]

A different type of duality of ligand function from that occurring in system (**85**) is observed in σ-cyclopentadienyl π-cyclopentadienyl complexes, e.g., $(\sigma\text{-}C_5H_5)Cr(NO)_2(\pi\text{-}C_5H_5)$[179] and the

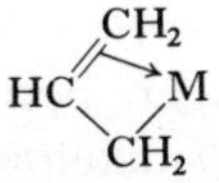

σ or σ and π bonding
e.g. $(C_3H_5) Mo (CO)_5$
$ABCX_2$ spectra

82

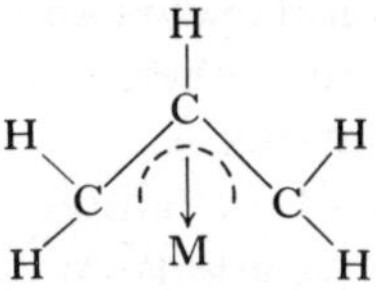

π bonding
e.g. $[(C_3H_5)PdCl]_2$
AM_2X_2 spectra.

83

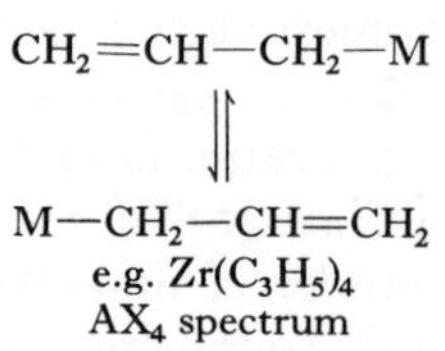

CH$_2$=CH—CH$_2$—M

$\updownarrow$

M—CH$_2$—CH=CH$_2$
e.g. Zr(C$_3$H$_5$)$_4$
AX$_4$ spectrum

84

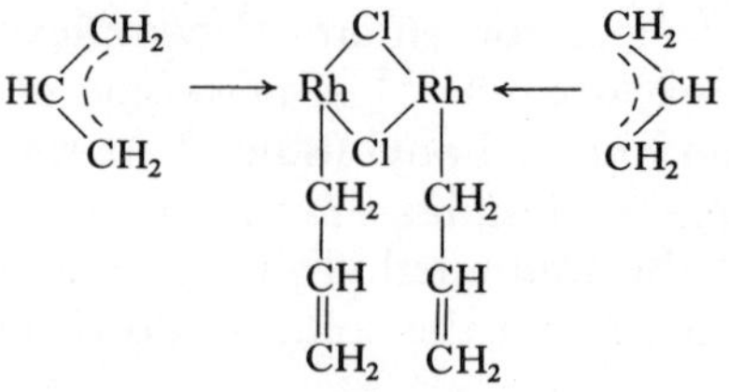

85

(σ-C$_5$H$_5$)Fe(CO)$_2$(π-C$_5$H$_5$) described earlier.[180] In these systems, the two cyclopentadienyl rings remain distinct and do not exchange their types of bonding (two peaks observed in the room temperature n.m.r. spectrum). The σ-bonded ligand however shows a time-averaged spectrum at room temperature due to rapid movement of the iron–carbon bond from one carbon to another by 1,2 shifts. At low temperature, the spectrum of the extreme forms is frozen out. σ-Cyclopentadienyl(triethylphosphine)copper (**86**) behaves similarly.[181]

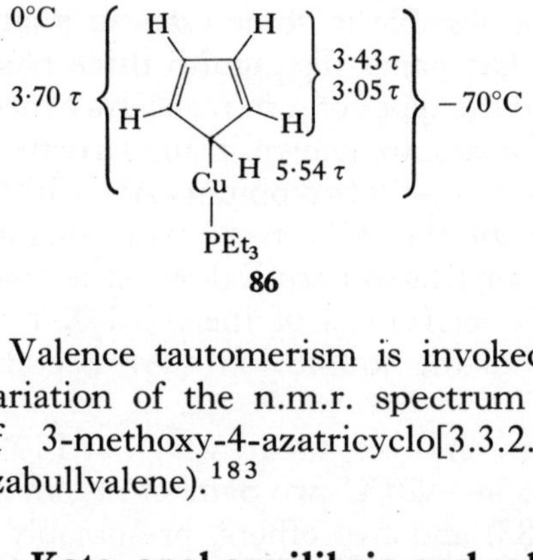

86

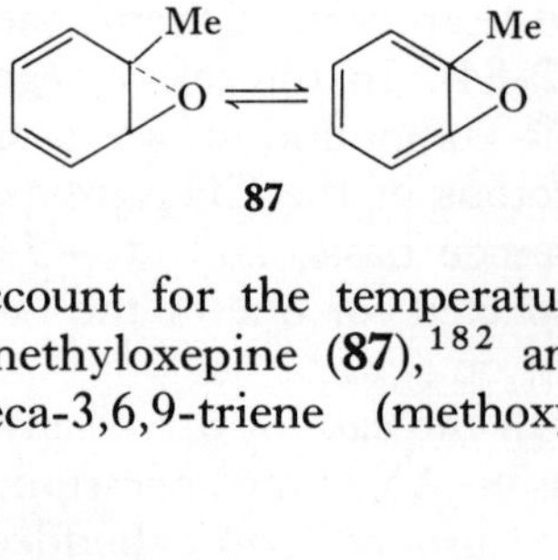

87

Valence tautomerism is invoked to account for the temperature variation of the n.m.r. spectrum of α-methyloxepine (**87**),[182] and of 3-methoxy-4-azatricyclo[3.3.2.0^{2,8}]deca-3,6,9-triene (methoxy-azabullvalene).[183]

G. Keto–enol equilibria and related phenomena

This type of equilibrium is characterized by forward and reverse rates that are affected by traces of catalysts. The information that n.m.r. spectrometry can give usually is confined to the position of the equilibrium. For example, it has been shown that the enol content of acyclic ketones and cycloalkanones is negligibly small,[184] in contrast to results from earlier chemical determinations,[185] which showed substantial enol contents.

The spectra of intramolecularly hydrogen bonded enol systems continue to receive attention. In the case of β-diketones and o-hydroxy-aromatic aldehydes and ketones, the width of the enolic proton peak is inversely related to the rate of intermolecular proton exchange.[186]

Multiple hydrogen bond systems have been examined; for example 2-(acetoacetyl)-1-naphthol (88) shows separate peaks for the two enol protons in the dienol form (88A) and for the one enol proton in the keto–enol form (88B).[187] Very strong enolic hydrogen bonds are found[188] in thiocarboxamides derived from dimedone, e.g. (89).

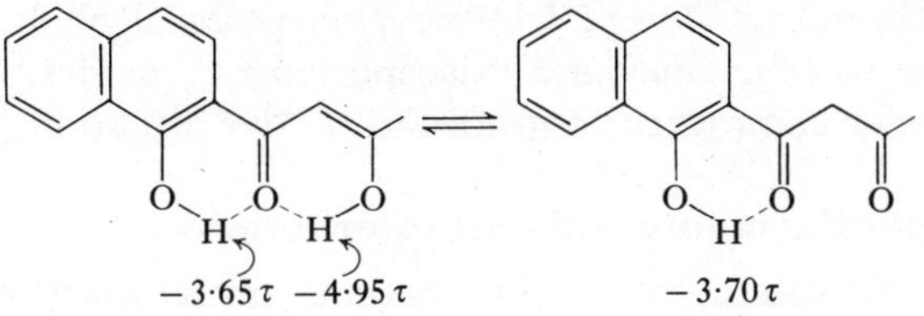

$-3\cdot65\,\tau$ $-4\cdot95\,\tau$ $-3\cdot70\,\tau$

88A   88B

$0\cdot3\,\tau$ $-8\cdot13\,\tau$

Me

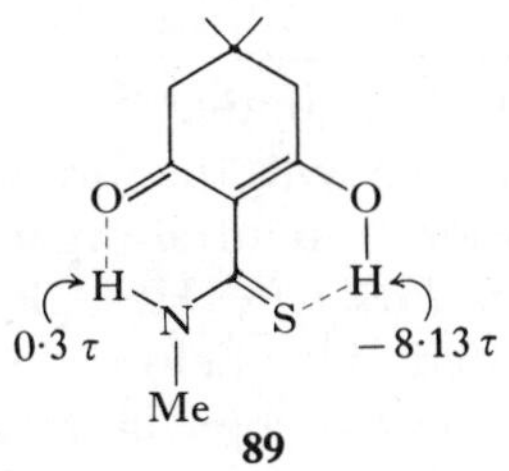

89

H. Molecular aggregation and self-association

The self-association of 9-anthraldehyde and 9-phenanthralde-hyde,[189] dibenzyl phenylboronate[190] and t-butylphenol[191] have been studied by n.m.r. techniques. Molecular-aggregation phenomena have been studied with metallochlorophylls (e.g., zinc phaeophytin-a)[192] and with the dye acridine orange (90) in dilute aqueous solution.[193]

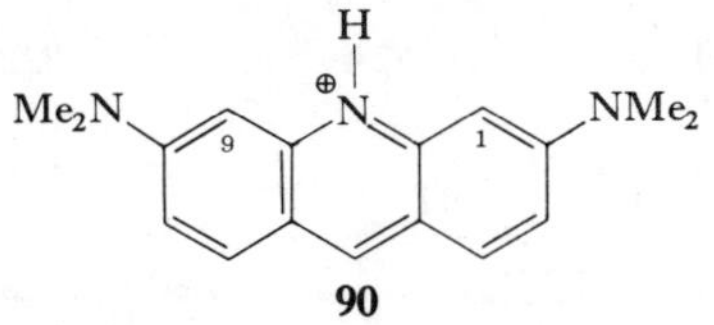

Me_2N NMe_2

90

In the latter case, the pairs of flat molecules are arranged with C_9 and C_1 of one molecule arranged over the terminal rings of the second.

I. Complex formation and hydrogen bonding

N.m.r. studies of hydrogen-bonded complex formation include work on the systems chloroform–pyridine,[194] phenol–base (bases included pyridine and derivatives, ethers, amides and carbonyl compounds),[195] chloroform–organometallic base (e.g., Me_3SnNEt_2),[196] dimethylformamide–benzene[197] and *sym*-trinitrobenzene and aliphatic amines.[198] Though not really an equilibrium phenomenon, intramolecular hydrogen bonding is considered here. Amongst work in this field can be cited that on intramolecular hydrogen bonding[199] and hydroxyl–π bonding[200] in [2.2.1]-bicycloheptane alcohols, and hydrogen bonding in sparteine- and α-isosparteine-N-oxides.[201] Work on charge-transfer complexes continues to receive attention.[202, 203]

J. Other specific solute–solvent interactions

Non-specific solute–solvent interactions are reviewed elsewhere in this Volume (p. 83). However certain interactions that are chemical in nature and can be studied by n.m.r. will be mentioned. These include the hydration of pyruvic acid[204] and hydration and hemiacetal formation from carbonyl compounds.[205]

The spate of papers dealing with the formation of stable carbonium ions formed via protonation of neutral organic molecules in strongly acidic solvents, such as HSO_3F, $HSO_3F–SbF_5–SO_2$ and 100% H_2SO_4, continues unabated. This field is dominated by Olah and his co-workers, and n.m.r. spectroscopy is an essential technique. Examples of compounds studied are (the structures given are those of the protonated forms before cleavage) aliphatic alcohols (**91**),[206] aldehydes (**92**),[207, 208] ketones (**93**)[208, 209] and carboxylic acids (**94**),[208, 210] aliphatic thiols (**95**) and sulphides (**96**)[211] and aliphatic ethers (**97**).[212] β-p-Anisylethyl chloride (**98**) in $SbF_5–SO_2$ gives the

$$\overset{\oplus}{ROH_2}$$
91

$$R-C\overset{\displaystyle O-H}{\underset{\displaystyle H}{\diagup}}$$
92A

$$\rightleftharpoons$$

$$R-C\overset{\displaystyle \overset{H}{\diagdown}\overset{\oplus}{O}}{\underset{\displaystyle H}{\diagup}}$$
92B

93A $\rightleftharpoons$ **93B**

$$R-C\overset{\displaystyle \overset{\oplus}{OH}}{\underset{\displaystyle OH}{\diagup}}$$
94

$$\overset{\oplus}{R.SH_2}$$
95

$$\overset{\oplus}{R'.S.R''}\;\;H$$
96

$$\overset{\oplus}{R'.O.R''}\;\;H$$
97

p-anisonium cation (**99**).[213] Tertiary alkyl carbonium ions are formed directly from hydrocarbons in FSO_3H–SbF_5, e.g., *n*-butane or isobutane give the t-butyl cation (5·50 τ).[214] Acetylacetone, when dissolved in HF–SbF_5, gives a mixture of the mono- (**100**) and di-cation (**101**) species.[215]

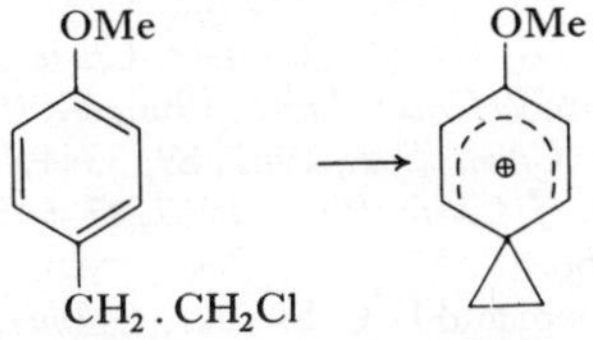

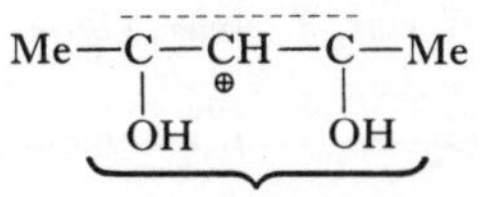

K. **Proton-exchange processes**

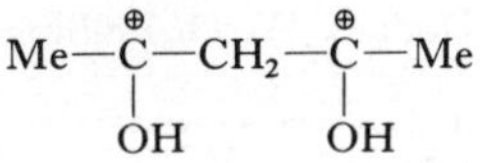

Proton–deuteron exchange reactions are most easily studied by n.m.r. Examples are the exchange of aromatic protons in phenols under alkaline conditions,[216,217] exchange of the α-protons in methoxyacetone in aqueous solution,[218] exchange of NH protons in triethylammonium ion,[219] exchange of the nuclear protons of hydroxyindoles in deuterium oxide under mildly basic conditions[220] and exchange of aromatic protons of substituted benzophenones in deuterosulphuric acid.[221]

REFERENCES

1. R. R. Ernst, R. Freeman, B. Gestblom and T. R. Lusebrink, *Mol. Phys.*, 1967, **13**, 283.
2. R. Freeman and B. Gestblom, *J. Chem. Phys.*, 1967, **47**, 2744.
3. R. R. Ernst, *Adv. Magnetic Resonance*, 1966, **2**, 1.
3a. G. E. Hall, *Ann. Rev. N.M.R. Spectroscopy*, 1968, **1**, 227.
4. L. Petrakis, *J. Chem. Educ.*, 1967, **44**, 432.
5. T. M. Connor, D. H. Whiffen and K. A. McLauchlan, *Mol. Phys.*, 1967, **13**, 221.
6. G. Govil and D. H. Whiffen, *Mol. Phys.*, 1967, **12**, 449.
7. H. R. Ward and R. G. Lawler, *J. Amer. Chem. Soc.*, 1967, **89**, 5518; R. G. Lawler, *ibid.*, p. 5519.
7a. J. Bargon, H. Fischer and U. Johnsen, *Z. Naturforsch.*, 1967, **22a**, 1551; J. Bargon and H. Fischer, *ibid.*, 1556.

8. L. C. Snyder and S. Meiboom, *J. Chem. Phys.*, 1967, **47**, 1480; S. Meiboom and L. C. Snyder, *J. Amer. Chem. Soc.*, 1967, **89**, 1038.
9. M. Cocivera, *J. Chem. Phys.*, 1967, **47**, 3061.
10. C. S. Yannoni, G. R. Ceasar and B. P. Dailey, *J. Amer. Chem. Soc.*, 1967, **89**, 2833.
11. R. A. Bernheim and B. J. Lavery, *J. Amer. Chem. Soc.*, 1967, **89**, 1279.
12. C. M. Woodman, *Mol. Phys.*, 1967, **13**, 365.
13. R. A. Bernheim and T. R. Krugh, *J. Amer. Chem. Soc.*, 1967, **89**, 6784; L. C. Snyder and S. Meiboom, *J. Chem. Phys.*, 1966, **44**, 4057; A. D. Buckingham and E. E. Burnell, *J. Amer. Chem. Soc.*, 1967, **89**, 3341.
14. A. Saupe and J. Nehrin, *J. Chem. Phys.*, 1967, **47**, 5459; J. I. Musher, *ibid.*, 1967, **46**, 1537; 1967, **47**, 5460.
15. E. Sackmann, S. Meiboom and L. C. Snyder, *J. Amer. Chem. Soc.*, 1967, **89**, 5981.
16. K. D. Lawson and T. J. Flautt, *J. Amer. Chem. Soc.*, 1967, **89**, 5490.
17. C. C. McDonald and W. D. Phillips, *J. Amer. Chem. Soc.*, 1967, **89**, 6332.
18. C. C. McDonald, W. D. Phillips and J. Lazar, *J. Amer. Chem. Soc.*, 1967, **89**, 4166.
19. G. J. Karabatsos, G. C. Sonnichsen, N. Hsi and D. J. Fenoglio, *J. Amer. Chem. Soc.*, 1967, **89**, 5067.
20. G. J. Karabatsos and N. Hsi, *J. Amer. Chem. Soc.*, 1965, **87**, 2864.
21. J. W. ApSimon, W. G. Craig, P. V. Demarco, D. W. Mathieson, L. Saunders and W. B. Whalley, *Tetrahedron*, 1967, **23**, 2339.
22. H. M. McConnell, *J. Chem. Phys.*, 1957, **27**, 226.
23. J. W. ApSimon, W. G. Craig, P. V. Demarco, D. W. Mathieson, L. Saunders and W. B. Whalley, *Tetrahedron*, 1967, **23**, 2357.
24. J. W. ApSimon, W. G. Craig, P. V. Demarco, D. W. Mathieson and W. B. Whalley, *Tetrahedron*, 1967, **23**, 2374.
25. A. Daniel and A. A. Pavia, *Tetrahedron Letters*, 1967, 1145.
26. A. C. Huitric, D. B. Roll and J. R. DeBoer, *J. Org. Chem.*, 1967, **32**, 1661.
27. N. Nakagawa, S. Saito, A. Suzuki and M. Itoh, *Tetrahedron Letters*, 1967, 1003.
28. Y. L. Chow, *Angew. Chem.*, 1967, **79**, 51.
29. S. Takada, K. Yamada, S. Nakamura and Y. Hirate, *Chem. Comm.*, 1967, 538.
30. J. A. Claisse and D. I. Davies, *J. Chem. Soc. B*, 1967, 679.
31 E. Pretsch, H. Immer, C. Pascual, K. Schaffner and W. Simon, *Helv. Chim. Acta*, 1967, **50**, 105.
32. "Aromaticity, An International Symposium held at Sheffield on 6th and 8th July, 1966." Special Publication No. 21 London, The Chemical Society, 1967.
33. F. Sondheimer, I. C. Calder, J. A. Elix, Y. Gaoni, P. J. Garratt, K. Grohmann, G. Di Maio, J. Mayer, M. V. Sargent and R. Wolovsky, Ref. 32, p. 75.
34. H. C. Longuet-Higgins, Ref. 32, p. 109.
35. I. C. Calder and F. Sondheimer, *Chem. Comm.*, 1966, 904.
36. F. Baer, H. Kuhn and W. Regel, *Z. Naturforsch.*, 1967, **22a**, 103.
37. H. P. Figeys, *Chem. Comm.*, 1967, 495.
38. W. H. Okamura and F. Sondheimer, *J. Amer. Chem. Soc.*, 1967, **89**, 5991.
39. R. Wolovsky and F. Sondheimer, *J. Amer. Chem. Soc.*, 1965, **87**, 5720; F. Sondheimer, R. Wolovsky, P. J. Garratt and I. C. Calder, *ibid.*, 1966, **88**, 2610.
40. K. G. Untch and D. C. Wysocki, *J. Amer. Chem. Soc.*, 1966, **88**, 2608.
41. C. C. Leznoff and F. Sondheimer, *J. Amer. Chem. Soc.*, 1967, **89**, 4247.
42. M. J. S. Dewar and G. J. Gleicher, *J. Amer. Chem. Soc.*, 1965, **87**, 685.
43. J. M. Brown, *Chem. Comm.*, 1967, 638.

44. S. Winstein, M. Ogliaruso, M. Sakai and J. M. Nicholson, *J. Amer. Chem. Soc.*, 1967, **89**, 3656.
45. D. G. Farnum and C. F. Wilcox, *J. Amer. Chem. Soc.*, 1967, **89**, 5379.
46. R. W. Murray and M. L. Kaplan, *Tetrahedron Letters*, 1967, 1307.
47. A. J. Leusink, W. Drenth, J. G. Noltes and G. J. M. van der Kerk, *Tetrahedron Letters*, 1967, 1263.
48. V. Boekelheide and J. B. Phillips, *J. Amer. Chem. Soc.*, 1967, **89**, 1695.
49. V. Boekelheide and T. Miyasaka, *J. Amer. Chem. Soc.*, 1967, **89**, 1709.
50. H. Meier, E. Muller and H. Suhr, *Tetrahedron*, 1967, **23**, 3713.
51. S. C. Dickerman and J. R. Haase, *J. Amer. Chem. Soc.*, 1967, **89**, 5458.
52. E. Clar, B. A. McAndrew and M. Zander, *Tetrahedron*, 1967, **23**, 985.
53. T. B. Cobb and J. D. Memory, *J. Chem. Phys.*, 1967, **47**, 2020.
54. M. L. Heffernan, A. J. Jones and P. J. Black, *Austral. J. Chem.*, 1967, **20**, 589.
55. E. Mühle, *Ann. Physik.*, 1966, **18**, 130.
56. A. J. Fry, B. W. Bowen and P. A. Leermakers, *J. Org. Chem.*, 1967, **32**, 1970.
57. K. G. Kidd, G. Kotowycz and T. Schaefer, *Canad. J. Chem.*, 1967, **45**, 2155.
58. M. Flammang-Barbieux, J. Nasielski and R. H. Martin, *Tetrahedron Letters*, 1967, 743.
59. L. S. Rattet, L. Mandell and J. H. Goldstein, *J. Amer. Chem. Soc.*, 1967, **89**, 2253.
60. F. Kaplan and J. D. Roberts, *J. Amer. Chem. Soc.*, 1961, **83**, 4666.
61. R. R. Fraser and P. Hanbury, *Canad. J. Chem.*, 1967, **45**, 1485.
62. K. Kondo and K. Mislow, *Tetrahedron Letters*, 1967, 1325.
63. E. Bullock, E. E. Burnell and B. Gregory, *Chem. Comm.*, 1967, 193.
64. G. E. Hall, D. Hughes, D. Rae and A. P. Rhodes, *Tetrahedron Letters*, 1967, 241.
65. M. Kajtár and L. Radics, *Chem. Comm.*, 1967, 784.
66. B. Halpern, J. W. Westley and B. Weinstein, *Chem. Comm.*, 1967, 160.
67. T. S. Sorensen, *Canad. J. Chem.*, 1967, **45**, 1585.
68. R. J. Seymour and R. G. Jones, *Tetrahedron Letters*, 1967, 2021.
69. V. J. Morlino and R. B. Martin, *J. Amer. Chem. Soc.*, 1967, **89**, 3107.
70. W. H. Pirkle and T. G. Burlingame, *Tetrahedron Letters*, 1967, 4039.
71. W. H. Pirkle and S. D. Beare, *J. Amer. Chem. Soc.*, 1967, **89**, 5485.
72. W. H. Pirkle, *J. Amer. Chem. Soc.*, 1966, **88**, 1837.
73. T. G. Burlingame and W. H. Pirkle, *J. Amer. Chem. Soc.*, 1966, **88**, 4294.
74. J. C. Jochims, G. Taigel and A. Seelinger, *Tetrahedron Letters*, 1967, 1901.
75. W. T. Dixon, *Tetrahedron Letters*, 1967, 2531.
76. W. T. Dixon, *Chem. Comm.*, 1967, 402.
77. N. Jonathan, S. Gordon and B. P. Dailey, *J. Chem. Phys.*, 1962, **36**, 2443.
78. W. B. Smith, W. H. Watson and S. Chiranjeevi, *J. Amer. Chem. Soc.*, 1967, **89**, 1438.
79. D. T. Witiak, D. B. Patel and Y. Lin, *J. Amer. Chem. Soc.*, 1967, **89**, 1908.
80. K. C. Ramey, D. C. Lini, R. M. Moriarty, H. Gopal and H. G. Welsh, *J. Amer. Chem. Soc.*, 1967, **89**, 2401.
81. D. Gagnaire, M. Taieb and P. Vottero, *Bull. Soc. chim. France*, 1967, 753.
82. W. J. Mijs, *Rec. Trav. chim.*, 1967, **86**, 220.
83. C. Pascual and W. Simon, *Helv. Chim. Acta*, 1967, **50**, 94.
84. M. Anteunis and D. Tavernier, *Bull. Soc. chim. belges*, 1967, **76**, 432.
85. K. Hayamizu and O. Yamoto, *J. Mol. Spectroscopy*, 1967, **23**, 121.
86. D. C. Ayres and J. W. Mundy, *Chem. Comm.*, 1967, 222.
87. J. T. Wang and C. H. Van Dyke, *Chem. Comm.*, 1967, 612.

88. R. R. Dean and W. McFarlane, *Mol. Phys.*, 1967, **12**, 289.
89. S. Mohanty and P. Venkateswarlu, *Mol. Phys.*, 1967, **12**, 277.
90. J. Meinwald and B. E. Kaplan, *J. Amer. Chem. Soc.*, 1967, **89**, 2611.
91. E. A. V. Ebsworth, *Pure Appl. Chem.*, 1966, **13**, 189.
92. E. A. V. Ebsworth, G. Rocktäschel and J. C. Thompson, *J. Chem. Soc. A*, 1967, 362.
93. E. A. V. Ebsworth and J. C. Thompson, *J. Chem. Soc. A*, 1967, 69.
94. E. O. Bishop and M. A. Jensen, *Chem. Comm.*, 1966, 922.
95. E. R. Malinowski and T. Vladimiroff, *J. Amer. Chem. Soc.*, 1964, **86**, 3375.
96. W. McFarlane, *J. Chem. Soc. A*, 1967, 528.
97. W. Kitching, V. G. K. Das and P. R. Wells, *Chem. Comm.*, 1967, 356.
98. J. P. Kintzinger and J. M. Lehn, *Chem. Comm.*, 1967, 660.
99. K. Tori, M. Ohtsuru and K. Aono, *J. Amer. Chem. Soc.*, 1967, **89**, 2765.
100. A. K. Bose and I. Kugajevsky, *Tetrahedron*, 1967, **23**, 1489.
101. J.-F. Biellmann and H. Callot, *Bull. Soc. chim. France.*, 1967, 397.
102. P. Diehl, R. K. Harris and R. G. Jones, *Progr. N.M.R. Spectroscopy*, 1967, **3**, 1.
103. J. A. Musso and J. Metzger, *Bull. Soc. chim. France*, 1968, 463.
104. S. M. Castellano and A. A. Bothner-By, *J. Chem. Phys.*, 1967, **47**, 5543.
105. G. Govil, *Mol. Phys.*, 1967, **12**, 293.
106. J. M. Read, R. E. Mayo and J. H. Goldstein, *J. Mol. Spectroscopy*, 1967, **22**, 419.
107. S. Castellano, C. Sun and R. Kastelnik, *J. Chem. Phys.*, 1967, **46**, 327.
108. E. M. Arnett, J. C. Sanda, J. M. Bollinger and M. Barber, *J. Amer. Chem. Soc.*, 1967, **89**, 5389.
109. E. A. Hill and J. D. Roberts, *J. Amer. Chem. Soc.*, 1967, **89**, 2047.
110. E. Lustig and E. P. Ragelis, *J. Org. Chem.*, 1967, **32**, 1398.
111. R. Breslow and G. Ryan, *J. Amer. Chem. Soc.*, 1967, **89**, 3073.
112. T. A. Wittstruck and E. N. Trachtenberg, *J. Amer. Chem. Soc.*, 1967, **89**, 3810.
113. E. Lustig, E. P. Ragelis, N. Duy and J. A. Ferretti, *J. Amer. Chem. Soc.*, 1967, **89**, 3953.
114. A. J. Carty and R. K. Harris, *Chem. Comm.*, 1967, 234.
115. E. G. Finer and R. K. Harris, *Mol. Phys.*, 1967, **12**, 457.
116. E. G. Finer and R. K. Harris, *Mol. Phys.*, 1967, **13**, 65.
117. E. O. Bishop, P. R. Carey and M. A. Jensen, *Mol. Phys.*, 1967, **12**, 589.
118. S. Mohanty, *Mol. Phys.*, 1967, **13**, 83.
119. A. Kumar, *Mol. Phys.*, 1967, **12**, 593.
120. A. G. Horfmann and D. A. Robertson, *J. Amer. Chem. Soc.*, 1967, **89**, 5974.
121. R. A. Hoffman, *J. Chem. Phys.*, 1967, **46**, 3277.
122. J. J. Bolmarcich and J. Macomber, *J. Chem. Phys.*, 1967, **46**, 392.
123. A. Allerhand, H. S. Gutowsky, J. Jonas and R. A. Meinzer, *J. Amer. Chem. Soc.*, 1966, **88**, 3185.
124. F. A. L. Anet and A. J. R. Bourn, *J. Amer. Chem. Soc.*, 1967, **89**, 760.
125. A. Allerhand, F. Chen and H. S. Gutowsky, *J. Chem. Phys.*, 1965, **42**, 3040.
126. R. K. Harris and N. Sheppard, *J. Mol. Spectroscopy*, 1967, **23**, 231.
127. G. Govil and H. J. Bernstein, *J. Chem. Phys.*, 1967, **47**, 2818.
128. K. K. Deb and R. J. Abraham, *J. Mol. Spectroscopy*, 1967, **23**, 393.
129. H. S. Gutowsky, J. Jonas and T. H. Siddall III, *J. Amer. Chem. Soc.*, 1967, **89**, 4300.
130. A. Mannschreck, A. Mattheus and G. Rissmann, *J. Mol. Spectroscopy*, 1967, **23**, 15.
131. G. M. Whitesides, J. P. Sevenair and R. W. Goetz, *J. Amer. Chem. Soc.*, 1967, **89**, 1135.

132. R. J. Abraham and M. A. Cooper, *J. Chem. Soc. B*, 1967, 202.
133. H. R. Buys, C. Altona and E. Havinga, *Tetrahedron Letters*, 1967, 3067.
134. J. R. Cavanaugh, *J. Amer. Chem. Soc.*, 1967, **89**, 1558.
135. G. W. Wood and E. P. Woo, *Canad. J. Chem.*, 1967, **45**, 1293.
136. S. Wolfe and J. R. Campbell, *Chem. Comm.*, 1967, 877.
137. R. W. Murray and M. L. Kaplan, *Tetrahedron*, 1967, **23**, 1575.
138. R. W. Murray, P. R. Story and M. L. Kaplan, *J. Amer. Chem. Soc.*, 1966, **88**, 526.
139. C. H. Bushweller, *J. Amer. Chem. Soc.*, 1967, **89**, 5978.
140. S. Wolfe and J. R. Campbell, *Chem. Comm.*, 1967, 874.
141. H. Bodot and Y. Gounelle, *Bull. Soc. chim. France*, 1967, 870.
142. P. Duféy, J. Delmau and J.-C. Duplan, *Bull. Soc. chim. France*, 1967, 1336.
143. J. Altman, H. Gilbea, D. Ginsburg and A. Loewenstein, *Tetrahedron Letters*, 1967, 1329.
144. I. Gault, B. J. Price and I. O. Sutherland, *Chem. Comm.*, 1967, 540.
145. H. S. Gutowsky and P. A. Temussi, *J. Amer. Chem. Soc.*, 1967, **89**, 4358.
146. J. M. Lehn, F. G. Riddell, B. J. Price and I. O. Sutherland, *J. Chem. Soc. B*, 1967, 387.
147. F. G. Riddell, *J. Chem. Soc. B*, 1967, 560.
148. K. F. Purcell and J. R. Berschied, Jr., *J. Amer. Chem. Soc.*, 1967, **89**, 1579.
149. J. B. Lambert, R. G. Keske, R. E. Carhart and A. P. Jovanovich, *J. Amer. Chem. Soc.*, 1967, **89**, 3761
150. J. B. Lambert, *J. Amer. Chem. Soc.*, 1967, **89**, 1836.
151. J. P. Kintzinger, J. M. Lehn and J. Wagner, *Chem. Comm.*, 1967, 206.
152. J. E. Anderson and J. M. Lehn, *J. Amer. Chem. Soc.*, 1967, **89**, 81.
153. E. L. Allred, C. L. Anderson, R. L. Miller and A. L. Johnson, *Tetrahedron Letters*, 1967, 525.
154. B. J. Price and I. O. Sutherland, *J. Chem. Soc. B*, 1967, 573.
155. F. Conti and W. von Philipsborn, *Helv. Chim. Acta*, 1967, **50**, 603.
156. J. P. Chupp and J. F. Olin, *J. Org. Chem.*, 1967, **32**, 2297.
157. T. H. Siddall III and W. E. Stewart, *Chem. Comm.*, 1967, 393.
158. R. C. Neuman, Jr., D. N. Roark and V. Jonas, *J. Amer. Chem. Soc.*, 1967, **89**, 3412.
159. E. Lustig, W. R. Benson and N. Duy, *J. Org. Chem.*, 1967, **32**, 851.
160. K. Nagarajan, M. D. Nair and P. M. Pillai, *Tetrahedron*, 1967, **23**, 1683.
161. G. Fraenkel, M. P. Cava and D. R. Dalton, *J. Amer. Chem. Soc.*, 1967, **89**, 329.
162. G. J. Bishop, B. J. Price and I. O. Sutherland, *Chem. Comm.*, 1967, 672.
163. R. M. Moriarty, Sr., M. R. Murphy, S. J. Druck and L. May, *Tetrahedron Letters*, 1967, 1603.
164. S. van der Werf, T. Olijnsma and J. B. F. N. Engberts, *Tetrahedron Letters*, 1967, 689.
165. J. P. Marsh, Jr. and L. Goodman, *Tetrahedron Letters*, 1967, 683.
166. D. J. Bertelli and J. T. Gerig, *Tetrahedron Letters*, 1967, 2481.
167. A. P. Downing, W. D. Ollis and I. O. Sutherland, *Chem. Comm.*, 1967, 143.
168. Y. Shvo, E. C. Taylor and J. Bartulin, *Tetrahedron Letters*, 1967, 3259.
169. A. Mannschreck and U. Koelle, *Tetrahedron Letters*, 1967, 863.
170. G. P. Newsereff and S. Sternhell, *Tetrahedron Letters*, 1967, 2539.
171. R. K. Harris and R. A. Spragg, *Chem. Comm.*, 1967, 362.
172. F. A. L. Anet, H. D. Kaesz, A. Maasbol and S. Winstein, *J. Amer. Chem. Soc.*, 1967, **89**, 2489.

173. M. I. Bruce, M. Cooke, M. Green and F. G. A. Stone, *Chem. Comm.*, 1967, 523.
174. F. A. L. Anet, *J. Amer. Chem. Soc.*, 1967, **89**, 2491.
175. R. Ben-Shoshan and R. Pettit, *J. Amer. Chem. Soc.*, 1967, **89**, 2231.
176. J. K. Becconsall, B. E. Job and S. O'Brien, *J. Chem. Soc. A*, 1967, 423.
177. F. A. Cotton, J. W. Faller and A. Musco, *Inorg. Chem.*, 1967, **6**, 179.
178. W. B. Wise, D. C. Lini and K. C. Ramey, *Chem. Comm.*, 1967, 463.
179. F. A. Cotton, A. Musco and G. Yagupsky, *J. Amer. Chem. Soc.*, 1967, **89**, 6136.
180. M. J. Bennett, F. A. Cotton, A. Davidson, J. W. Faller, S. J. Lippard and S. M. Moorehouse, *J. Amer. Chem. Soc.*, 1966, **88**, 4371.
181. G. M. Whitesides and J. S. Fleming, *J. Amer. Chem. Soc.*, 1967, **89**, 2855.
182. H. Günther, R. Schubart and E. Vogel, *Z. Naturforsch.*, 1967, **22b**, 25.
183. L. Paquette, T. J. Barton and E. B. Whipple, *J. Amer. Chem. Soc.*, 1967, **89**, 5481.
184. N. L. Allinger, L. W. Chow and R. A. Ford, *J. Org. Chem.*, 1967, **32**, 1994.
185. A. Gero, *J. Org. Chem.*, 1954, **19**, 469, 1960; 1961, **26**, 3156.
186. D. C. Nonhebel, *Tetrahedron*, 1968, **24**, 1869.
187. G. Dudek and E. P. Dudek, *Tetrahedron*, 1967, **23**, 3245.
188. E. P. Dudek and G. Dudek, *J. Org. Chem.*, 1967, **32**, 823.
189. Gurudata, R. E. Klinck and J. B. Stothers, *Canad. J. Chem.*, 1967, **45**, 213.
190. E. F. Mooney and P. H. Winson, *Chem. Comm.*, 1967, 341.
191. F. Strohbusch and H. Zimmermann, *Ber. Bunsengesellschaft Phys. Chem.*, 1967, **71**, 679.
192. L. J. Boucher and J. L. Katz, *J. Amer. Chem. Soc.*, 1967, **89**, 4703.
193. D. J. Blears and S. S. Danyluk, *J. Amer. Chem. Soc.*, 1967, **89**, 21.
194. T. J. V. Findlay, J. S. Keniry, A. D. Kidman and V. A. Pickles, *Trans. Faraday Soc.*, 1967, **63**, 846.
195. G. Socrates, *Trans Faraday Soc.*, 1967, **63**, 1083.
196. E. W. Abel, D. A. Armitage and S. P. Tyfield, *J. Chem. Soc. A*, 1967, 554.
197. R. Radeglia, *Ber. Bunsengesellschaft Phys. Chem.*, 1967, **71**, 1145.
198. M. R. Crampton and V. Gold, *J. Chem. Soc. B.*, 1967, 23.
199. R. J. Ouellette, K. Liptak and G. E. Booth, *J. Org. Chem.*, 1967, **32**, 2394.
200. D. C. Kleinfelter, *J. Amer. Chem. Soc.*, 1967, **89**, 1734.
201. P. J. Krueger and J. Skolik, *Tetrahedron*, 1967, **23**, 1799.
202. N. M. D. Brown, R. Foster and C. A. Fyfe, *J. Chem. Soc. B*, 1967, 406.
203. R. Foster and C. A. Fyfe, *Nature*, 1967, **213**, 591.
204. V. S. Griffiths and G. Socrates, *Trans. Faraday Soc.*, 1967, **63**, 673.
205. D. L. Hooper, *J. Chem. Soc. B*, 1967, 169.
206. G. A. Olah, J. Sommer and E. Namanworth, *J. Amer. Chem. Soc.*, 1967, **89**, 3576.
207. G. A. Olah, D. H. O'Brien and M. Calin, *J. Amer. Chem. Soc.*, 1967, **89**, 3582.
208. M. Brookhart, G. C. Levy and S. Winstein, *J. Amer. Chem. Soc.*, 1967, **89**, 1735.
209. G. A. Olah, M. Calin and D. H. O'Brien, *J. Amer. Chem. Soc.*, 1967, **89**, 3586.
210. G. A. Olah and A. M. White, *J. Amer. Chem. Soc.*, 1967, **89**, 3591.
211. G. A. Olah, D. H. O'Brien and C. U. Pittmann, Jr., *J. Amer. Chem. Soc.*, 1967, **89**, 2996.
212. G. A. Olah and D. H. O'Brien, *J. Amer. Chem. Soc.*, 1967, **89**, 1725.
213. G. A. Olah, E. Namanworth and M. B. Comisarow, *J. Amer. Chem. Soc.*, 1967, **89**, 711; G. A. Olah, M. B. Comisarow, E. Namanworth and B. Ramsey, *ibid.*, p. 5259.
214. G. A. Olah and J. Lukas, *J. Amer. Chem. Soc.*, 1967, **89**, 4739.

215. D. M. Brouwer, *Chem. Comm.*, 1967, 515.
216. J. Massicot, *Bull. Soc. chim. France*, 1967, 2204.
217. J. Massicot and F. Zonszajh, *Bull Soc. chim. France*, 1967, 2206.
218. J. Hine, G. Hampton and B. C. Menon, *J. Amer. Chem. Soc.*, 1967, **89**, 2664.
219. E. K. Ralph III and E. Grunwald, *J. Amer. Chem. Soc.*, 1967, **89**, 2963.
220. J. W. Daly and B. Witkop, *J. Amer. Chem. Soc.*, 1967, **89**, 1032.
221. G. L. Elan and C. A. Kingsbury, *J. Org. Chem.*, 1967, **32**, 1864.

Nuclear Magnetic Resonance Spectroscopy in the Study of Carbohydrates and Related Compounds

T. D. INCH

Chemical Defence Experimental Establishment,
Porton Down, Nr. Salisbury, Wiltshire, England

I. INTRODUCTION

THE EARLY pioneering papers of Lemieux *et al.*[1] in 1958 demonstrated the tremendous potential of n.m.r. techniques in the study of carbohydrate molecules and opened new vistas to the carbohydrate chemist. Between 1958 and 1964 many n.m.r. studies of carbohydrates were reported and several empirical rules were formulated to assist the carbohydrate chemist in structural, configurational and conformational studies. An excellent summary of the state of affairs up to 1964 has been presented by Hall.[2] In the comparatively short time that has elapsed since Hall's review, ever increasing use has been made of n.m.r. spectroscopy in the study of carbohydrates. Consequently, the mass of evidence now available has drawn attention to the shortcomings of some of the earlier empirical rules, and at the same time has led to the formulation of new ones. Also, many of the more sophisticated techniques, such as spin-decoupling, spectrum subtraction and spectrum accumulation, that were still in their early days in 1964 have now been extensively employed and examples will be given in this review. It has become apparent that suitable choice of solvent can simplify spectrum analysis and that a better understanding of long-range coupling effects has enabled the detection of these effects to become a considerable aid to configurational and conformational analysis. Examples of these phenomena will be discussed. This review essentially covers the period 1965–1967, and is concerned principally with those papers that further our understanding of the n.m.r. characteristics of carbohydrates, while at the same time describing the structural information n.m.r. studies provide. No attempt has been made to cover all the reports in which n.m.r. spectroscopy has been used routinely to establish the primary structure of carbohydrates.

II. CONFORMATIONAL STUDIES OF PYRANOID DERIVATIVES

(WITH THE HYDROXYL GROUPS PREPONDERANTLY PROTECTED)

Since the pioneering studies of Lemieux and his co-workers,[1] the application of n.m.r. for establishing the conformation of pyranoid derivatives has received extensive attention. The original generalizations that equatorially orientated hydrogens resonate at lower field than chemically similar, but axially orientated, hydrogens and that vicinal coupling constants are two to three times greater when the projected valency angle is about 180° than when the angle is 60° have almost acquired the status of chemical laws. The latter generalization in conjunction with the Karplus equation,[3] which relates the coupling constant between vicinal protons to the dihedral angle they subtend, has been extensively used to determine the conformation of many pyranoid and furanoid sugars. Over the last few years however it has become abundantly clear that the Karplus equation can only be used directly in a few limited cases,[4] since a variety of variables affect the precise relationship between coupling constants and dihedral angles.[5–8]

Consequently, more recent conformational studies have utilized the Karplus equation only as a guide to conformation and have not attempted the precise calculation of dihedral angles. In addition, various chemical-shift correlations have been shown to be of value in providing conformational information.

Lemieux and Stevens[9] have introduced a set of empirical rules to enable the chemical shift of any proton relative to β-D-glucopyranose tetra-acetate (1) to be calculated. The rules are (τ values p.p.m.)—

(1) If the proton under consideration has remained axial (a) subtract 0·20 p.p.m. for an axial acetoxy group at a neighbouring position, (b) subtract 0·25 p.p.m. for an opposition of the proton by an axial acetoxy group.

(2) If the proton under consideration has achieved the equatorial orientation (a) subtract 0·6 p.p.m. because of the change of environment of an axial hydrogen to that of an equatorial hydrogen, (b) add 0·20 p.p.m. for an axial acetoxy group at a neighbouring position.

1

Table I shows the agreement between the observed and calculated chemical shifts at H-1 and H-5 in a series of hexopyranose acetates.

TABLE I

Chemical shifts in a series of hexopyranose acetates

| Compound | Chemical shift (τ values) in $CDCl_3$ as solvent | | | |
| | H-1 | | H-5 | |
	Found	*Calculated*	*Found*	*Calculated*
β-D-glucopyranose	4·24	4·25	6·1	6·1
β-D-mannopyranose	4·07	4·05	6·1	6·1
β-D-allopyranose	4·00	4·00	5·8	5·85
β-D-galactopyranose	4·26	4·25	5·9	5·9
β-D-gulopyranose	4·00	4·00	5·7	5·65
α-D-glucopyranose	3·66	3·65	5·9	5·85
α-D-mannopyranose	3·91	3·85	5·9	5·85
α-D-galactopyranose	3·64	3·65	5·6	5·65
α-D-altropyranose	3·98	4·05	5·5	5·6
α-D-gulopyranose	3·78	3·85	5·4	5·4

The value of these chemical-shift correlations for determining configuration is best exemplified by consideration of the α- and β-D-manno-pyranose acetates. The anomers cannot be distinguished by their J_{12} coupling constants since H-1 and H-2 occupy a gauche relationship in each case. The anomers can be distinguished by the relative chemical shifts of H-1 and H-5. The equatorial H-1 in the α-D-anomer resonates at lower field than the axial H-1 in the β-D-anomer. Also the effect of the axial acetoxy group in the α-D-anomer causes H-5 to resonate at 0·2 p.p.m. to lower field than in the β-D-anomer in accordance with rule 1(b).

Lemieux and Stevens[9] also demonstrated that there are exceptions to the generalization that equatorial protons resonate at lower field than chemically similar, but axially orientated, protons, but did not report any anomeric pairs controversing this generalization. Anomeric exceptions have been subsequently reported.[10]

Lemieux and Stevens[9] have reported one of the first clear cases of virtual long-range coupling[11] in carbohydrate chemistry. The anomeric proton signal for β-D-galactopyranose penta-acetate appeared as a quartet with a smaller spacing of 1 c./sec. at 60 Mc./sec. Long-range coupling was precluded when this splitting disappeared when the spectrum was measured at 100 Mc./sec. The virtual long-range coupling was not surprising since H-2 and H-3 differed by only 0·2 p.p.m. in chemical shift, but were strongly coupled (10·2 c./sec.). It should be noted that whereas long-range coupling itself provides a great deal of configurational and conformational information, virtual long-range coupling does little to further our understanding of molecular geometry.

The chemical-shift rules obtained from a study of hexopyranose acetates have been applied to pentopyranose acetates. Measured coupling constants and chemical shifts were in good agreement with calculated parameters. For β-D-ribopentopyranose tetra-acetate (2)

2

the chemical shift data was consistent with either a C-1 or 1-C conformation,[12] but the coupling constants indicated that the ribopento-pyranose derivative was a mixture of the two chair conformations at room temperature. It has subsequently been shown,[13] by a 220 Mc./sec. study, that β-D-ribopentopyranose tetra-acetate does exist as a rapidly equilibrating mixture at room temperature and that at lower temperatures both the 1-C and C-1 forms may be identified.

An attempt has been made[10] to utilize chemical-shift data to establish the molecular conformation of some N-acyl-2-acylamido-D-hexopyranose acetates. The effect of a di-N-acyl substituent on the chemical shift of the anomeric proton was most outstanding. For example N-benzoylation of (3) caused a chemical shift change for H-1 (axial) of 0·78 p.p.m. from 4·23 to 3·45 τ, whereas N-benzoylation of (4) caused a chemical shift change for H-1 (equatorial) of 0·20 p.p.m.

3   R = H
3A R = COC₆H₅

4   R = H
4A R = COC₆H₅

from 3·80 to 3·60 τ. The net effect of this and like changes is that the di-N-acyl derivatives of 2-amino-2-deoxy-D-pyranose acetates represent the first examples in which the axial anomeric protons resonate at lower field than the equatorial anomeric protons. Di-N-acyl substituents produced other configuration-dependent chemical-shift changes and following a study of these changes in gluco- and galacto-pyranose derivatives an attempt was made to utilize the conclusions reached, to determine the conformations adopted by α- and β-N-acetylbenzamido-D-mannopyranose tetra-acetates.

An interesting summary[14] of the subtleties of the anomeric effect[15] that have been brought to light by n.m.r. studies has appeared recently. An example of the importance of the anomeric effect in controlling conformation is provided by β-D-xylopyranosyl chloride triacetate where all the substituent groups adopt axial orientations.[16] A detailed study of a series of acetylated aldopyranosyl halides has indicated that in all cases the chair conformation adopted permits the halogen substituent to occupy an axial orientation.[17] Similarly, an example of a "reverse anomeric effect" has been indicated by n.m.r. studies of N-(tetra-O-acetyl-α-D-glucopyranosyl)pyridinium and 4-methyl-pyridinium bromides, whose spectra require a 1-C conformation for these compounds, wherein the pyridinium group is in an equatorial orientation.[18]

Coxon[19] has shown that for a series of 2,3,4-tri-O-acyl-D-ribo-pyranose derivatives (e.g., **2**) the particular chair conformation adopted depends principally on the operation or non-operation of the anomeric effect. It was found unexpectedly that although the protons H-2–H-3 and H-3–H-4 have the same type of *gauche* (axial–equatorial) orientation in the C-1 and 1-C conformations, the values of J_{23} and J_{34} (2·8–3·4 c./sec. and 2·6–3·3 c./sec., respectively) in the C-1 chair conformation are characteristically smaller than those (3·6–4·0 c./sec.) in the compounds that exist predominantly in the 1-C conformation. Conformational rather than electronegativity effects were invoked to rationalize these differences.

Also in D-ribopyranose derivatives there appears to be a conformational dependence of the geminal $J_{5e, 5a}$ coupling. The numerical values of $J_{5e, 5a}$ (10·8–10·9 c./sec.) for the α-halides and the α-benzoate in the C-1 conformation are appreciably smaller than those (13·4–14·0 c./sec.) of the β-halides in the 1-C conformation. If it is assumed that these geminal couplings have negative signs, then the results agree with the predictions of a molecular orbital theory of geminal coupling,[20] namely, that the methylene protons in vicinal *gauche* and *trans*-orientations show a geminal coupling more negative than that of protons both in a *gauche* relationship with the substituent.

To facilitate the n.m.r. studies of the series of D-ribopyranose derivatives, use was made of a facility for the electronic subtraction of spectra.[19] The spectrum of α-D-ribopyranose tetrabenzoate, which is not known in the pure form, was obtained at 100 Mc./sec. by electronic subtraction of the spectrum of β-D-ribopyranose tetrabenzoate from the mixture of anomers using the Varian C-1024 computer.

In a series of acetylated 1-thioaldopyranose derivatives the use of solvent effects, as an aid in spectral analysis, is well illustrated.[21] The spectrum of 1-thio-β-D-glucose penta-acetate (Fig. 1) may for convenience be divided into two regions. It is seen that although in benzene-d_6 and deuterochloroform the low-field region of the spectrum between 4 and 6τ is complex, in acetone-d_6 this region of the spectrum approaches first order. In like fashion, the higher-field region between 5·5 and 6·5 τ is complex in deuterochloroform and acetone-d_6, but approached first order in benzene-d_6. The same spectra were measured at 220 Mc./sec. as well as at 100 Mc./sec., and it was demonstrated that there was a slight variation between the 100 Mc./sec. and 220 Mc./sec. coupling constants, thus indicating that the observed spectra were not absolutely first order even in the optimum solvent. Only a few results from 220 Mc./sec. spectra have as yet been reported, but the advantages offered are already clearly apparent.

The conformational dependence on the nature of the aglycon for a series of D-mannopyranosides has been reported.[22]

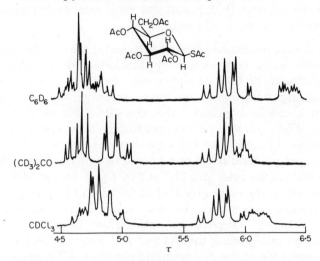

FIG. 1. The low-field portion of the 100 Mc./sec. spectrum of 1-thio-β-D-gluco-pyranose penta-acetate in deuterochloroform, acetone-d_6 and benzene-d_6. (From Holland *et al.*[21])

III. CONFIGURATION AND CONFORMATION OF ALDOSES

Lemieux and Stevens[23] have examined the 100 Mc./sec. spectra of D-xylose, D-lyxose, D-arabinose, D-ribose, D-glucose, D-mannose and D-galactose in deuterium oxide and have shown that the p.m.r. parameters provide considerable information on the conformations and tautomeric equilibria for sugars in aqueous solution. Earlier similar experiments[24] were equivocal, since at lower frequencies only the anomeric proton signals could be clearly observed, and at that time the limitations of the Karplus equation and complications that could arise from virtual long-range coupling were not fully appreciated. Extensive use of spin-decoupling techniques in conjunction with studies of specifically deuterated aldoses have permitted the development of a set of empirical rules analogous to those previously described for acetylated pyranoid derivatives.[9] With β-D-xylopyranose and β-D-glucopyranose as reference compounds, the following rules were formulated—

(1) If the proton under consideration is in an equatorial orientation subtract 0·6 p.p.m. (τ values).

(2) If the proton under consideration is in an axial orientation (a) subtract 0·3 p.p.m. for each neighbouring axial hydroxyl group and (b) subtract 0·35 p.p.m. for each axial hydroxyl group in opposition to the axial proton.

These rules are not as complicated as those for the acetylated pyranoses and have some very simple applications. For example, if the chemical shifts of the H-2, of a pyranose structure, as determined by spin-decoupling of the signals for the anomeric protons are nearly the same, then it can be concluded that the OH-2 group is in an axial orientation. The rules also permit conclusions to be reached concerning the position of the C-1 ⇌ 1-C equilibrium for those aldoses which do not exist preponderantly in one form. For α-D-lyxopyranose in the 1-C conformation the rules give H-1 at 5·00 τ and H-2 at 6·09 τ. In the C-1 conformation the rules give H-1 at 4·75 τ and H-2 at 6·14 τ. The observed resonance positions for H-1 and H-2 are 4·92 and 6·10 τ, respectively, which suggests an equilibrium mixture comprising approximately equal parts of the C-1 and 1-C forms, a result consistent with the magnitude of the J_{12} coupling constant (4·2 c./sec.).

By integration of the signals for the anomeric protons of pyranoid sugars the relative amounts of the anomeric forms were measured and compared with values obtained by other methods (Table II). The

TABLE II

Percentage proportions of the α-aldopyranose form at equilibrium

Sugar	N.m.r. at 35°C	Rotation	Bromine oxidation	Calculated
Xylose	33	34·8	32·1	36
Glucose	36	36·2	37·4	36
Lyxose	71	76	79·7	73
Mannose	67	68·8	68·9	68
Ribose	38	—	—	11
Allose	<10	—	—	—
Arabinose	63	73·5	67·6	61
Galactose	27	29·6	31·4	36
Talose	66	—	65·9	77·5

results show excellent agreement for xylose, glucose, mannose and galactose. The values for lyxose and arabinose agree well with calculated values of Eliel et al.,[25] but differ greatly from those obtained by rotation and bromine oxidation.[26]

Similar results concerning the anomeric composition of mono-saccharides in solution have been reported.[27] However, since these were at 60 Mc./sec. and only the signals for the anomeric protons were analysed, the conclusions reached concerning the preferred ring conformation, though probably correct, are less dependable. For example, Rudrum and Shaw[27] concluded that β-D-arabinopyranose had a C-1 conformation. Lemieux and Stevens point out,[23] however, that the values for J_{12} and J_{34} in β-D-arabinopyranose do not distinguish between the 1-C and C-1 conformations and that the chemical-shift data available are as in good agreement for one conformation as for the other. Perhaps solution to the problem must await studies at 220 Mc./sec. or at higher frequencies.

Although the n.m.r. method does not give anomeric compositions to the degree of accuracy that careful polarimetric studies can furnish, its advantages have been summarized.[28] Whereas accurate compositions by polarimetry require that both pure pyranose anomers be available and that the mixture at equilibrium must not contain appreciable proportions of furanose or acyclic forms, n.m.r. can give approximate tautomeric compositions even when no crystalline form of the sugar is available and it can indicate whether a sugar is a single tautomeric form or a co-crystallized mixture of forms.

It has been severally reported that no mutarotation of 2-amino-2-deoxy-β-D-mannose hydrochloride occurs in water, and suggestions why the β-D-anomer might be stabilized in the C-1 conformations have been made. It has now been shown[29] by n.m.r. studies that crystalline 2-amino-2-deoxy-D-mannose hydrochloride mutarotates very rapidly indeed in deuterium oxide to give a mixture of 43% of the α-D-anomer and 57% of the β-D-anomer proportions obtained by integrating the anomeric proton signals at 4·60 and 4·78 τ, respectively. The low-field signal was confidently assigned to the equatorial proton because of the close similarity to the α- and β-D-mannopyranoses. Since no signals in the region 4·3–4·4 τ were observed, it was concluded that no detectable proportion of furanose forms was present.

N.m.r. spectroscopy has been used to study the equilibrium between pyranoid and furanoid forms of sugars. 2,3-O-Isopropylidene-L-rhamnose was selected for careful study,[30] since it is known that this compound exists appreciably in the furanose form. For this sugar it was not convenient to observe the anomeric proton signals in order to assess the composition of the equilibrium mixture. However it was observed that with 2,3-O-isopropylidene-L-rhamnofuranose derivatives the separation of methyl signals was 0·09–0·11 p.p.m., whereas with the pyranoid derivatives the separation was 0·14 p.p.m. Consequently as 2,3-O-isopropylidene-L-rhamnose equilibrated, the observed change in the methyl signal pattern could be interpreted and an estimation made of the proportion of furanose and pyranose forms present in the equilibrium mixture.

IV. USE OF DIMETHYL SULPHOXIDE AS SOLVENT FOR CARBOHYDRATE STUDIES

Hydroxyl protons of alcohols dissolved in dimethyl sulphoxide give magnetic resonance signals that, in contrast to their properties in more common n.m.r. solvents, are generally well resolved and permit the detection of H—C—O—H coupling. The magnetic resonance characteristics of hydroxyl protons may then be utilized to provide information concerning compounds that are capable of adopting more than one type of structure.[31-33] For example, α-D-glucose can be shown to exist in a pyranose form in dimethyl sulphoxide. Specific deuteration and spin–spin decoupling techniques show (see Fig. 2)

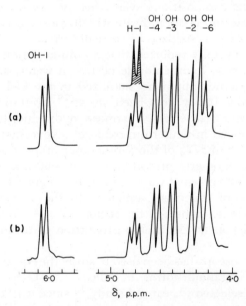

FIG. 2. The partial n.m.r. spectra at 100 Mc./sec. of (a) α-D-glucose and (b) α-D-glucose-5,6,6′-d_3 in dimethyl sulphoxide solution, showing hydroxyl proton signals (OH) and the anomeric proton signal (H-1). The insert doublet in (a) represents the only signal (H-1) detected after the addition of deuterium oxide to the solution. (From Perlin.[31])

unequivocally that C-4 carries a hydroxyl group whereas C-5 does not, since the secondary OH signals are the same in α-D-glucose and α-D-glucose-5,6,6′-d_3. Partially acetylated sugar derivatives may be distinguished by their n.m.r. spectra in dimethyl sulphoxide solution. In the spectra of 1,2,3,6-tetra-*O*-acetyl-β-D-glucose and 1,3,4,6-tetra-*O*-acetyl-β-D-glucose, addition of deuterium oxide causes one doublet to collapse to a singlet, but in 1,2,3,4-tetra-*O*-acetyl-β-D-glucose, deuterium oxide addition causes collapse of a triplet. This clearly confirms the presence of a free primary hydroxymethyl group in the latter compound.

Observation of the hydroxyl proton resonance is also of value in differentiating between cyclic and acyclic forms of compounds. Thus D-erythrose-2,5-dichlorophenylhydrazone shows two doublets (OH-2 and OH-3) and a triplet (OH-4) and D-fucose-toluene-*p*-phenylhydrazone shows four doublets (OH-2 to OH-5).

The n.m.r. spectrum of the crystalline hydrated dialdehyde, obtained by oxidative scission of methyl 4,6-*O*-benzylidene-α-D-glucopyranoside, shows two hydroxyl proton doublets (at 3·20 and 3·66 τ) in dimethyl sulphoxide. This evidence clearly favours **5**, since **6** would be expected to show hydroxyl resonances corresponding to four protons.

The periodate oxidation products of methyl α- and β-D-xylopyranosides have been examined by n.m.r. in both deuterium oxide and in dimethyl sulphoxide.[34] In deuterium oxide each product exists mainly in two forms, one of which is the hydrated dialdehyde and the other a hemialdal. In dimethyl sulphoxide, the dialdehyde cyclizes slowly to yield the hemialdal. In the cases reported, specific deuteration and spin–spin decoupling techniques were required to allow the spectra to be interpreted.

Casu and co-workers[35] have examined the spectra of glucose and some di, oligo and polyglucoses in dimethyl sulphoxide and have suggested that such studies provide information concerning the conformations and hydrogen-bonding patterns of these compounds. The anomeric hydroxyl in glucose and related sugars give a proton resonance at lowest field and its chemical shift and coupling constant are characteristic of the configuration of the anomeric linkage. Thus for α-D-anomers (OH is axial) $\tau = 3\cdot70 - 4\cdot05$, $J = 4\cdot0 - 4\cdot5$ c./sec., for β-D-anomers (OH is equatorial $\tau = 3\cdot40 - 3\cdot68$, and $J = 6\cdot0 - 7\cdot0$ c./sec. Non-anomeric hydroxyls of glucose and most related sugars give n.m.r. peaks in the range 5–6 τ, and it has been suggested that these signals are characteristic of OH groups free to associate with dimethyl sulphoxide by hydrogen bonding. In maltose a signal at lower field than 5 τ corresponding to two protons, has been assigned to O_2H and O_3^1H in the separate glucose units, a finding considered consistent with intramolecular bonding between O_2H and O_3^1H. The shift downfield from 5 τ increases from β-maltose → amylose → α-cyclodextrin → β-cyclodextrin. The strongest hydrogen bond found in the cyclodextrins is explained by the limited rotation of glucose units in the macrocycle. It has been observed that in certain cases $H—O—C—H$ couplings occur in acetone and chloroform.[36]

The vicinal coupling constant between hydroxyl protons and the α-proton, J_{CHOH}, may be used as a conformational probe.[37–39] It is found that the coupling is larger for equatorial alcohols than for axial ones (e.g., $4\cdot5$ c./sec. and $3\cdot2$ c./sec. for *trans* and *cis*-4-t-butylcyclohexanols). If such an approach for determining conformation is employed, care should be taken to examine only closely related systems. In some cases neighbouring groups may profoundly affect the magnitude of the J_{CHOH} coupling. For example, 4-oxo-1-phenyl-5-phenyl-azo-3-pyridazinecarboxaldehyde methylhemiacetal (7) displays a

7

J_{H_A, H_B} coupling of 11·5–12 c./sec. in chloroform-*d*.[40] It was suggested that the geometry of the CH_AOH_B group was markedly influenced by the carbonyl group on the neighbouring heterocyclic ring.

V. SUBSTITUENT RESONANCES AND CARBOHYDRATE CONFIGURATIONS

Lemieux and his co-workers[1] suggested that the methyl protons of axially orientated acetoxy-substituents in pyranose derivatives have lower chemical shifts than those of equatorially orientated groups.

These original findings were supposedly confirmed by other workers[17,41-44] and have been used in support of configurational assignments. Attempts have been made, principally on the basis of these generalizations, to specifically assign all the acetoxy-resonances in 2-deoxy-2-amino-glucopyranose derivatives.[43] It has been suggested that such assignments are unreliable,[9,10] and Horton and his co-workers[45,46] have demonstrated this by specific deuteration studies.

The anomeric 2-acetamido-1,3,4,6-tetra-O-acetyl-2-deoxy-α-(and β)-D-glucopyranoses were compared by n.m.r. with the corresponding analogues that had been specifically deuterated in the N-acetyl methyl group. Thus the signal at 8·09 τ in (3) and (4) was unequivocally assigned to the N-acetyl methyl group. This was the highest-field signal, a signal that had been previously assigned[43] to the acetoxy-group on the primary hydroxyl at C-6. In 2-acetamido-2-deoxy-mannopyranose derivatives the signal for the axial acetamido-group was at 7·92–7·96 τ. These definite assignments were in accord with assignments proposed for inosamine derivatives and acetylated derivatives of some amino-sugars and antibiotics.[47-51]

In the presence of trityl groups, large upfield shifts of acetoxy resonances are observed.[45] Since it is known that groups near an aromatic nucleus experience either shielding or deshielding according to whether they are perpendicular or parallel to the plane of the aromatic ring, it is possible that firm assignments for acetoxy-groups will provide a means for determining the favoured disposition of aryl substituent groups.

Horton and his co-workers have also reported complete specific deuteration studies on 2-acetamido-1,3,4,6-tetra-O-acetyl-2-deoxy-α-D-glucopyranose[46] (see Table III).

TABLE III

Chemical shifts of acetyl methyl groups in 2-acetamido-1,3,4,6-tetra-O-acetyl-2-deoxy-α-D-glucopyranose as assigned by synthesis of specifically deuterated derivatives

| Solvent | Chemical shifts (τ) of acetyl group signals | | | | |
	1-OAc	NAc	3-OAc	4-OAc	6-OAc
Chloroform-d	7·81	8·09	7·97	7·97	7·93
Acetone-d_6	7·90	8·20	†	†	8·05
Benzene	8·42	8·52	8·32	8·32	8·30

† Two three-proton singlets, at 8·05 and 8·09 τ assigned to 3-OAc and 4-OAc, but not specifically differentiated.

It is particularly noteworthy that although the acetamido signal is at highest field in all three solvents, the axial 1-acetoxy group is not the lowest field signal when benzene is the solvent. This finding emphasizes the difficulties likely to arise if the spectra of carbohydrate derivatives that do not contain aromatic functions are compared.

An interesting example of the unreliability of acetoxy-group resonance position as probes of molecular configuration and conformation is provided by the spectra of (8) and its hydrochloride.[52] In carbon tetrachloride, (8) had acetoxy signals at 8·08 and 8·04 τ, i.e.,

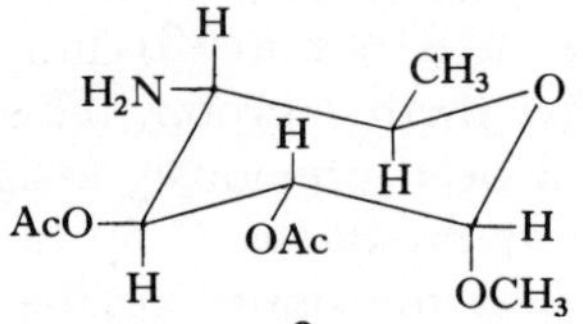

8

the signals were within the range normally associated with equatorial acetoxy resonances.[2] However the hydrochloride of (8) showed a signal, suggested to be characteristic of an axial acetoxy group, at 7·85 τ even though the coupling constants of the ring protons indicated that the conformation of (8) and its hydrochloride were essentially the same.

Although attempts[50, 53] have been made to assign configuration on the evidence provided by acetoxy chemical shifts, and although no serious errors have been propagated by this approach, the dangers of using this approach without recourse to adequate supporting evidence should now be clearly apparent. However, present results indicate[21, 54] that an acetoxy signal at 7·65 τ (deuterochloroform) is characteristic of a S-acetyl group, and that this resonance might therefore be a useful diagnostic aid. Use has also been made of acetoxy chemical shifts to follow the migration of acetyl groups[55] in partially acylated polyols under mildly alkaline conditions.

VI. SUBSTITUENTS THAT AID CONFIGURATIONAL ASSIGNMENTS

Horton and his co-workers[45] have shown that the anisotropy of aryl substituents affects the chemical shifts not only of certain acetyl groups but also those of certain ring protons. Preparation of suitable aryl substituted sugars may thus constitute a useful technique for obtaining first-order interpretations of ring proton signals, without the necessity for measurements at higher field strengths. For example, if the 6-acetoxy-group in (**9**) is replaced by a trityl group, the H-4, H-5, H-6, H-6[1] complex is resolved into an ABXY system, which can be analysed easily.

9

Similarly it has been shown that the introduction of a second N-acyl substituent into 2-acetamido-1,3,4,6-tetra-O-acetyl-2-deoxy-D-hexo-pyranoses affords clear first-order spectra.[10] A typical example is the spectrum simplification observed when 2-acetamido-1,3,4,6-tetra-O-acetyl-2-deoxy-β-D-glucopyranose (Fig. 3) is N-benzoylated (Fig. 4).

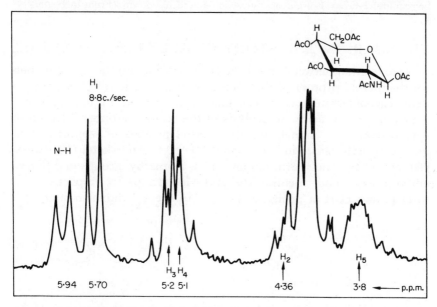

Fig. 3. The 100 Mc./sec. n.m.r. spectrum of 2-acetamido-1,3,4,6-tetra-O-acetyl-2-deoxy-β-D-glucopyranose in deuterochloroform. (From Inch *et al.*[10])

In this case, the increased resolution appears due to the anisotropic effects of the new carbonyl function. The specific ring proton chemical shift changes caused by the second N-acyl group have been discussed, and it has been suggested that the method might prove of general value for elucidating the structure of unknown amino-sugars.

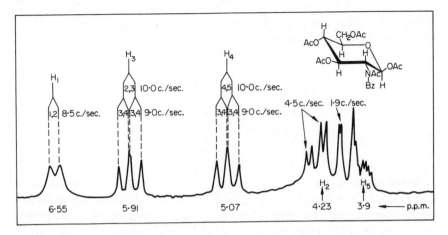

FIG. 4. The 100 Mc./sec. n.m.r. spectrum of 1,3,4,6-tetra-O-acetyl-2-(N-acetyl-benzamido)-2-deoxy-β-D-glucopyranose in deuterochloroform. (From Inch *et al.*[10])

VII. N.M.R. IN THE STUDY OF ACETALS AND KETALS

A correlation between the steric environment and the n.m.r. signals for the methyl protons of the ketal groups in a series of O-isopropylidene carbohydrate derivatives has been utilized in following the course of graded acidic hydrolysis of the acetone groups.[56] In n.m.r. spectroscopy, the signals for the methyl protons of isopropylidene groups usually occur in the region 8·0–9·0 τ. An α-ketal (10) (using Barker and Bourne's terminology[57]) has its methyl groups in different environments, and thus the Me$^\alpha$ and Me$^\beta$ groups are respectively *cis* to H/H and H/R at positions 4 and 5 in the 1,3-dioxolan ring. It is

10 α (terminal)   11 α T (threo)

suggested[58] that because of the greater proximity to the group R, Me$^\beta$ is (usually) more effectively deshielded than Me$^\alpha$, and this causes the Me$^\beta$ protons to appear at lower field. In αT(*threo*) ketals (11), which contain two Me$^\beta$ groups, whether two signals of three protons each or one of six protons is observed will depend on the nature of R^1 and R^2. In any case, the chemical-shift differences will be expected to be small. The αC ketal (*erythro*) (12) has Me$^\alpha$ and Me$^\gamma$ groups and since the latter group is *cis* to non-protonic substituents at positions 4 and 5 in the

1,3-dioxolan ring its signal should appear at lower field than for Me$^\beta$. For example, 1,2 : 5,6-di-O-isopropylidene-α-D-glucofuranose has signals at 8·87, 8·83, 8·77 and 8·72 τ corresponding to Me$^\alpha$, Me$^\alpha$, Me$^\beta$ and Me$^\gamma$ groups, respectively.

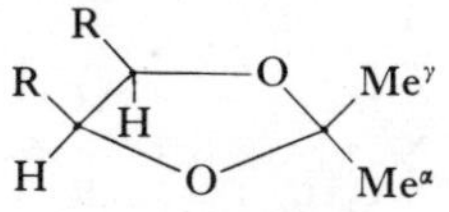

12 αC (erythro)

The general validity of these observations remains to be proven, but the careful application of the principles involved has undoubted utility for establishing the graded hydrolysis patterns and hence the structures of isopropylidene derivatives of polyhydric alcohols and other carbohydrate derivatives. An example of the application of these principles has been claimed.[59] The n.m.r. spectrum of 1,2 : 3,5-di-O-isopropylidene-α-D-apio-L-furanose (**13**) showed methyl peaks at 8·70, 8·65, 8·60 and 8·57 τ. The external peaks (8·70 and 8·57 τ) were considered to be of the Me$^\alpha$ and Me$^\gamma$ types, respectively, whereas the internal peaks (8·65 and 8·60 τ) were of the Me$^\beta$ type. Graded acidic hydrolysis of (**13**) removed the internal peaks, which were attributed to the 3,5–O-isopropylidene ring, showing the monoisopropylidene derivative to be the expected 1,2-O-isopropylidene-α-apio-L-furanose. It must be pointed out, however, that the generalization proposed by Foster and his co-workers[56] was based only on a study of 5-membered isopropylidene ketals, and any extension to 6-membered rings must be considered carefully. The isopropylidene derivatives of 2,4-O-methylene-D-glucitol have been examined and structures assigned, which are based on these empirical generalizations.[60]

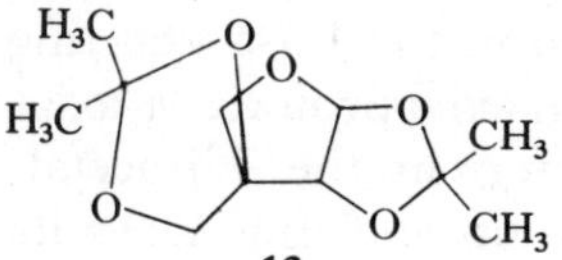

13

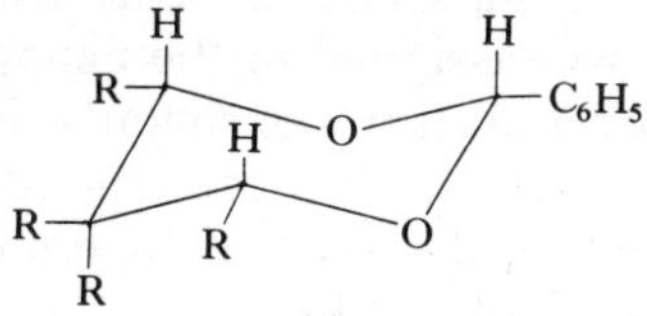

14

The absolute configuration of the benzylic centre in some benzylidene derivatives of acyclic polyhydric alcohols[61] and of some carbohydrate benzylidene acetals[62] containing fused-ring systems have been established. The method utilizes the observation that 2-phenyl-1,3-dioxan derivatives (**14**) in which the benzylic proton is axial, displays a signal for that proton in the range 4·82–5·02 τ. In a series of 4-

alkyl-2-phenyl-1,3-dioxolans, produced by acid catalysed benzylide-
nation of various 2-alkylethane-1,2-diols two benzylic proton signals
of comparable intensity were observed in the ranges 4·62–4·67 and
4·46 and 4·52 τ and which were assigned to the *cis* (15) and *trans* (16)

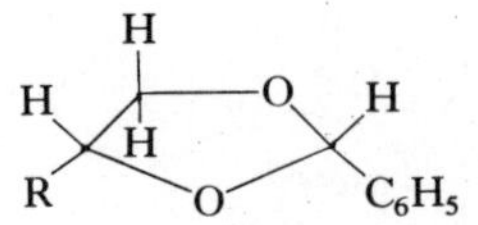

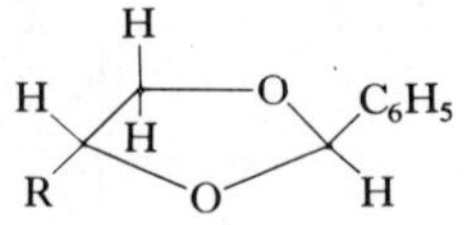

isomers, respectively (the ranges quoted are for 10% solutions in
dioxan). The information obtained from a study of a series of mono-
cyclic compounds has been utilized to assign structures to, for example, two 2,4:5,6-di-O-benzylidene derivatives of 3-O-methyl-D-
glucitol.

1,3:2,4-Di-O-benzylidene-L-arabinitol (17) had benzylic proton

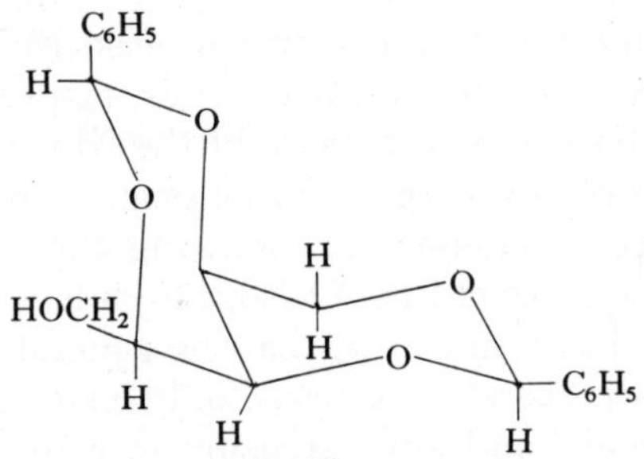

signals at 4·48 and 4·80 τ which was considered indicative of the existence of the molecule in the "O" inside structure with equatorial
phenyl groups and an axial hydroxymethyl group[63] The signal at
4·80 τ was assigned to the benzyl proton in the 1,3-acetal ring, since
the chemical shift was characteristic of an axial proton *syn*-axial to two
ortho protons. The corresponding proton in the 2,4-acetal is deshielded by the axial hydroxymethyl group and thus gives its signal
at lower field (4·48 τ).

Similar studies of diastereoisomeric forms of benzylidene derivatives have been reported where the benzylidene derivatives are formed
under basic conditions by the condensation of diols with benzylidene
bromide.[64] It is possible to isolate conformationally unfavoured
isomers from such reactions, which on acid treatment revert to the
thermodynamically favoured forms normally isolated from acid-
catalysed benzylidenations. Each pair of compounds that are diastereo-

isomeric at the benzylic carbon display a characteristic proton signal, and consequently the course of equilibrations may be followed by n.m.r. It must be pointed out that the choice of solvent systems, used by Foster and his co-workers, was governed by the experimental requirements, and because of the variation in solvent there is a parallel variation in chemical shift parameters. The configurational assignment for cis and trans-4-substituted derivatives of 2-phenyl-1,3-dioxolan, which were based originally on the evidence provided by the chemical shifts of their benzylic protons, have been substantiated by chemical evidence.[65]

The empirical information obtained concerning the relationship of the benzylic proton to its environment in cyclic acetals has helped provide information about the course of the acid-catalysed reactions of aldehydes with polyhydric alcohols.[66] Benzylidination of 1,4-anhydroerythritol under homogeneous conditions at 25°–30°C (in nitromethane containing toluene-p-sulphonic acid was conveniently followed by observing the appearance of the benzyl proton signals in the n.m.r. spectrum. The rapid development of a signal at relatively high field 4·96 τ was followed by the slow appearance of a signal at 4·67 τ paralleled by diminution in intensity of the first signal. At equilibrium the two signals were of comparable integrated area. These

18

results were interpreted as indications that (18; endo-Ph) is the kinetically favoured product. Similarly the proportions of cis and trans-5-hydroxy-2-phenyl-1,3-dioxan and cis and trans-2-hydroxymethyl-2-phenyl-1,3-dioxolan in acid-catalysed equilibrated O-benzylidene glycerol mixtures were determined by observation of the signals for the benzylic protons of these compounds and a rationalization for the course of the reactions observed was presented.[67]

N.m.r. studies have proved to be of value for assigning structures to 1,2-O-trichloroethylidene-α-D-glucofuranoses differing in configuration at the acetal carbon atom.[68] The relevant parameters for (19) and (20) are listed in Table IV.

By analogy with the results of Baggett and co-workers,[62] who showed that in 2-phenyl-1,3-dioxolans the acetal proton is at higher field when cis to protons at C-4 and C-5 than when cis to other substituents at C-4 and C-5, compound (19) was assigned the structure shown, with the

3

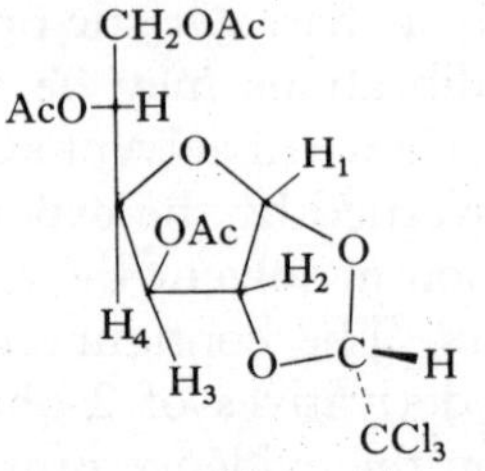

19

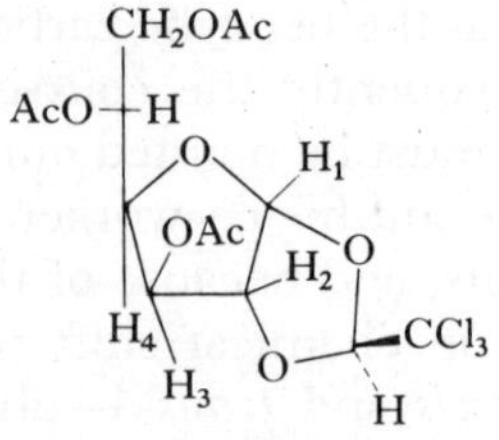

20

TABLE IV

Parameters for 19 and 20

	Chemical shifts, τ values					Coupling constants, c./sec.		
	H-1	H-2	H-3	H-4	Acetal	J_{12}	J_{23}	J_{34}
19	3·88	5·31	4·46	5·13	4·66	3·8	<0·5	3·0
20	3·76	5·15	4·55	5·70	4·37	3·7	<0·5	3·0

acetal proton in an *exo*-position. Other chemical-shift changes provide evidence concerning the ring conformation. It was shown previously[69] that in 1,2-O-isopropylidene derivatives of hexofuranoses carbon atoms C-2 and C-3 are displaced in opposite senses from the plane of the other ring atoms, C-2 being below the plane of the ring. The coupling constants for (19) and (20) indicate that these compounds have a similar conformation (e.g., 21). Comparison of the chemical shifts of (19) and (20) shows a bigger difference in the shifts of H-2 than H-1. This indicates that the C–Cl$_3$ group is closer to H-2 than H-1. Even more striking is the difference in chemical shifts of H-4, a result in accord with the structure shown (21) where H-4 is closer than H-3 to the C–Cl$_3$ group. Had the furanoid ring been puckered in the opposite

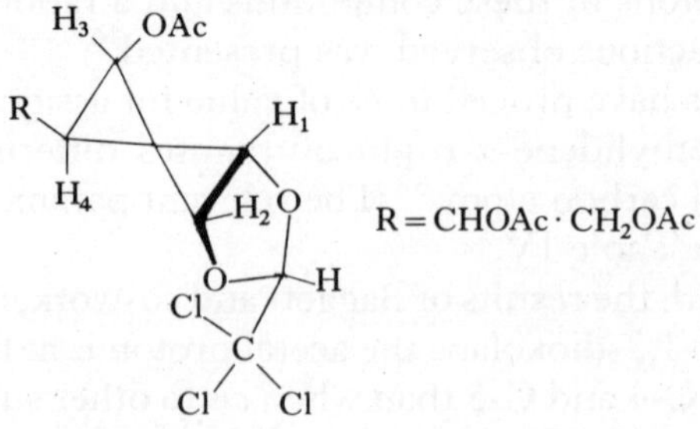

$R = CHOAc \cdot CH_2OAc$

21

sense with C-2 above and C-3 below the ring, appreciable H-3 chemical-shift differences between the two isomers would be expected. In fact the H-3 chemical shifts are very similar.

Similar arguments were used to establish the structures of some diastereoisomeric 1,2:5,6-di-O-trichloroethylidene-α-D-glucofurano-ses.

VIII. FUSED-RING SYSTEMS

Hall has drawn attention[2] to the conformational problems associated with bicyclic fused ring systems, particularly where one or both of the rings is five-membered. Several n.m.r. studies of such systems (and similar systems with more rings) have been described subsequently, and these studies are discussed below.

The *cis* fusion of one isopropylidene ring to a cyclohexane[70] or a pyranose[71] ring causes the six-membered ring to be distorted little from the original chair form except for some 1,2-O-alkylidene-α-D-glucopyranose derivatives.[72] A skewed boat conformation was assigned to the 1,2-O-alkylidene-α-D-glucopyranoses, as a result of a comparison of dihedral angles measured from a molecular model and dihedral angles calculated from coupling constants using a modified Karplus equation. Support for the postulated skew boat form (22) was provided by the observation that H-2 and H-4 were long-range coupled. In the conformation described (22) H-2 and H-4 are in the planar zig-zag conformation that favours strong long-range coupling.

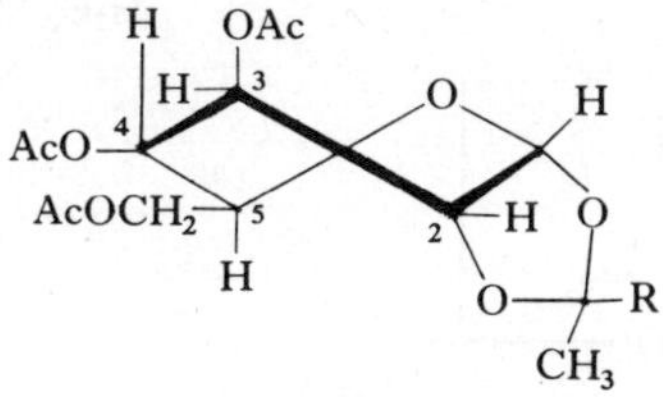

22

Cone and Hough[73] have studied the conformations of some derivatives of di-O-isopropylidenearabinopyranose. From these and other studies it is apparent that although it is usually possible to decide without invoking the Karplus relationship whether or not a molecule adopts a chair conformation, a modified Karplus equation must be used to determine the ring shape if a chair conformation is precluded. Cone and Hough found that the conformation that best fitted the observed parameters for the di-O-isopropylidenearabinopyranoses, was essentially the same as that suggested for the 1,2-O-alkylidene-glucopyranoses.

The glycol scission products of 1,2-O-isopropylidene-α-D-glucofuranose have been identified by n.m.r. studies.[74] The aldehyde (23) is

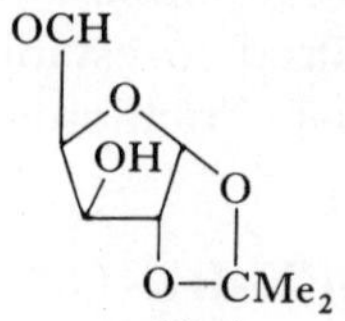

OCH

OH

O—CMe$_2$

23

unstable and dimerizes to give (24) and reacts with the formaldehyde produced by the glycol cleavage to give (25). Complete first-order analysis of the acetates of (24) and (25) have unequivocally established the configurations of the asymmetric centres formed during the condensation processes and also provided strong evidence that the 1,3-dioxan rings have ideal chair conformations. For this reason, there was no necessity for precise application of the Karplus relationship.

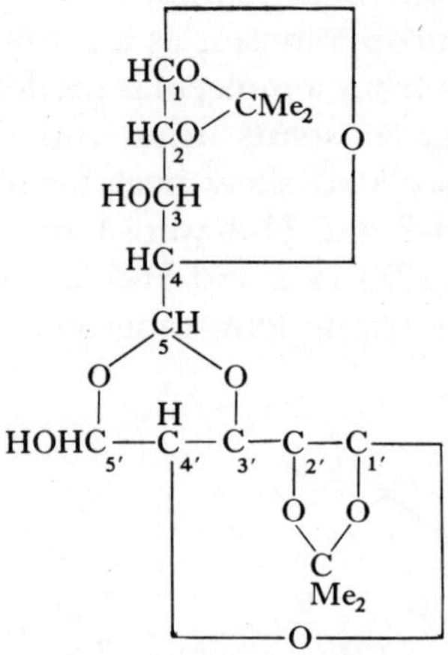

HCO 1
HCO 2 CMe$_2$ O
HOCH 3
HC 4
CH 5
O   O
H
HOHC 5' —C 4'—C 3'—C 2'—C 1'
O   O
C
Me$_2$
O
24

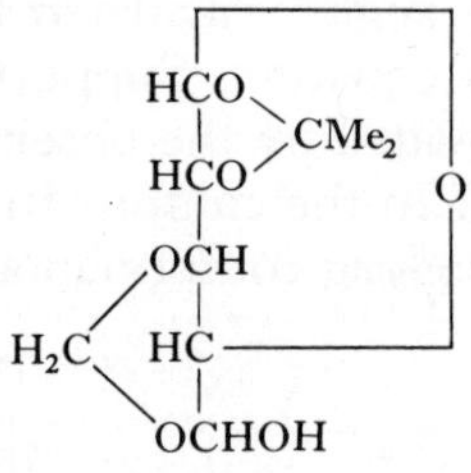

HCO
HCO CMe$_2$ O
OCH
H$_2$C HC
OCHOH
25

A study of a series of carbohydrate 2,3-epoxides[75] and related compounds of the type shown (26) has provided information concerning the stereodependence of the J_{12} and J_{34} vicinal couplings where the precise hybridization of C-2 and C-3 is uncertain. It has been shown that the coupling from the *epi* ring hydrogens at C-2 (and C-3) to

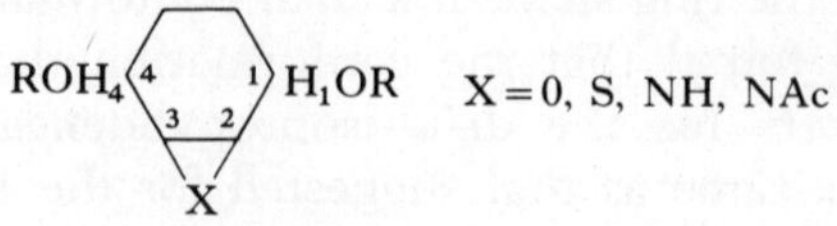

ROH$_4$ 4   1 H$_1$OR   X = O, S, NH, NAc
3 2
X
26

adjacent hydrogens at C-1 (and C-4) is smaller when these hydrogens have a *trans* relationship than when they are *cis*, and this effect is independent of the hetero atom in the *epi* ring. This result is in contrast to the more general observation[76] that $J_{trans} > J_{cis}$ for protons attached to sp^3 hybridized carbon atoms.

Coxon[77] has examined a series of 36 methyl 4,6-O-benzylidene-aldohexopyranosides with the α-D-*altro*, α-D-*manno*, α-D-*allo*, α-D-*gluco* and 2-deoxy-α-D-*arabino* configurations. The value of the coupling constants $J_{1\,2}, J_{1\,3}, J_{2\,3}$ and $J_{3\,4}$ obtained by first-order analysis support the assignment of the chair conformation to the pyranoid ring for all five configurations. It has been found that a small splitting (0·6–1·7 c./sec.) is characteristic of equatorial H-1–equatorial H-2 proton arrangements (as found in the α-D-*altro*, α-D-*manno* and 2-deoxy-α-D-*arabino*hexopyranosides) whereas a larger splitting (3·3–3·8 c./sec.) (as found in the α-D-*allo*, α-D-*gluco* and 2-deoxy-α-D-*arabino*hexo-pyranosides) is characteristic of the equatorial H-1–H-2 arrangement. Coxon points out that in an ideal chair conformation $\phi_{ee} = \phi_{ea} = \phi_{ae} = 60°$ and that if the Karplus equation was strictly applicable these couplings should be equal in magnitude. Possible geometrical reasons for the different couplings are discussed, and an attempt was also made to explain these differences in terms of Booth's rationalization[7] of an electronegativity effect with orientation.[6] Booth has suggested that the coupling constant is diminished to the greatest extent when the electronegative substituent is *trans* coplanar (*trans* antiparallel) to one proton of the coupling pair. Coxon has found that although in many cases his results fit the rationalization there are exceptions, and hence concludes that geometrical factors are also important. Coxon describes some stereospecific long range $H_{1e}–H_{3e}$ couplings and also describes some virtual long-range coupling effects. Musher and Corey's[11] conditions for virtual long-range coupling are restated and applied to the carbohydrate systems involved. Since the n.m.r. study of bicyclic α-D-altropyranoside derivatives indicated no appreciable distortion for normal chair conformations a study of potentially flexible altropyranose derivatives was also undertaken.[78] It was concluded that penta-O-acetyl-α-D-altropyranose exists predominantly in a C-1 chair conformation at 40°C in various solvents. The vicinal coupling constants and also an unequivocal stereospecific long-range $H_{1e}–H_{3e}$ coupling constant were in full support of this formulation.

The n.m.r. spectrum of 1,6-anhydro-2,3-O-isopropylidene-β-D-*lyxo*-hexopyranos-4-ulose (**27**) in deuterochloroform provides a good example of virtual long-range coupling.[79] Since H-2 and H-3 have identical chemical shifts at 5·52 τ the signal for H-1 at 4·37 τ appears as a triplet. The spectrum of the ketone (27) in deuterium oxide was similar to that observed[80] in deuterochloroform. The signals for H-2,3,5 and the *endo* hydrogen at C-6 were incompletely resolved.

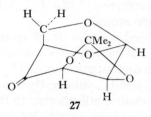

27

The H-1 signal was observed at 4·61 τ as a narrow triplet and the signal for the *exo* hydrogen at C-6 was observed at 6·25 τ as a quartet. A route to sugars specifically deuterated or tritiated at positions adjacent to the carbonyl group is afforded by base-catalysed enolization of compounds such as (27). It was easily shown by n.m.r. that treatment of (27) with NaOD in deuterium oxide afforded a product labelled with deuterium only at C-3, since the signal for H-1 collapsed to a sharp doublet ($J_{1\,2}$ 3 c./sec.) whereas H-6 (*exo*) was unchanged. It has been possible to use n.m.r. to demonstrate the formation of epoxides from glycopyranosiduloses.[81, 82]

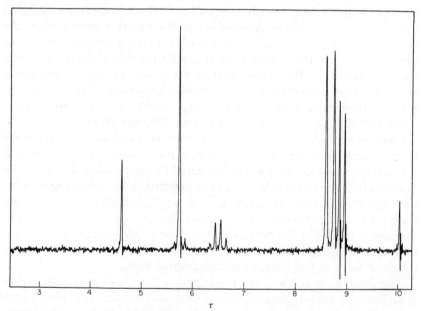

FIG. 5. The n.m.r. spectrum of 1,4-anhydro-6-deoxy-2,3-*O*-isopropylidene-β-L-talopyranose in deuterochloroform at 60 Mc./sec. (From Brimacombe and Tucker.[83])

An extremely simple n.m.r. spectrum has been obtained from 1,4-anhydro-6-deoxy-2,3-isopropylidene-β-L-talopyranose[83] (Fig. 5). No coupling is observed between H-1–H-2, H-3–H-4 and H-4–H-5, which subtend dihedral angles of ca. 80°, and H-2 and H-3 appear to be equivalent.

IX. UNSATURATED CARBOHYDRATES

The recent interest[84] in unsaturated carbohydrates has been both stimulated and furthered by advantageous application of n.m.r. The studies of shkimic acid[85] and of D-glucal triacetate[86] that showed that these compounds adopt a half-chair conformation also demonstrated the potentiality of n.m.r. in the study of unsaturated carbohydrates. It has now been shown that stereodependent long-range coupling effects associated with the double bond enhance the structural information n.m.r. provides.

A detailed n.m.r. study of six isomeric conduritols[87] (1,2,3,4-tetrahydroxycyclohex-5-enes) in deuterium oxide has shown that the conduritols also adopt a half-chair conformation (**28**). In order to

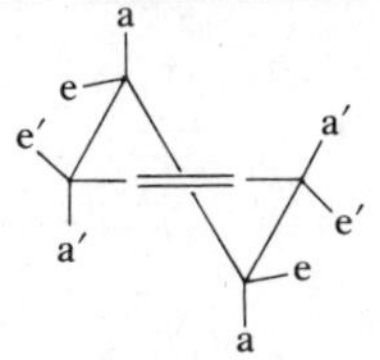

28

estimate the various coupling constants, the conduritol spectra were analysed as A_2B_2, A_2X_2 or ABXR spectral sub-systems. The parameters were adjusted until a good fit between observed and calculated spectra was obtained. The treatment adopted permitted the determination of the signs of the coupling constants for long-range (J_{13}, J_{24}) homoallylic (positive constants) and allylic (negative constants) couplings. The allylic couplings (H·C·C=C·H) exhibit angular dependence, since theory predicts[88] that these couplings, which result from σ–π interactions, are proportional to the overlap of the double bond π orbital and the 1s orbital of the C—H proton. The observed conduritol values support the theory, which predicts that the angle between the C—H bond and the plane of the olefinic group will exhibit a $\sin^2\phi$ dependence. Homoallylic couplings (CH·C=C·CH) are considered[89] to arise from the same σ–π mechanism as allylic couplings and have a similar orientation dependence. The conduritols provide evidence in support of this contention.

Long-range couplings found in the conduritols are of three types,[90] *viz.*, $J_{e,e'}$, $(J_{e',a'}-J_{a',e})$ and $J_{a',a}$. Theory predicts a relatively high value for equatorial–equatorial coupling across four bonds and such a coupling in the conduritols (2·1 c./sec.) is much higher than the axial–axial (0·3 c./sec.) or axial–equatorial (0·4–0·8 c./sec.) couplings.

A detailed n.m.r. examination of some -D-*glycero*-pent-2-enopyranosyl derivatives has been reported.[91] Frequency-sweep decoupling

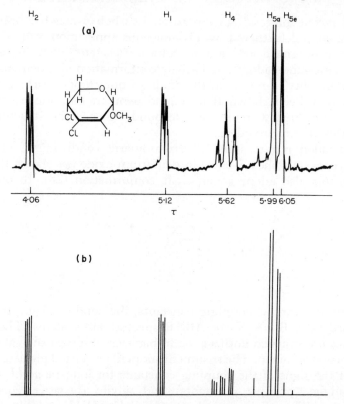

FIG. 6. The p.m.r. spectrum of methyl 3,4-dichloro-4-deoxy-α-D-*glycero*-pent-2-enopyranoside: (a), in deuterochloroform at 100 Mc./sec.; (b), the computed spectrum. The methoxy resonance is not shown. (From Coxon *et al.*[91])

experiments at 100 Mc./sec. showed that bi-allylic (homoallylic) and vicinal couplings have the same sign whereas vicinal couplings and allylic couplings are of opposite sign. The spectrum of methyl 3,4-dichloro-4-deoxy-α-D-*glycero*-pent-2-enopyranoside is shown in Fig. 6 and the expanded H-4 signal is shown in Fig. 7. Figure 7(a) shows the normal H-4 signal, and Fig. 7(b) shows the H-4 signal when the

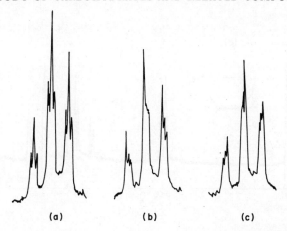

$$(a) \qquad\qquad (b) \qquad\qquad (c)$$

FIG. 7. Frequency-swept spin-decoupling experiments with methyl-3,4-dichloro-4-deoxy-α-D-*glycero*-pent-2-enopyranoside in deuterochloroform at 100 Mc./sec.: (a), unperturbed resonance due to H_4; (b), with irradiation of the low-field pair of lines of the H_2 quartet; (c), with irradiation of the low-field pair of lines of the H_1 quartet. (From Coxon *et al.*[91])

lowest-field pair of lines in H-2 is irradiated. It is seen that this has affected the lowest-field pair due to the J_{24} coupling in each line of the H-4 resonance, which implies J_{14} and J_{12} are of like sign.[92] Similarly, as seen in Fig. 7(c), irradiation of the low-field pair of lines in the H-1 quartet, due to J_{14} coupling, affects the high-field pair in each of the H-4 lines and demonstrates that J_{24} is of opposite sign to J_{12}.

Figure 8 shows the observed and calculated spectrum for methyl 3,4-dichloro-4-deoxy-β-D-*glycero*-pent-2-enopyranoside **(29)** and Table V lists chemical shifts and coupling constants for the same compound. Analysis of the H-4, H-5a and H-5e group was performed initially as an ABX system and the parameters were then further refined by computing the parameters of the five-ring proton using the Frequint IV program.

TABLE V

Chemical shifts (τ values) and coupling constants (c./sec.) for (29)

H-1	H-2	H-4	H-5e	H-5a
5·08	4·07	5·86	6·10	5·73
$J_{12}=3\cdot3$		$J_{4,\,5e}=1\cdot04$	$J_{5e,\,5a}=-12\cdot49$	
$J_{1,\,5a}=-0\cdot4$		$J_{4,\,5a}=2\cdot70$		

3*

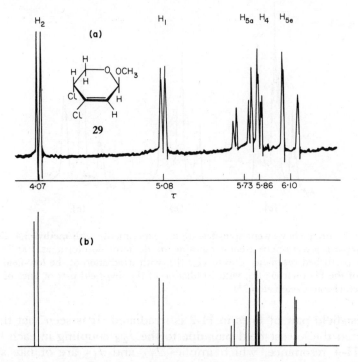

FIG. 8. The p.m.r. spectrum of methyl 3,4-dichloro-4-deoxy-β-D-*glycero*-pent-2-enopyranoside (**29**); (a) in deuterochloroform at 100 Mc./sec.; (b) the computed spectrum. The methoxy resonance is not shown. (From Coxon *et al.*[91])

The appearance of H-5a at lower field than H-5e (see Table V) may be explicable in terms of deshielding of H-5a by the almost *trans* coplanar chlorine at C-4 and the *syn* quasiaxial methoxyl group.[93] It is of interest that H-1 is long-range coupled to H-5a and not to H-5e. An H-1–H-5e coupling would perhaps be expected, since these protons exist in a planar zig-zag arrangement. However, the magnitude (0·4 c./sec.) of the long-range couplings observed is in agreement with other observations[87, 94] of long-range couplings of this type.

It is apparent that as theoretical calculations become more advanced the magnitude and signs of long-range, allylic and homoallylic couplings will prove of considerable advantage in conformational studies. Even at present, these relatively small couplings have been used to establish the configuration and conformation of unsaturated carbohydrate derivatives. For example, the relative magnitudes of allylic coupling constants have been used to distinguish between the four glycosides (**30**)–(**33**) that could exist in either of the half chair forms[95]

(34) and (35). The relationship between coupling constants and dihedral angles[96]—

$$J = 1\cdot3 \cos^2 \phi - 2\cdot6 \sin^2 \phi \quad (0° \leqslant \phi \leqslant 90°)$$

was used to show that those forms having the H-1 bond equatorial have $\phi = 30°$ ($J = 0\cdot32$ c./sec.) and those forms having the H-1 bond axial have $\phi = 80°$ ($J = -2\cdot6$ c./sec.). Therefore the anomers showing

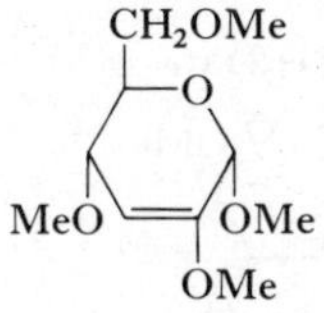

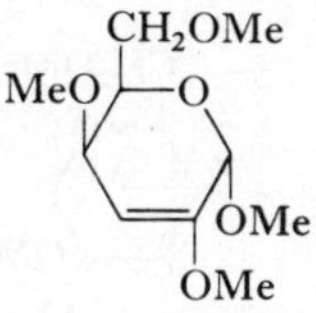

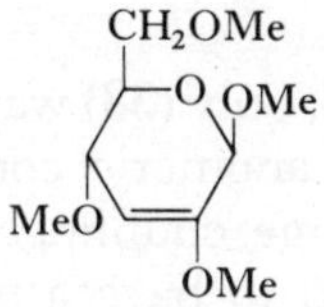

	R'	R''	R'''	R''''
30	H	OMe	H	OMe
31	H	OMe	OMe	H
32	OMe	H	H	OMe
33	OMe	H	OMe	H

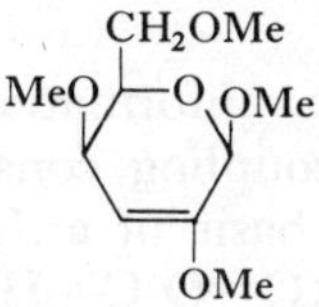

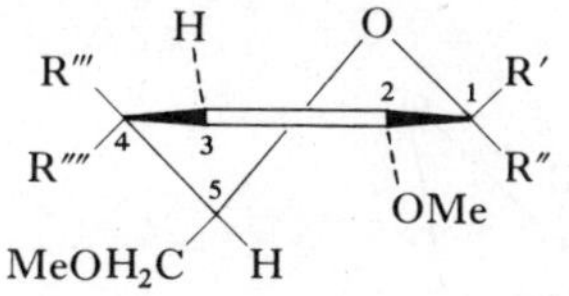

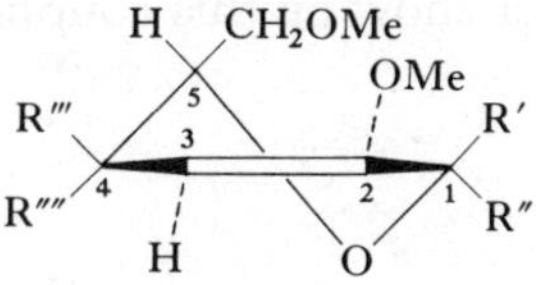

no appreciable allylic coupling are either the α-D-anomers in conformation (34) or the β-D-anomers in conformation (35). Since the β-D-anomers in conformation (35) have bulky C-1 and C-5 axial substituents, this conformation was considered unfavourable and conformation (34) in which the allylic couplings should be apparent, was favoured for the β-D-anomers.

The study of compounds (36) and (37) is of considerable interest. The coupling constants for (36) and (37) are listed in Table VI.

TABLE VI

Coupling constants (c./sec.) of the two anomers (36) and (37)

	J_{13}	J_{15}	J_{34}	J_{35}	J_{45}	J_{56}
(36) (α-D)	0·75	0·3	10·7	2·7	1·7	4·5
(37) (β-D)	0·2	1·1	10·7	2·6	2·3	5·0

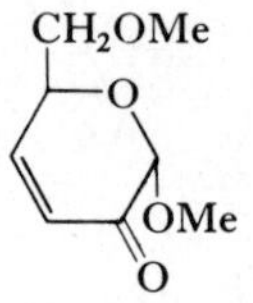

36 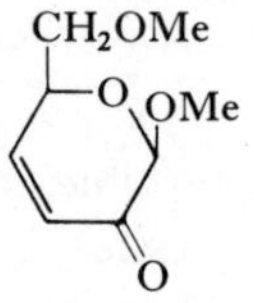   **37**

Of the two sofa conformations possible, only (38) was in accord with the J_{35} allylic coupling constant. The anomeric configuration was assigned on the basis of a J_{13} long-range coupling. As long-range couplings H—C(C=O)C—H are known to have a maximum value when the two protons and three carbon atoms are in the same plane the anomer showing this coupling ($J_{13} = 0.75$ c./sec.) is the α-D-form.

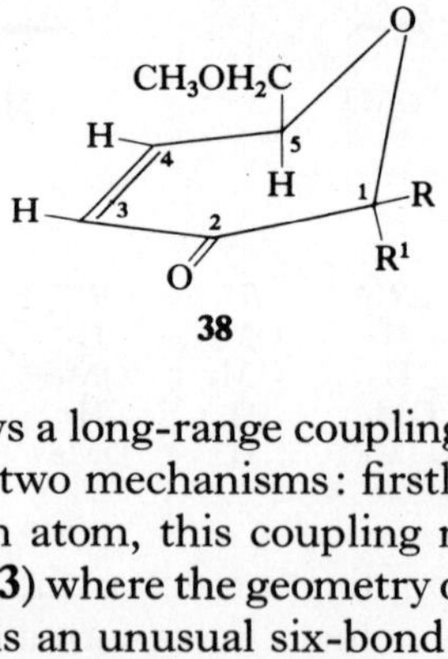

38

The β-D-anomer displays a long-range coupling ($J_{15} = 1.1$ c./sec.) that could arise by either of two mechanisms: firstly, a four σ-bond coupling through the oxygen atom, this coupling not being visible in the β-D-hexenosides (32), (33) where the geometry of the bonds is identical. The second possibility is an unusual six-bond coupling involving the π-electrons of the unsaturated system. The position here is somewhat similar to that of 3-deoxypent-2-enofuranose rings where J_{14} is large (up to 4 c./sec.) for β-D-anomers.[97, 98] For example, in compounds (39) and (40), H-1, H-3 and H-4 were well resolved and approximately first order. The significant differences between the two spectra were the values of J_{14} (0·9 c./sec. for 39 and 4·0 c./sec. for 40). The spatial disposition of H-1 and H-4 differed for the two anomers H-1 and H-4 being *trans* for (**39**) and *cis* for (**40**). An analogous structure occurs in the pyrrolizidine alkaloids (**41**) where the hetero ring atom is nitrogen instead of oxygen.[99] These alkaloids give J_{bc} values of ca. 5 c./sec. (*cis* protons) and lower values for J_{ac} (*trans* protons). Culvenor *et al.*[99] explained the large coupling in the *cis* compounds as being due to the addition of a long-range coupling, via the rear residual lobes of their C—H σ-orbitals to the π-orbital, homoallylic interaction.

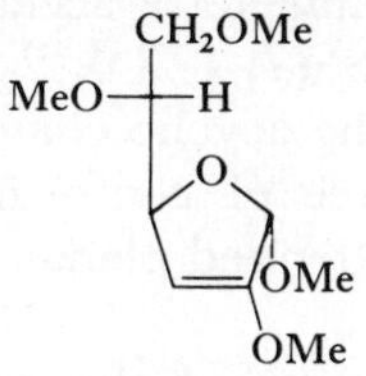

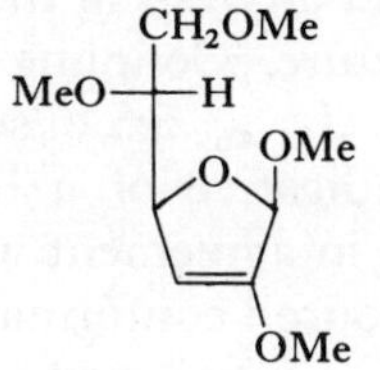

In addition to some detailed examinations of the n.m.r. of unsaturated sugars, extensive use has been made of n.m.r. simply to establish the structure of unsaturated sugars.[100–103] It has been shown that 2-hydroxy-glucals probably adopt a half-chair conformation and in this series n.m.r. spectroscopy has been used to show up some exceptions to Hudson's isorotation rule.[104] It has also been shown that in unsaturated carbohydrates, allylic ester groupings on pyranoid rings prefer a *quasi*-axial to a *quasi*-equatorial orientation.[105] The suggestion has been made that rotamer preference may be used to assign configuration to derivatives of 1-heptyne-L-*gluco*- and L-*manno*-3,4,5,6,7-pentals.[106]

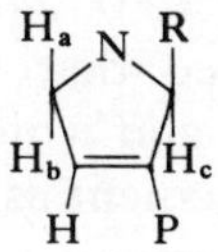

X. ACYCLIC SUGAR DERIVATIVES

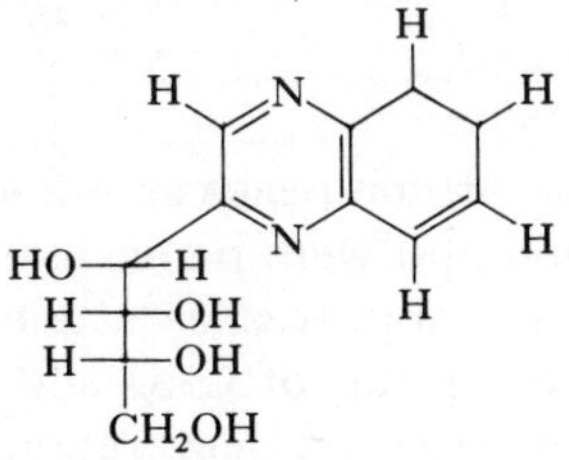

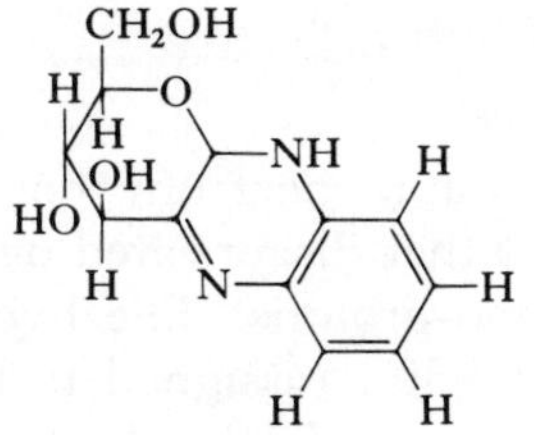

The product formed from the oxidative condensation of 2-amino-2-deoxy-D-glucose hydrochloride with *o*-phenylenediamine is 2(D-*arabino*-tetrahydroxybutyl)quinoxaline (**42**) and not the alternate formulation[107] (**43**). The spectrum of the quinoxaline in dimethyl sulphoxide shows a sharp low-field unit-proton signal at $0.80\ \tau$. Apart from the four protons from the benzene ring centred at $2.00\ \tau$, no other signals are observed below $4.5\ \tau$. These facts were considered indicative of structure (42), since in the formulation (43) the proton at C-1 of the sugar would appear in the non-exchanging solvent as a doublet through coupling with the proton on nitrogen, and the latter proton would also be observed at low field as a doublet, probably broadened by nitrogen quadrupole broadening.

A complete first-order analysis of the quinoxaline tetra-acetate confirms the acyclic structure. Coupling constants $(J_{1'2'}\ 3.0,\ J_{2'3'}\ 8.5,\ J_{4'a,4b}\ 12.0,\ J_{3',4a'}\ 3.0,\ J_{3',4b'}\ 5.5$ c./sec.) for the acyclic chain, were obtained that were indicative of a high degree of conformational purity and which were in agreement with an extended planar zig-zag arrangement as the favoured conformation.

For many years the precise structures of some of the products obtained from reaction of sugars with phenylhydrazine have been the subject of much discussion.[108] Reaction of D-mannose phenyl-hydrazone with acetic anhydride in pyridine yields D-*arabino*-3,4,5,6-tetraacetoxyl-1-phenylazo-1-hexene. The n.m.r. spectrum of this compound clearly establishes its structure.[109] Acyclic structures have similarly been assigned to various phenylhydrazones and osazones.[110] The work of Wolfrom and his co-workers perhaps best illustrates the kind of approach that has been adopted.[111] The n.m.r. spectrum of D-*lyxo*hexose phenylosazone was measured in dimethyl sulphoxide. The three possible structures of the osazone (44, 45, 46) were considered in terms of the spectrum.

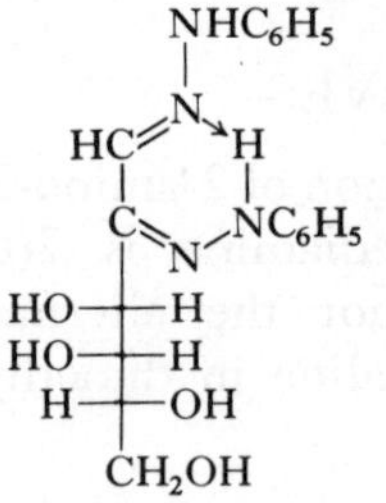

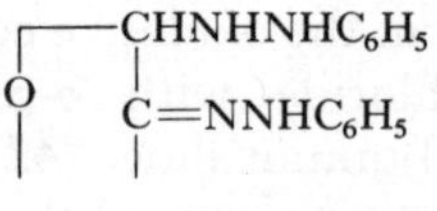

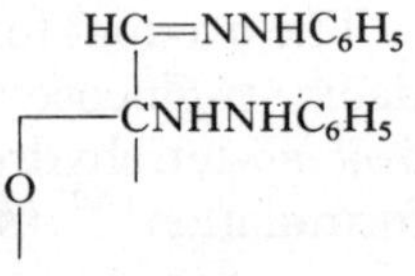

The n.m.r. spectrum showed two one proton peaks at $-2.40\ \tau$ and $-0.55\ \tau$ that disappeared on deuteration and were hence assigned to the imino-protons. The hydroxyl groups appeared as a one-proton peak at $4.50\ \tau$ (assigned to the hydroxyl group of C-3) and a three proton peak at $5.50\ \tau$; both peaks disappeared on deuteration. These facts were consistent only with structure (44), and if the cyclic structures **(45)** and **(46)** are present they constitute a small and undetected portion of the equilibrium mixture. The tetra-*O*-acetate of **(44)** had imino-proton signals at -2.48 and -1.58 τ. When the spectrum of the mixed osazone D-*arabino*hexosulose-1-(methylphenylhydrazone)-2-(phenylhydrazone) tetra-acetate **(47)** was examined, the imino-proton signal was at -2.5 τ, analogous with the low-field proton

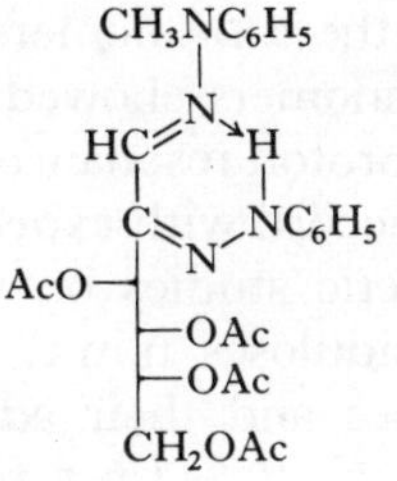

$$CH_3NC_6H_5$$

47

signal of **(44)** and its tetra-acetate. It was therefore concluded that the bond in **(44)** with the higher τ value was due to the imino-proton of the C-1 hydrazone residue and the low τ value peak was due to that of the C-2 hydrazone residue. This is in agreement with the formulation of the osazone in the chelated form with the proton of the C-2 hydrazone chelated, and hence of lower τ value, rather than the tautomeric form in which the proton of the C-1 hydrazone would be chelated.

In similar studies on the structures of osazones,[112] but using 100 Mc./sec. n.m.r. spectroscopy, a long-range coupling between the C-1 proton and the non-chelated imino-proton was observed, and was confirmed by double resonance and deuteration techniques.

The structure of Percival dianhydro-osazone[113] has been established, and Mester and Moczar[114] have shown that dehydro-D-glucosazone has the cyclic structure **(48)** rather than an acyclic structure as has previously been suggested. The observed chemical shifts and coupling constants are in accord with the conformation shown **(49)**.

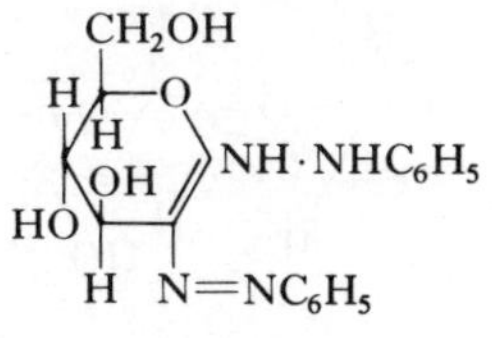

48

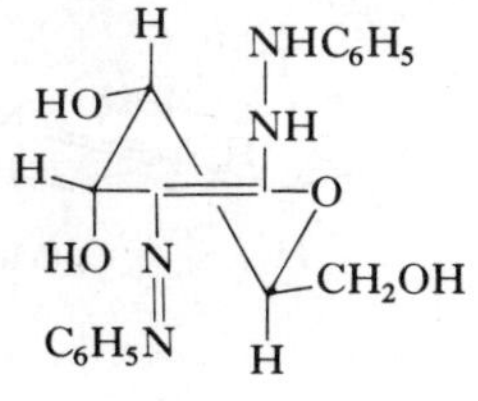

49

The n.m.r. analyses of the osazones and anhydro-derivatives have been reported by El. Khadem and his co-workers.[115,116]

XI. SUGARS THAT CONTAIN EXOCYCLIC NITROGEN
(OTHER THAN $-NH_2$ DERIVATIVES)

The anomeric configuration of some N-aryl-D-glucosylamines has been established[117] since the α-D-anomers showed $J_{1\,2}$ couplings of ca. 4 c./sec. and the β-D-anomers showed $J_{1\,2}$ couplings of 8 c./sec. In all cases the equatorial proton resonance was at lower field than the axial proton resonance in accord with expectation.

In the course of synthetic studies on the preparation of amino-sugars from glycopyranosiduloses n.m.r. spectroscopy was used to distinguish between oximes and their addition products.[118] Compound (50) showed a signal at $-1\cdot6$ τ from a proton that readily exchanged with deuterium oxide, whereas (51) showed three exchangeable protons in the regions $2\cdot7$–$3\cdot2$ τ and $4\cdot4$–$5\cdot2$ τ. *Syn* and

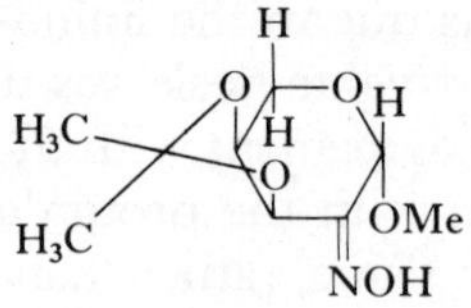

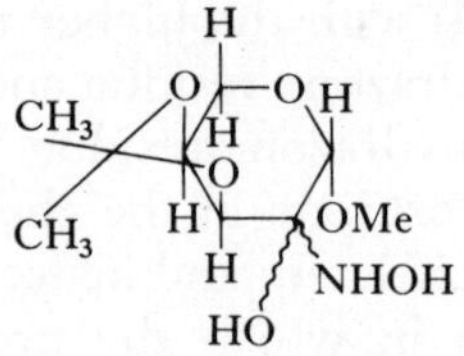

anti isomers of the oxime prepared from methyl-2,3-O-isopropylidene-β-L-erythro pentopyranosidulose have been isolated and n.m.r. has been used to distinguish between them[119] It has been shown[120] that aldoximes of the type $R_2CH\cdot C(=NOH)H$ show a low field α-methine proton when the oxime hydroxyl is *cis* to it. This has been explained by the preferred rotamer being the one in which the α-methine proton is situated in the plane of the $C=N-OH$ group. In one isomer of the pentopyranosidulose oxime (52) H-1 is at $6\cdot63$ τ and H-3 is at $8\cdot07$ τ in dimethyl sulphoxide-d_6. In the other isomer (53) H-1 is at $6\cdot88$ τ

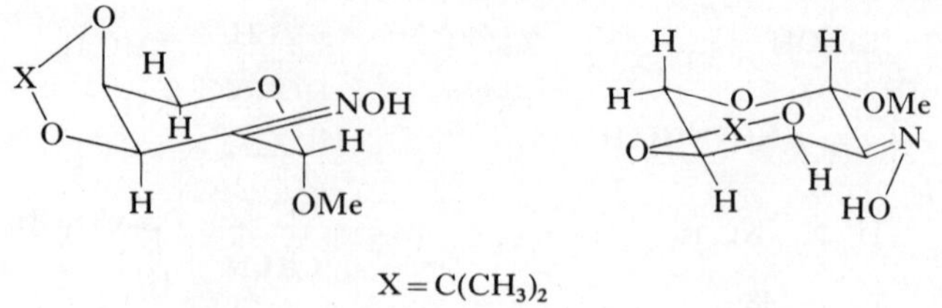

$$X = C(CH_3)_2$$

52   53

and H-3 is at 6·75 τ, i.e., at lower field than H-1. Thus (52) is assigned the *syn* structure in which the hydroxyl is *cis* to the C-1 proton and (53) is assigned the *anti* structure in which the hydroxyl is *cis* to the C-3 proton, thus causing H-3 to resonate at lower field than H-1.

An attempt has been made to assign the structures of geometric isomers (54 and 55) of *ribo*hexoside-3-ulose phenylhydrazone.[121] The relevant parameters are listed in Table VII.

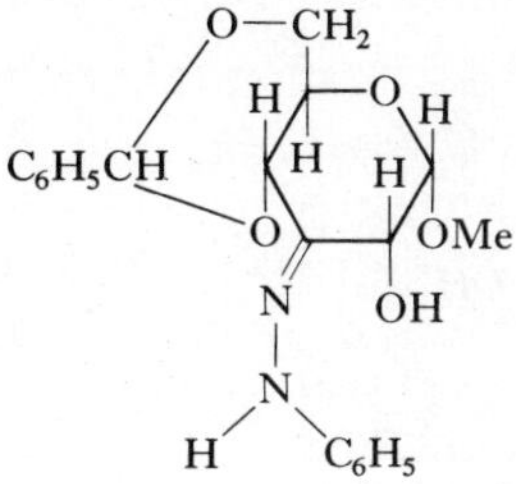

54 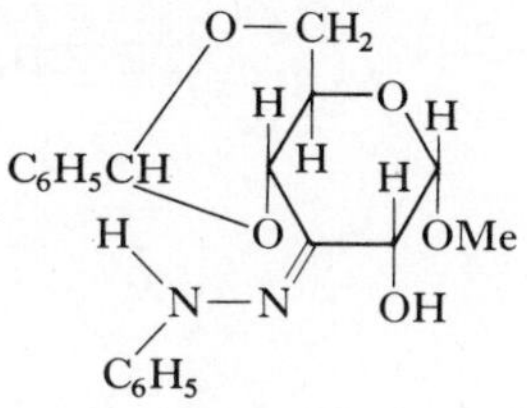   55

TABLE VII

N.m.r. parameters of the *ribo*hexoside-3-ulose phenylhydrazone isomers

Compound	Signal (τ value)	Assignment
(54)	4·29 (singlet)	Acetal proton
	5·15 (2-proton singlet)	H-1, H-2
	5·4–6·5 (4-proton multiplet)	H-4, H-5, H-6, H-6′
(55)	4·13 (singlet)	Acetal proton
	5·07 (doublet)	H-1
	5·40–6·50 (5-proton multiplet)	H-2, H-3, H-4, H-5, H-6, H-6′

Compound (54) was formulated as *syn-ribo*hexoside-3-ulose phenyl-hydrazone, since the H-2 signal was moved downfield from (55) to be coincident with the anomeric proton signal. Molecular models indicate that such deshielding, attributed to the anisotropic effect of the phenyl group, could best occur in the *syn* form.

Baer and his co-workers[44, 122] have used n.m.r. to assist in the con-figurational assignments of nitro-sugars.

XII. SUGARS IN WHICH THE RING OXYGEN IS REPLACED BY NITROGEN

N.m.r. has greatly facilitated studies of the new classes of sugar derivatives in which the ring oxygen atom is replaced by nitrogen.[123]

In the case of the pyrollidine type of sugar, various rotational isomers have been detected. For example, in deuterium oxide at ambient temperature, the spectrum of 4,5-diacetamido-4,5-dideoxy-L-xylose[124] (56) shows a peak corresponding to three protons at 7·97 τ and a double peak (7·79 and 7·84 τ) also corresponding to three protons. At 80°C however the double peak sharpens to a singlet. This behaviour suggests two rotational isomers such as (57, 58). Other workers have

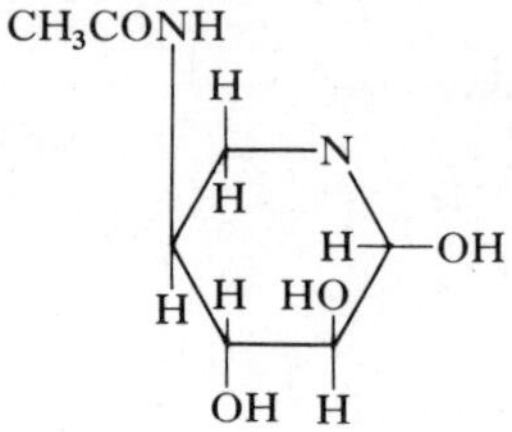

56

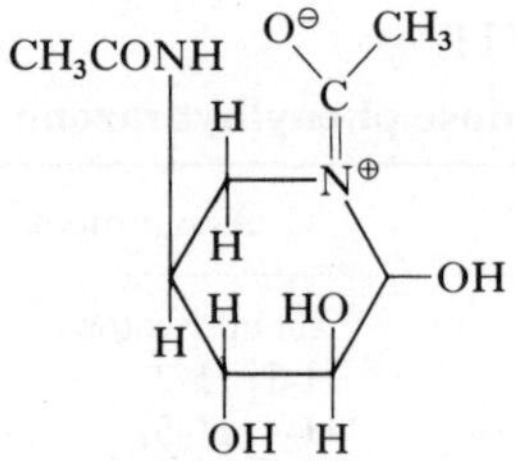

57

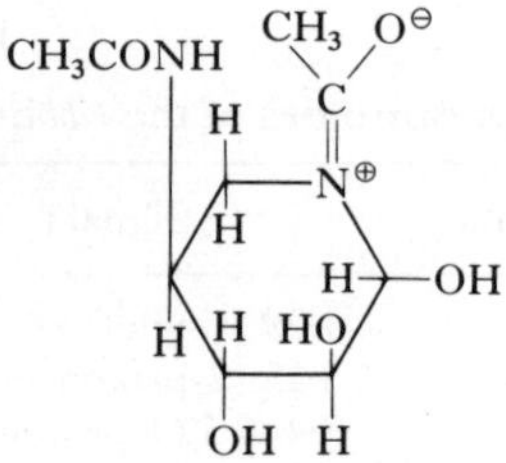

58

reported similar behaviour.[125-127] In certain cases the restricted rotation of the acetamido-group causes some splitting of other signals in the molecule[128] in addition to the signals from the acetamido methyl group. In methyl 4-acetamido-4-deoxy-D-*ribo* furanoside, the methoxyl resonance, rather than appearing as a clean singlet appeared as two singlets at 6·45 and 6·51 τ with relative intensities of 5:1 respectively. Additionally, the absorption that was assigned to H-1 also occurred as two doublets ($J = 1·5$ c./sec.) at 4·88 and 4·69 τ again with relative intensities of 5:1. When the spectrum was measured at 70°C one singlet was observed for the methoxyl group and one doublet was observed for the anomeric proton.

Several *N*-acetyl piperidine derivatives have been examined and reasons for the anisotropic effects displayed by the *N*-acetyl group have been discussed.[129]

N.m.r. can be successfully used to distinguish between a pyrollidine sugar or some alternative structure. The choice between (59) and

(60) is easily resolved.[128] The actual compound showed all the acetoxy resonances between 7·88 and 8·02 τ, and it is known that N-diacetates resonate at lower field at about 7·60 τ.[10, 130]

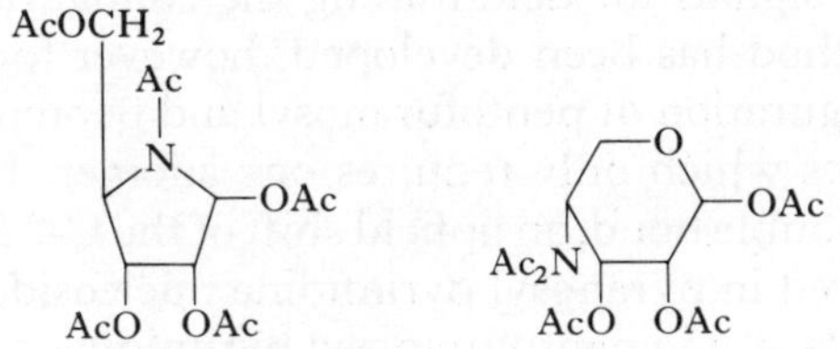

AcOCH$_2$
Ac
|
N
—OAc
AcO OAc

59

O
—OAc
Ac$_2$N
AcO OAc

60

XIII. FURANOID DERIVATIVES AND NUCLEOSIDES

Hall[2] has given a full account of early conformational studies of furanoid derivatives by n.m.r. and has shown that although such studies are of undoubted value, over-zealous application of the Karplus equation can perhaps lead to erroneous conclusions. Not surprisingly, therefore, few conformational studies of furanoid derivatives have been reported.

In favourable circumstances, however, n.m.r. can be used to determine the anomeric configuration of furanoid derivatives, particularly when both anomers are available. For example, in many cases where H-1 and H-2 are *cis* the observed coupling is ca. 5 c./sec., whereas when H-1 and H-2 are *trans* the observed coupling constant approaches zero.[131, 132] However even when H-1 and H-2 are *trans* it is possible for quite a large coupling to be observed if the furanoid ring adopts a conformation in which the dihedral angle between H-1–H-2 is of the order 150–160°.[133] Such examples are not uncommon in the nucleoside field. The α- and β-anomers of 9-(2-amino-2-deoxy-D-ribofuranosyl)adenine have $J_{1 2}$ coupling constants of 6·6 and 7·9 c./sec., respectively.[134] It is possible that these relatively large couplings truly reflect the furanoside conformation and do not, as has been suggested,[134] provide an example of a gross exception to the Karplus rule. Because comparisons of anomeric coupling constants do not provide unambiguous results, it has been severally suggested[135–137] that the chemical shifts of nucleoside anomeric protons might be utilized to assign anomeric configuration. The anomeric proton in C-1, C-2 *cis* nucleosides appears at lower field than the anomeric proton in C-1, C-2 *trans* nucleosides, and this difference has been suggested to be indicative of anomeric configuration.

In a detailed study of acetylated nucleosides, Cushley and co-workers[138] have demonstrated the unreliability of using the chemical shifts of acetyl signals for determining the configuration of the sugar portion. A method has been developed, however for establishing the anomeric configuration of pentofuranosyl and pentopyranosyl pyrimidine nucleosides which only requires one anomer. Upon hydrogenation of the 5,6 double bond, an upfield shift of the C-2 acetoxy resonance signal is observed in pyranosyl pyrimidine nucleosides having *cis* C-1, C-2 substituents and in pentofuranosyl pyrimidine nucleosides having a *trans* C-1, C-2 relationship. Similar hydrogenation of pyranosyl pyrimidine nucleosides having a *trans* C-1, C-2 relationship and pentofuranosyl pyrimidine nucleosides having a *cis* C-1, C-2 relationship causes a downfield shift of the C-2 acetoxyl signal. It is also possible to distinguish between isomeric 2′- and 3′-ribonucleoside derivatives,[139] such as (61) and (62). The $J_{1,2}$ coupling constant is less in (61) than in (62), and $H_{1'}$ is at lower field in (61) than in (62).

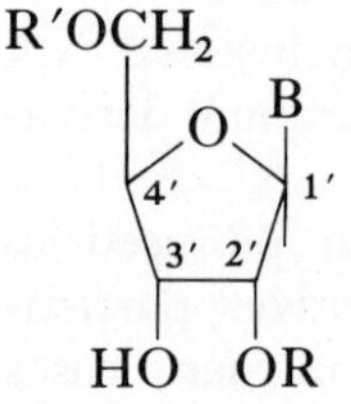

61 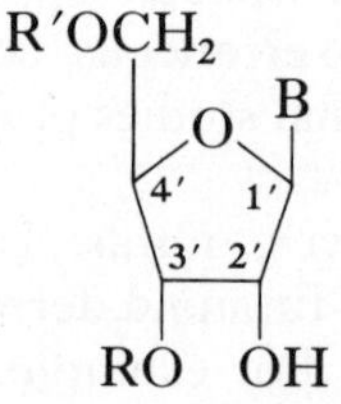   62 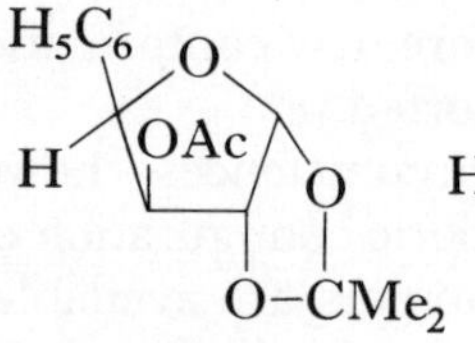   63 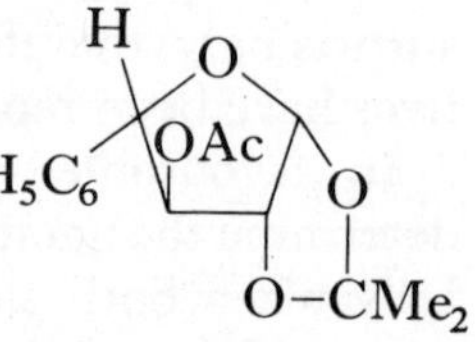   64

A study of compounds such as (63) and (64) has provided an interesting example of the use of chemical-shift data for determining configuration in furanoid derivatives.[140] Neither the coupling constants nor the chemical shifts of the ring protons were indicative of the configuration of the benzylic centre. However, in (63) the aromatic protons gave a sharp signal at 7·30 τ and the 3-O-acetate gave a signal at 1·72 τ. In (64) the aromatic protons gave a complex multiplet and the 3-O-acetate signal was at 2·12 τ. These facts were consistent with the assigned structures, since it was considered that the higher-field acetoxy methyl signal in (63) resulted from shielding by the phenyl substituent and that the complex aromatic multiplet in (64) arose because interaction between the phenyl and isopropylidene methyl groups hindered the rotation of the phenyl substituent.

XIV. RARE NATURALLY OCCURRING SUGARS

It has been stated previously[2] that the carbohydrate components of antibiotics have proved particularly amenable to analysis by n.m.r. spectroscopy. Thus, the structures of chalcose,[141] desosamine,[142] mycarose and cladinose[143] have been established by n.m.r. spectroscopy. To this list may be added oleandrose,[144] chromose[145, 146] and arcanose.[147] By making suitable model compounds it was possible to show[144] that in oleandomycin, L-oleandrose exists in a 1-C conformation and has a α-L- linkage, whereas D-desosamine exists in a C-1 conformation and has a β-D- anomeric linkage.

Methyl thiolincosaminide (65),[148] a carbohydrate component of the antibiotic lincomycin has been identified by n.m.r. An unusually

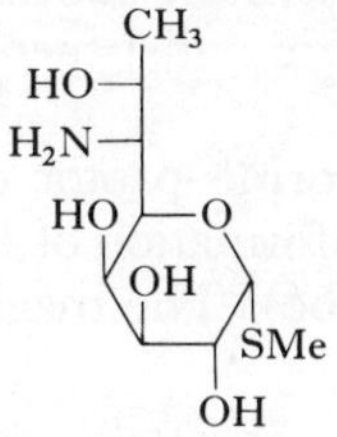

65

complete n.m.r. analysis permitted even the configuration of the side chain to be determined. A similar analysis of 2-hydroxyethylthiocelestosaminide, a sugar component from celesticetin, indicated the essential similarity of the two compounds.

XV. FLUORINE-CONTAINING CARBOHYDRATES

The studies of fluorine–proton couplings in fluorocarbohydrates that have so far been reported have proven of value both for elucidating the structures of the carbohydrates and in providing fundamental information concerning the nature of fluorine–proton coupling. A study of some glycopyranosyl fluorides[149] of known configuration was undertaken to determine the ^{19}F n.m.r. parameters that might be expected to aid configurational assignments. It was shown that for compounds in which the substituent at C-2 was axially orientated, fluorine came into resonance within the range $+52\cdot4$ to $63\cdot3$ p.p.m. (relative to trifluoroacetic acid) when it was equatorially orientated and between $+68\cdot6$ and $+72\cdot4$ p.p.m. when fluorine was axially orientated. This behaviour is analogous to the chemical shifts of carbohydrate anomeric protons in that the equatorial resonance is to low field of the axial resonance. The $^{19}F-^1H$ coupling constants for the glycopyranosyl fluorides provided a further criterion for determining the configuration at the anomeric centre. For $^{19}F_1-^1H_2$ axial–axial vicinal couplings, couplings of the order 23·4–25·4 c./sec. were observed, whereas for $^{19}F_1-^1H_2$ equatorial–axial couplings the order was 4·9–11·7 c./sec.

The relative signs of fluorine–proton spin coupling constants in glycopyranosyl halides have been determined.[150] It was confirmed that the relative signs of vicinal proton–proton and vicinal fluorine–proton couplings are the same whilst geminal proton–proton and geminal fluorine–proton couplings have different signs.

The configuration of some derivatives of 2-deoxy-α-D-hexopyranosyl fluoride have been determined by n.m.r. methods.[151] The observation was made that the geminal $J_{2a,2e}$ coupling is smaller (ca. 12 c./sec.) when the electronegative anomeric substituent is equatorially orientated than when the anomeric substituent is in the axial orientation (13·5–13·9 c./sec.).

The magnitude of the fluorine–proton coupling constants have been invoked to establish the conformation of 1,3,4-tri-O-benzoyl-2-deoxy-2-fluoro-β-D-ribose[152] as (66). The magnitude of the proton–proton

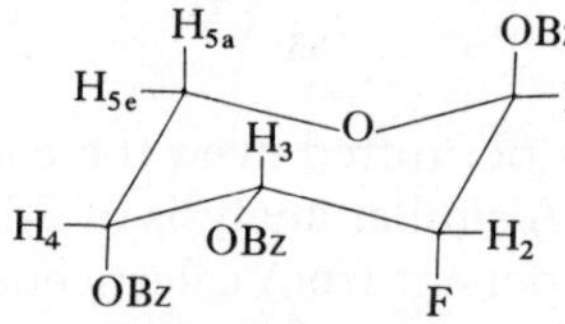

66

couplings were consistent with either the α- or β-D-anomer in the 1-C form. However the coupling constants $J_{H-1,F}$ 6·7 c./sec., $J_{H-3,F}$ 28 c./sec. were compatible only with the 1-C (β-D) isomer shown.

Derivatives of 2,5-anhydro-1-deoxy-1,1-difluoro-D-mannitol have been examined.[153]

XVI. N.M.R. DATA RELEVANT TO CARBOHYDRATES FROM STUDIES OF OTHER HETEROCYCLES

Studies of heterocycles such as dioxans, dioxolanes, dithians, oxathians and morpholines have furnished much information that is relevant to carbohydrates. For example, studies of substituted 1,3-dioxans[94] have demonstrated the complex nature of long-range coupling effects. For a 4-substituted 1,3-dioxan (67) the following long-range coupling constants have been reported:[94] $J_{2e,6e} = 1·5$;

$J_{2e,5e}=0{\cdot}9$; $J_{2e,6a}=0{\cdot}5$; $J_{6e,4a}=0{\cdot}5$; $J_{6e,2a}=0{\cdot}4$; $J_{6a,4a}=0{\cdot}4$; and $J_{6a,2a}=0{\cdot}3$ c./sec. These values show that although a planar zig-zag arrangement (e.g., $J_{2e,6e}$) favours long-range coupling it is not a necessary requirement for the observation of small (ca. $0{\cdot}5$ c./sec.) couplings. From studies of other 1,3-dioxans some possible reasons have been suggested[154] for the enhanced long-range coupling constants in cyclic systems.

67

A very detailed analysis of the A_2B_2 spectrum of 2-methyl-1,3-dioxolan has been reported,[155] and it has been shown that the Karplus $\cos^2 \theta$ law cannot account precisely for the magnitude of the couplings in dioxolan and dioxan rings.

Interest has centred on the influence on geminal coupling constants of vicinal groups particularly where the neighbouring group is a heteroatom carrying a lone pair of electrons. Geminal coupling constants cover the range $+42$ to $-22{\cdot}3$ c./sec., and ranges of values for various types of CH_2 have been reviewed;[156] some of the factors that influence the magnitude of the geminal couplings have been discussed. In this connection a molecular orbital treatment[20] of geminal coupling has justified various empirical conclusions. By considering the four possible transitions to triplet excited states of a CH_2 group, Pople and Bothner-By[20] showed that withdrawal of electrons from orbitals symmetric to the plane at right angles to the H–H axis (inductive effect of an electronegative substituent) should lead to a positive change in coupling constant, whereas withdrawal of electrons from orbitals antisymmetric between the hydrogen atoms (hyperconjugation) should produce a negative change in coupling constant. Supply of electrons to the CH_2 should give opposite results. [Geminal couplings are negative so a smaller coupling (or negative change) in fact means a larger measured line spacing and a larger coupling (or positive change) means a smaller measured line spacing.] Anteunis[157, 158] has studied the influence of vicinal free orbitals on both geminal and vicinal coupling constants. He has proposed that increments of $+2{\cdot}3$ and $+1{\cdot}8$ c./sec. be added to vicinal and geminal coupling values, respectively, each time an α-oxygen (or α-nitrogen) atom has one of its free-electron pair p orbitals parallel with the C—H bond of one of the protons involved in the coupling under consideration. The geminal increment is consistent with the molecular orbital treatment, and the vicinal increment increases the reliability of the Karplus rule. There is no doubt that in future small changes in geminal coupling constants in carbohydrate systems (and particularly in furanoid systems) will be interpreted in terms of molecular geometry.

The n.m.r. spectra of some substituted 1,3-dithians have been described[159] and methods for the determination of the preferred conformation of potentially flexible molecules have been discussed. It is suggested that invariance of coupling constants with solvent may be considered as evidence favouring conformational homogeneity. In the 1,3-dithians the C-4(6) axial protons resonate at lower field than the C-4(6) equatorial protons in contrast to the generally accepted rule for cyclohexanes.[76] A similar result for geminal protons adjacent to sulphur has been reported by other workers.[160,161] In cyclohexanones, the axial α-protons also resonate at lower field than the equatorial α-protons.[162] Foster and his co-workers[163,164] have prepared a series of 2,6-disubstituted-1,4-oxathians (68) and S-oxide and S-dioxide derivatives. In the oxathians the axial protons in the C-3 and

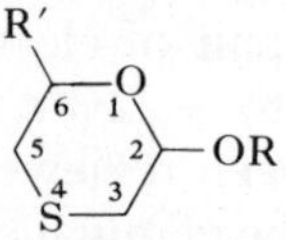

68

C-5 methylene groups resonate at lower field than the corresponding equatorial protons, but in the S-oxides and S-dioxides the more normal situation, where equatorial protons resonate at lower field than axial protons, is observed.[164] The magnitude of the vicinal coupling constants together with the observation of strong long-range $J_{3e,5e}$ couplings (ca. 2 c./sec.) unequivocally establish the conformational homogeneity of this series of compounds.

Attempts have been made to use n.m.r. data to establish the absolute configuration of the sulphoxide group in 1,4-oxathian S-oxides[165] (e.g., 69 and 70) and in other cyclic systems.[166,167] To distinguish

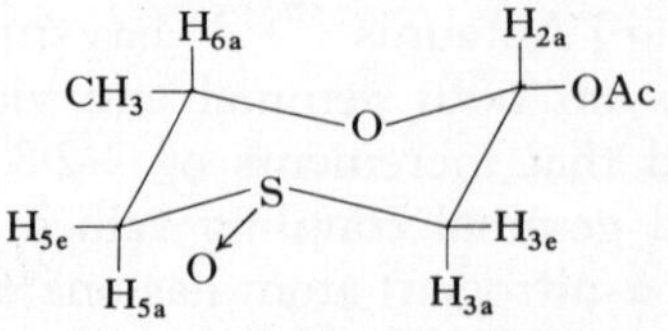

69

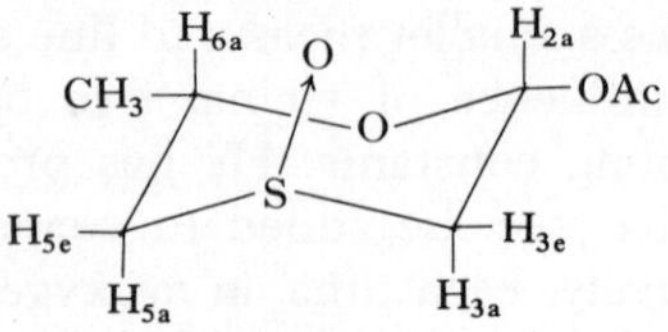

70

between axial and equatorial S→O bonds three different spectral parameters may be used. It has been suggested that for molecules having a chair conformation—

(1) The geminal coupling constants ($J_{3a, 3e}$ and $J_{5a, 5e}$) in compounds where the S → O bond is equatorial are smaller than when the S → O bond is axial [and moreover smaller than in the parent sulphide (e.g., **71**)].

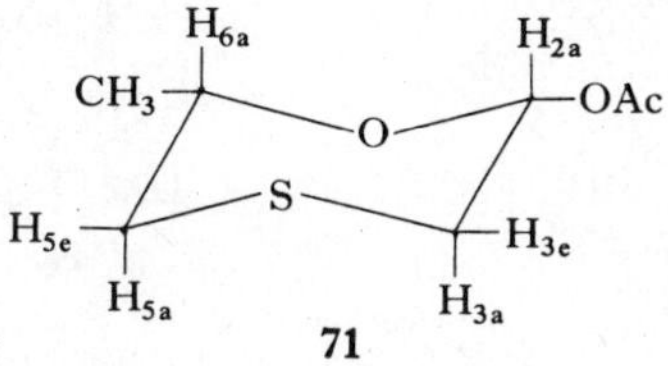

(2) The chemical-shift difference between geminal protons vicinal to the sulphoxide centre is larger when the S → O bond is equatorial than when the S → O bond is axial.[166] In the 1,4-oxathian S-oxides the chemical shift difference ranges from 0·69 to 0·95 p.p.m. for equatorial S → O bonds and from 0·28 to 0·68 p.p.m. when the S → O bond is axial.[164]

(3) In compounds where the S → O bond is axially orientated any protons situated *syn* axially will be at lower field (by ca. 1 p.p.m.) than when the S → O bond is equatorially orientated.[165]

The empirical validity of these generalizations has been substantiated[164] by a study of a series of 1,4-oxathian derivatives in which the configuration and conformation of some members was established by chemical[163] and X-ray methods.[168] The parameters of compounds (**69**)–(**71**) are listed in Table VIII as an illustration of the utility of n.m.r. for establishing sulphoxide configuration.

TABLE VIII

Parameters of compounds (69)–(71)

Compound	Chemical shift, τ values						Coupling constants, c./sec.						
	H_{2a}	H_{3e}	H_{3a}	H_{5e}	H_{5a}	H_{6a}	$J_{2a, 3e}$	$J_{2a, 3e}$	$J_{3a, 3e}$	$J_{3a, 5e}$	$J_{5a, 6a}$	$J_{5a, 5e}$	$J_{5e, 6a}$
69	4·26	6·40	7·30	6·59	7·47	6·20	10·1	1·6	11·3	1·8	11·5	12·0	1·8
70	3·52	6·93	7·47	7·05	7·62	5·20	9·8	1·9	14·2	2·2	10·8	13·8	1·9
71	4·17	7·55	7·31	7·80	7·52	5·98	9·0	2·7	13·1	1·2	9·9	13·5	1·9

The configurations of the conformationally rigid S-oxides of methyl 3,4-di-O-acetyl-2,6-anhydro-2-thio-α-D-altropyranoside[167] (**72** and

73) have been established by n.m.r. considerations. When the S → O bond is *syn* axially orientated to H-1 (**72**), H-1 is at much lower field than when the S → O bond is *syn* axially orientated to H-3 and H-4 (**73**). Alternatively, when the S → O bond is *syn* axial to H-3 and H-4

72   73

(**73**), H-3 and H-4 are at much lower field than when the S → O bond is *syn* axial to H-1 (**72**). It was concluded originally that the *syn* axial shielding effects in the 1,4-oxathians and in the altropyranoside derivatives, could be attributed to an acetylenic type anisotropy of the S → O bond.[165] It is now clear that this is an over-simplification and that the chemical-shift differences in epimeric sulphoxides must be rationalized in terms of its total electron distribution and not simply in terms of the anisotropy of the S → O bond.[164]

REFERENCES

1. R. U. Lemieux, R. K. Kullnig, H. J. Bernstein and W. G. Schneider, *J. Amer. Chem. Soc.*, 1958, **80**, 6098.
2. L. D. Hall, *Adv. Carbohydrate Chem.*, 1964, **19**, 51.
3. M. Karplus, *J. Chem. Phys.*, 1959, **30**, 11.
4. M. Karplus, *J. Amer. Chem. Soc.*, 1963, **85**, 2870.
5. K. L. Williamson, *J. Amer. Chem. Soc.*, 1963, **85**, 516.
6. D. H. Williams and N. S. Bhacca, *J. Amer. Chem. Soc.*, 1964, **86**, 2742.
7. H. Booth, *Tetrahedron Letters*, 1965, 411.
8. R. J. Abraham and K. G. R. Pachler, *Mol. Phys.*, 1963, **7**, 165.
9. R. U. Lemieux and J. D. Stevens, *Canad. J. Chem.*, 1965, **43**, 2059.
10. T. D. Inch, J. R. Plimmer and H. G. Fletcher Jr., *J. Org. Chem.*, 1966, **31**, 1825.
11. J. I. Musher and E. J. Corey, *Tetrahedron*, 1962, **18**, 791.
12. R. E. Reeves, *Adv. Carbohydrate Chem.*, 1951, **6**, 107.
13. N. S. Bhacca and D. Horton, *J. Amer. Chem. Soc.*, 1967, **89**, 5993.
14. A. C. Richardson, *Ann. Reports*, 1966, **63**, 489.
15. R. U. Lemieux, in "Molecular Rearrangements, Part 2" (P. de Mayo, Ed.). Interscience, New York, 1963.
16. C. V. Holland, D. Horton and J. S. Jewell, *J. Org. Chem.*, 1967, **32**, 1818.
17. D. Horton and W. N. Turner, *J. Org. Chem.*, 1965, **30**, 3387.
18. R. U. Lemieux and A. R. Morgan, *Canad. J. Chem.*, 1965, **43**, 2205.

19. B. Coxon, *Tetrahedron*, 1966, **22**, 2281.
20. J. A. Pople and A. A. Bothner-By, *J. Chem. Phys.*, 1965, **42**, 1339.
21. C. V. Holland, D. Horton, M. J. Miller and N. S. Bhacca, *J. Org. Chem.*, 1967, **32**, 3077.
22. K. Onodera, S. Hirano, F. Masuda and N. Kashimura, *J. Org. Chem.*, 1966, **31**, 2403.
23. R. U. Lemieux and J. D. Stevens, *Canad. J. Chem.*, 1966, **44**, 249.
24. R. W. Lenz and J. P. Heeschen, *J. Polymer. Sci.*, 1961, **51**, 247.
25. E. L. Eliel, N. L. Allinger, S. J. Angyal and G. A. Morrison, "Conformational Analysis", p. 408. Wiley, New York, 1965.
26. H. S. Isbell, *J. Res. Natl. Bur. Std.*, 1962, **66A**, 233.
27. M. Rudrum and D. F. Shaw, *J. Chem. Soc.*, 1965, 52.
28. D. Horton, J. S. Jewell and K. D. Philips, *J. Org. Chem.*, 1966, **31**, 4022.
29. D. Horton, J. S. Jewell and K. D. Philips, *J. Org. Chem.*, 1966, **31**, 3843.
30. S. J. Angyal, V. A. Pickles and R. Ahluwalia, *Carbohydrate Res.*, 1967, **3**, 300.
31. A. S. Perlin, *Canad. J. Chem.*, 1966, **44**, 539.
32. O. L. Chapman and R. W. King, *J. Amer. Chem. Soc.*, 1964, **86**, 1256.
33. B. Casu, M. Reggiani, G. G. Gallo and A. Vigevani, *Tetrahedron Letters*, 1964, 2839; 1965, 2253.
34. A. S. Perlin, *Canad. J. Chem.*, 1966, **44**, 1757.
35. B. Casu, M. Reggiani, G. G. Gallo and A. Vigevani, *Tetrahedron*, 1966, **22**, 3061.
36. T. D. Inch and P. Rich, *J. Chem. Soc. C*, 1968, 1784.
37. J. J. Uebel and H. W. Goodwin, *J. Org. Chem.*, 1966, **31**, 2040.
38. R. J. Ouellitte, *J. Amer. Chem. Soc.*, 1964, **86**, 4378.
39. W. B. Morris, C. F. Poranski and T. N. Hall, *J. Am. Chem. Soc.*, 1966, **88**, 190.
40. H. S. Isbell and A. J. Fatiadi, *Carbohydrate Res.*, 1966, **2**, 204.
41. A. C. Richardson and K. A. McLauchlan, *J. Chem. Soc.*, 1962, 2499.
42. L. D. Hall, L. Hough, S. H. Shute and T. J. Taylor, *J. Chem. Soc.*, 1965, 1154.
43. D. Horton, *J. Org. Chem.*, 1964, **29**, 766.
44. H. H. Baer and F. Kienzle, *Canad. J. Chem.*, 1967, **45**, 983.
45. D. Horton, J. B. Hughes, J. S. Jewell, K. D. Philips and W. N. Turner, *J. Org. Chem.*, 1967, **32**, 1073.
46. D. Horton, W. E. Mast and K. D. Philips, *J. Org. Chem.*, 1967, **32**, 1471.
47. H. Agahigian, G. D. Vickers, M. H. van Saltza, J. Reid, A. I. Cohen and H. Gauthier, *J. Org. Chem.*, 1965, **30**, 1085.
48. F. W. Lichtenthaler, *Chem. Ber.*, 1963, **96**, 2047.
49. M. Nakajuna, A. Hasegawa and F. W. Lichtenthaler, *Annalen*, 1964, **630**, 21.
50. H. H. Baer, L. D. Hall and F. Kienzle, *J. Org. Chem.*, 1964, **29**, 2014.
51. F. W. Lichtenthaler and H. P. Albrecht, *Chem. Ber.*, 1966, **99**, 575.
52. C. L. Stevens, P. Blumbergs, F. A. Daniker, D. H. Otterback and K. G. Taylor, *J. Org. Chem.*, 1966, **31**, 2822.
53. B. R. Baker and D. H. Buss, *J. Org. Chem.*, 1966, **31**, 217.
54. D. Horton and M. J. Miller, *Carbohydrate Res.*, 1965, **1**, 335.
55. S. J. Angyal and G. J. Melrose, *J. Chem. Soc.*, 1965, 6494.
56. N. Baggett, K. W. Buck, A. B. Foster, R. Jefferis, B. H. Rees and J. M. Webber, *J. Chem. Soc.*, 1965, 3382.
57. S. A. Barker and E. J. Bourne, *J. Chem. Soc.*, 1952, 905.
58. N. Baggett, K. W. Buck, A. B. Foster, M. H. Randall and J. M. Webber, *Proc. Chem. Soc.*, 1964, 118.
59. F. A. Carey, D. B. Ball and L. Long Jr., *Carbohydrate Res.*, 1966, **3**, 205.

60. K. W. Buck, A. B. Foster, B. H. Rees, J. M. Webber and J. Lehmann, *Carbohydrate Res.*, 1965, **1**, 329.
61. N. Baggett, K. W. Buck, A. B. Foster, M. H. Randall and J. M. Webber, *J. Chem. Soc.*, 1965, 3394.
62. N. Baggett, K. W. Buck, A. B. Foster and J. M. Webber, *J. Chem. Soc.*, 1965, 3401.
63. A. B. Foster, A. H. Haines, T. D. Inch, M. H. Randall and J. M. Webber, *Carbohydrate Res.*, 1965, **1**, 145.
64. N. Baggett, J. M. Duxbury, A. B. Foster and J. M. Webber, *Chem. Ind.*, 1964, 1832; *Carbohydrate Res.*, 1965, **1**, 22.
65. N. Baggett, J. M. Duxbury, A. B. Foster and J. M. Webber, *J. Chem. Soc. C*, 1966, 208.
66. F. S. Al-Jeboury, N. Baggett, A. B. Foster and J. M. Webber, *Chem. Comm.*, 1965, 222.
67. N. Baggett, J. M. Duxbury, A. B. Foster and J. M. Webber, *Carbohydrate Res.*, 1966, **2**, 216.
68. S. Forsen, B. Lindberg and B.-G. Silvander, *Acta. Chem. Scand.*, 1965, **19**, 359.
69. R. J. Abraham, L. D. Hall, L. Hough and K. A. McLauchlan, *J. Chem. Soc.*, 1962, 3699.
70. S. J. Angyal and R. M. Hoskinson, *J. Chem. Soc.*, 1962, 2991.
71. L. D. Hall, L. Hough, K. A. McLauchlan and K. Pachler, *Chem. and Ind.*, 1962, 1465.
72. B. Coxon and L. D. Hall, *Tetrahedron*, 1964, **20**, 1685.
73. C. Cone and L. Hough, *Carbohydrate Res.*, 1965, **1**, 1.
74. T. D. Inch, *Carbohydrate Res.*, 1967, **5**, 53.
75. D. H. Buss, L. Hough, L. D. Hall and J. F. Manville, *Tetrahedron*, 1965, **21**, 69.
76. L. M. Jackman, "Applications of Nuclear Magnetic Spectroscopy in Organic Chemistry". Pergamon, London, 1959.
77. B. Coxon, *Tetrahedron*, 1965, **21**, 3481.
78. B. Coxon, *Carbohydrate Res.*, 1966, **1**, 357.
79. D. Horton and J. S. Jewell, *Carbohydrate Res.*, 1966, **2**, 251.
80. D. Horton and J. S. Jewell, *Carbohydrate Res.*, 1966, **3**, 255.
81. R. D. King, W. G. Overend, J. Wells and N. R. Williams, *Chem. Comm.*, 1967, 726.
82. B. Flaherty, W. G. Overend and N. R. Williams, *Chem. Comm.*, 1966, 434.
83. J. S. Brimacombe and L. C. N. Tucker, *Carbohydrate Res.*, 1967, **5**, 36.
84. R. J. Ferrier, *Adv. Carbohydrate Chem.*, 1965, **20**, 67.
85. L. D. Hall, *J. Org. Chem.*, 1964, **29**, 297.
86. L. D. Hall and L. F. Johnson, *Tetrahedron*, 1964, **20**, 883.
87. R. J. Abraham, H. Gottschalk, H. Paulsen and W. A. Thomas, *J. Chem. Soc.*, 1965, 6268.
88. J. A. Pople, W. G. Schneider and H. J. Bernstein, "High Resolution Nuclear Magnetic Resonance". McGraw-Hill, London, 1959.
89. M. Karplus, *J. Chem. Phys.*, 1960, **33**, 1842.
90. S. Sternhell, *Rev. Pure and Appl. Chem.*, 1964, **14**, 15.
91. B. Coxon, H. J. Jennings and K. A. McLauchlan, *Tetrahedron*, 1967, **23**, 2395.
92. R. Freeman and D. H. Whiffen, *Mol. Phys.*, 1961, **4**, 321.
93. N. S. Bhacca and D. H. Williams, "Applications of N.M.R. Spectroscopy in Organic Chemistry: Illustrations from the Steroid Field", p. 185. Holden Day, San Francisco, 1964.

94. K. C. Ramey and K. Messick, *Tetrahedron Letters*, 1965, 4423.
95. E. F. L. Anet, *Carbohydrate Res.*, 1966, **1**, 348.
96. E. W. Garbish, *J. Am. Chem. Soc.*, 1964, **86**, 5561.
97. E. F. L. Anet, *Austral. J. Chem.*, 1965, **18**, 837.
98. E. F. L. Anet, *Carbohydrate Res.*, 1966, **2**, 448.
99. C. C. J. Culvenor, M. L. Hefferan and W. G. Woods, *Austral. J. Chem.*, 1965, **18**, 1605.
100. E. Albano, D. Horton and T. Tsuchiya, *Carbohydrate Res.*, 1966, **2**, 349.
101. D. Horton and W. N. Turner, *Carbohydrate Res.*, 1966, **1**, 444.
102. R. U. Lemieux, D. R. Lineback, M. L. Wolfrom, F. B. Moody, E. G. Wallace and F. Komitsky, *J. Org. Chem.*, 1965, **30**, 1092.
103. U. G. Nayak, M. Sharma and R. K. Brown, *Canad. J. Chem.*, 1967, **45**, 1767.
104. R. J. Ferrier, W. G. Overend and G. H. Sankey, *J. Chem. Soc.*, 1965, 2830.
105. R. J. Ferrier and G. H. Sankey, *J. Chem. Soc. C*, 1966, 2345.
106. D. Horton and J. M. Tranchet, *Carbohydrate Res.*, 1966, **2**, 315.
107. D. Horton and M. J. Miller, *J. Org. Chem.*, 1965, **30**, 2457.
108. L. Mester, *Adv. Carbohydrate Chem.*, 1958, **13**, 105.
109. M. L. Wolfrom, A. Thompson and D. R. Lineback, *J. Org. Chem.*, 1962, **27**, 2563.
110. M. L. Wolfrom, G. Fraenkel, D. R. Lineback and F. Komitsky Jr., *J. Org. Chem.*, 1964, **29**, 457.
111. H. El. Khadem, M. L. Wolfrom and D. Horton, *J. Org. Chem.*, 1965, **30**, 838.
112. L. Mester, E. Moczar and J. Parello, *J. Amer. Chem. Soc.*, 1965, **87**, 596.
113. H. El. Khadem and M. M. A. Abdel Rahman, *J. Org. Chem.*, 1966, **31**, 1178.
114. L. Mester and E. Moczar, *J. Org. Chem.*, 1964, **29**, 247.
115. H. El. Khadem, *J. Org. Chem.*, 1964, **29**, 3072.
116. H. El. Khadem, Z. M. El-Shafei and M. M. A. Abdel Rahman, *Carbohydrate Res.*, 1965, **1**, 31.
117. B. Capon and B. E. Connett, *J. Chem. Soc.*, 1965, 4492.
118. P. M. Collins and W. G. Overend, *J. Chem. Soc.*, 1965, 3448.
119. P. M. Collins, *Chem. Comm.*, 1966, 164.
120. G. J. Karabatsos, R. A. Taller and F. M. Vane, *J. Amer. Chem. Soc.*, 1963, **85**, 2327.
121. G. J. F. Chittenden and R. D. Guthrie, *J. Chem. Soc. C*, 1966, 697.
122. H. H. Baer, T. Neilson and W. Rank, *Canad. J. Chem.*, 1967, **45**, 991.
123. H. Paulsen, *Angew. Chem. (Internat. Ed.)*, 1966, **5**, 495.
124. M. L. Wolfrom, J. L. Minor and W. A. Szarek, *Carbohydrate Res.*, 1965, **1**, 156.
125. W. A. Szarek, S. Wolfe and J. N. K. Jones, *Tetrahedron Letters*, 1962, 2743.
126. A. E. El. Ashmairy and D. Horton, *Carbohydrate Res.*, 1965, **1**, 164.
127. J. S. Brimacombe and J. G. H. Bryan, *J. Chem. Soc. C*, 1966, 1725.
128. E. J. Reist, D. E. Gueffroy, R. W. Blackford and L. Goodman, *J. Org. Chem.*, 1966, **31**, 4025.
129. H. Paulsen and K. Todt, *Chem. Ber.*, 1967, **100**, 3385.
130. F. A. L. Anet, R. A. B. Bannard and L. D. Hall, *Canad. J. Chem.*, 1963, **41**, 2331.
131. B. Capon and D. Thacker, *Proc. Chem. Soc.*, 1964, 396.
132. T. D. Inch and P. Rich, *J. Chem. Soc. C*, 1968, 1784.
133. R. U. Lemieux and J. W. Lown, *Canad. J. Chem.*, 1963, **41**, 889.
134. M. L. Wolfrom and M. W. Winkley, *J. Org. Chem.*, 1967, **32**, 1823.
135. T. Nishimura and B. Shimizu, *Chem. Pharm. Bull.*, 1965, **13**, 803.
136. K. R. Darnall and L. B. Townsend, *J. Heterocyclic Chem.*, 1966, **3**, 371.

137. M. J. Robins and R. K. Robins, *J. Am. Chem. Soc.*, 1965, **87**, 4934.
138. R. J. Cushley, K. A. Watanabe and J. J. Fox, *J. Am. Chem. Soc.*, 1967, **89**, 394.
139. H. P. M. Fromageot, B. E. Griffin, C. B. Reese, J. E. Sulstan and D. R. Trentham, *Tetrahedron*, 1966, **22**, 705.
140. T. D. Inch, R. V. Ley and P. Rich, *J. Chem. Soc. C*, 1968, 1683.
141. P. K. W. Woo, H. W. Dion and L. F. Johnson, *J. Amer. Chem. Soc.*, 1962, **84**, 1066.
142. P. K. W. Woo, H. W. Dion, L. Durham and H. S. Mosher, *Tetrahedron Letters*, 1962, 735.
143. W. Hofheinz, H. Grisebach and H. Friebolin, *Tetrahedron*, 1962, **18**, 1265.
144. W. D. Celmer and D. C. Hobbs, *Carbohydrate Res.*, 1965, **1**, 137.
145. M. Miyamoto, Y. Kawamatsu, M. Shinohara, K. Nakanishi, Y. Nakadaira and N. S. Bhacca, *Tetrahedron Letters*, 1964, 2371.
146. J. S. Brimacombe and D. Portsmouth, *Carbohydrate Res.*, 1965, **1**, 128.
147. G. Roncari and W. Keller-Schierlen, *Helv. Chim. Acta.*, 1966, **49**, 705.
148. G. Slomp and F. A. MacKellar, *J. Amer. Chem. Soc.*, 1967, **89**, 2454.
149. L. D. Hall and J. F. Manville, *Chem. and Ind.*, 1965, 991.
150. L. D. Hall and J. F. Manville, *Chem. and Ind.*, 1967, 468.
151. L. D. Hall and J. F. Manville, *Canad. J. Chem.*, 1967, **45**, 1299.
152. R. J. Cushley, J. F. Codington and J. J. Fox, *Carbohydrate Res.*, 1967, **5**, 31.
153. K. R. Wood and P. W. Kent, *J. Chem. Soc. C*, 1967, 2442.
154. J. E. Anderson, *J. Chem. Soc. B*, 1967, 712.
155. R. J. Abraham, *J. Chem. Soc.*, 1965, 256.
156. R. C. Cookson, T. A. Crabb, J. J. Frankel and J. Hudec, *Tetrahedron*, 1966, Suppl. No. 7, 355.
157. M. Anteunis, D. Tavernier and F. Borremans, *Bull. Soc. chim. belges*, 1966, **75**, 396.
158. M. Anteunis, *Bull. Soc. chim. belges*, 1966, **75**, 413.
159. R. J. Abraham and W. A. Thomas, *J. Chem. Soc.*, 1965, 335.
160. E. Campaigne, N. F. Chamberlain and B. E. Edwards, *J. Org. Chem.*, 1962, **27**, 135.
161. Y. Allingham, R. C. Cookson and T. A. Crabb, *Tetrahedron*, 1968, **24**, 1989.
162. K. M. Wellman and F. G. Bordwell, *Tetrahedron Letters*, 1963, 1703.
163. K. W. Buck, A. B. Foster, A. R. Perry and J. M. Webber, *Chem. Comm.*, 1965, 433.
164. A. B. Foster, T. D. Inch, M. H. Qadir and J. M. Webber, *Chem. Comm.*, 1968, 1086.
165. K. W. Buck, A. B. Foster, W. D. Pardoe, M. H. Qadir and J. M. Webber, *Chem. Comm.*, 1966, 759.
166. J. B. Lambert and R. G. Keske, *J. Org. Chem.*, 1966, **31**, 3429.
167. A. B. Foster, J. M. Duxbury, T. D. Inch and J. M. Webber, *Chem. Comm.*, 1967, 881.
168. K. W. Buck, T. A. Hamor and D. J. Watkin, *Chem. Comm.*, 1966, 759.

Solvent Effects in Proton Magnetic
Resonance Spectroscopy

J. RONAYNE AND DUDLEY H. WILLIAMS

University Chemical Laboratory, Cambridge, England

I. INTRODUCTION

WITHIN the last few years n.m.r. spectroscopists have increasingly looked to solvents other than the usual "inert" materials, such as carbon tetrachloride or deuterochloroform as an aid in the simplification of spectra, in structural elucidation, in the investigation of weak interactions in solution, and in stereochemical studies.

Solvent effects were first observed by Bothner-By and Glick[1] and independently by Reeves and Schneider[2] in 1957. A summary appeared in 1964,[3] which emphasized the potential of solvent shifts in organic chemistry, but before that date little practical use was made of the phenomenon. This situation no longer pertains, as is evident from the increasing number of publications that are now appearing dealing with the application of solvent shifts to a wide variety of problems.

In n.m.r. experiments, nuclei with magnetic moments are effectively used as probes to measure the magnetic field H_{local} at the nucleus, i.e.—

$$H_{local} = (1-\sigma)H \tag{1}$$

H is the applied magnetic field strength and σ is the screening constant. The understanding of the observed screening constants for a particular proton is greatly facilitated by the splitting of the total screening constant σ_{total} into six contributions;[4,5] thus—

$$\sigma_{total} = \sigma_g + \sigma_b + \sigma_w + \sigma_a + \sigma_e + \sigma_c \tag{2}$$

where the subscripted symbols refer to the contributions to the total screening of the gaseous molecule (σ_g), bulk susceptibility of the medium (σ_b), van der Waals interactions (σ_w), anisotropy of the susceptibilities of the surrounding molecules (σ_a), reaction field of the medium (σ_e), and specific solute–solvent interactions (σ_c). In this review we are mainly concerned with the two contributions σ_e and σ_c, but we shall deal in turn with all of the contributions to the total screening.

II. THE BULK SUSCEPTIBILITY TERM (σ_b)

The total volume of a cylindrical sample may be divided into two regions by defining a sphere round any given molecule within the sample large enough to be of macroscopic dimensions and small compared with the size of the sample. If the sample is placed in a uniform magnetic field H_0, the field experienced by the nucleus at the centre of the sphere is made up of three parts—

  (a) the external field;
  (b) the field due to the induced magnetism in the region between the small sphere and the sample boundary;
  (c) the field due to induced magnetism in the inner sphere.

The bulk susceptibility arises from (b) and must be allowed for if an external reference is used. The effect of the bulk susceptibility on chemical shifts may in principle be calculated[6] and may also be obtained experimentally by a simple technique.[7]

If an internal reference substance is used, however, no correction is needed, since the bulk susceptibilities for the reference and the sample are the same and equal to the bulk susceptibility of the solution. The earlier studies of solvent effects were carried out using external references, and it has been found that repetition of some of these experiments using internal tetramethylsilane as reference can lead to differences in the observed shifts, even after the application of the bulk susceptibility correction. Probable factors in the observation of such discrepancies are errors in the calculation of the susceptibility correction on the one hand and neglect of the effect of the tetramethyl-silane on the solute molecules on the other.

III. THE VAN DER WAALS TERM (σ_w)

In 1960 Bothner-By[8] observed that for several simple organic compounds, a change from the gaseous to the liquid state was accompanied by a shift to low field of the protons in excess of that calculated using the classical bulk susceptibility correction. It was found possible to calculate the observed shift β_i^j of a solute proton i in a solvent j by use of the empirical relationship—

$$\beta_i^j = -x_i y_j \tag{3}$$

where x and y were numbers characteristic of the solute and solvent, respectively. In non-polar and non-aromatic solvents it was suggested that the shifts were due to dispersion (or van der Waals) forces. These forces between molecules in solution perturb the electronic structure of the molecules, and this leads to a change in the nuclear screening constant.[9] Two effects may contribute to σ_w (the contribution to the screening of such interactions)—

(a) Distortion of the electronic environment of the nucleus. This distortion is probably an expansion and the diamagnetic screening is therefore diminished, resulting in a paramagnetic shift. The shift should increase as the charges on the solvent nuclei rise so that halogenated solvents should produce relatively large paramagnetic shifts. This effect would not be expected to be temperature dependent.

(b) Departures from the equilibrium solvent configuration will lead to a "buffeting" of the solute and hence to a time-dependent distortion of the electronic structure. This also leads to a paramagnetic shift and is temperature dependent.

By taking methane gas as their reference in order to eliminate solute–solvent interactions, Buckingham and co-workers[9] have been able to

4

obtain an estimate of the shifts in the methane proton resonances due to the van der Waals effect of the solvent. The results given in Table I show qualitative agreement with the generalizations (*a*) and (*b*) above. The negative shifts of the methane proton resonances in solvents 1–15 are due to the van der Waals contribution of the solvent molecules to the total screening. The polyhalogenated solvents produce the largest shifts, as is expected for solvents with large numbers of electrons. The large negative and the positive shifts produced by solvents 16–21 are unexpected from a consideration of the simple van der Waals effect. These shifts are due to the anisotropy of the magnetic susceptibility of the solvents concerned and the effect of this anisotropy on the total screening constant will now be considered.

TABLE I

Proton chemical shifts (in c./sec. at 60 Mc./sec.) of dilute solutions of methane in various solvents relative to external chloroform

Number	Solvent	Chemical shift, c./sec.	Solvent shift, c./sec.
–	Methane (gas)	446·5	0
1	Neopentane	438·7	−7·8
2	Cyclopentane	437·1	−9·4
3	*n*-Hexane	434·7	−11·8
4	Cyclohexane	432·7	−13·8
5	Acetone	435·9	−10·6
6	Diethyl ether	435·0	−11·5
7	Methyl bromide	424·5	−22·0
8	Methyl iodide	418·6	−27·9
9	Methylene chloride	425·7	−20·8
10	Methylene bromide	419·0	−27·5
11	Methylene iodide	404·1	−42·4
12	Chloroform	423·1	−23·4
13	Bromoform	406·7	−39·8
14	Carbon tetrachloride	421·3	−25·2
15	Carbon tetrabromide	412·5	−34·0
16	Acetonitrile	418·9	−27·6
17	Carbon disulphide	412·5	−34·0
18	Dicyanoacetylene	401·2	−45·2
19	Benzene	457·3	+10·8
20	Toluene	454·3	+7·8
21	Nitrobenzene	462·6	+16·1

IV. THE ANISOTROPY TERM (σ_a)

The importance of magnetic anisotropy contributions to the chemical shift has been recognized for some time, and several quantitative calculations have been made for the aromatic hydrocarbons.[10–12] Buckingham and co-workers have suggested[9] *that in the absence of any specific solute–solvent interactions*, disc-like solvents, such as benzene will adopt the configuration (**1A**) rather than (**1B**), enabling the benzene to lie closer to the solute molecules. Similarly, rod-like solvents will have, on the average, the configuration (**2A**) rather than (**2B**). In view

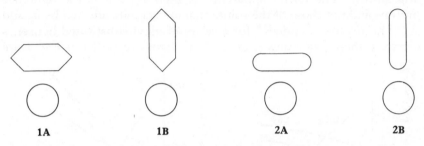

| 1A | 1B | 2A | 2B |

of the known anisotropy of the benzene ring, it is clear that an average solute–solvent configuration, such as that depicted in (**1A**) will result in a net upfield shift of the solute protons relative to a random arrangement. It is also to be expected that the rod-like solvents, carbon disulphide or acetylene, whose largest diamagnetic susceptibility is along the axis of the rod, will cause a net downfield shift of the solute protons.

In Table I it is seen that benzene causes an upfield shift of 10·8 c./sec. from the value in the gas phase, and that dicyanoacetylene, a rod-shaped, non-polar solvent causes a downfield shift of 45·2 c./sec.

Several authors have calculated the shifts due to anisotropy effects in cylindrically symmetrical solvent molecules,[1, 9, 13, 14] and some[9, 13] have succeeded in obtaining values comparable with experimental ones. Watts and Goldstein[14] have shown that the shift produced in α-chloroacrylonitrile by benzene in excess of that due to the reaction field (see Section VI) is almost identical with the value obtained by the use of Buckingham's equation[9] for the anisotropy effect of cylindrically symmetric solvents.

V. STERIC EFFECTS IN RELATION TO σ_w AND σ_a

It is to be expected that if an internal reference is used, then the reference protons will normally suffer the same contribution to their total screening from σ_w and σ_a as the protons of the solute. This will be the case provided that there is complete access to the solute and reference protons by the solvent and also that solute–solvent and reference–solvent physical interactions are similar by virtue of shape considerations (see Section IV). However, if there is steric hindrance to the approach of the solvent to a solute proton, an apparent *upfield* shift will be observed for the σ_a contribution of rod-like solvents and the σ_w contribution of such solvents as carbon tetrachloride. The anisotropic effect of aromatic solvents will produce an apparent *downfield* shift.[15] The term "apparent" is used since it is the reference protons and not those of the solute that are actually affected by σ_a and σ_w. The results obtained[15] for a series of alkyl-substituted benzenes illustrate these principles (Fig. 1). The values recorded in Fig. 1 are

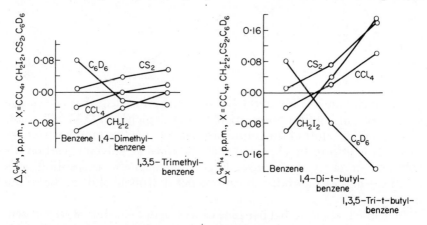

FIG. 1. The solvent dependence of the aromatic proton resonances of benzene, 1,4-di-t-butylbenzene and 1,3,5-tri-t-butylbenzene. (From Williams et al.[15])

solvent shifts of the aromatic protons in a solvent (X) relative to n-hexane solution (where only a relatively small σ_w term is applicable—see Table I). Thus, the marked "downfield shift" of the aromatic protons of 1,3,5-tri-t-butylbenzene in C_6D_6 solution relative to n-hexane solution ($\Delta = \delta_{C_6H_{14}} - \delta_X$ p.p.m.) reflects the steric congestion round this proton. Thus it is evident that sterically hindered protons may give "anomalous" chemical shift values when an internal reference is employed, and care must be exercised in the interpretation of such data.

VI. THE REACTION FIELD TERM (σ_e)

A polar molecule in solution can polarize the surrounding medium giving rise to an electric field, the reaction field (R) at the solute. In a definitive paper, Buckingham[4] has developed a theory of the effect of the reaction field on chemical shifts based on the Onsager model.[16]

In this model the solute molecule is regarded as a sphere of radius r containing a dipole of moment μ at its centre. If the solvent is considered to be a continuum of dielectric constant ε, then the reaction field at the solute is given by—

$$R = \frac{2(\varepsilon-1)}{(2\varepsilon+1)} \cdot \frac{m}{r^3} \qquad (4)$$

$$= \frac{2(\varepsilon-1)(n^2-1)}{3(2\varepsilon+n^2)} \cdot \frac{\mu}{\alpha} \qquad (5)$$

where $m = \mu + \alpha R$, the total dipole moment of the solute in the medium; α is the polarizability of the sphere and n is the refractive index of the pure solute. In the treatment of Marshall and Pople,[17] the reduction in the shielding of a proton in an s state is proportional to the square of the applied field, E. However, a field along an X—H bond that does not possess spherical symmetry will either increase or decrease the electron density at the proton, depending on the direction of E. Shifts proportional to E are therefore expected. A field perpendicular to the X—H bond destroys the axial symmetry of the bond leading to a low-field shift proportional to E^2. Buckingham[4] gives a calculated contribution to the shielding of a proton in an X—H bond of—

$$\sigma_e = -\chi.10^{-12}.E.\cos\theta - 10^{-18}.E^2 \qquad (6)$$

where $E\cos\theta$ is the component of the total field along the X—H bond, and χ is a constant. He suggests a value of $\chi = 2$, whereas Musher[18] lists values of $\chi = 2$ to $3\cdot4$ obtained by several methods. Equations (5) and (6), neglecting terms in E^2 yield a contribution to the shielding of the proton in an X—H bond due to the reaction field as—

$$\sigma_e = \chi.10^{-12}.\frac{2(\varepsilon-1)(n^2-1)}{3(2\varepsilon+n^2)}.\frac{\mu\cos\theta}{\alpha} \qquad (7)$$

Equation (7) predicts that the solvent shift due to the reaction field should be linear in $(\varepsilon-1)/(2\varepsilon+n^2)$ with a slope of

$$-\frac{2}{3}\frac{\chi(n^2-1)\mu\cos\theta.10^{-12}}{\alpha}$$

Such a relationship between solvent shift and dielectric constant has been found for various systems by a number of authors.[9, 14, 19–21]

For molecules such as p-dinitrobenzene, which has no net dipole moment, the appropriate reaction field equation is—

$$R' = \frac{6(\varepsilon-1)}{3\varepsilon+2} \cdot \frac{\theta}{r^5} \qquad (8)$$

where R' is the reaction field gradient and θ is the molecular quadrupole moment. In (3A) and (3B), the quadrupolar reaction fields of p-dinitrobenzene and acetylene are illustrated. The theory can be used to predict the proton resonance shifts in p-nitrotoluene on changing the solvent from hexane to acetone. From (3C) it is clear that a downfield

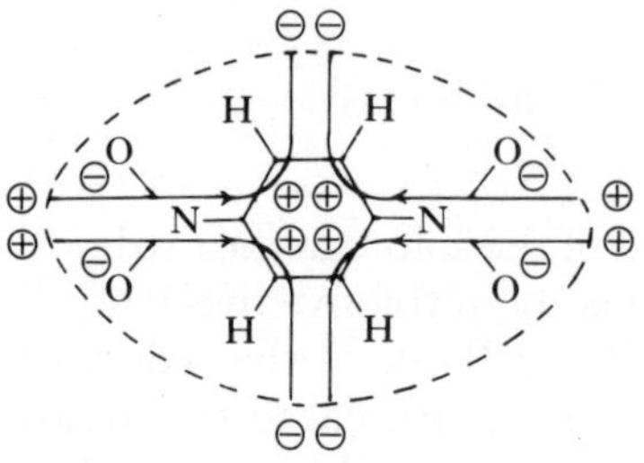

3A

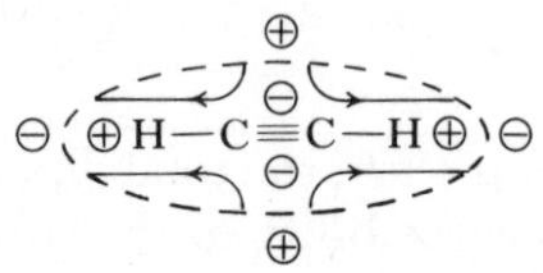

3B

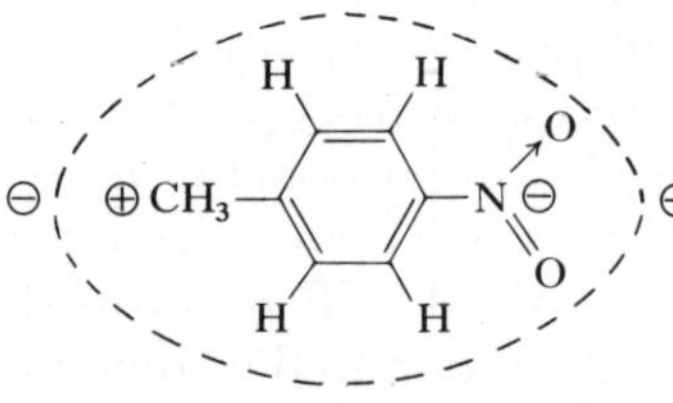

3C

shift would be expected for the protons *ortho* to the methyl group and an upfield shift for the *meta* protons. The experimental results[22] show a downfield shift of 0·29 p.p.m. for the *ortho* protons and a downfield shift of 0·06 p.p.m. for the *meta* protons. The latter shift is unexpected, but is explained by Buckingham as being due to the reaction field perpendicular to the bond, which always manifests itself in downfield shifts. A downfield contribution from the quadrupolar reaction field of the nitro-group would also be expected (see 3A). However, Schug and Smith[23] have found that a non-linear relationship exists between the dielectric function $(\varepsilon - 1)/(\varepsilon + 1)$ and solvent shift when the solute benzene is examined in an acetone–CCl$_4$ solvent mixture (results extrapolated to infinite dilution). Since the benzene quadrupole should produce a reaction field according to equation (8), this result is unexpected and the shift has been explained exclusively in terms of van der Waals forces.

Since few molecules approximate to a spherical shape, the Onsager model was considered inadequate by Diehl and Freeman to account for the reaction field in complex molecules; they have therefore derived a more sophisticated equation[24] for the reaction field effect based on an ellipsoidal cavity which takes into account the shape of the solute molecule, i.e.—

$$\sigma_e = -\chi.10^{-12}.\frac{3\mu}{abc}.\cos\theta.\xi_a\left[1+(n^2-1)\xi_a\right]\frac{\varepsilon-1}{\varepsilon+\beta} \qquad (9)$$

where $\beta=n^2\xi_a/(1-\xi_a)$, ξ_a is a shape factor and a, b, c are the ellipsoidal semi-axes. Ross and Sack[25] have previously evaluated ξ_a for cavities of various shapes and using their data Diehl and Freeman[24] have found that the chemical shifts of acetonitrile and paraldehyde were linear in $(\varepsilon-1)/(\varepsilon+\beta)$ for media of differing dielectric constant. A similar linear relationship has since been found[26] for some dihalo-ethylenes.

It has been shown[21] that the reaction field approach may be useful in the assignment of peaks in the n.m.r. spectra of polar molecules. The positions of the C-10, C-8 and C-13 methyl resonances of epi-manoyl oxide (**4**) in various solvents are given in Table II together with

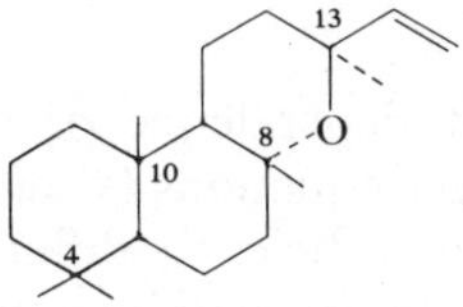

4

the dielectric constant of the solvents. It can be seen that the variations in the position of the C-10 methyl group are small compared with the corresponding variations for the C-8 and C-13 methyls. This is consistent with the explanation that the protons near the polar groups (in

TABLE II

Positions of C-10, C-8 **and** C-13 **methyl resonances of epimanoyl oxide (4) in various solvents**

	Dielectric constant, ε	c./sec. at 60 Mc.			
		v_{C-10}	v_{C-8}	v_{C-13}	$v_{C-13}-v_{C-8}$
Cyclohexane	2·02	51·3	60·4	67·1	6·7
Carbon tetrachloride	2·24	51·0	62·4	69·0	6·6
Carbon disulphide	2·64	50·6	60·2	67·1	6·9
Chloroform	4·81	52·0	69·0	74·2	5·2
Methylene chloride	9·1	51·1	64·2	71·7	7·5
Cyclohexanone	18·03	52·0	62·8	72·0	9·2
Acetone	20·7	51·9	62·6	72·1	9·5

this case the ether function of the tetrahydropyran ring) will be affected most by the reaction field.

A. Some criticisms of the reaction field theory

In view of the approximations inherent in the derivation of the reaction field theory, it is not surprising that some instances are known in which a non-linear relationship exists between the solvent shift and dielectric constant in polar solvents. As pointed out by Buckingham,[4] the reaction field model is only valid for a solute that reacts in no way with the solvent or with other solute molecules but simply presents a continuum of certain dielectric properties. Protons are normally on the "surface" of the molecule and are therefore exposed to direct contact with the surrounding molecules, so that the Onsager model is a poor approximation of the actual reaction field acting on a molecule.

Laszlo and Musher[27] have examined some dibromocyclohexanones of known conformation in acetone–carbon tetrachloride mixtures (providing media of varying dielectric constant) and have reached the following conclusions—

(a) Dielectric constant dependence of the reaction field is not given by the Onsager equations (4) and (5).
(b) The reaction field is sufficiently different at various points in a molecule that some of its components not only differ in magnitude, but actually change sign; this means that the solute cannot be treated as a point molecule in a cavity, so that the solvent shifts in complex molecules are not adequately defined by the linear reaction field theory.

These conclusions were based on the severe curvature of the plots of chemical shift against reaction field calculated from both the simple Onsager and the more complex Diehl and Freeman equations. Fontaine et al.[28] have found similar curvature in plots of σ_e for acetone versus the Onsager reaction field of cyclohexane–acetone mixtures. Some interesting results recently obtained[29–31] show that if $\varepsilon^{\frac{1}{2}}$ is substituted for the dielectric function $(\varepsilon-1)/(\varepsilon+\frac{1}{2}n^2)$ of equation (5), the curvature of these plots is effectively removed, especially for protons near the dipole location in the large molecules studies by Laszlo and Musher. No explanation for the dependence of σ_e on $\varepsilon^{\frac{1}{2}}$ has been offered. Deviations from linearity in plots of σ_e versus $\varepsilon^{\frac{1}{2}}$ in some haloethylenes are explained[31] by the occurrence of excess dispersion forces in the solvents producing the deviations.

The conclusions that may be drawn from the foregoing discussion on the reaction field theory are that it satisfactorily explains many of the observed shifts in polar solvents but it is not entirely adequate in the general case where the solute molecules do not approximate to the spherical shape and solute–solvent interactions cannot be ruled out. Alternative suggestions for specific systems have been made that account for low field shifts of polar solutes in polarizable solvents; notably hydrogen bonding,[22, 32–35] lone-pair co-ordination,[36–38] breakup of aggregates[32, 39–41] and effects on rotamer populations.[42] In a recent publication Kuntz and Johnson[43] have rejected the reaction field as the causative factor of the low-field shifts of nitromethane and some halides in various polar solvents. They propose instead a solute–solvent collision complex with an approximate heat of formation of $-1 \cdot 5$ kcal./mole. This value is a reasonable one for such an interaction and is closely similar to that observed for weakly hydrogen-bonded systems. Supporting evidence for the proposals is forthcoming from the precise mathematical description of the concentration and temperature dependence of the solvent shifts in the systems studied.

B. Solvent dependence of spin–spin coupling constants

The dependence of spin–spin coupling constants on the nature of the solvent is now well established.[44–46] For example, geminal coupling constants vary by as much as 100% in the vinyl halides[47] and are roughly proportional to the dielectric constant of the medium; vicinal couplings may also vary (by 2% in the vinyl halides[47] and 30% in 1-chloro-2-ethoxyethylene[48]). Solvent dependence is usually found in polar solvents and it is generally believed[14, 20, 44–53] that the reaction field is the primary causative factor. However, the difficulties in trying to account for the solvent dependence of chemical shifts by one mechanism only are also encountered in any attempt to explain the solvent-dependent coupling constants; hydrogen bonding,[35, 46, 54] solvent effects on π-contribution to the couplings[55] and dispersion forces[55, 56] have also been implicated.

Solvent effects are more pronounced on geminal than on vicinal coupling constants and only a few investigations have been carried out on the latter.[48, 52, 55] Some studies have also been made on the solvent dependence of $J_{^{13}C-H}$,[54] $J_{^{13}C-F}$,[44] J_{H-F}[44, 52] and J_{Si-F}.[56]

A recent summary by Smith and Cox[46] which was based on their own (see for example, Table III) and other experimental evidence gives the following information for the solvent dependence of geminal coupling constants ($^2J_{H-H}$) —

   (a) The reaction field is of primary importance in causing changes in the coupling constants.

4*

(b) At a fixed concentration in different solvents, $^2J_{H-H}$ always changes in the same direction in the absolute sense (probably negative) as the dielectric constant of the medium is increased.

(c) Hydrogen bonding solvents appear to have the same effect on $^2J_{H-H}$ as an increase in the dielectric constant.

(d) With a few exceptions, changes in $^2J_{H-H}$ $[\Delta(^2J_{H-H})]$ parallel the solvent-induced changes in chemical shift of the protons involved.

(e) The magnitude of $\Delta(^2J_{H-H})$ is largest for molecules possessing large permanent dipoles; for molecules having dipoles of similar magnitude, the more polarizable molecules exhibit the largest $\Delta(^2J_{H-H})$.

(f) The orientation of the solute dipole is an important factor in determining the magnitude of $\Delta(^2J_{H-H})$.

TABLE III

J_{gem} for styrene oxide and styrene sulphide in various solvents

Solvent	Dielectric constant	Styrene oxide J_{gem}	Styrene sulphide J_{gem}
Cyclohexane	1·99	6·00	−1·15
Carbon tetrachloride	2·20	5·85	−1·18
Benzene	2·26	5·81	−1·37
Toluene	2·35	5·79	. .
Deuterochloroform	4·55	5·55	−1·52
Pyridine	12·3	5·69	−1·41
Acetophenone	16·99	5·67	. .
Acetone	19·8	5·56	−1·46
o-Nitrotoluene	25·15	5·68	. .
Nitrobenzene	32·22	5·53	−1·47
Nitromethane	35·0	5·42	−1·61
Acetonitrile	35·1	5·40	−1·54
Dimethylsulphoxide	46	5·31	−1·55
Neat	. .	5·63	−1·34

The obvious implication of (b) is that the changes in coupling constants induced by solvents may be used in the determination of the signs of the coupling constants and this may well prove to be an important application of the technique in the future.

A molecular orbital theory of nuclear spin–spin coupling recently proposed by Pople and Bothner-By[57] has been extended by Smith and Cox[46] to account for the observed changes in $^2J_{H-H}$. The electronic structure of the isolated CH_2 group is discussed in terms of four molecular orbitals that are delocalized over both bonds. Two of these are bonding (ψ_1 and ψ_2) and the other two are antibonding (ψ_3 and ψ_4) (see **5A**). The bonding orbitals may be classified further into symmetric

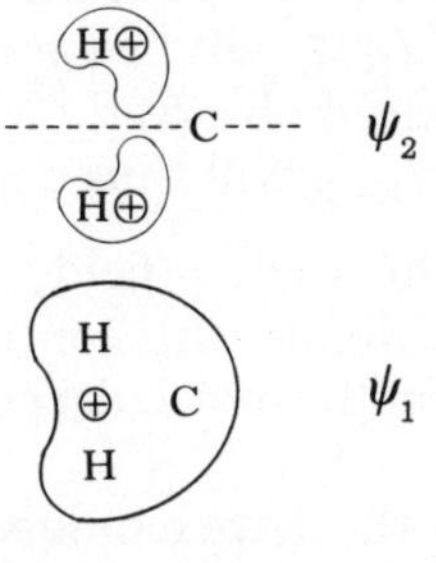

5A: nodal behaviour of the bonding orbitals of a methylene group

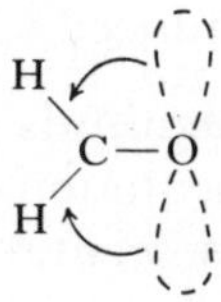

5B

(ψ_1) and antisymmetric (ψ_2) types. According to Pople and Bothner-By—

(a) withdrawal of electrons from symmetric orbitals between the hydrogen atoms (usually inductive) leads to a positive change in $^2J_{H-H}$, whereas

(b) withdrawal of electrons from antisymmetric orbitals (hyperconjugative effect) leads to a negative change.

Application of these two "rules" to the *isolated* formaldehyde molecule for example leads to the expectation of a positive contribution to $^2J_{H-H}$ both from inductive withdrawal of electrons by the directly bonded oxygen from the symmetric orbital ψ_1 and concurrent contribution of electrons from the doubly occupied $2p_y$ orbital of the oxygen atom back into the antisymmetric orbital ψ_2 (see **5B**). Thus $^2J_{H-H}$ for formaldehyde should be large and positive as is observed.

In *solution*, the large permanent dipole of the formaldehyde molecule will induce an appreciable solvent reaction field, the orientation of this field being, in all probability, parallel to the dipole moment (see **6**). It is clear that the orientation of the permanent dipole and the reaction field will produce a shift of electrons out of ψ_1 and ψ_2. Electron shift out of ψ_1 will cause $^2J_{H-H}$ to become more positive, whereas

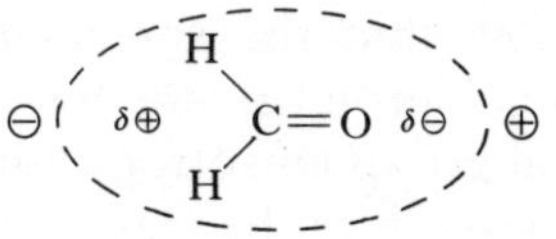

6

shift of electrons out of ψ_2 will cause it to become more negative. On the reasonable assumption that the antisymmetric orbital ψ_2 involved in π-like hyperconjugative interactions is more polarizable than the symmetric orbital ψ_1, the conclusion may be reached that in a solvent which produces a reaction field, $^2J_{H-H}$ will become more negative in the case of formaldehyde, as is indeed observed.[58] The magnitude of the solvent-induced variation in $^2J_{H-H}$ will thus depend on—

(a) the magnitude of the solvent reaction field;

(b) the orientation of the solute dipole; this controls the orientation of the solvent reaction field in the molecular co-ordinate system; and

(c) the relative magnitude of the hyperconjugative contribution to $^2J_{H-H}$.

These generalizations suggest[46] that hydrogen bonding solvents should produce a negative shift in $^2J_{H-H}$. Solvents such as chloroform bond to the solute via the non-bonding electrons (e.g., at oxygen), greatly decreasing the back donation to ψ_2. Thus, a more negative coupling constant than might be expected from the reaction field alone may be observed; such an observation has been made.[46]

VII. SUMMARY OF σ_b, σ_w, σ_a and σ_e TERMS

At this point we may summarize the main "physical" (as opposed to "chemical") effects that solvents may have on proton resonances—

(a) Bulk susceptibility effects cause paramagnetic shifts in all cases where an external reference is used and a correction must be made. An internal reference removes, for all practical purposes, the necessity for such a correction.

(b) Van der Waals effects are responsible for paramagnetic shifts only.

(c) Anisotropy effects cause paramagnetic or diamagnetic shifts depending on the orientation of the axis of largest diamagnetic susceptibility in the solvent molecule.

(d) The presence of steric hindrance to the approach of bulk solvent to a solute proton reverses the trends in the observed shifts for anisotropic and van der Waals effects. Studies of steric effects show that the so-called inert solvents, carbon tetrachloride and chloroform, are unsuitable for the determination of functional group anisotropies if the introduction of the functional group modifies the steric environment of the neighbouring protons.

(e) The reaction field and associated effects generally cause paramagnetic shifts in polar solvents and must be taken into account
in any study of functional group anisotropies and coupling
constants. A recent study by Karabatsos et al.,[59] which supports
the model proposed by ApSimon et al.[60] for the anisotropy of
the carbonyl group, relies for its conclusions on the fact that a
downfield shift is observed for the methine proton of dichloro-
acetaldehyde when the dielectric constant of the solvent is increased. The solvents, which ranged in polarity from dimethyl
sulphoxide to n-pentane, were believed to change the rotamer
populations of the aldehyde, thus changing the average position
of the methine proton with respect to the carbonyl group (see 7).

7

No account was taken of the reaction field of the solvents and
therefore the conclusions drawn can be regarded as correct
only if the chemical shift change is in excess of that which
would be expected from the reaction field of the solvent in
going from a solvent of low dielectric constant (n-pentane) to
one of high dielectric constant (dimethyl sulphoxide). A determination[61] of the reaction field-induced shift for the protons
of methylene chloride (as a model compound for dichloro-
acetaldehyde) supports the conclusions regarding the anisotropy of the carbonyl group.

(f) Coupling constants vary with the dielectric constant of the
solvent, and this variation may have considerable potential in
the evaluation of the absolute signs of nuclear spin–spin coupling constants.

VIII. THE SPECIFIC ASSOCIATION TERM (σ_c)

The term σ_c has previously[5, 62] been applied to the effect on chemical
shift of specific solute–solvent interactions in solution, and it has been
pointed out that these should cause a small paramagnetic solvent shift;
in this usage, shifts due to anisotropy effects associated with specific
interactions are included in the σ_a term. In this discussion, however,
we shall take σ_c to represent the effect of solvent anisotropy in a geometrically specific solute–solvent orientation which has been brought

about by "chemical association". We shall be wholly concerned with the effects of aromatic solvents, both carbocyclic and heterocyclic, on the proton screening constants of di-, and quadrupolar solute molecules.

When a polar molecule is dissolved in an aromatic solvent, the solute protons are usually shifted with respect to their positions in an inert solvent, such as neopentane or hexane (even if an internal reference is employed, as is assumed in the following discussion, and even if the previously discussed σ_w, σ_a and σ_e terms due to change of solvent are negligible). The solvent shift for a particular proton is represented by Δ_y^x where $\Delta_y^x = (\delta_x - \delta_y)$ p.p.m.; δ_x is the chemical shift in the "inert" solvent x and δ_y the chemical shift in the aromatic solvent y. A diamagnetic solvent shift is denoted by a positive value for Δ_y^x; a paramagnetic shift has a negative value.

The mechanism by which benzene solvent molecules are able to produce differential solvent shifts in the proton resonances of the same molecule has been widely interpreted[63, 64] in terms of a benzene–solute collision complex. The term collision complex is meant to imply a short-lived orientation of the benzene molecule(s) that has been brought about by dipole–induced dipole, dipole–quadrupole, or other weak chemical association. Any mechanism that is proposed for benzene-induced solvent shifts should take into account the nature, stoicheiometry, strength and time-averaged stereochemical environment of the interaction and we shall deal with each of these points in turn.

A. The nature of the interaction

In 1962, Schneider[5] suggested that the large $\Delta_{\text{benzene}}^{\text{neopentane}}$ values he observed for alkyl—X and vinyl—X solutes (X = CN, CHO, NO$_2$, Cl, Br and I) could be explained by a dipole–induced dipole interaction leading to the solute–solvent orientation depicted in (8) for acetonitrile. In this orientation the benzene ring lies as far away as possible from the region of negative charge. In view of the known anisotropy of the benzene ring this arrangement would obviously lead to a large

8

diamagnetic shift of the methyl protons, as is observed ($\Delta_{benzene}^{neopentane}$ = 0·94 p.p.m.).

Corroborative evidence for the proposed type of interaction was forthcoming from the linear plots which were obtained for μ/V versus Δ, where μ is the dipole moment and V is the molecular volume of the various solutes used (see Fig. 2). Similar linearity between molecular dipole moment and solvent shift of the methyl protons has

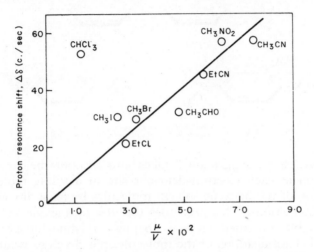

FIG. 2. Plot of proton shifts against μ/V. (From Schneider.[5])

been observed in some organometallic compounds of the type $(CH_3)_nSnX_{4-n}$ (X = Cl, Br and I).[65]

The interaction between benzene and aromatic solutes is somewhat more complicated however, and the simple dipole is no longer adequate to account for the observations. Schneider[62] was unable to account for the following results—

(a) $\Delta_{benzene}^{cylohexane}$ for the ring protons of the non-dipolar solute p-benzoquinone is 0·50 p.p.m.;

(b) the ring protons of NN-dimethylaniline are deshielded in benzene relative to their positions in cyclohexane.

Klinck and Stothers[66, 67] have reported strong evidence that benzene acts as an electron donor to electron-deficient sites in aromatic solutes and have suggested the orientations shown in (9A) and (9B) for the benzene collision complex with p-nitrobenzaldehyde and p-NN-dimethylaminobenzaldehyde, respectively.

The results obtained for these and other p-substituted benzaldehydes

qualitatively support such a picture. A plot of chemical shift of the
N-methyl and formyl protons versus mole fraction of benzene (added
to a solution in an inert solvent) was found to be approximately linear
for (9A) and (9B), consistent with the occurrence of a 1:1 collision
complex.

9A   9B

A more recent suggestion[64] takes into account the possibility of
interaction at each electron-deficient site in a solute molecule and
orientation of the benzene solvent molecules by local dipole-induced
dipole interactions. This precludes the idea of a single 1:1 collision
complex, but provided there is no phase relationship between the
various 1:1 associations in the molecule, the Δ values would still be
proportional to the mole fraction of benzene added, as is suggested by
the dilution studies. In the case of p-NN-dimethylaminobenzaldehyde
(9B), solvation at the carbonyl carbon may be drastically reduced or
even non-existent due to the influence of the electron-donating di-
methylamino-group, so that the local dipole-induced dipole concept
"reduces" to that shown in (9B). However, for p-nitrobenzaldehyde
the observation that ΔH_{ortho} is greater than ΔH_{meta} (see 9A) will be a
consequence of association not only in the region of the formyl group
but also in the region of the nitro-group.

   Schneider's results[5] for the aromatic solutes may be readily understood in terms of the foregoing principles. In (10A) stereospecific
solvation at the most important electron-deficient sites in p-benzoquinone is schematically represented. Such solvation would be expected to produce the observed shielding of the ring protons irrespective of the lack of a solute dipole; the reason for the slightly non-
planar arrangement of the solvating molecules is discussed in Section
VIIID. Schneider et al.[62] have alternatively suggested a quadrupole-
induced quadrupole association for the p-benzoquinone–benzene
collision complex (10B), and Baker and Davis,[68] who obtained a 2:2

stoicheiometry for the system by dilution studies, have proposed the cage-like structure shown in (**10C**).

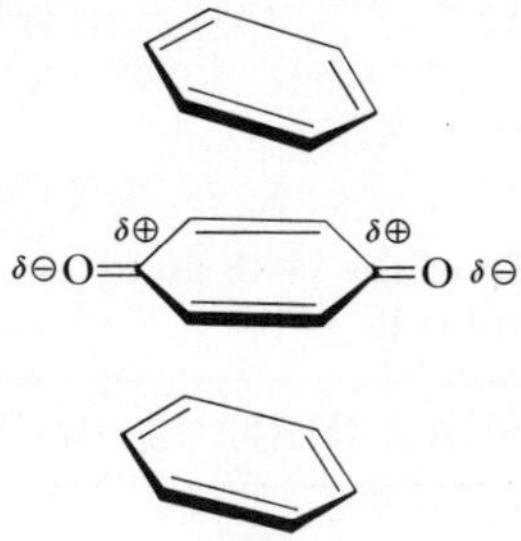

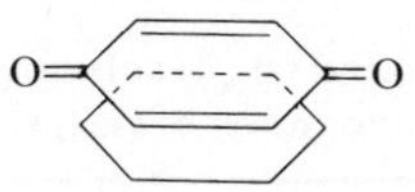

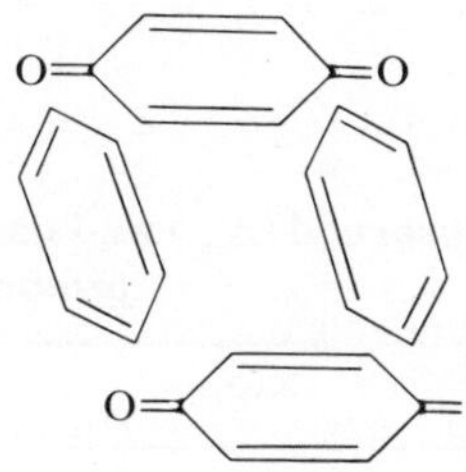

                    10A   10B   10C

The negative shifts of the ring protons of *NN*-dimethylaniline are the result of solvation in the dimethylamino-region of the molecule by the benzene with subsequent deshielding of the ring protons (see **11**).

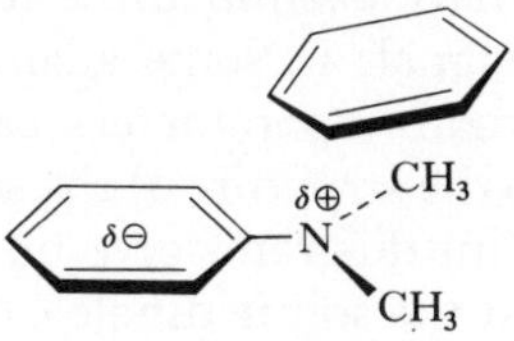

11

B. The stoicheiometry of the interaction

It has been widely assumed that the stoicheiometry of the benzene–solute collision complex is 1:1, and consistent with this assumption is the observation[67–70] that the solvent shift at various concentrations of benzene in carbon tetrachloride is approximately proportional to the mole fraction of benzene. Dilution studies such as these do not exclude the co-occurrence to a small extent of other solute–solvent combinations, such as 2:1 or 1:2. Phase-independent 1:1 associations at isolated polar sites can account for the additivity of benzene-induced solvent shifts. For example, addition of the solvent shifts $(\Delta = \delta_{CDCl_3} - \delta_{C_6H_6})$ of the H-18 and H-19 protons of 5α-androstan-11-one (**12**) and 5α-androstan-2-one (**13**) gives Δ values which are in

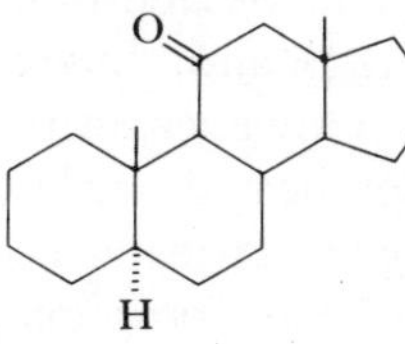

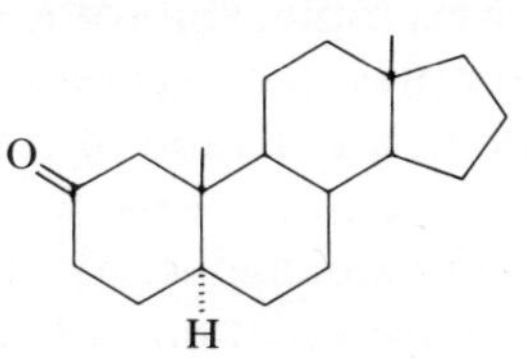

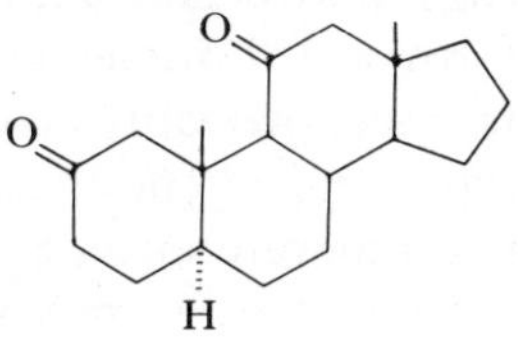

          12   13   14

excellent agreement with the experimentally determined solvent shifts of the H-18 and H-19 protons of 5α-androstan-2,11-dione (14) (see Table IV).[71]

TABLE IV

Observed (Δ_{obs}) and calculated (Δ_{calc}) solvent shifts of the H-18 and H-19 proton resonances of (12), (13) and (14)

Solute	Δ_{obs} (H-18)	Δ_{obs} (H-19)	Δ_{calc} (H-18)	Δ_{calc} (H-19)
5-α-Androstan-11-one (12)	+0·11	−0·14	..	..
5α-Androstan-2-one (13)	+0·06	+0·16	..	..
5α-Androstan-2,11-dione (14)	+0·17	+0·02	+0·17	+0·02

Fort and Lindstrom[72] have examined the temperature dependence of the proton resonance signals in some adamantyl halides and have found that the thermodynamic parameters calculated therefrom are significantly insensitive to the structure of the solute and solvent. They note also that freezing-point diagrams give no evidence of compound formation and suggest that the solute dipole causes a weak ordering of the solvent, geometrically, but not thermodynamically, equivalent to a 1:1 complex. However, Stothers and co-workers[73] have found clear evidence from variable-temperature n.m.r. studies at various concentrations in deuterochloroform, that tricyclic aldehyde molecules such as 9-anthraldehyde associate with each other in solution in a 1:1 ratio. There is no *a priori* reason, therefore, why the related systems we are discussing might not associate in this way also; indeed Baker and Davis[68] have recently suggested from dilution studies that benzene associates with camphor, 3-ethylenedioxybornan-2-one and bornane-2,3-dione in a 1:1 stoicheiometry. In those cases where a specific stoicheiometry is involved, the actual ratios (1:1, 1:2, 2:2, etc.), may obviously depend on the solutes and solvents involved.

Physically, it is most reasonable to assume that a wide spectrum of aggregates, ranging from 1:1 to something best described as a solvent cage, may occur. Thus, for example, chloroform and toluene definitely form a 1:1 molecular complex (cryoscopic evidence[2]) and, by inference, probably associate in a 1:1 ratio in solution. However, at the other end of the spectrum, some systems are perhaps best described without reference to specific stoicheiometries and geometries;[73a] in such instances, pictorial representations of the collision complexes do not have any physical significance.

C. The strength of the interaction

The concept of a transient $1:1$ association at least provides a useful working hypothesis for thermodynamic measurements of the strength of the interaction. The association between benzene and polar solutes has often been represented by the reversible equilibrium—

$$\text{BENZENE} + \text{SOLUTE} \leftrightharpoons \text{``COMPLEX''} \qquad (10)$$

If this equilibrium has any real significance, then the benzene-induced solvent shifts should be temperature dependent. This has been shown to be true for aliphatic[19, 62, 72, 74, 75] and aromatic[63, 67, 76, 77] solutes. On the basis of a $1:1$ collision complex, Abraham[19] has developed a method by which the heat and entropy of formation together with the equilibrium constant of the complex may be calculated. Briefly, if a fraction p of the solute is complexed at a temperature T, the equilibrium constant, K, for a dilute solution is given by—

$$K = p/(1-p) \qquad (11)$$

The value of p may be calculated by the use of the equation—

$$p = v_T - v_0/v_C - v_0 \qquad (12)$$

where v_T is the chemical shift of the proton resonance in question at temperature T, and v_C and v_0 are the chemical shifts of that proton in the pure complex and the complex-free solution respectively. Since—

$$K = \exp{(\Delta S/R)} \exp{(-\Delta H/RT)} \qquad (13)$$

then a plot of $\log_{10} K$ should be linear in $1/T$, giving a slope of $-\Delta H/R$ and intercept $\Delta S/R$. Linear plots of $\log_{10} K$ versus $1/T$ have been obtained by many authors[19, 72, 74, 76, 77] and the values obtained from the data for various systems indicate that the heat of formation for the benzene-solute interaction is of the order of 1 kcal./mole.

An alternative method for calculating K from dilution studies has been described by Hanna and Ashbaugh[78] and the association constants for several donor–acceptor complexes have been determined by this method.[69, 78–81]

The significance of the thermodynamic parameters obtained in this way has been questioned in view of the assumption of a $1:1$ collision complex, and the gross approximations involved in the calculation. The values are probably most meaningful for aliphatic solutes containing a single polar site, but even in such cases they are probably of limited significance. However, the weak nature of the interaction is usefully demonstrated by such techniques.

D. The stereochemistry of the interaction

In the earlier studies of benzene-induced solvent shifts it has been assumed that the solute–solvent collision complex is planar. For example, the solvent shifts of the methyl groups of dimethylfor-mamide[82] are consistent with a planar association between the benzene and the amide as shown in (15). The nitrogen atom, with its fractional positive charge, is situated close to the π-electron density of the aromatic ring with the negatively charged carbonyl oxygen as far away as possible from the centre of the ring. Such a geometrical arrangement qualitatively explains the relative Δ values ($\Delta = \delta_{\text{neat liquid}} - \delta_{\text{benzene}}$) for $CH_3^{(a)}$ and $CH_3^{(b)}$ in the molecule ($\Delta CH_3^{(a)} = 1 \cdot 08$ p.p.m.; $\Delta CH_3^{(b)} = 0 \cdot 41$ p.p.m.).

However, it has recently been observed[83] that the solvent shifts for certain protons in 5α-androstan-11-one are more easily accommodated in terms of solvation of the positive end of the carbonyl dipole by a benzene molecule such that the plane of the benzene ring is steeply inclined with respect to the plane of the steroid molecule (see **16**, which represents the time-averaged picture at room temperature).

15   16

The observed solvent shifts ($\Delta_{C_6H_6}^{CDCl_3}$) for the 1β-, 19-, 12β-, 12α- and 18-protons are given subsequently in Table VI.

It would seem energetically improbable that all benzene–solute collision complexes should be planar, since it is reasonable to suppose that steric requirements would play an important role in the determination of the geometrical preferences of the interacting molecules. Anderson has found, for example, that the solvent shifts of some 1,3-dioxans are highly dependent on the size of the axial substituent in the 5-position and a non-planar solute–solvent complex accounts for the observed shifts.[70] The solvent shifts of adamantyl halides,[72] steroidal ketones,[83] β-dicarbonyl compounds,[84] and anisoles[85] are best understood in terms of a non-planar association. However, there are a few cases known in which the observed solvent shifts are surprisingly insensitive to steric effects in the region of the functional group.

Connolly and McCrindle have shown that the protons of the geminal methyl groups in the tricyclic ketone (**17**) have appreciable solvent shifts ($\Delta^{CDCl_3}_{C_6H_6} = 0.13$ and 0.14 p.p.m.).[86] A study of models indicates severe steric hindrance to the approach of the solvent to the rear of the carbonyl group. In this case it is impossible to rationalize the results on the basis of a preferred benzene–solute collision complex, and these solvent shifts must have a different origin.

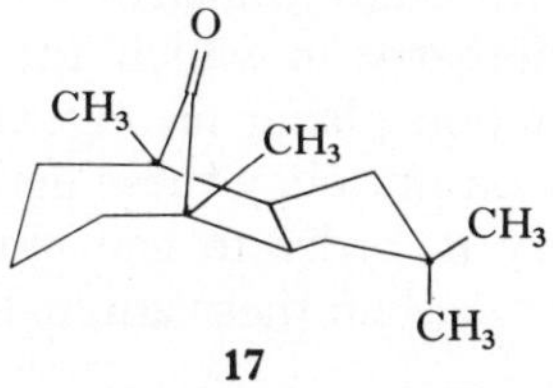

17

Meakins *et al.*[87] have also observed an apparent insensitivity to steric environment in the solvent shifts experienced by the protons of the 18-, and 19-methyl groups in some steroidal ketones. The relevant shifts are given in Table V.

TABLE V

Solvent shifts of the 18- and 19-methyl protons in some steroidal ketones[87]

Solute	$\Delta_{18\text{-}CH_3}$, p.p.m.	$\Delta_{19\text{-}CH_3}$, p.p.m.
5α-Androstan-17-one	0·18	0·12
5β-Androstan-17-one	0·21	0·12
5α-Cholestan-6-one	0·11	0·06
5β-Cholestan-6-one	0·13	0·06
5α-Androstan-6-one	0·16	0·09

Two points are to be noted from the data given in Table V—

(a) The shifts of the angular methyl groups are insensitive to the stereochemistry about the 5-position.

(b) In the 6-ketones, the shift of the methyl group remote from the oxo function (18–CH$_3$) is greater than the shift of the more proximate methyl group (19-CH$_3$).

Both of these observations are unexpected on the basis of a benzene–solute collision complex involving the electron-deficient carbonyl carbon and the π-electron system of the benzene ring.

Fort and Lindstrom[72] have demonstrated that there is no significant difference in the magnitude of the benzene-induced shifts of t-butyl and adamantyl halides. They have suggested on this evidence that in these cases the closeness of approach of the solute dipole to the solvent molecule is not of prime importance in determining the solvent shifts.

In summary, we may say that most of the solvent shift data so far reported is consistent with a local (or molecular) dipole-induced dipole interaction between benzene and solute so that the benzene ring avoids the negative end of the dipole and solvates electron deficient centres. The strength of the interaction is of the order of 1 kcal./mole, and probably occurs through transient associations of varying or indeterminate stoicheiometry in which the participating molecules may adopt a planar or non-planar arrangement depending on steric factors. Some systems do not obey these generalizations, and further work may be necessary in order to gain an insight into alternative mechanisms that might explain these anomalies.

IX. APPLICATIONS OF AROMATIC SOLVENT-INDUCED SHIFTS

Extensive studies have been carried out on the empirical use of benzene solvent-induced shifts in structural and stereochemical correlations. Saturated aliphatic ketones in particular have been the subject of many investigations,[71, 88-101] and an important generalization, the so-called "carbonyl plane rule", has been proposed by Williams and Bhacca[71] and independently by Connolly and McCrindle.[86] This rule states that in the specific case of an isolated carbonyl group, as found in 5α-androstan-11-one for example, the benzene-induced solvent shift $(\Delta_{C_6H_6}^{CDCl_3})$ will be positive for protons lying behind a plane drawn through the carbonyl carbon atom and perpendicular to the direction of the C—O bond (see **18**); protons lying in front of the plane will have a negative shift, and protons lying very near or in the reference plane will have a small or zero shift.

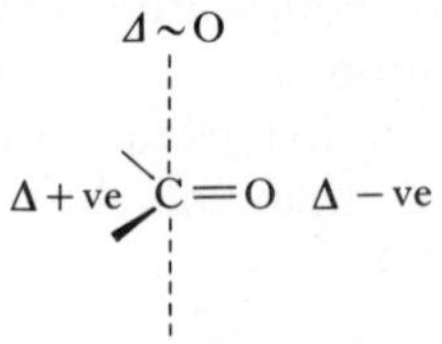

18 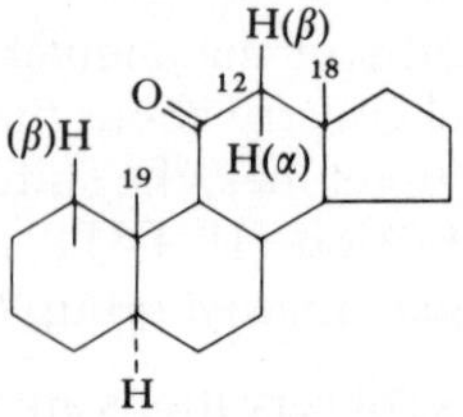   **19**

Thus in benzene solution the 1β-H and 19-H resonances of (**19**) move downfield relative to their positions in deuterochloroform, the 12β-H is hardly affected, and the 12α-H and 18-H resonances move upfield (see Table VI).

TABLE VI

Solvent shifts ($\Delta = \delta_{\mathrm{CDCl_3}} - \delta_{\mathrm{C_6H_6}}$) **of the** 1β-, 19-, 12α-, **and** 18-H
resonances of 5α-**androstan**-11-**one** (19)

Proton(s)	$\Delta^{\mathrm{CDCl_3}}_{\mathrm{C_6H_6}}$ (p.p.m.)
1β-H	$-0 \cdot 36$
19-H	$-0 \cdot 14$
12β-H	$-0 \cdot 02$
12α-H	$+0 \cdot 34$
18-H	$+0 \cdot 11$

This rule has found wide applicability in the field of structure elucidation. For example, in the oxidative hydroboration of ($+$)car-2-ene and ($+$)car-3-ene,[96] corroborative evidence for the proposed stereochemistry of the respective products (20) and (21) has been obtained from the solvent shifts of the 10-methyl protons ($\Delta = \delta_{\mathrm{CDCl_3}} - \delta_{\mathrm{C_6H_6}}$).

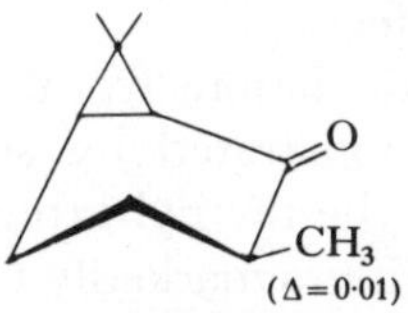

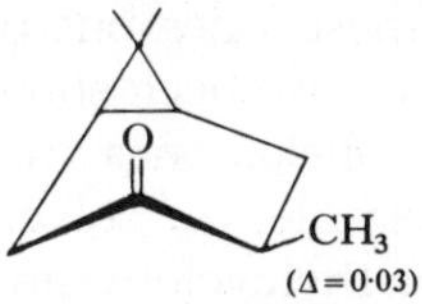

Another example that may be cited is the use of the rule in the confirmation of the stereochemistry of α- and β-thujone.[97] If we represent α-thujone (22) in its two possible conformations, then it is to be expected that in the boat form (24A) a relatively high positive solvent shift will be observed for the protons of the 10-methyl group. In the chair form (24B) a negligible solvent shift is expected. The β-isomer (23) will show the reverse of these trends in its boat and chair forms.

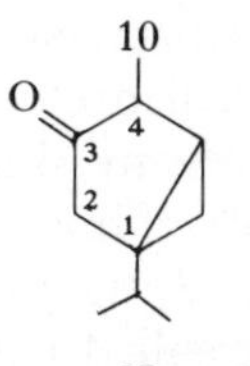

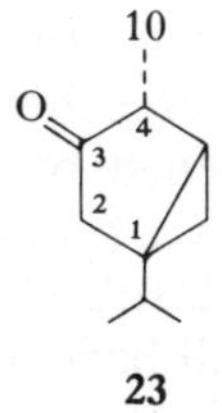

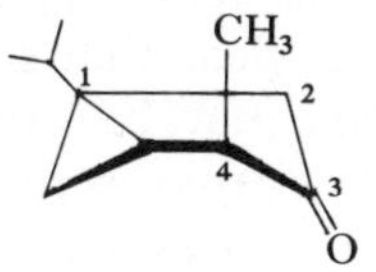

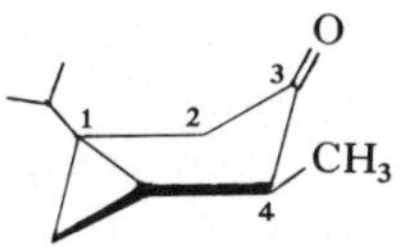

The observed shifts, shown in Table VII, show that α- and β-thujone exist in the boat form.

TABLE VII

Solvent shifts of some proton resonances in α- and β-thujone

Isomer	Solvent shift Δ ($=\delta_{CDCl_3}-\delta_{C_6H_6}$) for				
	2α-H	2β-H	4α-H	4β-H	10-CH$_3$
α-thujone (22)	+0·07	+0·15	+0·03	..	+0·15
β-thujone (23)	+0·12	+0·25	..	+0·34	−0·01

The carbonyl plane rule leads to two further important conclusions—

(a) Axial protons or methyl groups adjacent to a carbonyl function in a cyclohexane system will have positive Δ values (most frequently 0·20–0·40 p.p.m.), whereas equatorial substituents will have very small positive or negative Δ values (usually in the range 0·06 to −0·10 p.p.m.).[88] The observed shifts of 2,6,6-trimethylcyclohexanone (25) ($\Delta^{CCl_4}_{C_6H_6}$ values shown in parentheses) demonstrate this effect.[90]

It has also been shown[90] that deviations from the chair form in cyclohexanones may be demonstrated by solvent shifts; for example, the solvent shift of the methyl groups of 2,2,6,6-tetramethylcyclohexanone (26) differs markedly from the value calculated (0·09 p.p.m.), assuming interconversion between true chair forms. This observation suggests that (26) exists in a flattened chair form.

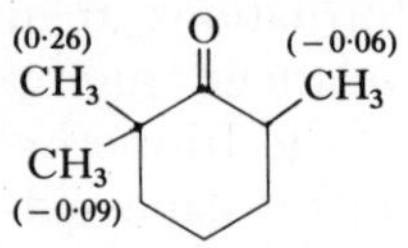

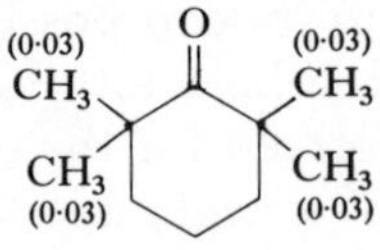

(b) Since the rule is also applicable to α,β-unsaturated ketones,[102, 103] it is clear that the stereochemical preferences of such compounds may be established by solvent shifts in cases where s-*cis* or s-*trans* isomerism is possible. Thus, in the conformationally mobile system depicted in Fig. 3, the protons of a β-*cis* substituent (H or CH$_3$) will have a small Δ value in the s-*cis* form and a relatively large Δ value in the s-*trans* form.

A study of some fixed s-*cis* and s-*trans* and mobile s-*cis* and s-*trans* systems has confirmed these deductions.[75, 102, 103] The solvent shifts

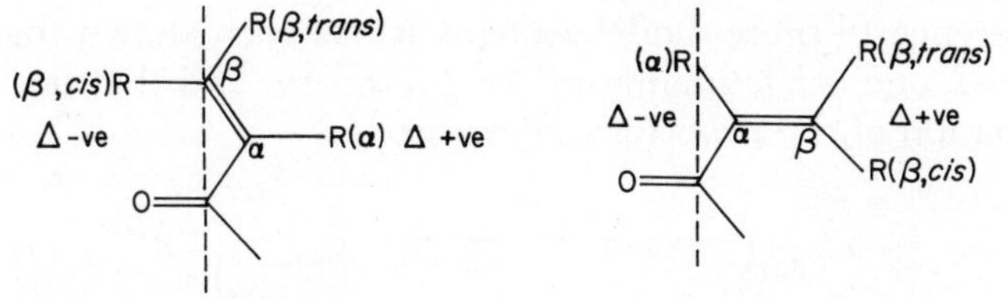

FIG. 3. The plane of shielding in the s-*cis* and s-*trans* configuration of α,β-unsaturated ketones.

obtained for some representative fixed and mobile s-*cis* and s-*trans* ketones[103] are shown in (27)–(32).

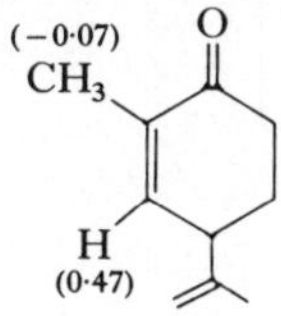

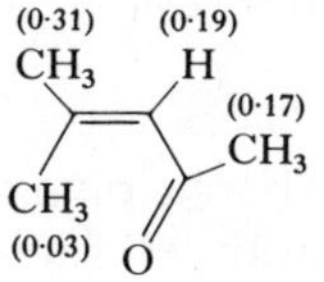

The result obtained for mesityl oxide (32) is of special interest. This molecule has previously been drawn[82] in the s-*trans* conformation in order to explain the solvent shifts of the methyl protons. It has been shown by an alternative method[104] that it exists mainly in the s-*cis* form. This conclusion is confirmed by the recent solvent shift studies.[75, 103]

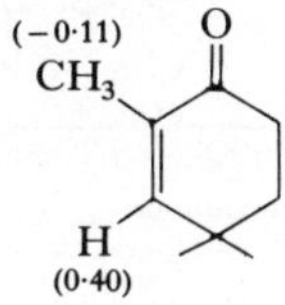

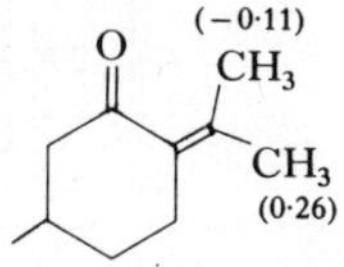

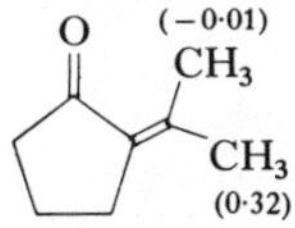

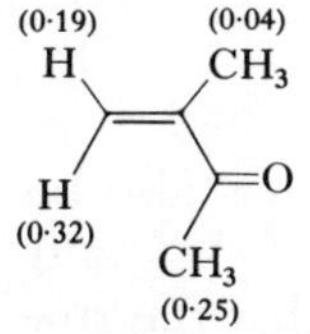

In any conformationally mobile α,β-unsaturated ketone that exists as a mixture of s-*cis* and s-*trans* isomers at room temperature there will usually be one conformer that will be energetically more favourable. It is therefore to be expected that a decrease in temperature will increase the population of the favoured isomer, and this may be detectable in the benzene-induced solvent shifts of the substituents. Variable-temperature studies in toluene-d_8 solution of some model fixed s-*cis* and s-*trans* α,β-unsaturated ketones have been carried out[75] and the data for 3-methyl-cyclohexenone (33) are fairly typical (see Fig. 4; the chemical shift is given in c./sec. at 100 Mc./sec. relative to internal TMS).

By reference to these model systems it has been shown that *trans*-pent-3-en-2-one exists mainly in the *trans* form and that on cooling, the population of the *trans* form increases.

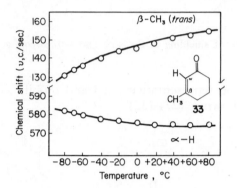

FIG. 4. The temperature dependence of the chemical shifts (c./sec. at 100 Mc./sec.) of the α-olefinic hydrogen and the β-methyl group of 3-methylcyclohex-2-en-1-one. (From Ronayne et al.[75])

The carbonyl plane rule has also been applied with some success in the study of lactones[105–110] and quinones.[111] Connolly and McCrindle[105] have found that the rule is apparently not affected by groups such as ethereal oxygen, double bond or acetoxy-group close to the lactone ring. Solvent shifts have been applied successfully in the problem of the stereochemistry of the 13-methyl group of α- and β-santonin (34) and (35), respectively.[106]

34   35

The 13-methyl group of α-santonin has only recently been proved by X-ray crystallography[112] to be α-oriented. Based on solvent shift data for many sesquiterpene lactones with α- and β-oriented 13-methyl groups, Narayanan and Venkatasubramanian[106] have found that an α-methyl resonance gives Δ values ($\Delta = \delta_{CDCl_3} - \delta_{C_6H_6}$) of 0.23 ± 0.06 p.p.m., whereas β-methyl resonances give Δ values of 0.46 ± 0.06 p.p.m.

A. Methoxy-compounds

The solvent dependence of the resonance position of methoxyl groups has been recognized as having considerable potential in structural studies of methoxyl-containing compounds.[77, 85, 109, 111, 113–117] Benzene usually causes upfield shifts of aromatic methoxyl (proton) resonances; a notable exception is the case of a methoxyl situated between two others, as in 1,2,3-trimethoxybenzene, in which case the central methoxyl group exhibits a negative Δ value [see (36) where the solvent shifts ($\Delta_{C_6H_6}^{CDCl_3}$) of the methoxyl proton resonances are given in parentheses].

In aromatic solutes PhR (R=Me, CH_2OH, OCH_3, $COCH_3$) there is a marked tendency for the $\Delta_{C_6H_6}^{CDCl_3}$ values of the protons in R to become more negative when methoxy-groups are substituted in the 2- or the 2,6-positions.[85] This is dramatically illustrated for the methylene protons of benzyl alcohol (37) and the methoxylated derivatives (38) and (39). The dependence of the solvent shifts of methoxy resonances on electronic, steric and conformational factors has been discussed.[77, 85]

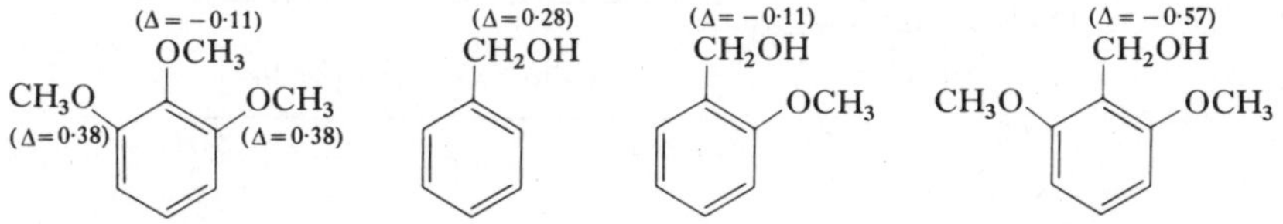

In view of the frequency with which methoxy substituents occur in natural products, the use of benzene-induced solvent shifts as an aid in structural elucidation has obvious possibilities. A recent study of the benzene-induced shifts of the methoxy resonances of some flavones[115] has resulted in the following observations—

(a) "Isolated" methoxy groups at C_5, C_7, $C_{2'}$ and $C_{4'}$ have large upfield shifts ($\Delta_{C_6H_6}^{CDCl_3}$) and can be differentiated from C_3 methoxyls, which have a small positive or a negative shift. The ranges of Δ values are given in Table VIII.

(b) The central methoxyl of three adjacent methoxyl substituents has a small positive or a negative shift; this situation is analogous to the shift of the 2-methoxyl of 1,2,3,-trimethoxybenzene. In the flavones studied, the solvent shift range for the central methoxyls was between $+0\cdot13$ and $-0\cdot12$ p.p.m. In an analogous manner, since the heterocyclic oxygen atom should

TABLE VIII

**Range of solvent shifts of the methoxyl protons attached to
C-3, C-5, C-7, C-2′ and C-4′ of some flavones[115]**

Position of methoxyl	Range of Δ values
C-3	−0·07 to +0·34
C-5	+0·43 to +0·58
C-7	+0·54 to +0·76
C-2′	+0·46 to +0·53
C-4′	+0·54 to +0·71

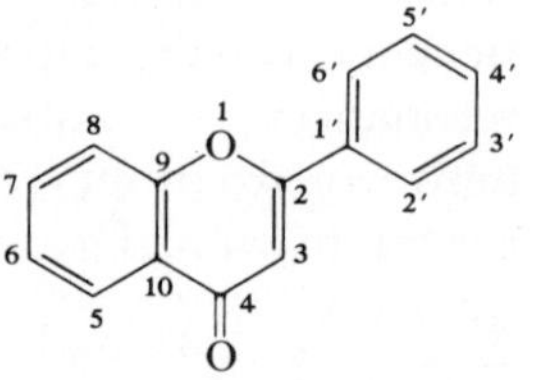

have an effect similar to a hypothetical methoxy substituent
at C-9, the C-8 methoxyl has a small solvent shift in 7,8-di-
methoxyflavones. In Fig. 5, the observed solvent shifts for
5,7,8,3′,4′-pentamethoxyflavene (**40**) are schematically represented.

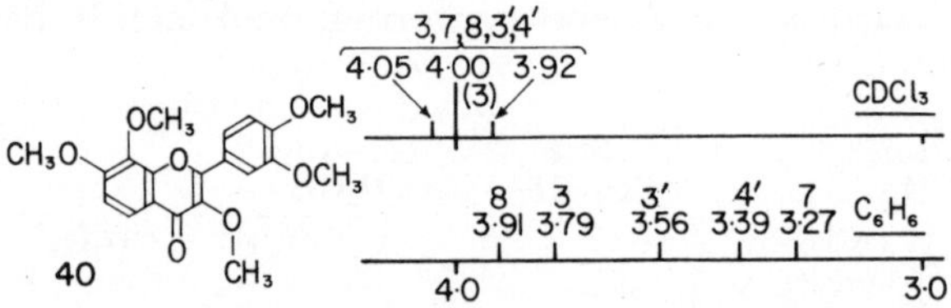

FIG. 5. The schematic representation of the solvent shifts of 5,7,8,3′,4′-penta-
methoxyflavene (**40**). (From Wilson et al.[115])

(c) The solvent shift of a methoxy group at C-5 suffers a drastic
change in magnitude from a relatively large positive value
(see Table VIII) to a small or negative value (see the range of Δ
values in p.p.m. for hexamethylquercetagetin given in parentheses in **41**). This characteristic shift has proved to be useful
in the structural elucidation of zapotin (**42**).[116]

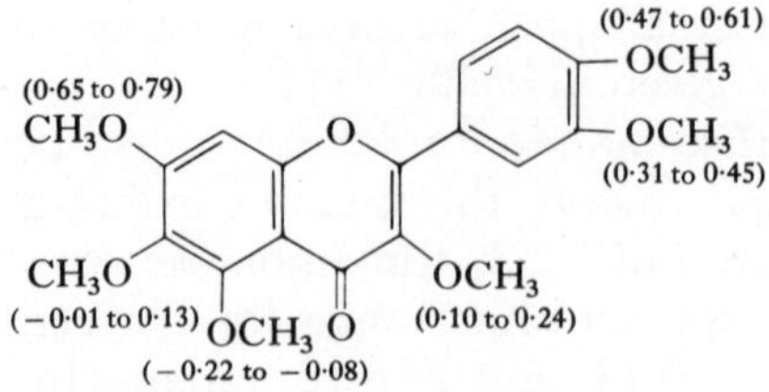

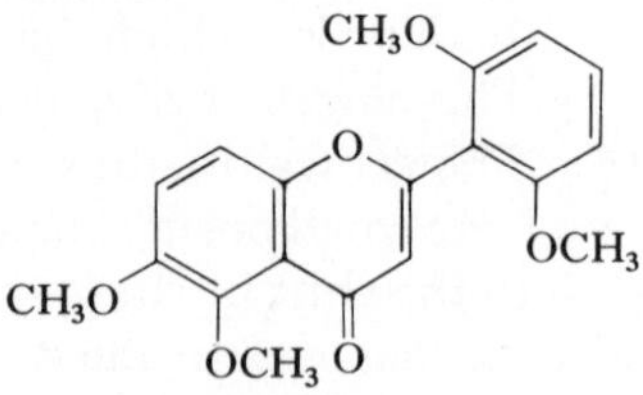

B. Nitrogen Heterocycles

Differential solvent shifts have been observed[118-122] for azabenzenes, pyrroles, quinolines and indoles. In the pyridines that have been studied,[118, 122] protons α to the heterocyclic atom have a small positive or a negative shift; the β- and γ-protons have positive shifts ranging from 0·20 to 0·50 p.p.m. Similar shifts are observed for the heterocyclic ring protons of the quinolines.[122] In the carbocyclic ring of the quinolines there is a characteristic downfield shift of the 8-substituents (H or CH$_3$).

In contrast, the α-protons in pyrroles and indoles have positive shifts (0·05–0·30 p.p.m.), and the β-protons have negative shifts ($\leqslant$0·50 p.p.m.). N-Alkyl protons have large positive shifts, decreasing in magnitude with increase in length of the alkyl chain.[122] Some typical Δ values for some nitrogen heterocycles are shown in parentheses with the appropriate molecular formulae (**43–46**).

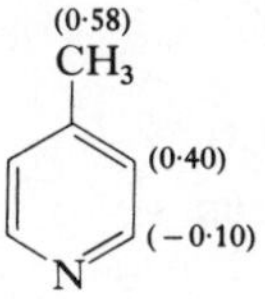

43 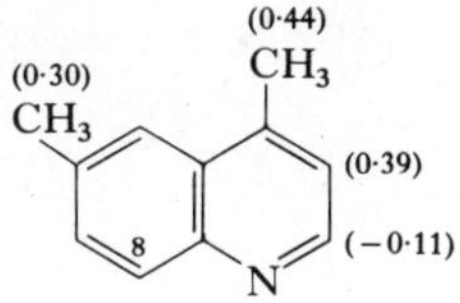   **44** 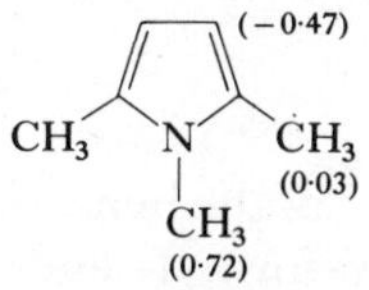   **45** 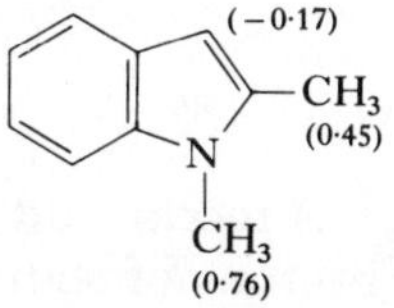   **46**

The observed shifts are in complete accord with the generalizations of Section VIII; namely that solvation of the positive end of the molecular dipole by the benzene occurs so that the benzene ring avoids the negative end of the dipole[121] (see **47** and **48**).

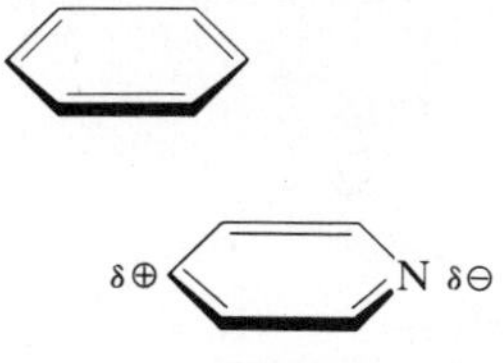

47 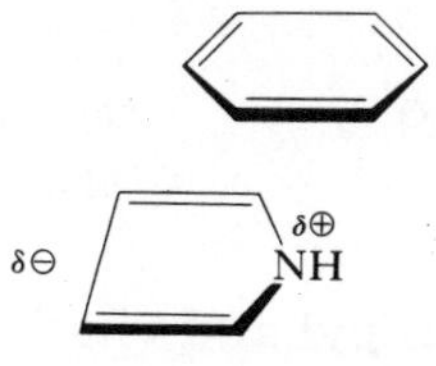   **48**

C. Amides and lactams

Hindered rotation about the carbonyl carbon–nitrogen bond in amides results in the substituent *trans* to the oxygen being shielded to a greater extent in benzene than the substituent *cis* to it (see **15**).[82, 123–125] Moriarty and Kliegman[126, 127] have studied the solvent shifts of N-methyl lactams and have demonstrated the occurrence of hindered rotation about the carbonyl carbon–nitrogen bond in these compounds. An example that may be cited is N-methylcaprilactam (49), which displays doublet N-methyl absorption in its n.m.r. spectrum in carbon tetrachloride. When benzene is used as solvent, one of the signals moves upfield by 0·62 p.p.m., whereas the other moves upfield by 1·10 p.p.m. The methyl group responsible for the former signal is that of the "s-*cis*" form (50A). The latter signal is due to the methyl group of the "s-*trans*" form (50B). From their results for many lactams, these authors have been able to calculate the conformer ratios in mixtures of "s-*cis*" and "s-*trans*" isomers.

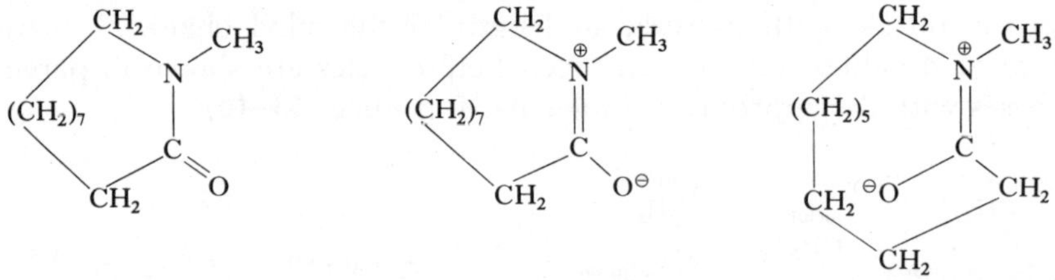

A recent study[128] of the benzene-induced solvent shifts of the 2-CH_2 protons of some N-formyl- and N-thioacetylindolenes demonstrates admirably the elegance of the method in distinguishing between various conformational isomers [see 51–54; the solvent shifts Δ $(=\delta_{CDCl_3} - \delta_{C_6H_6}$ p.p.m.) are shown in parentheses].

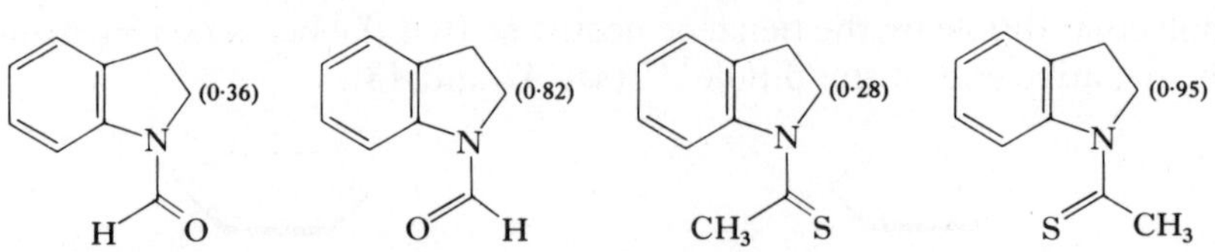

D. Cyclopropyl and vinyl derivatives

Wharton and Bair[129] have demonstrated that in the cyclopropane derivatives of the type shown in (55), the methyl group *trans* to the ester group suffers a larger positive benzene-induced solvent shift than the methyl group *cis* to it. These studies have been extended by Seyden-Penne and co-workers[130–132] and Boykin *et al.*,[133] to many cyclopropyl derivatives, all of which display the same trends in solvent shift, i.e., protons (H or CH_3) *trans* to a substituent X (X=$COOCH_3$,

COOH, $CONH_2$, $COCH_3$, CN) in the ring have a larger solvent shift than protons *cis* to it.

Analogous to the results for the cyclopropyl derivatives are the benzene-induced solvent shifts observed for a number of vinyl derivatives of the type shown in (56).[134] In such systems also, $\Delta R' > \Delta R''$

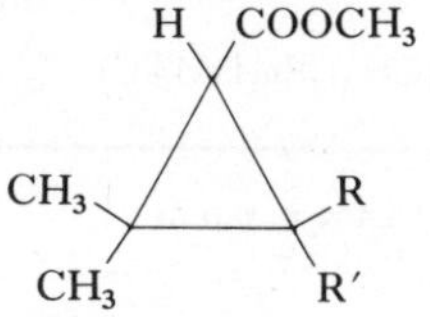

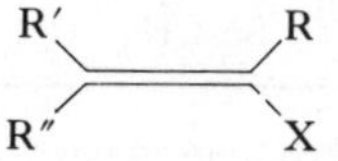

and the shifts may be reliably used in the assignment of the configuration of *cis–trans* isomers, such as the geranic acids (57) and (58), or angelic and tiglic acids (59) and (60), respectively. The results obtained for these acids are shown in parentheses with their molecular formulae.[135]

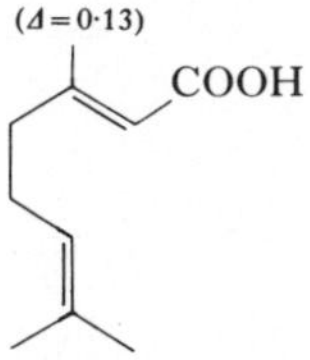

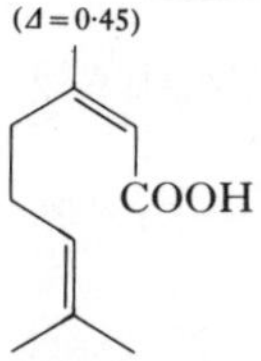

E. Miscellaneous applications

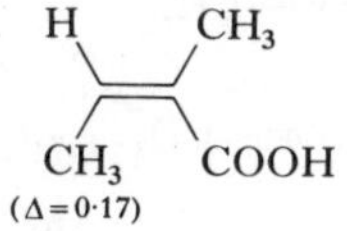

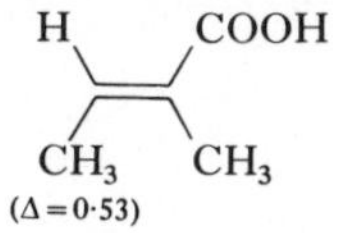

Benzene-induced solvent shifts have been used in structural and stereochemical studies in a number of sulphur-[136–139] and phosphorus-containing[140] compounds, ethylenedi-imine complexes[141] and nitrosamines.[142] Of particular interest is the study by Honda *et al.*[136] on some bis(*NN*-dialkyldithiocarbamato)methyltin halides. The complex shown in (61) is proposed to account for the observed solvent shifts (see Table IX).

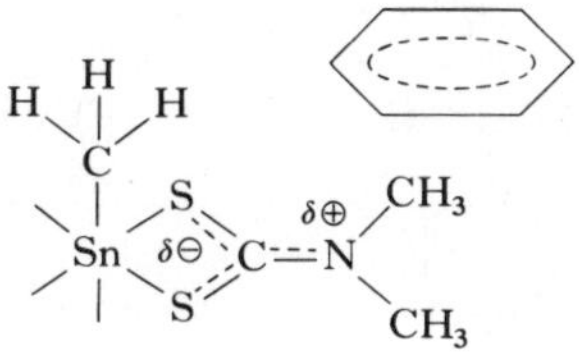

TABLE IX

Chemical shifts of protons in $(CH_3)XSn(DMTC)_2$†, and $(CH_3)_2Sn(DMTC)_2$

		$\Delta_{CHCl_3}^{C_6H_6}$ ‡			$\Delta_{CHCl_3}^{C_6H_6}$ ‡
$(CH_3)ClSn(DMTC)_2$	N-CH_3	+1·06	$(CH_3)_2Sn(DMTC)_2$	N-CH_3	+0·94
	Sn-CH_3	−0·34		Sn-CH_3	−0·68
$(CH_3)BrSn(DMTC)_2$	N-CH_3	+1·09	$(CH_3)_2Sn(DMTC)_2$	N-CH_3	+0·93
	Sn-CH_3	−0·31		Sn-CH_3	−0·32

The values are taken from an internal tetramethylsilane in p.p.m.
† DMTC = NN-dimethyldithiocarbamate.   ‡ $\Delta_{CHCl_3}^{C_6H_6} = \tau_{C_6H_6} - \tau_{CHCl_3}$

A similar type of solute–solvent complex has been proposed by Benezra and Ourisson[140] to account for the solvent shifts of many phosphonates. The solvent shifts $\Delta(=\delta_{CDCl_3}-\delta_{C_6H_6})$ for a representative molecule are shown in parentheses in (62).

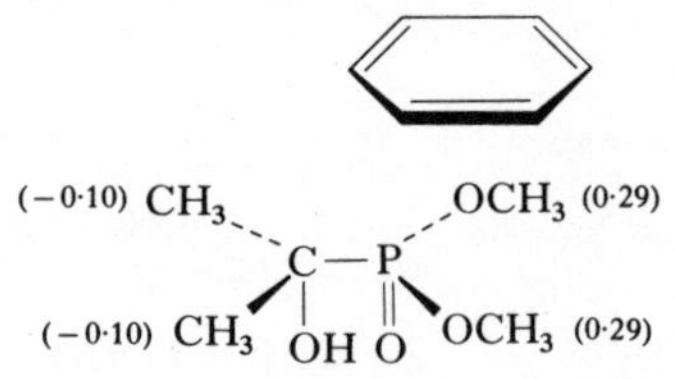

62

Recent developments in the field of benzene-induced solvent shifts have been (*a*) the enhancement of the shifts by the addition of a small amount of a protic solvent, such as trifluoracetic acid,[143] and (*b*) the use of optically active aromatic solvents to generate diastereoisomeric collision complexes.[144–146] This latter development is of particular importance, since it may be used in the determination of optical purity and the assignment of absolute configuration. For example, Pirkle[146] has examined the ^1H and ^{19}F spectra of enantiomeric 2,2,2-trifluorophenylethanol (63) in optically active α-(1-napthyl)ethylamine (64) solvent.

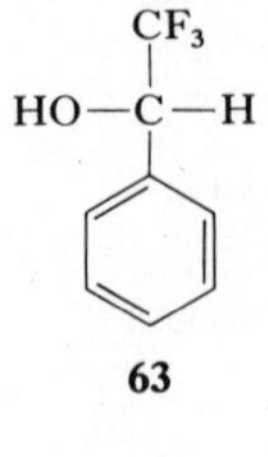

63 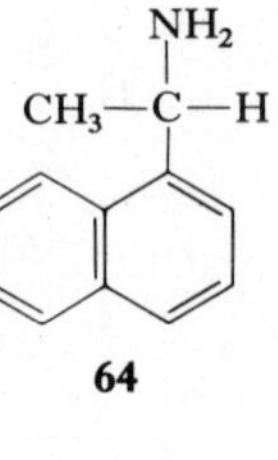   64

Figure 6 shows the methine ^{1}H resonance (100 Mc./sec.) and the trifluoromethyl ^{19}F resonance (94·1 Mc./sec.) in (a) racemic and (b) optically active α-(1-naphthyl)ethylamine. In the optically active solvent, the solute gives rise to distinct signals for each enantiomer.

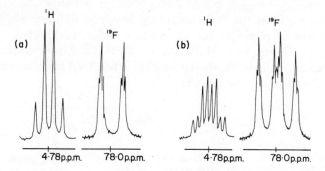

FIG. 6. Portions of the n.m.r. spectra of partially resolved 2,2,2-trifluorophenyletha-nol in: (a), racemic; (b), optically active α-(1-naphthyl)ethylamine. (From Pirkle.[146])

From a study of isomers of known absolute configuration, it is found that the high-field methine proton resonances and low-field fluorine resonances are due to enantiomers having the configuration shown in (65).

The hypothesis that a solute–solvent conformation depicted in (66) is responsible for the spectral non-equivalence allows explanation of the experimental data. In this conformation, the aromatic rings of the amine and the carbinol overlap, the methine proton being shielded by the diamagnetic anisotropy of the rings. The more distant trifluoro-methyl group experiences comparatively less shielding. In the enantio-mer shown in (67) the positions of the trifluoromethyl group and the

methine proton are reversed, so that the solute–solvent association will produce in this case strong shielding of the trifluoromethyl group and little effect on the methine proton. Hence in the optically active solvent non-equivalence is observed.

5

X. PYRIDINE-INDUCED SOLVENT SHIFTS

Pyridine is a useful alternative solvent when the use of benzene is precluded on solubility grounds. In the compounds so far studied, the shifts ($\varDelta = \delta_{CDCl_3} - \delta_{C_5H_5N}$ p.p.m.) observed for pyridine are in general more negative than the corresponding benzene-induced shifts. The empirical use of pyridine for the simplification of spectra was first reported by Slomp and McKellar in 1960.[147] An example of the simplification achieved is shown in Fig. 7 for 4,4,17α-trimethyl-17β-hydroxy-5-androsten-3-one (**68**).

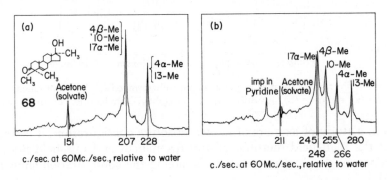

FIG. 7. Portion of the spectra of 4,4,17α-trimethyl-17β-hydroxy-5-androsten-3-one in: (a), deuterochloroform; (b), pyridine. (From Slomp and McKellar.[147])

The 1:1 complex shown in (**69**) has been proposed by Danyluk[148] to account for the pyridine-induced shifts ($\varDelta^{C_6H_{14}}_{C_6H_5N}$ p.p.m.) observed for benzyl acetone (**70**). These shifts are given in parentheses with its

molecular formula. The effect of pyridine on the methyl protons of *N*-methyl-*N*-cyclohexylacetamide (**71**) has been interpreted by Moriarty[149] in terms of a solute-solvent complex of the type shown in (**74**).

Dilution of a carbon tetrachloride solution of (**71**) results in a downfield shift of both the C-methyl and one of the N-methyl signals associated with the resonance forms (72) and (73). The remaining N-methyl signal suffers a very small upfield shift. The solute–solvent orientation shown in (74) would lead to predominantly downfield shifts because of the ring anisotropy of the pyridine. Unique solvent–solute complexes have also been invoked to explain the solvent shifts of the methyl groups in related sulphinamides, sulphonamides and nitrosamines.[149]

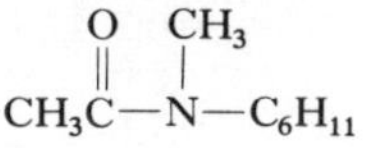

71 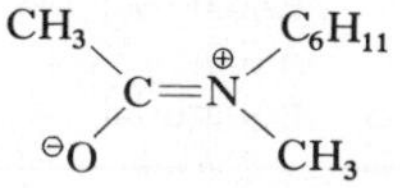   **72**

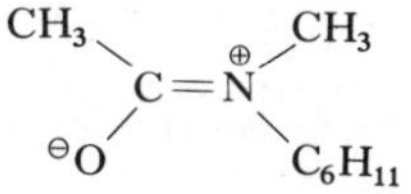

73 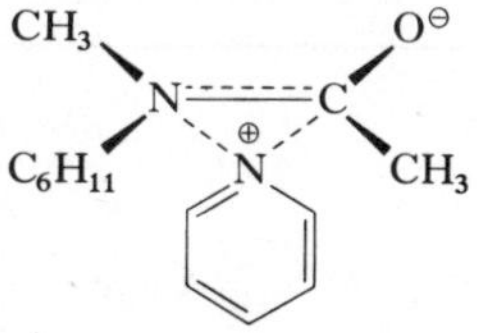   **74**

Johnson and co-workers[150] have utilized the pyridine-induced solvent shifts $(\varDelta = \delta_{CDCl_3} - \delta_{C_5H_5N}$ p.p.m.) of some model cyclohexanones in the determination of the cyclohexanone ring stereochemistry of cycloheximide (75) and some of its derivatives. For their model

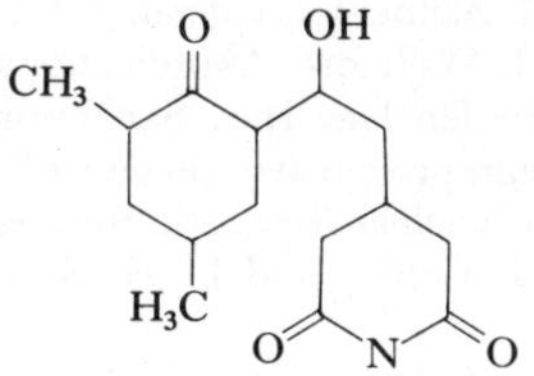

75

compounds these authors observed that 2-equatorial methyl substituents had very small positive or even negative shifts whereas 2-axial, 4-axial or 4-equatorial methyls had relatively large shifts (see Table X).

The carbonyl plane "rule" is also applicable to pyridine-induced solvent shifts in some ketones.[102] However, the reference plane is displaced so that it passes through the α-carbons rather than the carbonyl carbon (see **76**). The shifts of α-tetralone (**77**) shown in parentheses with its molecular formula serve as an example to illustrate the modified rule.

TABLE X

Pyridine-induced solvent shifts of the methyl protons of some model cyclohexanones[150]

Solute	Methyl group stereochemistry	Δ c./sec. at 60 Mc./sec.
2-Methylcyclohexanone	Largely equatorial	0·3
4-Methylcyclohexanone	Largely equatorial	8·8
trans-4-t-Butyl-2-methylcyclohexanone	Axial	4·7
cis-4-t-Butyl-2-methylcyclohexanone	Equatorial	−0·7
trans-2-t-Butyl-4-methylcyclohexanone	Axial	6·0
cis-2-t-Butyl-4-methylcyclohexanone	Equatorial	7·5

76   77 $\Delta \begin{smallmatrix} CCl_4 \\ C_5H_5N \end{smallmatrix}$ values

REFERENCES

1. A. A. Bothner-By and R. E. Glick, *J. Chem. Phys.*, 1957, **26**, 1651.
2. L. W. Reeves and W. G. Schneider, *Canad. J. Chem.*, 1957, **35**, 251.
3. N. S. Bhacca and D. H. Williams, "Applications of N.M.R. Spectroscopy in Organic Chemistry", Holden-Day Inc., San Francisco, 1964; since this article was written, another comprehensive review of solvent shifts has appeared (P. Laszlo, "Progress in Nuclear Magnetic Resonance Spectroscopy", Vol. III, p. 231 (J. W. Emsley, J. Feeney and L. H. Sutcliffe, Eds.), Pergamon Press, London, 1968.
4. A. D. Buckingham, *Canad. J. Chem.*, 1960, **38**, 300.
5. W. G. Schneider, *J. Phys. Chem.*, 1962, **66**, 2653.
6. W. C. Dickinson, *Phys. Rev.*, 1951, **81**, 717.
7. K. Frei and H. J. Bernstein, *J. Chem. Phys.*, 1962, **37**, 1891.
8. A. A. Bothner-By, *Mol. Phys.*, 1960, **5**, 52.
9. A. D. Buckingham, T. Schaefer and W. G. Schneider, *J. Chem. Phys.*, 1960, **32**, 1227.
10. C. E. Johnson and F. A. Bovey, *J. Chem. Phys.*, 1958, **29**, 1012.
11. B. P. Dailey, *J. Chem. Phys.*, 1964, **41**, 2304.
12. E. D. Becker, R. B. Bradley and C. J. Watson, *J. Amer. Chem. Soc.*, 1961, **83**, 3743.
13. J. C. Schug, *J. Phys. Chem.*, 1966, **70**, 1816.
14. V. S. Watts and J. H. Goldstein, *J. Mol. Spectroscopy*, 1966, **21**, 260.
15. D. H. Williams, J. Ronayne and R. G. Wilson, *Chem. Comm.*, 1967, 1089.
16. L. Onsager, *J. Amer. Chem. Soc.*, 1936, **58**, 1486.

17. T. W. Marshall and J. A. Pople, *Mol. Phys.*, 1958, **1**, 199.
18. J. I. Musher, *J. Chem. Phys.*, 1962, **37**, 34.
19. R. J. Abraham, *Mol. Phys.*, 1961, **4**, 369.
20. V. S. Watts, G. S. Reddy and J. H. Goldstein, *J. Mol. Spectroscopy*, 1963, **11**, 325.
21. P. Laszlo, *Bull. Soc. chim. France*, 1964, 85.
22. T. Schaefer and W. G. Schneider, *J. Chem. Phys.*, 1960, **32**, 1218.
23. J. C. Schug and B. P. Smith, *J. Chem. Phys.*, 1967, **47**, 849.
24. P. Diehl and R. Freeman, *Mol. Phys.*, 1961, **4**, 39.
25. I. G. Ross and R. A. Sack, *Proc. Phys. Soc.*, 1950, **63B**, 893.
26. F. Hruska, E. Bock and T. Schaefer, *Canad. J. Chem.*, 1963, **41**, 3034.
27. P. Laszlo and J. I. Musher, *J. Chem. Phys.*, **41**, 3906.
28. B. Fontaine, M. Chenon and N. Lumbroso-Bader, *J. Chim. Phys.*, 1965, 1075.
29. G. Kotowycz and T. Schaefer, *Canad. J. Chem.*, 1967, **45**, 1093.
30. H. M. Hutton and T. Schaefer, *Canad. J. Chem.*, 1967, **45**, 1111.
31. C. J. Macdonald and T. Schaefer, *Canad. J. Chem.*, 1967, **45**, 3157.
32. T. Schaefer and W. G. Schneider, *J. Chem. Phys.*, 1960, **32**, 1224.
33. P. Bates, S. Cawley and S. S. Danyluk, *J. Chem. Phys.*, 1964, **40**, 2415.
34. M. A. Weinberger, R. M. Heggie and H. L. Holmes, *Canad. J. Chem.*, 1965, **43**, 2585.
35. K. A. McLaughlin, L. W. Reeves and T. Schaefer, *Canad. J. Chem.*, 1966, **44**, 1473.
36. T. Matsuo and Y. Kodera, *J. Phys. Chem.*, 1966, **70**, 4087.
37. T. Matsuo, *Canad. J. Chem.*, 1967, **45**, 1829.
38. T. M. Spotswood and C. I. Tanzer, *Tetrahedron Letters*, 1967, 911.
39. P. J. Black and M. L. Heffernan, *Austral. J. Chem.*, 1964, **17**, 558.
40. P. J. Black and M. L. Heffernan, *Austral. J. Chem.*, 1966, **19**, 1287.
41. D. J. Blears and S. S. Danyluk, *J. Amer. Chem. Soc.*, 1967, **89**, 21.
42. S. S. Danyluk, *Canad. J. Chem.*, 1963, **41**, 387.
43. I. D. Kuntz and M. D. Johnson, *J. Amer. Chem. Soc.*, 1967, **89**, 6008.
44. C. L. Bell and S. S. Danyluk, *J. Amer. Chem. Soc.*, 1966, **88**, 2344 and references cited therein.
45. V. S. Watts, J. Loemaker and J. H. Goldstein, *J. Mol. Spectroscopy*, 1965, **17**, 348, and references cited therein.
46. S. L. Smith and R. H. Cox, *J. Chem. Phys.*, 1966, **45**, 2848, and references cited therein.
47. V. S. Watts and J. H. Goldstein, *J. Chem. Phys.*, 1965, **42**, 228.
48. P. Laszlo and H. J. T. Bos, *Tetrahedron Letters*, 1965, 1325.
49. B. L. Shapiro, E. J. Ebersole and R. M. Kopchik, *J. Mol. Spectroscopy*, 1963, **11**, 326.
50. S. L. Smith and A. M. Ihrig, *J. Mol. Spectroscopy*, 1967, **22**, 242.
51. S. L. Smith and A. M. Ihrig, *J. Chem. Phys.*, 1967, **46**, 1181.
52. P. Laszlo and P. Schleyer, *Bull. Soc. chim. France*, 1964, 87.
53. A. Kumar, *Mol. Phys.*, 1967, **12**, 593.
54. D. F. Evans, *J. Chem. Soc.*, 1963, 5575.
55. H. M. Hutton and T. Schaefer, *Canad. J. Chem.*, 1965, **43**, 3116.
56. H. M. Hutton, E. Bock and T. Schaefer, *Canad. J. Chem.*, 1966, **44**, 2772.
57. J. A. Pople and A. A. Bothner-By, *J. Chem. Phys.*, 1965, **42**, 1339.
58. M. Barfield and D. M. Grant, *J. Amer. Chem. Soc.*, 1961, **83**, 4726.
59. G. J. Karabatsos, G. C. Sonnischen, N. Hsi and D. J. Fenoglio, *J. Amer. Chem. Soc.*, 1967, **89**, 5067.

60. J. W. ApSimon, W. G. Craig, P. V. Demarco, D. W. Mathieson, A. K. G. Nasser, L. Saunders and W. B. Whalley, *Chem. Comm.*, 1966, 754.
61. J. Ronayne, R. G. Wilson and D. H. Williams, unpublished work.
62. J. V. Hatton and W. G. Schneider, *Canad. J. Chem.*, 1962, **40**, 1285.
63. J. V. Hatton and R. E. Richards, *Mol. Phys.*, 1962, **5**, 153.
64. J. Ronayne and D. H. Williams, *J. Chem. Soc. B*, 1967, 540, and references cited therein.
65. T. L. Brown and K. Stark, *J. Phys. Chem.*, 1965, **69**, 2679.
66. R. E. Klinck and J. B. Stothers, *Canad. J. Chem.*, 1962, **40**, 1071.
67. R. E. Klinck and J. B. Stothers, *Canad. J. Chem.*, 1962, **40**, 2339.
68. K. M. Baker and B. R. Davis, *J. Chem. Soc. B*, 261.
69. J. Tyrell, *Canad. J. Chem.*, 1965, **43**, 783.
70. J. E. Anderson, *Tetrahedron Letters*, 1965, 4713.
71. D. H. Williams and N. S. Bhacca, *Tetrahedron*, 1965, **21**, 2021.
72. R. C. Fort and T. R. Lindstrom, *Tetrahedron*, 1967, **23**, 3227.
73. Gurudata, R. E. Klinck and J. B. Stothers, *Canad. J. Chem.*, 1967, **45**, 213.
73a. P. Laszlo and J. L. Soong, *J. Phys. Chem.*, 1967, **47**, 4472; T. Matsuo, *J. Phys. Chem.*, 1968, **72**, 1819.
74. P. Laszlo and D. H. Williams, *J. Amer. Chem. Soc.*, 1966, **88**, 2799.
75. J. Ronayne, M. V. Sargent and D. H. Williams, *J. Amer. Chem. Soc.*, 1966, **88**, 5288.
76. R. E. Klinck and J. B. Stothers, *Canad. J. Chem.*, 1966, **44**, 37.
77. J. H. Bowie, J. Ronayne and D. H. Williams, *J. Chem. Soc. B*, 1966, 785.
78. M. W. Hanna and A. L. Ashbaugh, *J. Phys. Chem.*, 1964, **68**, 811.
79. R. Foster and C. A. Fyfe, *Trans. Faraday Soc.*, 1965, **61**, 1626.
80. R. Foster and C. A. Fyfe, *Trans. Faraday Soc.*, 1966, **62**, 1400.
81. R. Foster and C. A. Fyfe, *J. Chem. Soc. B*, 1966, 926.
82. J. V. Hatton and R. E. Richards, *Mol. Phys.*, 1962, **5**, 139.
83. D. H. Williams and D. A. Wilson, *J. Chem. Soc. B*, 1966, 144.
84. M. T. Rogers and J. L. Burdett, *Canad. J. Chem.*, 1965, **43**, 1516.
85. J. H. Bowie, J. Ronayne and D. H. Williams, *J. Chem. Soc. B*, 1967, 535.
86. J. D. Connolly and R. McCrindle, *Chem. and Ind.*, 1965, 379.
87. P. C. Cherry, W. R. T. Cottrell, G. C. Meakins and E. E. Richards, *J. Chem. Soc. C*, 1967, 181.
88. N. S. Bhacca and D. H. Williams, *Tetrahedron Letters*, 1964, 3127.
89. D. H. Williams and N. S. Bhacca, *Tetrahedron*, 1965, **21**, 1641.
90. S. Bory, M. Fetizon, P. Laszlo and D. H. Williams, *Bull. Soc. chim. France*, 1965, 2541.
91. M. Fetizon, J. Gore, P. Laszlo and B. Waegell, *J. Org. Chem.*, 1966, **31**, 4047.
92. J. D. Connolly and R. McCrindle, *J. Chem. Soc. C*, 1966, 1613.
93. C. W. Brooks and G. H. Draffan, *Chem. Comm.*, 1966, 393.
94. T. E. Bridgeman, P. C. Cherry, W. R. T. Cottrell, E. R. H. Jones and G. D. Meakins, *Chem. Comm.*, 1966, 561.
95. E. G. Glotter and D. Lavie, *J. Chem. Soc. C*, 1967, 2298.
96. W. Cocker, P. V. R. Shannon and P. A. Staniland, *J. Chem. Soc. C*, 1967, 485.
97. K. Tori, *Pharm. Bull. (Japan)*, 1964, **12**, 1439.
98. S. Bien and U. Michael, *Chem. and Ind.*, 1967, 664.
99. R. A. Appleton, J. B. Fulke, M. S. Henderson and R. McCrindle, *J. Chem. Soc. C*, 1967, 1943.
100. Y. Fujise and S. Ito, *Pharm. Bull. (Japan)*, 1966, **14**, 797.

101. M. Ohtsuru, M. Teraoka, K. Tori and K. Takeda, *J. Chem. Soc. B*, 1967, 1033.
102. D. H. Williams, *Tetrahedron Letters*, 1965, 2305.
103. C. J. Timmons, *Chem. Comm.*, 1966, 576.
104. J. K. Bailey, K. B. Everard, R. J. B. Marsden and L. E. Sutton, *J. Chem. Soc.*, 1949, 2957.
105. J. D. Connolly and R. McCrindle, *Chem. and Ind.*, 1965, 2068.
106. C. R. Narayanan and N. K. Venkatasubramanian, *Tetrahedron Letters*, 1966, 5865.
107. G. Di Maio, P. A. Tardella and C. Ivarone, *Tetrahedron Letters*, 1966, 2825.
108. T. B. H. McMurry and R. C. Mollan, *J. Chem. Soc. C*, 1967, 1815.
109. R. Grigg, J. H. Knight and P. Roffey, *Tetrahedron*, 1966, **22**, 3301.
110. K. C. Ramey, D. C. Lini, R. M. Moriarty, H. Gopal and H. G. Walsh, *J. Amer. Chem. Soc.*, 1967, **89**, 2401.
111. J. H. Bowie, D. Cameron, P. Schutz, D. H. Williams and N. S. Bhacca, *Tetrahedron*, 1966, **22**, 1771.
112. J. D. M. Asher and G. A. Sim, *J. Chem. Soc.*, 1965, 6041.
113. T. Matsuo, Y. Yoshida and O. Higuchi, *Bull. Soc. Chem. (Japan)*, 1967, **40**, 2526.
114. H. M. Fales and K. S. Warren, *J. Org. Chem.*, 1967, **32**, 501.
115. R. G. Wilson, D. H. Williams and J. H. Bowie, *Tetrahedron*, 1968, **24**, 1407.
116. P. J. Garratt, F. Scheinemann and F. Sondheimer, *Tetrahedron*, 1967, **23**, 2413.
117. N. Nakagawa and S. Fugiwara, *Bull. Soc. Chem. (Japan)*, 1961, **34**, 143.
118. J. N. Murrell and V. M. S. Gil, *Trans. Faraday Soc.*, 1965, **61**, 402.
119. T. Schaefer, *Canad. J. Chem.*, 1961, **39**, 1864.
120. N. Chatterjee and M. Bose, *Mol. Phys.*, 1967, **12**, 341.
121. J. Ronayne and D. H. Williams, *Chem. Comm.*, 1966, 712.
122. J. Ronayne and D. H. Williams, *J. Chem. Soc. B*, 1967, 805.
123. A. J. R. Bourn, D. G. Gillies and E. W. Randall, *Tetrahedron*, 1966, **22**, 1825.
124. L. A. LaPlanche and M. T. Rogers, *J. Amer. Chem. Soc.*, 1964, **86**, 337.
125. Y. Shvo, E. C. Taylor, K. Mislow and M. Raban, *J. Amer. Chem. Soc.*, 1967, **89**, 4910.
126. R. M. Moriarty and J. M. Kliegman, *Tetrahedron Letters*, 1966, 891.
127. R. M. Moriarty and J. M. Kliegman, *J. Org. Chem.*, 1966, **31**, 3007.
128. K. Nagarajan and M. D. Nair, *Tetrahedron*, 1967, **23**, 4493.
129. P. S. Wharton and T. I. Bair, *J. Org. Chem.*, 1965, **30**, 1681.
130. J. Seyden-Penne, T. Strzalko and M. Plat, *Tetrahedron Letters*, 1965, 4597.
131. J. Seyden-Penne, T. Strzalko and M. Plat, *Tetrahedron Letters*, 1966, 3611.
132. J. Seyden-Penne, P. Arnaud, J-L. Pierre and M. Plat, *Tetrahedron Letters*, 1967, 3719.
133. D. W. Boykin, A. B. Turner and R. E. Lutz, *Tetrahedron Letters*, 1967, 817.
134. J. Ronayne and D. H. Williams, *J. Chem. Soc. C*, 1967, 2642.
135. F. Hruska, D. W. McBride and T. Schaefer, *Canad. J. Chem.*, 1967, **45**, 1081.
136. M. Honda, Y. Kawasaki and T. Tanaka, *Tetrahedron Letters*, 1967, 3313.
137. G. Wood and M. Miskow, *Tetrahedron Letters*, 1966, 4433.
138. P. B. Solleman, R. Nagarajan and R. M. Dodson, *Chem. Comm.*, 1967, 553.
139. A. P. Schroff and G. Karmas, *Steroids*, 1966, **8**, 739.
140. C. Benezra and G. Ourisson, *Bull. Soc. chim. France*, 1966, 2270.
141. G. O. Dudek and R. H. Holm, *J. Amer. Chem. Soc.*, 1961, **83**, 2099.
142. Y. L. Chow and M. M. Feser, *Chem. Comm.*, 1967, 239.

143. T. Yonezawa, I. Morishima and K. Takeuchi, *Bull. Chem. Soc. (Japan)*, 1967, **40**, 1807.
144. W. H. Pirkle, *J. Amer. Chem. Soc.*, 1966, **88**, 1937.
145. T. G. Burlingame and W. H. Pirkle, *J. Amer. Chem. Soc.*, 1966, **88**, 4294.
146. W. H. Pirkle and S. D. Beare, *J. Amer. Chem. Soc.*, 1967, **89**, 5485.
147. G. Slomp and F. McKellar, *J. Amer. Chem. Soc.*, 1960, **82**, 999.
148. S. S. Danyluk, *Canad. J. Chem.*, 1963, **41**, 387.
149. R. M. Moriarty, *J. Org. Chem.*, 1963, **28**, 1296.
150. F. Johnson, W. D. Gurowitz and N. A. Starkovsky, *J. Amer. Chem. Soc.*, 1965, **87**, 3492.

Nitrogen Magnetic Resonance
Spectroscopy

E. F. MOONEY AND P. H. WINSON

University of Birmingham, P.O. Box 363, Birmingham 15, England

IT IS only in the last few years that interest in the study of high resolution n.m.r. spectra of nitrogen has begun to increase. The difficulties encountered in the study of both the nitrogen nuclei, namely nitrogen-14, with a spin of 1 and nitrogen-15 with a spin of $\frac{1}{2}$, are well known.[1] The nitrogen-14 isotope, although in nearly 100% natural abundance, has a low magnetic moment and is therefore insensitive to n.m.r. detection. Additionally, quadrupolar broadening is also a difficulty with this nucleus, and detection of spin–spin coupling is therefore limited. The low natural abundance (0·365%) of the nitrogen-15 isotope precludes measurement on all but the isotopically enriched molecules; however this nucleus has no quadrupole moment and spin–spin coupling is readily detected under suitable conditions. The advent of sensitivity enhancement devices, and the use of more sophisticated measuring techniques, has inevitably led to a resurge in the interest of studies of nitrogen magnetic resonance.

I. NITROGEN CHEMICAL SHIFTS

There was very little consistency in the choice of the resonance signal to be used as the reference for chemical shifts, in the earlier nitrogen resonance studies. A unified scale for chemical shift measurements, δ_{14N}, has recently been proposed by Witanowski[2] for both organic and aqueous solutions. The primary standards proposed are nitromethane and the nitrate ion for organic and aqueous solutions, respectively, and tetranitromethane and dimethylformamide are suggested for cases where there are complications due to very small δ_N values (Table I). However our own experience, with nitrogen-14 resonance spectroscopy, has shown that the shifts of the nitromethane and the nitrate ion are not identical; the former is 3 p.p.m. to low field of the nitrate ion. No unified standards have yet been suggested for nitrogen-15, the choice of the reference usually being governed by the availability of suitable material.

TABLE I

Internal standards for ^{14}N measurements

	δ_N p.p.m.	Application
MeNO$_2$	0	Primary: For general use with organic solvents and concentrated mineral acids
NO$_3^{\ominus}$	0	Primary: For general use in aqueous solutions
C(NO$_2$)$_4$	+48	Secondary: For nitro-compounds
Me$_2$NCHO	+276	Secondary: For aromatic nitro-compounds and nitrogen heterocycles

Nitrogen chemical shifts are generally considered to be dominated by the paramagnetic term of Ramsey's[3] expression for the screening constant, and much effort has been directed towards the understanding and prediction of chemical shifts. The simple shielding theory of Karplus and Pople,[4] which considers only the paramagnetic contribution σ_p to the screening constant σ, has been found to account satisfactorily for the observed chemical shifts of a series of linear triatomic molecules and ions.[5] The chemical shifts, over a considerable range of values, vary linearly with the π electron densities calculated by the LCGO–MO theory. Bose et al.[6] have surveyed the nitrogen-14 resonance shifts, in both aliphatic and aromatic compounds, and drew similar conclusions to those of Richards.[7] The nitrogen chemical shifts can be interpreted in terms of the electronic environment around the nitrogen-14 nucleus. In the case of saturated compounds the electronegativity is an important factor, whereas for aromatic and conjugated compounds the paramagnetic term becomes increasingly dominant. Evidence for hyperconjugation and charge-transfer interaction has been presented for certain systems, and the large variation in the line widths observed for nitrogen-14 resonances are found to be dependent on hybridization and steric factors as well as on symmetry and molecular-charge distribution. Similar evidence has been presented by Roberts[8] in a study of nitrogen-15 shifts in oxygen–nitrogen compounds, where an attempt has been made to correlate the chemical shifts with the energy of the $n \rightarrow \pi^*$ absorption of the nitro-group (Table II). For the nitro–nitrate series, the transition in question is from a non-bonding orbital on oxygen, whereas in the nitroso–nitrite

TABLE II

^{15}N chemical shifts and absorption maxima of oxygen–nitrogen compounds

	λ_{max} ($n \rightarrow \pi^*$) nm.	$\sigma_{p.p.m.}^D,^9$ (Diamagnetic shielding)	Chemical shift,† p.p.m.
s-Butyl nitrate	270	500	−337
Nitrate ion	300	510	−367
Nitrobenzene	330	490	−372
n-Butyl nitrate	356	440	−572
Nitrite ion	380,300	450	−608
Nitrosobenzene	755	430	−913

† Measured from anhydrous ammonium.

series there is also a non-bonding orbital on nitrogen. It is therefore not surprising that nitrites exhibit a larger paramagnetic contribution than the nitrates, even though the u.v. absorptions occur within a range of 100 nm.

A study of closely related compounds, however, often reveals secondary influences on nitrogen chemical shifts. Poranski and Moniz[10] have shown that the chemical shifts of aliphatic nitro-compounds (Table III) depend on the inductive effect of substituent groups. Simple empirical rules for the prediction of chemical shifts in the system $R^1R^2R^3CNO_2$ have been devised, where $R = H$, NO_2, Cl or alkyl.[11] The contribution of the shift from CH_3, RCH_2 and Cl are additive and, with a further modification of the expression—

$$\delta_{(NO_2)} = \delta_0 + \Delta(R^1) + \Delta(R^2) + \Delta(R^3)$$

which allows prediction of chemical shifts on introduction of further nitro-groups, agreement is generally within 1–2% of the 70 p.p.m. range of shifts observed for alkanes (Table IV). A different type of behaviour is found for aromatic nitro-compounds: the chemical shifts of the nitro-group in substituted nitrobenzenes are almost identical for the *ortho*, *meta* and *para* isomers, showing that π electron conjugation is unimportant.[12] Only those substituents that have a strong inductive effect show any appreciable effect on the shifts, e.g., methoxy- and hydroxy-groups that exert a strong mesomeric but only

TABLE III

^{14}N chemical shifts of aliphatic nitro-compounds

	Chemical shift, δ_N p.p.m.	Line width at half height, c./sec.	Reference
$CH_3CH_2NO_2$	$-10\cdot8$	30	10
$CH_3CH_2CH_2NO_2$	$-9\cdot5$	..	10
$HOCH_2CH_2NO_2$	$-5\cdot5$	..	10
$CH_3CH_2CHClNO_2$	$-2\cdot5, -4\cdot5$	50	10, 11
$CH_3CH_2CHBrNO_2$	$-4\cdot0$	75	11
$CH_3CHClNO_2$	$-5\cdot5$	33	11
$CH_3(CH_2)_3CHClNO_2$	$-4\cdot5$	67	11
$CH_3CH_2CCl_2NO_2$	$+1$	31	11
$CH_3CH_2ONO_2$	$+37\cdot5$	12	10
$CH_3CH(NO_2)_2$	$+11$	28	11
$CH_3CH_2CH(NO_2)_2$	$+11$	35	11
$(CH_3)_2C(NO_2)_2$	0	34	11
$O_2NCH_2CH_2NO_2$	$+2\cdot5$	60	11
$O_2N(CH_2)_6NO_2$	-9	60	11
$O_2NCH(CH_3)CH(CH_3)NO_2$	-8	68	11
$CH_3C(NO_2)_3$	26	11	10
$OHCH_2C(NO_2)_3$	30	10	10

TABLE IV

Calculated and observed ^{14}N chemical shifts of nitro-groups in $R^1R^2R^3CNO_2$ systems

R^1	R^2	R^3	Nitro-group ^{14}N shifts, c./sec., at 4·33 Mc./sec.	
			Calculated	Observed
H	H	H	0	0
CH_3	H	H	-45	-49
C_2H_5	H	H	-41	-41
CH_3	CH_3	H	-90	-96
RCH_2	RCH_2	H	-82	-80
CH_3	CH_3	CH_3	-135	-128
NO_2	NO_2	H	$+150$	$+152$
NO_2	NO_2	NO_2	$+206$	$+206$
CH_3	NO_2	H	$+48$	$+46$
C_2H_5	NO_2	H	$+52$	$+48$
CH_3	CH_3	NO_2	0	0
CH_3	CH_3	Cl	-67	-53
CH_3	Cl	H	-22	-23
C_2H_5	Cl	H	-18	-20
C_4H_9	Cl	H	-18	-20
C_2H_5	Cl	Cl	$+5$	$+5$

a weak inductive effect have little influence. The substituted ring may be considered, in this context, as a single atom exerting a negative (i.e., electron-attracting) inductive effect. *Ortho* effects may be important in the shifts of some *ortho*-substituted nitrobenzenes, but there is no evidence for hydrogen bonding in nitrophenols from their ^{14}N resonances. ^{15}N chemical shifts in *para* substituted nitrobenzenes correlate with the *para* ^{13}C shifts in monosubstituted nitrobenzenes and ^{19}F shifts in *para* substituted fluorobenzenes.[13] It appears that the results for nitrobenzenes can be interpreted by considering the electron density at the nitrogen and neighbouring nuclei and the π

TABLE V

^{14}N and ^{15}N chemical shifts of aromatic nitro-groups

	Nitrobenzene derivatives		Perfluoronitrobenzene derivatives
	^{14}N†	^{15}N‡	^{14}N†
Nitrobenzene	6·1	0·0	27·5
o-Nitrophenol	7	. .	. .
m-Nitrophenol	9	. .	. .
p-Nitrophenol	7	. .	. .
o-Nitroanisole	6	. .	. .
m-Nitroanisole	8	. .	. .
p-Nitroanisole	7	4·38	. .
2-Fluoronitrobenzene	13·1	. .	. .
3-Fluoronitrobenzene	10·6	. .	. .
4-Fluoronitrobenzene	9·8	3·57	. .
2-Chloronitrobenzene	12·3	. .	23·3
3-Chloronitrobenzene	16·5	. .	26·9
4-Chloronitrobenzene	16·0	2·09	27·0
2-Bromonitrobenzene	9·9	. .	19·9
3-Bromonitrobenzene	16·0	. .	28·7
4-Bromonitrobenzene	9·0	1·32	26·9
2-Iodonitrobenzene	4·5	. .	16·7
3-Iodonitrobenzene	10·4	. .	24·9
4-Iodonitrobenzene	12·6	. .	25·9
o-Dinitrobenzene	12	. .	. .
m-Dinitrobenzene	13	. .	. .
p-Dinitrobenzene	13	−3·85	. .
o-Nitrobenzaldehyde	11	. .	. .
m-Nitrobenzaldehyde	12	. .	. .
p-Nitrobenzaldehyde	12·5	. .	. .
1,3,5-Trinitrobenzene	18·5	. .	. .
2,4,6-Trinitrotoluene	14	. .	. .
2,4,6-Trinitrophenol	18	. .	. .

† p.p.m. from nitrate resonance.   ‡ p.p.m. from nitrobenzene-^{15}N.

bond orders of the N—C and N—O bonds in a similar fashion to the theory of fluorine shifts. The nitrogen-14 chemical shift of p-nitroaniline appears to have an extra paramagnetic contribution, which may be explained by the increased $(+M)$ effect of the amino-group. It seems peculiar that there is no correlation between ^{14}N and ^{15}N shift values for corresponding *para* substituted compounds in these series (Table V). The nitrogen-14 shifts of the polyfluoronitrobenzenes have been compared with the corresponding hydrocarbon compounds[14] and some of the results are also shown in Table V. It is clear from the shifts for 2-fluoronitrobenzene, the substituted tetrafluoronitrobenzenes and pentafluoronitrobenzene that fluorine atoms *ortho* to the nitro-group cause a pronounced shielding effect upon the nitrogen-14 resonance. Nitrogen-14 resonance measurements have been used in a study of donor–acceptor interaction in boron halide–nitrobenzene and pentafluoronitrobenzene systems.[15] The absence of significant nitrogen-14 shifts of the nitro-group in the nitrobenzenes on complex formation indicates that the effect of co-ordination to the boron halide is confined to one of the two oxygen atoms of the nitrogroup. The nitrogen-14 line widths in these systems do however reflect the acceptor properties of the boron halides.

The nitrogen-14 shifts of nitriles and isocyanides[16,17] may correspondingly be interpreted, in terms of changes in bond order and the charge-density matrix, without assuming values for the mean excitation energy explicit in the expression for the screening constant. Although only two examples were considered,[17] it was suggested that the behaviour of the nitrogen-14 resonance in substituted isonitriles, $R—N≡C$, where $R = Me$ or Et, was very similar to that observed for the nitro-group in nitroalkanes, i.e., that there is a decrease in shielding with decreasing electronegativity of R. The very sharp resonance line observed for isocyanides indicates that there is a very low field gradient present around the nitrogen atom. The [14]N–[1]H coupling was observed in methyl isocyanide,[16] but was not reported in the later work[17] (see p. 142).

Nitrogen chemical-shift measurements can be useful in interpretation of hydrogen bonding[6,16,18] and complex formation[15,19,20] systems. Bose *et al.*[6] have presented values for the dissociation constant of the pyridine–pyridinium system in HCl, whereas the ^{14}N chemical shifts of the system pyridine–methanol at different concentrations can be interpreted in terms of hydrogen-bond formation between pyridine and methanol. The high-field shifts observed on formation of the hydrogen bond can be satisfactorily described using valence bond theory. The nitrogen-14 shifts of pyridine–borane complexes,

$RC_5H_4N \rightarrow BH_3$, $R = H$, Me or Et, are some 55–65 p.p.m. to high field of the resonance of the parent pyridine,[19] but are at lower field than the corresponding pyridinium chlorides. The nitrogen-15 resonance spectra have been used to ascertain the extent and type of complexing of alkaline earth metals ($Mg^{2\oplus}$, $Zn^{2\oplus}$) to adenosine triphosphate (ATP). The ^{15}N chemical shift values, shown in Table VI indicate that, although $Mg^{2\oplus}$ does not bind to the adenosine ring nitrogens in the ATP–$Mg^{2\oplus}$ complexes, the shifts for the $Zn^{2\oplus}$ case are consistent with a model in which $Zn^{2\oplus}$ interacts at both the 6-amino and the N–7 positions.[20]

TABLE VI

^{15}N shifts† of the nitrogen atoms in ATP and in equimolar metal ion–ATP solutions[20]

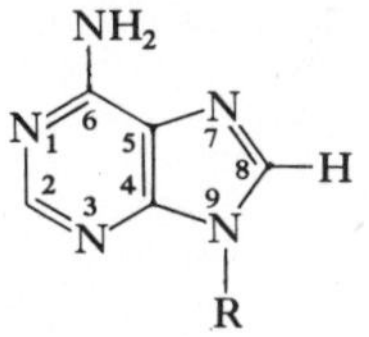

Coupling constants:
$J_{^{15}N-7-H-8} = 10$ c./sec.
$J_{^{15}N-1-H-2} = 16\cdot0$ c./sec.

	N-1	N-3	N-7	N-9	NH$_2$-6
ATP	144·7	135·6	129·5	191·6	282·8
$Mg^{2\oplus}$–ATP	144·9	135·0	129·5	191·6	282·3
$Zn^{2\oplus}$–ATP	144·9	135·0	132·5	190·1	279·7

† p.p.m. from $H^{15}NO_3$.

The nuclear magnetic double-resonance technique has been found particularly useful for measuring chemical shifts of ^{14}N directly bonded to protons. The ^1H resonance of the nitrogen-containing compound is observed with simultaneous irradiation of the ^{14}N nucleus at its resonance frequency, using a variable-frequency oscillator: the removal of fine structure or sharpening of the NH proton spectrum indicates when spin decoupling has been achieved. Since proton resonances are used, the indirect method is more sensitive, and furthermore ^{14}N chemical shifts can be readily obtained from dilute solutions. Complications can arise, however, when line broadening occurs due to labile protons or when the ^{14}N relaxation times are very short. This technique has been applied to a study of ^{14}N n.m.r. in amides,[21] thioamides,[22] benzthiazoles[23] and hydroxyquinolines.[24]

Primary amides exhibit upfield shifts relative to acetamide or formamide with changes in the group α to the carbonyl function. The localization of the nitrogen lone pair, resulting in a high-field shift is due, in acrylamide, cinnamide and benzamide, to cross-conjugation, that is a resonance structure such as that shown in (1) is important. Prevention of maximum overlap of the nitrogen lone pair and the carbonyl group arises, in the other primary amides, from twisting about the N—C bond. The larger variation in the ^{14}N chemical shifts of secondary aromatic amides probably arise from a superposition of various effects, especially since conjugation is also possible between the lone-pair nitrogen electrons and the aromatic ring (2). The ^{14}N chemical shifts of thioamides are substantially lower than their oxygen analogues.

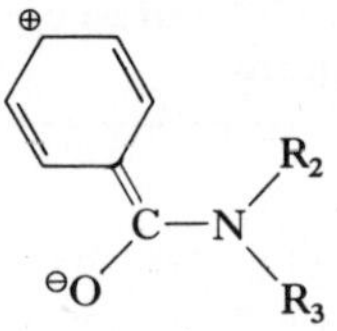

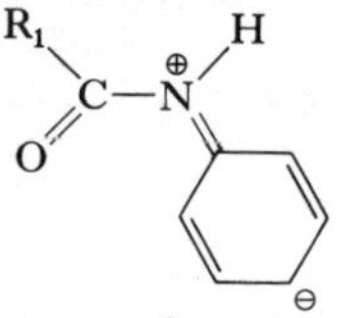

X = O, S

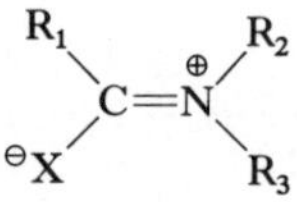

This indicates that there is a greater contribution from canonical structures of the form shown in (3); this is in accord with results obtained from i.r. and u.v. studies. Another corresponding trend is observed in the anilides and thioanilides, where introduction of sulphur in place of oxygen in the anilides should cause a smaller downfield shift than observed between the amides and the corresponding thioamides, since there will already be some delocalization of charge present through structures shown in (3). The value for selenobenzamide, only 3·8 p.p.m. downfield from thiobenzamide, perhaps reflects the similarity of bond order δ and π electron densities between the thio- and seleno-amides. A summary of the chemical shifts in these systems is shown in Table VII.

Nitrogen-14 spectroscopy can be very useful in deciding preferred tautomeric structures in nitrogen heterocyclic chemistry: an example of this is found in the 2-substituted benzthiazoles, which can exist in two tautomeric forms (4) and (5). The 4- and 6-substituted derivatives exhibit chemical shifts in the range expected for aromatic compounds,

TABLE VII

^{14}N **Shifts of amides and thioamides**[21, 22]

Amides	Shift, p.p.m.† (Error ~ 2·0 p.p.m.)	Thioamides	Shift, p.p.m.† (Error ~ 2·0 p.p.m.)
HCONH$_2$	267·8	..	..
CH$_3$CONH$_2$	269·6	CH$_3$CSNH$_2$	238·9
C$_2$H$_5$CONH$_2$	272·8	..	..
n-C$_3$H$_7$CONH$_2$	272·4	..	..
i-C$_3$H$_7$CONH$_2$	272·8	..	..
CH$_2$ClCONH$_2$	278·5	..	..
CHCl$_2$CONH$_2$	280·8	..	..
CCl$_3$CONH$_2$	283·3	..	..
PhCH$_2$CONH$_2$	274·5	PhCH$_2$CSNH$_2$	228·7
Ph$_2$CHCONH$_2$	273·1	..	..
CH$_2$=CHCONH$_2$	276·4	..	..
PhCH=CHCONH$_2$	277·1	..	..
PhCONH$_2$	282·1	PhCSNH$_2$	238·9
CH$_3$CONHCH$_3$	268·7	..	..
CH$_3$CONHC$_2$H$_5$	253·3	..	..
CH$_3$CONHC$_3$H$_7$-n	246·6	..	..
CH$_3$CONHC$_4$H$_9$-n	248·6	..	..
C$_2$H$_5$CONHCH$_3$	270·3	..	..
HCONHCH$_3$	264·1	..	..
HCONHC$_2$H$_5$	248·7	..	..
HCONHPh	235·0	..	..
CH$_3$CONHPh	243·3	CH$_3$CSNHPh	210·9
C$_2$H$_5$CONHPh	243·6	..	..
PhCONHPh	251·6	PhCSNHPh	216·7
o-Nitroacetanilide	253·3	..	..
m-Nitroacetanilide	246·3	PhCSeNH$_2$	235·1
2,4-Dinitroacetanilide	254·1	..	..

† p.p.m. from ^{14}N resonance of the nitrate ion.

such as pyridine or isoquinoline. The 2-amino- and 2-methylamino-derivatives however, absorb in the range 310–320 p.p.m., and therefore exist in the amino form (**4**, X = NH or NMe) rather than the imino form (**5**, X = NH or Me). Both 2-hydroxy- and 2-mercapto-benzthiazole show absorption to low field, indicating the environment of

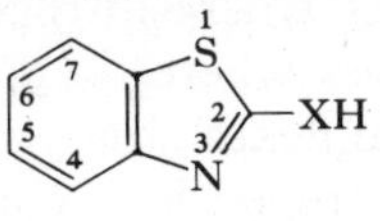

4

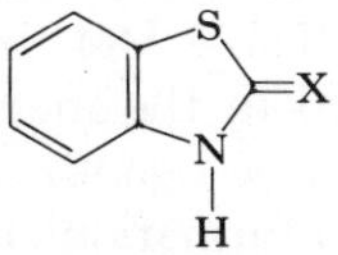

5
H

X = O, S, NH or NCH$_3$

the nitrogen to be of the thiazoline type (5). Similar behaviour is observed in 2- and 8-hydroxyquinolines, where only the 2-substituted isomers can exist in the oxo form (6).[24] 8-Hydroxyquinolines again show absorption in the range expected for ring-nitrogen atoms, e.g.,

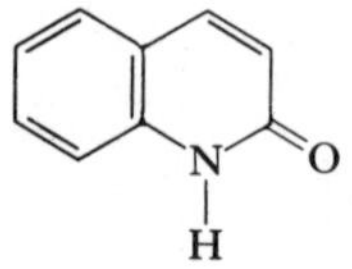

6

as in quinoline, whereas the high-field resonances associated with the 2-substituted isomers, and the existence of ^{14}N–H spin coupling, proves that the oxo form must exist almost exclusively (Table VIII).

TABLE VIII

[14]N **chemical shifts of substituted hydroxyquinolines**

Compound	Solvent	Chemical shift, δ_N p.p.m.†
Quinoline	Ether	72 ± 2
8-Hydroxyquinoline	Acetone	95 ± 4
5-Chloro-8-hydroxyquinoline	Acetone	93 ± 7
8-Hydroxy-7-methylquinoline	Acetone	91 ± 4
8-Hydroxy-5-methylquinoline	Acetone	90 ± 5
6-Chloro-8-hydroxyquinoline	Acetone	∼90
8-Hydroxy-6-nitroquinoline	Acetone	∼90
Acetanilide	CDCl₃	243 ± 2
2-Hydroxyquinoline	CDCl₃	238 ± 3
2-Hydroxy-4-methylquinoline	CDCl₃	238 ± 4
2-Hydroxy-3-methoxyquinoline	Acetate	229 ± 4
4-Chloro-2-hydroxyquinoline	CDCl₃	∼230

† p.p.m. from nitrate resonance.

Bramley et al.[25] have discussed the range of ^{14}N chemical shifts observed in transition-metal complexes where nitrogen is contained in the ligand (Table IX). In those cases where the nitrogen atom is directly bonded to the metal, the complexes show high-field shifts, relative to the free ligand, since the nitrogen lone pair is constricted on ligand-bond formation and thus contributes less to the negative or paramagnetic part of Ramsey's formula. Low-field shifts, relative to free ligand, are observed when nitrogen is not directly bonded to the

TABLE IX

^{14}N chemical shifts of some transition–metal complexes[25]

	δ_N,† p.p.m.	Stereo- chemistry		δ_N,† p.p.m.	Stereo- chemistry
$NaNO_2$	-385	..	$K_2Ni(CN)_4$	-46	Square planar
$Na_2Pd(NO_2)_4$	-134	Square planar	$K_2Pd(CN)_4$	-33	Square planar
$Na_2Pt(NO_2)_4$	-136	Square planar	$K_2Pt(CN)_4$	-20	Square planar
$Na_3Co(NO_2)_6$	-135	Octahedral	$K_2Zn(CN)_4$	-35	Tetrahedral
$Co(NH_3)_6Cl_3$	$+286$	Octahedral	$K_2Cd(CN)_4$	-45	Tetrahedral
$Rh(NH_3)_6Cl_3$	$+295$	Octahedral	$Na_4Os(CN)_6$	-31	Octahedral
$Ru(NH_3)_6Cl_2$	$+316$	Octahedral	$Na_3Co(CN)_6$	-34	Octahedral
$Fe(CO)_2NO_2$	-167	Tetrahedral	$NaAu(CN)_2$	-16	Linear
$Co(CO)_3NO$	-149	Tetrahedral	$Hg(CN)_2$	-40	Linear
H_2RuCl_5NO	-107	Octahedral	KCN	-5	..

† Chemical shifts relative to the ^{14}N resonance of acetonitrile.

metal. In these cases mixing is possible between metal d orbitals and nitrogen electrons similar to those of the ligand π orbitals in the MO description. More complex concepts are involved when the ligands contain NO or CO groups. Similar conclusions have been reached by Shporer et al.[26] in a study of the ^{14}N chemical shifts and line widths of some cyano–metal complexes. The diamagnetic complexes show little variation from the reference, whereas the shifts in paramagnetic metal cyanides and metal complexes with pyridine and ethylenedia-mine[27] are dependent upon the contact term. Line widths in both types of complex are predominantly determined by quadrupolar rather than electron spin relaxation. Nitrogen-14 resonance line-width studies have been reported for the exchange of ammonia in nickel–ammine complexes for both aqueous ammonia and anhydrous liquid ammonia solutions[26, 27] and for the electron exchange between ferri- and ferrocyanide ions.[28]

II. SPIN–SPIN COUPLING INVOLVING NITROGEN NUCLEI

The quadrupole moment associated with the ^{14}N nucleus (spin $I=1$) precludes observation of spin–spin coupling to nitrogen in all but a few compounds. Detection of coupling is only possible when there is a highly symmetrical field gradient around the nitrogen nucleus. This symmetry results in a sufficient increase of the spin–lattice relaxation time (T_1) of the nucleus to allow coupling to be observed. No complications due to quadrupolar decoupling are present for ^{15}N, and splittings may be readily observed in isotopically enriched compounds.

A. Nitrogen-14 coupling

The observed direct $^{14}N-^1H$ and *gem* $^1H-^1H$ coupling constants in ammonia are $43\cdot6\pm0\cdot6$ and $10\cdot35\pm0\cdot8$ c./sec., respectively. Kato *et al.*[29] have used the second-order perturbation theory of Pople and Santry to evaluate the signs of $J_{^{14}N-H}$ and $J_{^1H-^1H}$. Within the single-determinant MO formalism, the theoretical estimation of the contact term for coupling constants gives reasonable agreement with experiment, and suggests that both $J_{^{14}N-H}$ and $J_{^1H-^1H}$ are positive. The existence of a deuterium isotope effect on certain $^{14}N-^1H$ coupling constants has been shown to be erroneous.[30-32] The value of the $^{14}N-H$ coupling constant of ammonium nitrate in nitric acid on successive deuteration, i.e., $NH_4^\oplus$, $NH_3D^\oplus$, $NH_2D_2^\oplus$, $NHD_3^\oplus$, was essentially invariant with $J_{^{14}N-^1H} = 52\cdot7 \pm 0\cdot2$ c./sec.; deuterium substitution has therefore very little effect on the $^{14}N-H$ couplings. There is however evidence of a downfield shift of the proton resonance on successive deuteration in the ammonium nitrate–nitric acid system, which has been attributed to electrostatic effects arising from hydrogen bonding with the solvent molecules.[32]

The existence of $^{14}N-H$ coupling in alkylammonium salts is well known. In quaternary ethyl ammonium halides, for example, coupling of nitrogen and the β-CH_3 group is of larger magnitude than that to the adjacent methylene protons. Gassman and Heckert[33] have studied the long-range $^{14}N-C-C-H$ couplings in acyclic and cyclic quaternary ammonium iodides (Table X). The coupling in the acyclic salts appears to depend upon the nature of the substituent at the β-carbon, with electron-inducing groups tending to decrease the value of the coupling constant. Generally, values for $^{14}N-C-C-H$ couplings in cyclic salts are of the same order of magnitude, though when the nitrogen atom is constricted into a four-membered ring, e.g., N-methyl-N-ethyl-6-aza-bicyclo[3,2,0]heptyl iodide no coupling is observed. Spin–spin interactions are therefore restricted to tetra-alkylammonium salts in which hybridization of bonds to nitrogen is sp^3. A slight distortion of configuration results in a sufficiently large change of symmetry to cause decoupling. Symmetry considerations are also important in the proton spectra of compounds of the type $(CH_3CH_2)_3\overset{\oplus}{N}(CH_2)_n\overset{\oplus}{N}(CH_2CH_3)_32Br^\ominus$.[34] For long chains (*n* large) the compounds behave as two symmetrical, independent $(CH_3CH_2)_4\overset{\oplus}{N}Br^\ominus$ entities, and coupling is observed between ^{14}N and

TABLE X

^{14}N–methyl coupling constants in acyclic and cyclic quarternary ammonium iodides†

Acyclic iodides	J_{14N-^1H}, c./sec.	Cyclic iodides	R	J_{14N-^1H}, c./sec.
$(CH_3CH_2)_4\overset{\oplus}{N}$	1·80	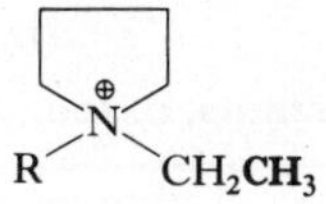	CH_3	1·90
$(CH_3CH_2)_3\overset{\oplus}{N}CH_3$	1·85		C_2H_5	1·88
$(CH_3CH_2)_2\overset{\oplus}{N}(CH_3)_2$	2·01	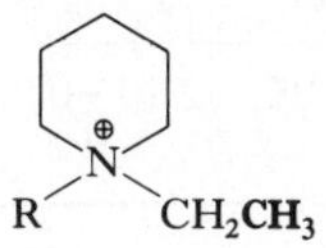	CH_3	1·67
$(CH_3CH_2\overset{\oplus}{N}(CH_3)_3$	2·15		C_2H_5	1·75
$(CH_3)_3\overset{\oplus}{N}C(CH_3)_3$	1·74			
$(CH_3)_3\overset{\oplus}{N}CH(CH_3)_2$	1·83	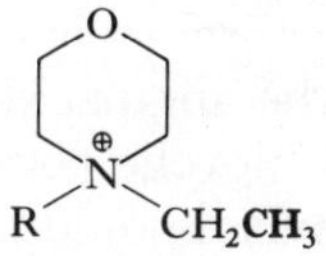	CH_3	1·75
			C_2H_5	1·69
$(CH_3)_3\overset{\oplus}{N}CHCH_3$ $\quad\quad\;\; \mid$ $\quad\quad\; CH_2CH_3$	1·87	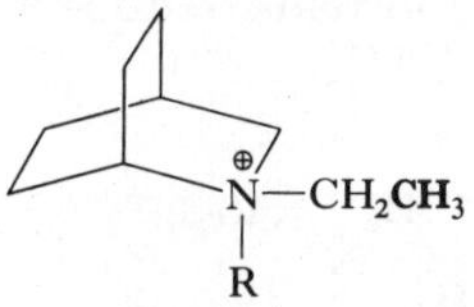	CH_3	1·79
			H	No spin coupling
$(CH_3CH_2)_3\overset{\oplus}{N}CH_2CH{=}CH_2$	1·50	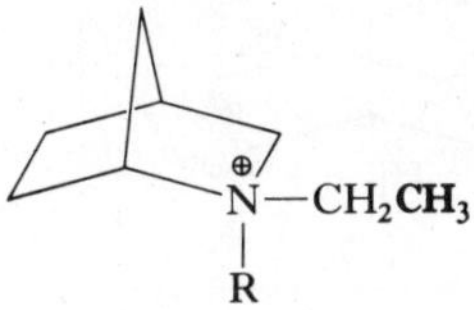	CH_3	1·82
			C_2H_5	1·62
$(CH_3CH_2)_3\overset{\oplus}{N}CH_2CH_2CH_2CH_3$	1·80	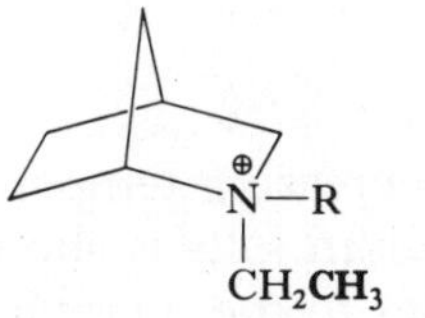	CH_3	1·80
			C_2H_5	1·62
$(CH_3CH_2)_3\overset{\oplus}{N}CH_2CH_2CH_3$	1·78	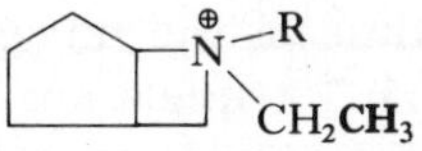	CH_3	No spin coupling

† The coupling involves the methyl group shown in **bold** type.

the α and β protons. As n decreases and the two $(CH_3CH_2)_3N^{\oplus}$ units come closer together, the quadrupolar relaxation of the ^{14}N nucleus becomes more effective and coupling is destroyed. Coupling may be observed in these latter compounds at higher temperatures, when the correlation time, τ, and thus the quadrupolar relaxation, is decreased due to easier orientation of the molecules in solution. Both $^{14}N\!-\!C\!-\!^1H$ and $^{14}N\!-\!C\!-\!C\!-\!^1H$ are observed in the proton resonance spectra of quaternary ammonium iodides (Table XI),[35, 36] and the magnitude

TABLE XI

^{14}N–H **coupling constants, c./sec., for quarternary ammonium iodides**

Coupling	NEt_4I	NEt_3MeI	NEt_2Me_2I	$NEtMe_3I$	NMe_4I
$J_{^{14}N-C-C-H}$	$1\cdot80\pm0\cdot05$	$2\cdot10\pm0\cdot05$	$2\cdot10\pm0\cdot05$	$2\cdot10\pm0\cdot05$	..
$J_{^{14}N-C-H}$	..	$<0\cdot2$	$<0\cdot2$	$<0\cdot3$	$0\cdot55$

of both the coupling constants is independent of the gegen ion. Terui et al.[37] have shown the angular dependence of the vicinal $^{14}N\!-\!^1H$ coupling in the rigid bicyclic compounds dibenzobicyclo[2,2,2]octa-2,5-dien-7-yl trimethylammonium bromide (**7**) and the 2-exo- and 2-endo-hydroxybornan-3-endo-yl trimethylammonium bromides (**8A** and **8B**) (Table XII).

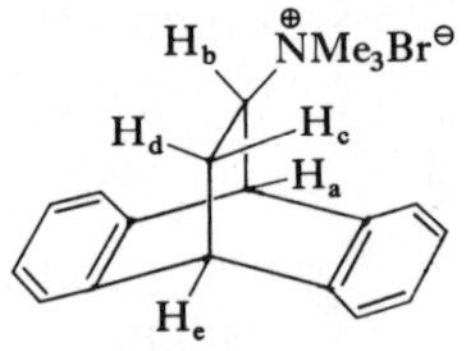

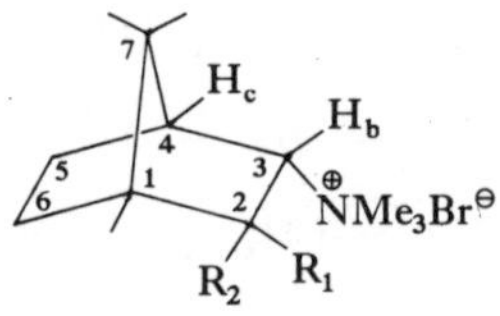

A: $R_1 = OH$, $R_2 = H_a$
B: $R_1 = H_a$, $R_2 = OH$

The effect of increasing temperature on the methyl proton spectra of N-ethylpyridinium salts is shown in Fig. 1.[36] At 25°C the methyl group only couples to the methylene group, but at 80°C the quadrupolar relaxation time of the nitrogen nucleus is sufficiently reduced and additional $1:1:1$ triplets are observed in the methyl resonance signal with a $^{14}N\!-\!C\!-\!CH_3$ coupling constant of $2\cdot4\pm0\cdot1$ c./sec. The effect of substituents in the 4-position is shown in Fig. 2; electron-attracting groups, such as CN or CF_3 are capable of decreasing the relaxation sufficiently to permit the observation of nitrogen–proton coupling at ambient temperatures and a relationship between τ and the σ para Hammett function of various substituents was described.

TABLE XII

The angular dependence of ^{14}N–H coupling constants[37]

Compound	Dihedral angle		$J(^{14}\mathrm{N}-^{1}\mathrm{H})$ vic., c./sec.
7	0	N–H$_c$	2·7
	60	N–H$_a$	≤0·3
	120	N–H$_d$	0·8
8A	0	N–H$_a$	1·4
	44	..	..
	79	N–H$_c$	≃0·0
	120	..	..
8B	0	..	..
	44	..	..
	79	N–H$_c$	≃0·0
	120	N–H$_a$	≤0·3

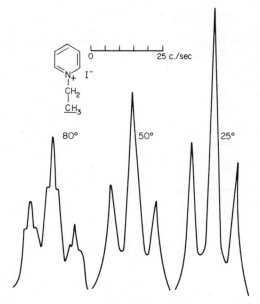

FIG. 1. The effect of temperature upon the methyl resonance signal of the *N*-ethylpyridinium iodide recorded in deuterium oxide. (From Biellmann and Callot.[36])

This effect is also shown in the proton spectra of 1-methyl-pyrazinium iodide (**9**), 2,4-dimethylpyrazinium (**10A**), 2-amino-4-methylpyrazinium iodide (**10B**) and 1-methylquinoxalinium iodide (**11**) in deuterium oxide solution at 100 Mc./sec.[38] The reduction of the

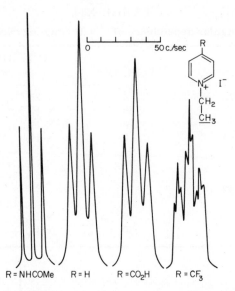

FIG. 2. The effect of substituents in the 4-position on the methyl resonance of the
N-ethyl group of 4-substituted N-ethyl pyridinium iodides recorded at 25°C. (From
Biellman and Callot.[36])

9

$J_{N_1-H_2} = 1 \cdot 0$ c./sec.

10

A: R = CH$_3$ · $J_{N_4-H_3} = 1 \cdot 0$ c./sec.
$J_{N_4-H_5} = 1 \cdot 1$ c./sec.
$J_{N_4-H_6} = 2 \cdot 9$ c./sec.
B: R = NH$_2$ $J_{N_4-H_3} = 1 \cdot 0$ c./sec.
$J_{N_4-H_5} = 1 \cdot 2$ c./sec.
$J_{N_4-H_6} = 3 \cdot 0$ c./sec.

11

$J_{N_1-H_2} = 0 \cdot 0$ c./sec.
$J_{N_1-H_3} = 2 \cdot 1$ c./sec.

electric-field gradient resulting from the strong electron-attracting nitrogen atom at the *para* position is sufficient to allow long-range $^{14}N-^1H$ coupling to be observed.

Analysis of the AMKX spectra of the trimethylvinylammonium salts (Fig. 3)[39, 40] shows that the nitrogen couples, not only to the

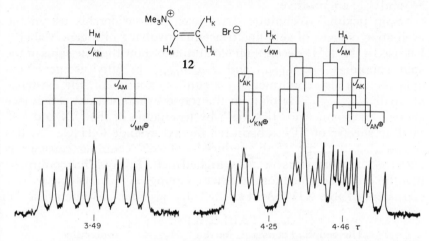

FIG. 3. The vinyl proton resonance signals of trimethylvinylammonium bromide (**12**) recorded in deuterium oxide at 100 Mc./sec. (From Ohtsuru and Tori.[40])

TABLE XIII

$^{14}N-H$ coupling constants of quaternary enammonium salts (13) measured at 90°C[39, 40]

Substituents in (13)				Coupling constants, c./sec.			
A	M	K	Y	($^{14}N-CH_3$)	($^{14}N-A$)	($^{14}N-M$)	($^{14}N-K$)
H	H	H	Br	~0·5	5·6	2·6	3·6
H	H	Br	Br	0·5	~3·5	†	..
H	H	Cl	Cl	0·5	~3·5	†	..
H	H	OEt	Br	0·5	3·8	†	..
CO_2H	H	H	Br	0·5	..	~1·8	~2·5
C_6H_5	H	H	Br	0·5	..	2·2	2·9

† Coupling not observed.

methyl groups, but also to the vinylic protons A, K and M. However, even at 90°C, the presence of certain substituents is sufficient to remove the *cis* ^{14}N–^{1}H coupling (Table XIII). By using "tickling" techniques, and by analogy with proton couplings in vinylic systems, the authors suggest that all three ^{14}N–^{1}H couplings, namely J_{trans}, J_{cis} and J_{gem} are positive.

"Spin tickling" techniques have been of considerable use in the evaluation of signs of coupling constants involving nitrogen. Maher[41] has used a ^{1}H–$\{^1$H$\}$ decoupling technique to show that the signs of the spin couplings $J_{^{14}N-^1H(CH_2)}$ and $J_{^{14}N-^1H(CH_3)}$ in ethyl isonitrile are opposite and also confirmed, by a similar experiment, the existence of small $J_{^{14}N-^1H(CH_2)}$ coupling in the tetraethylammonium cation (see above). Heteronuclear "tickling", by irradiation of the ^{15}N and ^{13}C satellite spectra of ^{15}N substituted methyl cyanide $C_aH_3C_b{}^{15}$N, has shown that the sign of the reduced —C≡N coupling constant is positive.[42] Experiments on ^{13}C-enriched methyl cyanide has confirmed that the values obtained for the other couplings in the molecule are self consistent (Table XIV). McFarlane[43] has also demonstrated that the

TABLE XIV
The coupling constants for the $C_aH_3C_b{\equiv}^{15}$N molecule

Coupled nuclei	Coupling constant, c./sec.	Reduced coupling constant, $K \times 10^{-20}$ cm^{-3}
$^{13}C_a$–^{15}N	±3·0±0·4	−9·77
^{15}N–^{1}H	±1·80±0·1	+1·48
$^{13}C_b$–^{15}N	±17·5±0·4	+57·0

reduced coupling constant of singly bonded nitrogen and carbon in methyl isocyanide is positive, in agreement with theory. The absolute signs of the geminal and vicinal ^{14}N–^{1}H couplings in isocyanides were shown to be negative and positive respectively, thus confirming Maher's earlier predictions.[41] The vicinal ^{14}N–^{1}H coupling constant in the tetraethylammonium cation was also found to be positive.

Since the original recognition of ^{14}N–^{1}H coupling in isocyanides,[44] most of the work, dealing with the ^{14}N–^{1}H coupling in these compounds, has utilized the proton resonance spectra. Only one paper has however reported the observation of the ^{14}N–^{1}H coupling in the nitrogen-14 resonance spectrum of methyl isocyanide.[16] However, we have recently studied the high-resolution nitrogen-14 resonance spectra of alkyl isocyanides, using 8·5 mm. spinning tubes, in our laboratories.[14] The coupling of the nitrogen-14 to both α and β protons is easily seen in the spectra; some examples are shown in Fig. 4.

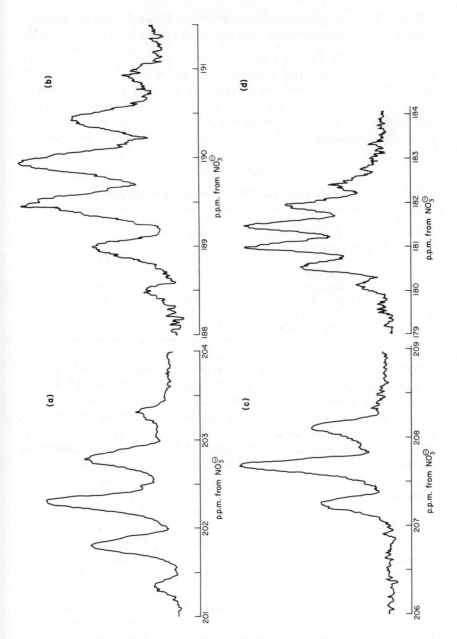

Fig. 4. The high-resolution nitrogen-14 spectra of: (a), n-propyl isonitrile; (b), isopropyl isonitrile; (c), neopentyl isonitrile; and (d), t-butyl isonitrile, recorded at 4·34 Mc./sec.

The ^{19}F n.m.r. spectrum of the product obtained from *cis*-difluoro-diazine and arsenic pentafluoride has been interpreted in terms of the ionic structure $N_2F\overset{\oplus}{A}sF_6^{\ominus}$; the magnitude of the N–F coupling was also consistent with the formation of the fluorodiazonium salt.[45] Similarly the triplet structure found in the ^{19}F n.m.r. spectra of NF_4SbF_6 and NF_4AsF_6 dissolved in HF indicates the formation of the perfluoroammonium cation $NF_4^{\oplus}$.[46,47] The values of these and other N–F coupling constants are shown in Table XV. Birchall and

TABLE XV

Some values of ^{14}N–^{19}F coupling constants

Compound	^{14}N–^{19}F coupling constant, c./sec.	Ref.
NF_3	155	48
cis-N_2F_2	145	48
trans-N_2F_2	136	48
$[F—N≡N]^{\oplus}[AsF_6]^{\ominus}$	328	45
$[NF_4]^{\oplus}[SbF_6]^{\ominus}$	231	46
$[NF_4]^{\oplus}[AsF_6]^{\ominus}$	234	47

Jolly[49] have shown that acids may be characterized by their behaviour in liquid ammonia. Acids of intermediate strength (pK 15–42) exchange their protons slowly with liquid ammonia and show distinct signals for both the acid and the anion. The proton spectrum of ammonia is observed as a sharp multiplet, with $J_{^{14}N–H}=43·5$ c./sec. and $J_{^{15}N–H}=61·0$ c./sec., or in various states of collapse depending on the acid–anion ratio. The behaviour of the ammonia resonance is interpreted in terms of exchange processes involving protons and solvent.

B. Nitrogen-15 coupling

The observation of spin coupling involving ^{15}N is limited to isotopically enriched molecules. Despite this drawback, ^{15}N coupling studies are capable of providing insight into structural problems concerning nitrogen-containing compounds in which spin interaction of ^{14}N are normally not observable. Nitrogen-15 n.m.r. spectroscopy has been used to determine the structure of the thiotriazyl cation formed by the reaction of ammonium chloride, disulphur dichloride and carbon tetrachloride.[50] The ^{15}N spectrum showed two peaks in the ratio 1:2 consistent with the symmetrical structure shown in (14).

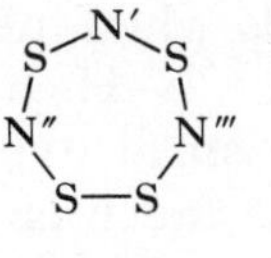

$$\begin{array}{ccc}
 & S-N'-S & \\
 N'' & & N''' \\
 & S-S &
\end{array}$$

14

The ^{15}N–^{15}N coupling of 7 c./sec. is the first to be reported for a system containing nitrogen-15 separated by two bonds. Bose and Kugajevsky[51] have studied the ^{15}N–H coupling in several ^{15}N labelled compounds (Tables XVI, XVII). Large ^{15}N–H couplings

TABLE XVI

Some selected examples of ^{15}N–H coupling constants

Compound	Solvent	Coupling constants, c./sec.		
		$J_{^{15}N-H}$	$J_{^{15}N-C-H}$	$J_{^{15}N-C-C-H}$
Ph—^{15}NH—C(=S)—NH—Ph	DMSO-d_6	89.8 ± 0.2	..	..
Ph—^{15}NH—C(=O)—NH—Ph	DMSO-d_6	89.7 ± 0.1	..	..
Ph—^{15}NH—CH=C(CO$_2$Et)$_2$	CDCl$_3$	91.4 ± 0.2	..	..
Ph—CH=N—^{15}NH—Ph†	DMSO-d_6	92.7 ± 0.2	..	..
Ph—^{15}NH—N=C(COMe)(CO$_2$Et)	CCl$_4$	$\begin{cases} 94.7 \pm 0.3 \\ 96.1 \pm 0.3 \end{cases}$	..	..
H,MeO$_2$C—C=C—CO$_2$Me,^{15}NHPh	CCl$_4$	91.2 ± 0.4	..	3.5 ± 0.2
H,MeO$_2$C—C=C—^{15}NHPh, CO$_2$Me	CCl$_4$	92.8 ± 0.3	..	1.7 ± 0.1
MeCO·^{15}NH—Ph	CDCl$_3$	89.9	..	..
Ph—CH=^{15}N—Ph	CDCl$_3$	..	3.8 ± 0.1	..
Ph—^{15}N=CH·NMe$_2$	CCl$_4$	..	2.4 ± 0.1	..
Ph—N=CH—^{15}NMe$_2$	CCl$_4$	..	8.4 ± 0.1	..
p—MeOC$_6$H$_4$N=CH—^{15}NMe$_2$	CCl$_4$	..	8.3 ± 0.1	..
p—NO$_2$C$_6$H$_4$N=CH—^{15}NMe$_2$	CCl$_4$	..	7.5 ± 0.1	..
Ph—^{15}N=C(Me)·NMe$_2$	CCl$_4$	..	..	1.1 ± 0.1

† $J_{^{15}N-N-CH}$ is 6.6 ± 0.1 c./sec.

are observed for compounds where nitrogen is bonded to trigonally hybridized carbon. Geminal ^{15}N–H couplings through sp^3 hybridized carbon atoms are generally small (0·6–1·4 c./sec.), though a certain similarity exists between the much larger nitrogen-15 coupling with a *gem* proton on sp^2 hybridized carbon atom and the *gem* proton–proton coupling in a similar environment (Table XVII). Long-range

TABLE XVII

Correlation of *gem*-^{15}N–^{1}H and *gem*-^{1}H–^{1}H coupling constants

Gem-^{15}N–^{1}H coupling		Gem-^{1}H–^{1}H coupling	
compound	$J_{^{15}N-CH}$, c./sec.	compound	J_{H-CH}, c./sec.
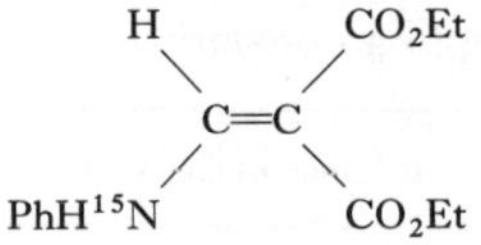 H, CO$_2$Et / C=C / PhH^{15}N, CO$_2$Et	≃0·2	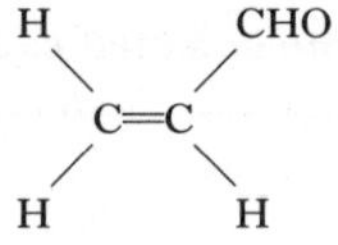 H, CHO / C=C / H, H	1·0
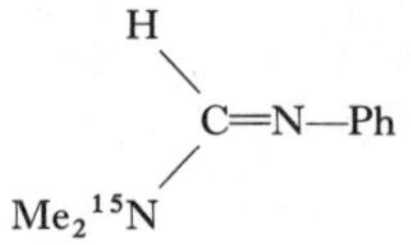 H, C=N—Ph / Me$_2$^{15}N	8·4	H, C=N—Bu^t / H	16·5
H, C=O / H$_2$^{15}N	+19·0	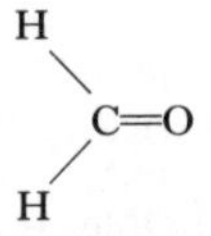 H, C=O / H	+40·2

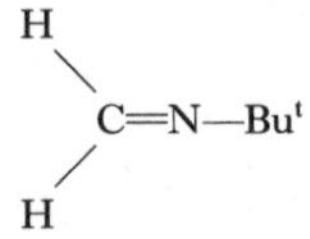

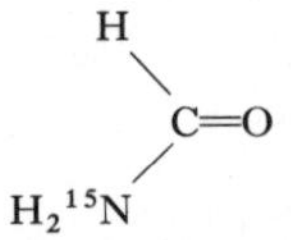

nitrogen-15 couplings to the 2, 3, 4 and 8 protons have been observed in substituted quinolines.[52, 53] The values of $J_{^{15}N-H_{(2)}}$ and $J_{^{15}N-H_{(3)}}$ are found to be dependent on the *s* character of the ^{15}N atom bonding orbitals to carbon. N-quaternization, oxygenation or solvent protonization on nitrogen results in an increase in coupling to $H_{(2)}$ and a simultaneous decrease in that to $H_{(3)}$.

If the dominant coupling mechanism is by the Fermi contact term, then nitrogen proton coupling constants can be useful parameters for the examination of nitrogen-atom hybridization.[54] An example of this occurs in the evaluation of $(p-d)\pi$ bonding in organic silicon compounds.[55] The proton spectrum of N-trimethylsilylaniline-^{15}N exhibits two ^{15}N–H couplings: $J_{^{15}N-H} = 76·0 \pm 0·2$ c./sec. and $J_{^{15}N-CH_3} = 1·0 \pm 0·1$ c./sec. The magnitude of the former, which is within the general range for sp^3 nitrogen coupling, indicates that there is no increase in the *s* character of the nitrogen orbital directed towards the proton, which would be expected if rehybridization had occurred with resulting $(p \rightarrow d)\pi$ bonding in the silicon–nitrogen bond.

The nitrogen–proton coupling constants for the separately observable *cis* and *trans* isomers of ^{15}N-n-butylformamide and N-n-propyl-acetamide are shown in **(15)**–**(17)**.[56] The value of the coupling across the C–N bond relative to that observed in ^{15}N-formamide ($J_{^{15}N-C-H}$ = 19·0 c./sec.) indicates that there is a decrease in the π electron density of the bond in the substituted compounds. This may arise either from the greater ease of hydrogen-bond formation in formamide or from the non-coplanarity of the atoms in the substituted amides.

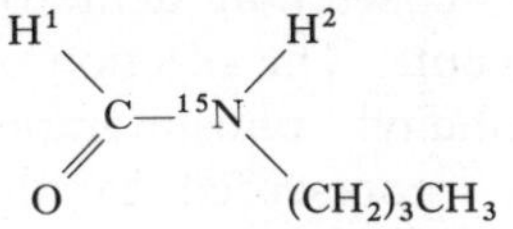

15

$J_{^{15}N-H(1)} = 15\cdot0$ c./sec.
$J_{^{15}N-H(2)} = 92\cdot2$ c./sec.

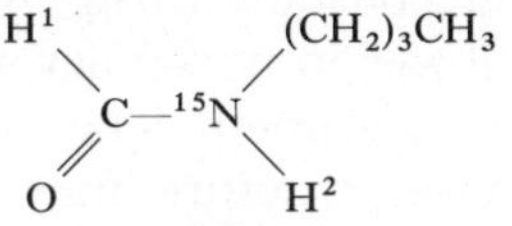

16

$J_{^{15}N-H(1)} = 14\cdot3$ c./sec.
$J_{^{15}N-H(2)} = 89\cdot8$ c./sec.

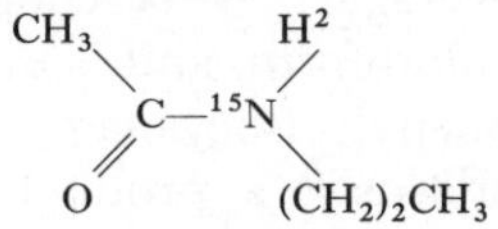

17

$J_{^{15}N-H(2)} = 92\cdot0$ c./sec.

The observation of ^{15}N coupling can be a particularly sensitive method of studying isomeric and valence tautomeric phenomena, which are a general feature of the chemistry of organic nitrogen-containing compounds. For example, if intramolecular proton exchange between the two sites, oxygen and nitrogen, is rapid, then the observed ^{15}N–H coupling provides a good measure of the residence time of the proton on nitrogen. This technique was used to determine the keto–enol equilibrium, as a function of solvent and temperature, in Schiff bases derived from anilides, aldehydes and ketones,[57–59] where the value of the ^{15}N–H coupling constants allowed an estimation of each tautomeric form and the thermodynamic constants for the equilibration process, to be made. For example 3-(^{15}N-phenylamino)-crotonophenone **(18)** exhibited ^{15}N–H coupling of 80–90 c./sec., a general feature of ^{15}N substituted Schiff bases that exist in the keto-amine form, e.g., 2-(^{15}N-phenylacetimidoyl)-5,5-dimethylcyclohex-ane-1,3-dione **(19)**. The predominance of the enolimine form of 1-(^{15}N-phenylformimdoyl)-2-naphthol **(20B)** is confirmed by the value of the

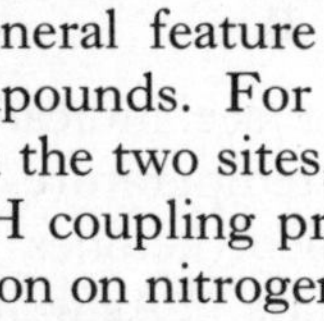

18

$J_{^{15}N-^{1}H} = 89\cdot2$ c./sec.

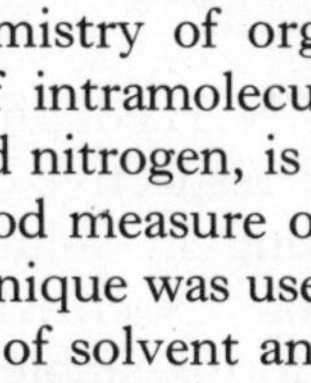

19

$J_{^{15}N-^{1}H} = 84\cdot7$ c./sec.

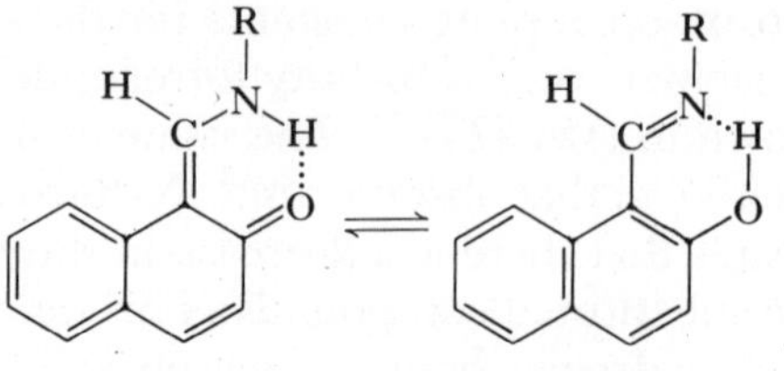

20A   **20B**

average ^{15}N–H coupling constant ($J_{15_{N-H}} = 33$ c./sec.) in deutero-chloroform, and is even lower in non-polar solvents. The reaction of phenyl isocyanate and acyl-methylene triphenyl phosphoranes affords[60] a product whose structure may be represented by the tautomeric equilibrium—

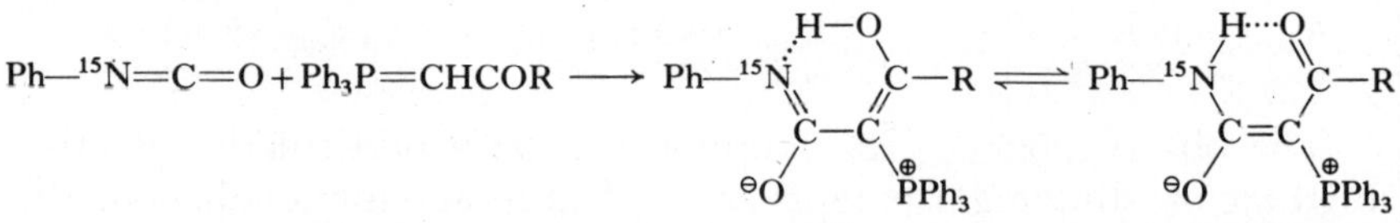

21   **22**

The observed ^{15}N–H coupling of 85–88 c./sec. indicates that form (**22**) predominates, irrespective of solvent or temperature. The tautomeric equilibria existing in solutions of 2-picolyketones have also been studied by use of ^{15}N-enriched compounds.[61] As well as the keto (**23**) and enol (**24**) forms stable at low temperatures, a new tautomeric species (**25**) is formed at higher temperatures. In accordance with HMO calculations the pyridinium structure (**25**) has been assigned to

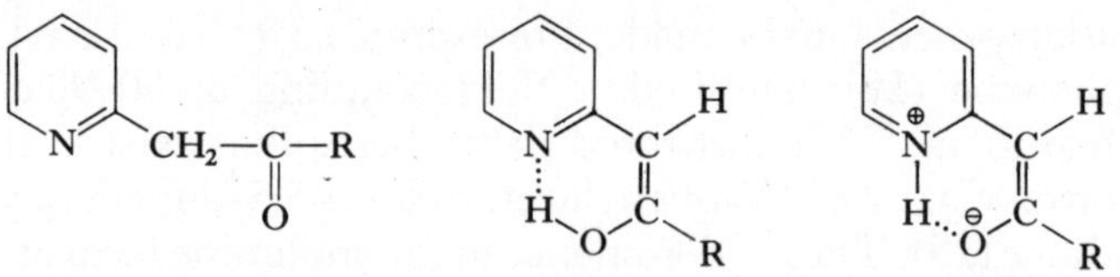

23   **24**   **25**

this tautomer. The temperature-dependence n.m.r. spectra of the imine protons of diphenyl- and sec-butylphenylketimines is ascribed to a bimolecular exchange of protons between imines as shown in (**26**).[62] At −60°C, four peaks were observed for the imine proton

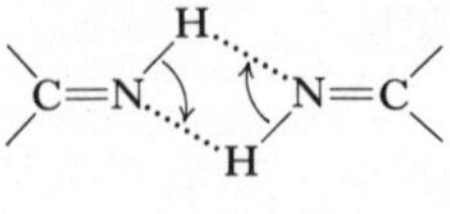

26

resonance spectrum of the unsymmetrical sec-butylphenylketimine-^{15}N, which must arise from two distinct *syn* and *anti* isomers. The free-energy difference between isomers was calculated to be 70 cal./mole.

Nitrogen-15 labelling is very useful in n.m.r. studies of nucleoside residues, since proton assignments are normally difficult, owing to the ^{14}N quadrupole moment. Becker *et al.*[63] have reported the p.m.r. spectra of ^{15}N labelled dimethylcytosines in sulphur dioxide and dimethyl sulphoxide solvent systems, and the $^{15}N–H$ coupling constants for these systems are shown in Table XVIII. Variations in the coupling-constant values are discussed in terms of the effect of temperature, salt

TABLE XVIII

$^{15}N–^{1}H$ coupling constants (c./sec.) in cytosine derivatives determined in either liquid sulphur dioxide or dimethyl sulphoxide solutions

Derivative	$J_{^{15}N-7H}$		$J_{^{15}N-CH_3}$		$J_{^{15}N-5H}$	
	SO$_2$	DMSO	SO$_2$	DMSO	SO$_2$	DMSO
1-Methylcytosine-7-^{15}N	..	90	..	..	..	..
1-Methylcytosine-7-^{15}N	⎰ 93·8	92·6	..	..	0·7	0·7
hydrochloride	⎱ 96·8	91·4	..	..	..	..
1,7-Dimethylcytosine-7-^{15}N	..	94	..	1·2	..	..
1,7-Dimethylcytosine-7-^{15}N	93·5	94	0·7	1·5	1·5	..
hydrochloride						
1,7-Dimethylcytosine-7-^{15}N	..	94	..	..	..	..
hydroiodide						

concentration and the nature of the solvent used. In agreement with earlier work it was found[64] that 1-methylcytosine-$^{15}N_2$ (27) protonates at $N_{(3)}$ and the same authors have measured the long-range $^{15}N–^{1}H$ coupling constants in uracil-$^{15}N_2$, 2,4-dichloropyrimidine-$^{15}N_2$,

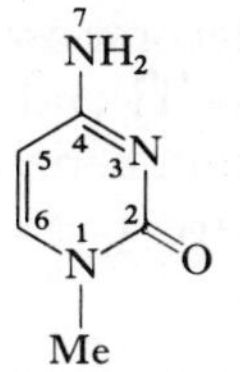

27

2,4-dimethoxypyrimidine-$^{15}N_2$ and methyl-4-methoxy-2-pyrimidine-$^{15}N_2$; these couplings are shown in (28–31).

Hogeveen[65] has shown that the imino-^{15}N-ethylcarbonium ion,

6

formed by protonation of propionitrile-^{15}N at $-81°$C, exists in one conformation only, namely R—$\overset{\oplus}{C}$=NH with $J_{^{15}N-^{1}H}=130$ c./sec. and $J_{^{15}N-C-CH_2}=1\cdot5-2\cdot0$ c./sec. At $-28°$C, rapid deprotonation occurs and, by measuring the line widths of the low-field ^{15}N–H signals at various temperatures, the rate constants for the deprotonation may be determined.

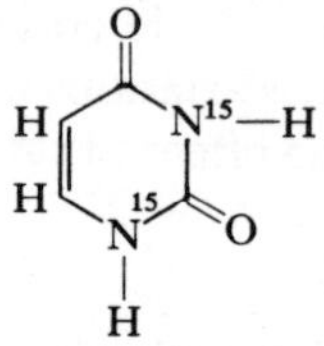

28

$J_{^{15}N-H}=91$ c./sec.
$J_{^{15}N-H}=97$ c./sec.
$J_{^{15}N-CH}=3\cdot5$ c./sec.

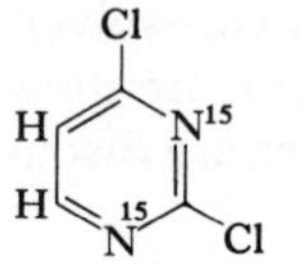

29

$J_{^{15}N_{(1)}-CH}=12\cdot5$ c./sec.
$J_{^{15}N_{(3)}-CH-5}=0\cdot9$ c./sec.

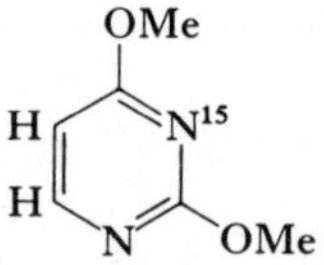

30

$J_{^{15}N_{(1)}-H-6}=12\cdot2$ c./sec.
$J_{^{15}N_{(3)}-H-5}=0\cdot6$ c./sec.

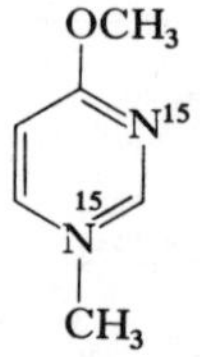

31

$J_{^{15}N_{(1)}-CH_3}=1\cdot2$ c./sec.
$J_{^{15}N_{(1)}-H-6}=1\cdot8$ c./sec.
$J_{^{15}N_{(3)}-H-5}=3\cdot9$ c./sec.

An interesting use of ^{15}N substitution occurs in the study of the production and reactions of the phenyldiazonium ion.[66] Earlier work had predicted a rearrangement of the nitrogen atoms of the generated cation before the salt was decomposed. By measuring the relative areas associated with the ^{15}N–^{1}H and the ^{14}N–^{1}H resonances of the condensation products with both benzaldehyde and ethylacetoacetate, the authors showed that there was no evidence of the following reaction taking place—

$$(C_6H_5{}^{15}N\equiv N)^{\oplus} \longrightarrow (C_6H_5N\equiv{}^{15}N)^{\oplus}$$

REFERENCES

1. J. W. Emsley, J. Feeney and L. H. Sutcliffe, "High Resolution Nuclear Magnetic Resonance Spectroscopy", Vol. 2, p. 1031, Pergamon Press, London, 1966.
2. M. Witanowski and H. Januszewski, *J. Chem. Soc. B*, 1967, 1063.
3. N. F. Ramsey, *Phys. Rev.*, 1952, **85**, 243.
4. M. Karplus and J. A. Pople, *J. Chem. Phys.*, 1963, **38**, 374.
5. J. E. Kent and E. L. Wagner, *J. Chem. Phys.*, 1966, **44**, 3530.
6. M. Bose, N. Das and N. Chatterjee, *J. Mol. Spectroscopy*, 1965, **18**, 32.
7. D. Herbison-Evans and R. E. Richards, *Mol. Phys.*, 1964, **8**, 19.
8. J. B. Lambert and J. D. Roberts, *J. Amer. Chem. Soc.*, 1965, **87**, 4087.
9. S. I. Chan, M. R. Baker and N. F. Ramsey, *Phys. Rev.*, 1964, 136 and 1224.
10. C. F. Poranski and W. B. Moniz, *J. Phys. Chem.*, 1967, **71**, 1142.
11. M. Witanowski and L. Stefaniak, *J. Chem. Soc. B*, 1967, 1061.
12. M. Witanowski, L. Stefaniak and G. A. Webb, *J. Chem. Soc. B*, 1967, 1065.
13. D. T. Clark and J. D. Roberts, *J. Amer. Chem. Soc.*, 1966, **88**, 745.
14. E. F. Mooney and P. H. Winson, unpublished work.
15. E. F. Mooney, M. A. Qaseem and P. H. Winson, *J. Chem. Soc. B*, 1968, 224.
16. A. Loewenstein and Y. Margalit, *J. Phys. Chem.*, 1965, **69**, 4152.
17. M. Witanowski, *Tetrahedron*, 1967, **23**, 4299.
18. H. Saitô, K. Nukada, H. Kato, T. Yonezawa and K. Fukui, *Tetrahedron Letters*, 1965, 111.
19. E. F. Mooney and M. A. Qaseem, *J. Inorg. Nuc. Chem.*, 1968, **30**, 1439.
20. J. A. Happe and M. Morales, *J. Amer. Chem. Soc.*, 1966, **88**, 2077.
21. P. Hampson and A. Mathias, *Mol. Phys.*, 1966, **11**, 541.
22. P. Hampson and A. Mathias, *Mol. Phys.*, 1967, **13**, 361.
23. A. Mathias, *Mol. Phys.*, 1967, **12**, 381.
24. P. Hampson and A. Mathias, *Chem. Comm.*, 1967, 371.
25. R. Bramley, B. N. Figgis and R. S. Nyholm, *J. Chem. Soc. A*, 1967, 851.
26. M. Shporer, G. Ron, A. Loewenstein and G. Navon, *Inorg. Chem.*, 1965, **4**, 358.
27. M. A. Glaeser, G. A. Lo, H. W. Dodgen and J. P. Hunt, *Inorg. Chem.*, 1965, **4**, 206.
28. M. Shporer, G. Ron, A. Loewenstein and G. Navon, *Inorg. Chem.*, 1965, **4**, 361.
29. Y. Kato, M. Miura and A. Saika, *Mol. Phys.*, 1967, **13**, 491.
30. N. Muller and R. H. Birkhahn, *J. Chem. Phys.*, 1965, **43**, 4540.
31. G. Fraenkel and W. J. Burlant, *J. Chem. Phys.*, 1965, **43**, 4541.
32. G. Fraenkel, Y. Asaki, H. Batiz-Hernandez and R. A. Bernheim, *J. Chem. Phys.*, 1966, **44**, 4647.
33. P. G. Gassman and D. C. Heckert, *J. Org. Chem.*, 1965, **30**, 2859.
34. J-M. Lehn and M. Franck-Neunamm, *J. Chem. Phys.*, 1965, **43**, 1421.
35. E. W. Randall and D. Shaw, *Spectrochim. Acta*, 1967, **23A**, 1235.
36. J-F. Biellmann and H. Callot, *Bull. Soc. chim. France*, 1967, 397.
37. Y. Terui, K. Aono and K. Tori, *J. Amer. Chem. Soc.*, 1968, **90**, 1069.
38. T. Gato, M. Isobe, M. Ohtsuru and K. Tori, *Tetrahedron Letters*, 1968, 1511.
39. J. M. Lehn and R. Seher, *Chem. Comm.*, 1966, 847.
40. M. Ohtsuru and K. Tori, *Chem. Comm.*, 1966, 750.
41. J. P. Maher, *J. Chem. Soc. A*, 1966, 1855.
42. W. McFarlane, *Mol. Phys.*, 1966, **10**, 603.
43. W. McFarlane, *J. Chem. Soc. A*, 1967, 1660.
44. I. D. Kuntz, P. von R. Schleyer and A. Allerhand, *J. Chem. Phys.*, 1961, **35**, 1533.

45. D. Moy and A. R. Young, *J. Amer. Chem. Soc.*, 1965, **87**, 1889.
46. W. E. Tolberg, R. T. Rewick, R. S. Stringham and M. E. Hill, *Inorg. Chem.*, 1967, **6**, 1156.
47. K. O. Christe, J. P. Guertin, A. E. Pavlath and W. Sawodny, *Inorg. Chem.*, 1967, **6**, 553.
48. J. Noggle, J. D. Baldeschweiler, C. B. Colburn, *J. Chem. Phys.*, 1962, **37**, 182.
49. T. Birchall and W. L. Jolly, *J. Amer. Chem. Soc.*, 1965, **87**, 3007.
50. N. Logan and W. L. Jolly, *Inorg. Chem.*, 1965, **4**, 1508.
51. A. K. Bose and I. Kugajevsky, *Tetrahedron*, 1967, **23**, 1489.
52. Y. Kawazoe, M. Ohnishi and N. Kataoka, *Chem. Pharm. Bull. (Tokyo)*, 1965, **13**, 396.
53. K. Tori, M. Ohtsuru, K. Aono, Y. Kawazoe and M. Ohnishi, *J. Amer. Chem. Soc.*, 1967, **89**, 2765.
54. G. Binsch, J. B. Lambert, B. W. Roberts and J. D. Roberts, *J. Amer. Chem. Soc.*, 1964, **86**, 5564.
55. E. W. Randall, J. J. Ellner and J. J. Zuckerman, *J. Amer. Chem. Soc.*, 1966, **88**, 622.
56. M. T. Rogers and L. A. LaPlanche, *J. Phys. Chem.*, 1965, **69**, 3648.
57. G. O. Dudek and E. P. Dudek, *J. Amer. Chem. Soc.*, 1964, **86**, 4283.
58. G. O. Dudek and E. P. Dudek, *Chem. Comm.*, 1965, 464.
59. G. O. Dudek and E. P. Dudek, *J. Amer. Chem. Soc.*, 1966, **88**, 2407.
60. M-L. Blanchard, H. Strzelecka, G. J. Martin and M. Simalty, *Bull. Soc. chim. France*, 1967, 2677.
61. G. Klose and E. Unlemann, *Tetrahedron*, 1966, **22**, 1373.
62. J. B. Lambert, W. L. Oliver and J. D. Roberts, *J. Amer. Chem. Soc.*, 1965, **87**, 5085.
63. E. D. Becker, H. T. Miles and R. B. Bradley, *J. Amer. Chem. Soc.*, 1965, **87**, 5575.
64. B. W. Roberts, J. B. Lambert and J. D. Roberts, *J. Amer. Chem. Soc.*, 1965, **87**, 5439.
65. H. Hogeveen, *Rec. Trav. chim.*, 1967, **86**, 1288.
66. A. K. Bose and I. Kugajevsky, *J. Amer. Chem. Soc.*, 1966, **88**, 2325.

Carbon-13 Nuclear Magnetic Resonance Spectroscopy: Carbon-13 Chemical Shifts and Coupling Constants

E. F. MOONEY AND P. H. WINSON

University of Birmingham, P.O. Box 363, Birmingham 15, England

I. INTRODUCTION

THE carbon-13 nucleus resonates at 15·09 Mc./sec. in a magnetic field of 14,092 gauss. Since this isotope has a low magnetic moment and is present in only 1% of natural carbon, the sensitivity of the ^{13}C resonance signal in "natural abundance" samples is only about 1/6500 of that of an equal number of proton nuclei. The spin lattice relaxation time (T_1) of the ^{13}C nucleus varies from a few seconds to several minutes; consequently unless the scan of the nuclear resonance is very fast, the ^{13}C multiplets show distorted peak intensities owing to magnetization transfer. Considerable modification of the general conditions used for the observation of nuclear magnetic resonance is thus necessary before spin coupling and chemical-shift parameters can be satisfactorily obtained for the ^{13}C nucleus.

Although the first report[1] of the direct observation of the ^{13}C resonance signals was in 1957, the general development of ^{13}C resonance spectroscopy has been very slow in gathering momentum. The subject has been reviewed by Lauterbur[2] and by Stothers,[3] and there is a section on this subject in the book by Emsley et al.[4a] Stothers was more concerned with the ^{13}C chemical-shift correlations, but some useful tables of ^{13}C coupling constants are given in Emsley et al. Since 1965, the advances that have been made in overcoming the difficulties associated with the low natural abundance have led to the appearance of an increasing number of papers on this subject.

For convenience, the review will be divided into two Sections, the first dealing with the chemical-shift correlations within different classes of organic compounds and the second specifically concerned with ^{13}C coupling constants.

II. DEVELOPMENTS IN EXPERIMENTAL TECHNIQUES

In order to overcome the low natural abundance and sensitivity of the ^{13}C isotope, large sample tubes and high values of r.f. power have generally been used to observe ^{13}C resonance signals. Rapid passage conditions, generally in the dispersion mode, with delayed sweep are necessary if saturation is to be avoided. The limitations of this method are well known; chemical-shift values can be inaccurate unless the spectra are averaged by recording with both increasing and decreasing field sweep, and additionally much of the spin–spin coupling fine structure of the resonance signals may be lost.

Flow techniques have also been used to avoid difficulties from saturation, and improved sensitivity can be achieved by using the internuclear double resonance technique (INDOR). Enhancement of ^{13}C resonance signals can be obtained by examining the sample in the presence of free radicals (Overhauser effect, see p. 338). Richards,[5] for example, has observed positive enhancement of ^{13}C signals in chloroform, methylene dichloride, dibromide and di-iodide, and in carbon tetrachloride. In these examples, contact between a radical electron and the large halogen atom facilitates scalar coupling, leading to a positive increase in the signal intensity. Negative enhancement has been observed for aromatic compounds, alcohols, ketones and carbon disulphide; but in contrast positive Overhauser signal enhancements have been obtained for aromatic polyfluorocarbons.[6] Proton-decoupling techniques, in addition to increasing signal intensity by collapse of the $^{13}C-^1H$ coupling, also give rise to Overhauser enhancement of the ^{13}C resonance. Ernst[7] has extended this heteronuclear decoupling technique by showing that complete decoupling of one or more nuclear species is possible by use of a second, incoherent r.f. source. For example, strong noise irradiation in the proton frequency region would cause improvement of sensitivity through collapse of all multiplets caused by $^{13}C-^1H$ couplings as well as possible enhancement of the ^{13}C resonance signal through Overhauser polarization.

The low signal-to-noise ratio inherent in the observation of the absorption mode of the ^{13}C resonance, with low r.f. power and delayed field sweep, can be largely overcome by use of repeated scanning of the ^{13}C resonance spectrum. The coherent resonance signal is allowed to build up progressively, while random background noise only builds up at a much reduced rate. Commercial CATs (Computer of Average Transients) are available, whereby the spectrum is scanned repeatedly at the usual speed for satisfactory resolution and a summed spectrum is thus obtained. The signal-to-noise ratio, compared to that obtained in a standard single-scan spectrum, improves as the square root of the number of scans accumulated. Another approach involves an extremely slow single scan, whereby the signal-to-noise improves as the square root of the ratio of the long sweep time to that of the normal spectrum sweep time. Dehlson and Robertson[8] have notified the latter DOG technique in a device known as SUPER SNAIL (Simple Uncomputerized Procedure for Experimentally Recording Signals above Noise by Accumulation of Integral Lines). The presentation of the accumulated repetitive integral scans in the form of a histogram may be improved by employing numerical smoothing procedures to suppress noise further.[9] Efficient spinning of large sample tubes will also increase signal-to-noise levels and resolution: Roberts[10] has shown the application of the above procedures in a study of the ^{13}C spectrum of benzene in natural abundance.

The observation of the ^{13}C satellite spectra of proton and fluorine resonances has been extensively used to provide information on the magnitude and signs of $^{13}C-^1H$ and $^{13}C-^{19}F$ coupling constants. The values of directly bonded couplings involving ^{13}C can generally be measured with greater precision from the ^{13}C satellite spectra than from direct ^{13}C resonance studies. Long-range coupling constants between ^{13}C and protons or fluorine can be observed in ^{13}C-enriched samples, but, because of the small magnitude of the coupling constants, are generally "swamped" by the intense signals arising from the protons or fluorine atoms directly attached to ^{12}C atoms. Freeman[11] has described a technique whereby the intense central lines may be effectively suppressed. The resonance of the protons associated with the ^{13}C nucleus is modified by slow pulse modulation of the second r.f. field (H_b) in conjunction with a long time constant filter in the recorder output.[12] The ^{13}C satellites will be of different appearance, according to whether H_b is on or off and are therefore not suppressed by the detection system, whereas the strong proton signals arising from the protons attached to ^{12}C are effectively cancelled. This "isotope-filter" technique, as well as allowing observation of inner satellites, is capable of providing information regarding the relative signs of spin coupling constants in the molecules by the use of the INDOR and spin "tickling" techniques. Observation of proton satellites with simultaneous irradiation at the ^{13}C resonance frequency also permits the chemical shift of the ^{13}C nuclei to be determined. This indirect method, which utilizes the favourable sensitivity and relaxation time of the proton, is capable of permitting ^{13}C chemical shifts to be determined with a high degree of accuracy.[13-15]

The discussion of developments in instrumentation and measurement techniques that may be utilized for ^{13}C n.m.r. has been of necessity quite brief. Excellent reviews of signal-to-noise enhancement[16] and double-resonance techniques and instrumentation[17] have been given in Volume 1 of this series.

III. CARBON-13 CHEMICAL SHIFTS

A. Theoretical considerations

The expression for the screening constant (σ_A) of a nucleus may be written as the sum of three separate parameters[18]—

(i) a diamagnetic contribution, σ_D, due to currents involving local electrons;

(ii) σ', the contribution from circulation of electrons on neighbouring atoms and the effect of anisotropic atoms, bonds or ring structures;

(iii) σ_p, paramagnetic term involving the mixing of electronic states by the applied field H_0.

For nuclei other than protons, σ' is relatively unimportant, and calculations of the diamagnetic circulation σ_D show that it does not contribute more than a few p.p.m. to the total shielding in ^{13}C chemical shifts. The paramagnetic term, σ_p, is therefore the dominant term in the expression for the calculation of the shielding for the ^{13}C nucleus, and considerable attention has been paid to the evaluation of this term using quantum mechanical treatments.

A LCAO–MO theory for σ electrons[19] has been used to calculate the ^{13}C chemical shifts of saturated hydrocarbons. The shielding constant of the carbon atom is found to be approximately proportional to the excess charge densities of the $2p$ electrons, which is in accordance with experimental results. The theory fails, however, to predict the so-called β- and γ-effects in ^{13}C chemical shifts. The β-effect, which gives an unexpectedly large downfield contribution to ^{13}C chemical shifts, may be interpreted in terms of the change of the mean excitation energy, ΔE, in the expression for the paramagnetic term or to the change in the effective nuclear charge Z^* of carbon, due to the influence of the β-methyl group on the radical part of the $2p$ atomic orbital. The γ-effect, another positive contribution to the ^{13}C chemical shifts, may be interpreted in terms of electronic effects. The γ-carbon atom can occupy both a *gauche* and *trans* position relative to the carbon atom under consideration, e.g., the *trans* (**1**) and *gauche* (**2**) forms of

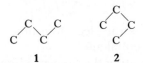

n-butane. Calculation of the atom population of the terminal carbon, using extended Hückel MO theory, shows that the terminal carbon atom of the *gauche* form is more shielded than in the *trans* form and thus causes a diamagnetic shift of the terminal carbon atom of n-butane. Sichel and Whitehead[20] have also shown that MO calculations for alkanes and halogenated-alkanes, while correlating well with the chemical shift of the substituted carbon atom, fails to correlate with the shifts of the adjacent carbon atoms. This defect was ascribed, by contrasting the EHMO and SCFLCAOMO methods, to the neglect of intra- and inter-orbital repulsion and the interatomic electrostatic interactions in the former method. The neglect of intra-orbital repulsion is responsible for the high bond polarities predicted by the EHT method, whereas the neglect of inter-orbital repulsions results in failure to predict inductive effects. It is therefore probable that charge distributions calculated by extended Hückel theory could be improved by making coulomb and resonance integrals depend upon molecular orbital charge distribution as is done in the SCFLCAOMO method.

Cheney and Grant,[21] using a valence bond treatment, have presented a somewhat different interpretation of ^{13}C chemical shifts in saturated hydrocarbons. The theory stresses that only changes in the immediate electronic environment of the ^{13}C nucleus can be expected to affect the chemical shifts. The availability of low-lying excited states will decrease the average excitation energy ΔE and cause shifts to low fields. Similarly, electron polarization affects the $\langle 1/r^3 \rangle$ value in the shielding expression. Enhancement of the paramagnetic term as a result of electron orbital contraction explains the downfield shift, due to steric crowding, at the β-carbon atom (see above). The steric polarization of electrons along the C—H bond accounts for remote substituent effects in the γ-position. Another important consideration is the effect of deviations from classical bond structure (perfect pairing).

Feeney et al. have used the electric-field theory to predict ^{19}F chemical shifts in various molecules.[22] The relation used was of the form—

$$\sigma_{\text{electric}} = -A\Delta E_z - B(\Delta E^2 + \Delta\langle E^2 \rangle)$$

where

$$\langle E^2 \rangle = \sum 3P_i I_i / r_i^6$$

p_i is the polarizability of the electron group
I_i is the ionization potential and
T_i is the distance separating the fluorine atom from the C–X grouping.

Application of the electric-field theory to ^{13}C chemical-shift calculations in compounds of the general type $^{13}CH_3CXYZ$ predicts shifts that are in good agreement with the experimentally determined values. The SCOBE (Self-Consistent group Orbital and Bond Electronegativity method) provides a useful method of evaluating charge distributions in simple alkyl chlorides.[23] The ^{13}C chemical shifts of chloromethanes are dependent on orbital charges, and a linear relationship of δ and the net electron charge at the carbon nucleus is found for these compounds.

The dependence of the ^{13}C chemical shifts on the π-electron charge density in aromatic molecules has frequently been observed. Karplus and Pople[24] showed that the magnetic shielding $\Delta\sigma_A$ (p.p.m. from benzene) of a ^{13}C nucleus (A) in a conjugated molecule is a function of the local charge density, ρ_A, the free valence, F_A, and the polarity of the C—H bonds, λ_H, and is given by the expression—

$$\Delta\sigma_A = (86\cdot7 + 46\cdot0\lambda_H)(\rho_A - 1) + 46\cdot0(F_A - 0\cdot399)$$

Application of this equation to some aromatic hydrocarbons affords ^{13}C chemical shifts in good agreement with experimental values.[25] Alger et al.[26] have extended this theory by inclusion of σ- as well as π-electron density terms. The ^{13}C chemical shifts in biphenyl, naphthalene, phenanthrene and pyrene all fall into a relatively narrow range of values ($-13\cdot0$ to $5\cdot5$ p.p.m. from benzene). The electronic environment of carbon atoms in various aromatic systems is therefore remarkably similar, and variations are minor compared to the total range of chemical shifts found for other classes of compounds.

The introduction of substituents into aromatic rings modifies the ground-state wave functions obtained by MO methods. Changes in electron distribution are reflected in ^{13}C chemical-shift values. The chemical shifts of carbon atoms *para* to the substituents show a linear correlation with π-electron density and lend support to the hypothesis that predicts that the ground state π-electron densities are largely determined by the π-inductive effects of the substituent groups (Fig. 1).[27] Calculations on fluorobenzene, chlorobenzene, aniline and

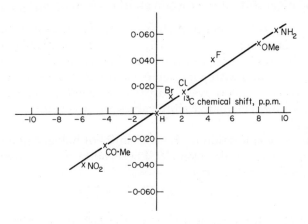

FIG. 1. Differences in π electron density, calculated by the "π inductive model", versus ^{13}C chemical shift of the *para* carbon in monosubstituted benzenes. (From Clark.[27])

phenol by the Parisier–Pople–Parr MO method, which includes both σ- and π-inductive effects, again confirms the dependence of the *para* [13]C shifts on π-electron charge densities.[28]

B. Aliphatic and alicyclic compounds

There has been considerable interest in the prediction of ^{13}C chemical shifts of derivatives of aliphatic compounds by the use of substituent parameters and other similar functions. The chemical shifts of simple unsubstituted hydrocarbons may be predicted using additivity relations,[29] although there are serious deviations from the constitutive additivity rule when the hydrocarbons are substituted by polar groupings. Savitsky et al.[30] have evaluated polar-bond contri-butions to the ^{13}C chemical shifts in various monosubstituted meth-anes. The deviation, D_X, from the constitutive rule, in p.p.m., for a given X in the series alkyl–X is given by—

$$D_X = n(1 \cdot 50 - d_X)22 \cdot 6$$

where n is the number of carbon atoms attached to the monosub-stituted α-carbon atom and d_X is the C—X bond distance. Using this relationship, the chemical shifts of the α-carbon atoms in C_2H_5X, i-C_3H_7X and t-C_4H_9X can be estimated to an accuracy of ± 3 p.p.m. for X=F, Cl, Br, I, OH, NO_2 and CO_2H. Malinowski et al.[31] have considered the so-called "pairwise-additivity" correlations in sub-stituted methane derivatives. The rule is perhaps unusually simple, and the chemical shift of the carbon atom is given by $\delta_{(1, 2, 3, 4)} = \sum_{i<j} \eta_{ij}$, where $\delta_{(1, 2, 3, 4)}$ is the chemical shift of the ^{13}C nucleus in a series of molecules containing substituents 1, 2, 3, 4 in chemically equivalent positions with respect to the nucleus. The term η_{ij} is an empirical parameter associated with parameters i and j, and is independent of all other substituents. There was a surprisingly good agreement between the observed and calculated shift values for a considerable range of compounds.

A recent reconsideration of the ^{13}C shifts of halogenated methanes $CH_{4-n}X_n$ has been undertaken.[32] These authors also found that a linear expression of the form—

$$\delta_{C^{13}}(m) = k + \sum_{i, v} p_i \delta_i + \sum p_{ij} \delta_{ij}$$

where $\delta_{C^{13}}(m)$ is the chemical shift of the mth halomethane, k is an arbitrary scale factor,

p_i and p_{ij} are population factors, and

δ_i and δ_{ij} are substituent factors corresponding to the direct effect of substituent i and to the interaction of the pair of groups i and j, respectively,

gave good agreement between the calculated and observed shift values. The authors consider these parameters in relation to charge polarization, the steric effect of the halogen substituents on the effective orbital radii and deviations from the classical bond structure.

Bucci[33] has attempted to correlate both the proton and the ^{13}C

shifts, in compounds of the type $(CH_3)_nM$ and $(CH_3CH_2)_nM$, where n is the valency of M, with the electronegativity and the number of lone pairs on M. The correlations of the observed shifts with those predicted by the relationship—

$$\delta = \delta_0 + aE + bm$$

where E is Pauling's electronegativity,
        m is the number of lone pairs of electrons on M
and δ_0, a and b are adjustable parameters,
are good, and it was suggested that the physical meaning of the above relationship was compatible with the electric field generated by the electric dipole moment of the lone pairs. It is evident from the above account that in simple hydrocarbon derivatives a reasonable prediction of the ^{13}C chemical shifts may be made.

The ^{13}C chemical shifts of polar molecules are frequently found to be solvent dependent. Becconsall and Hampson[13] have studied the solvent effects on the ^{13}C shifts of methyl iodide and acetonitrile. The results obtained from dilution studies in various solvents may be explained as arising from a reaction field around the solute molecules. The "spherical cavity" model due to Onsager was used to describe this effect, and this model was completely consistent with the experimental data when a modified value for the dielectric constant, ε, of the particular solvent was used.

The unusually large shielding of the ^{13}C nuclei of cyclopropane has been interpreted as the result of a diamagnetic ring current effect which originates from the peculiar hybridization of the three-membered ring system.[34] The chemical shifts of the ring carbon atoms are also influenced by substituents,[35] and Weiner and Malinowski[36] have demonstrated that the ^{13}C shift of the α-carbon atom of substituted cyclopropyl derivatives exhibits a linear correlation with the shift of the corresponding substituted methane.

The measurement of ^{13}C chemical shifts in alicyclic hydrocarbons also provides information regarding the conformational preference of substituted rings.[37, 38] The chemical shifts of the carbinol carbon atom (C-1) of *cis* and *trans* cyclohexyl systems, $4\text{-R}—C_6H_{10}—OR'$, differ substantially for each pair of isomers in the series (Table I).[37] The carbon atom having an axial oxygen substituent resonates about 5 p.p.m. to higher field and appears to be invarient of the substituent at C-4; thus a carbon atom with an equatorial hydroxy group has a shift of about 121·6, whereas that with an axial hydroxy is about 126·5 (p.p.m. from CS_2). This work has established the existence of substantial conformational effects on ^{13}C shieldings and would seem to

TABLE I

Carbinol carbon shieldings of some cyclohexyl systems of the form
cis **and** *trans* 4—R—C_6H_{10}—OR ′, **shifts given in p.p.m. from** CS_2

R	R ′	C—OR ′ Axial	C—OR ′ Equatorial	$\Delta\delta$ (i.e., $\delta_{ax} - \delta_{eq}$)
Bu^t	H	126·4	112·5	4·9
	Ac	123·6	119·6	4·0
	Me	117·5	112·6	4·9
Pr^i	H	..	121·8	..
	Ac	..	119·2	..
	Me	..	112·6	..
Me	H	..	121·4	..
	Ac	..	119·8	..
	Me	..	113·0	..

From Burke and Lauterbur.[34]

afford the basis of several useful chemical applications. For example, from the ^{13}C shift data, cyclohexanol exists in the equatorial form to the extent of 74%, which corresponds to a conformational equilibrium constant of ~2·8 and a $-\Delta G°$ value of 0·6 kcal./mole, values that are in good agreement with those obtained from other methods.

Dalling and Grant[38] have extended this type of study in an extensive paper on the ^{13}C shifts of methyl substituted cyclohexanes. The ^{13}C shifts of a large number of substituted cyclohexanes were measured by using the technique of simultaneous proton decoupling to give enhanced sensitivity of the ^{13}C resonance signals. Spectral assignments were made with the aid of additivity parameters, derived from compounds in the series studied where unequivocal assignments were possible, and refined substituent parameters determined for various carbon centres. Some useful ^{13}C shift correlations begin to emerge from the work; for example—

Equatorial methyl groups $105·6 \pm 0·3$ p.p.m. from C_6H_6
Carbon atom α to a methyl group $95·7 \pm 0·3$
Carbon atom β to a methyl group $92·4 \pm 0·4$
Carbon atom β to two methyl groups $83·9 \pm 0·5$
Carbon atom further removed from methyl group $101·9 \pm 0·3$ (this latter value compares with the shift in cyclohexane of 101·44 p.p.m.)

The results obtained for 1,1,2-trimethylcyclohexane are of interest. The sizeable deviation of the predicted and observed ^{13}C shift data, and the observation that the proton resonance of the ring methylene groups is a single peak indicates that the compound does not exist in either of the two chair forms (**3** and **4**). The data is consistent with contribution from conformational structures such as the skew boat form (**5**).

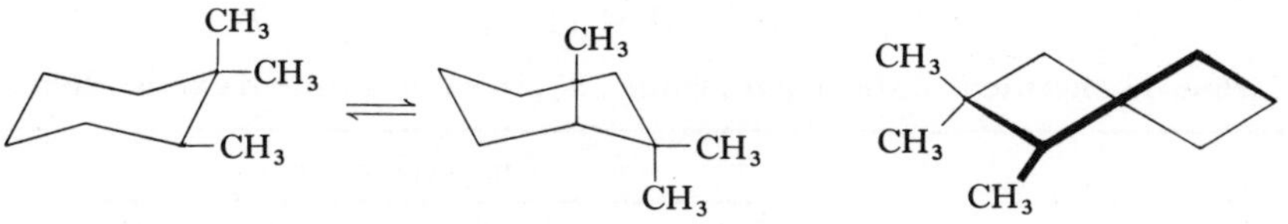

and the observation that the proton resonance of the ring methylene

Carbon-13 n.m.r. is therefore clearly a useful tool for the study of conformational analysis and is now established as a source of information in the molecular geometry of alicyclic rings.

C. Acyclic and cyclic olefins and acetylenes

Maciel[39] has presented ^{13}C shift data for the vinyl carbon atoms in the system $H_2C_\beta{=}C_\alpha HX$. Comparison of the shift values, allowing for neighbouring anisotropy effects, show that there is an approximately linear relationship between δC_α and the corresponding ^{13}C shifts of the substituted carbon atom and between δC_β and the corresponding *ortho* carbon shifts of monosubstituted aromatics (C_6H_5X). Deviations from these relationships are found for the acetyl and carboethoxy-substituents, which may be related to differences in the relative importance of the canonical structures in these particular compounds.

The chemical shift of the β-carbon atom is sensitive to the introduction of substituents into the *meta* and *para* positions of the aromatic ring of styrenes[40] and the shifts are dependent upon the polar characteristics of the substituent groups. The sensitivity of the ^{13}C resonance of the β-carbon is due to the effect of resonance contributions of the type (**6**). The β carbon atom is situated at the end of the resonance

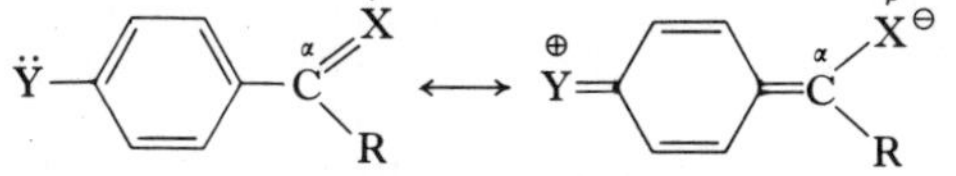

system when the substituent Y is either electron attracting or releasing. The behaviour of the β-carbon chemical shift of *ortho* substituted styrenes and certain α, β-unsaturated ketones[41] reflects the steric inhibition of resonance with the adjacent unsaturated centres in these compounds.

Carbon-13 n.m.r. studies may be used to investigate strain effects in cyclic olefins.[42] The values of the ^{13}C chemical shifts in some strained cyclic olefins are shown in Table II.

TABLE II

Carbon-13 chemical shifts, p.p.m. from CS_2, in some strained cyclic olefins

	Chemical shift			
	—CH_2	—CH_2—C=	C—H	—HC=
Cyclo-octane	166	..	..	..
Cyclo-octatetrene	..	..	..	61
Cyclo-octa-1,5-diene	..	164	..	64
cis-Cyclo-octene	167	..	..	63
trans-Cyclo-octene	157	..	..	59
trans, trans, as- Dodecatriene }	..	160	..	63
Norbornene	160,† 140‡	..	148	56
Bicyclpentadiene	140, 150‡	155	145	59
Norbornadiene	119	..	141	49

† 2,3 carbon.   ‡ 7 carbon. From Maciel.[39]

Unequivocal ^{13}C assignments for the α- and β-carbon resonances are possible for hex-1-yne derivatives[43] due to the doublet structure arising from coupling of both carbon atoms to the acetylenic proton.

TABLE III

Carbon-13 chemical shifts of the acetylenic carbons in 1-substituted hexynes, p.p.m.

$$n\text{-}C_4H_9\overset{\beta}{—}\overset{\alpha}{C}\equiv C—X$$

X	$\delta^{13}C_\alpha$	$\delta^{13}C_\beta$
H	123·7	108·0
CH_3	(115·4)	(112·0)
Cl	137·0	124·9
Br	155·3	113·9
I	197·0	96·9
$COCH_3$	106·7	96·3
C_6H_5—	110·6	101·7
n-$C_4H_9C\equiv C$—	125·7	115·0

Values given in parentheses are tentative assignments, and may be reversed.

Coupling also occurs between β-carbon and the alkyl fragment; this broadening of the β-resonance is sufficient to assign both ^{13}C acetylenic signals for 1-substituted hexynes. The shifts of the α-acetylenic carbon atoms covered a range of some 90 p.p.m. whereas that of the β-carbon atoms was only 26 p.p.m. (Table III). The shifts of the acetylenic carbon atoms did not correlate with inductive effects, and the authors ascribed the general pattern of shifts to anisotropy effects arising from the pseudo linearity of the systems.

D. Ketones, aldehydes, acids and their derivatives

In general, the carbonyl carbon nucleus resonates at low field, in regions free from interference from other absorptions and is uncoupled. Measurement of the carbonyl group ^{13}C chemical shifts has been a particularly fruitful method for gaining information about the electronic structural features of this polar grouping.

Maciel et al.[44] have observed an isotope effect of -0.28 p.p.m. on the ^{13}C chemical shift of the carbonyl group in acetone-d_6 with respect to that of the carbonyl shift of acetone. The authors discuss the results in terms of vibrational zero-point energies, and in addition the paper describes a useful method of observing ^{13}C resonances using a direct ^{13}C field–frequency lock system.

Many workers have been prompted, because of the abundance of ^{13}C shifts of the carbonyl carbon atom, to study the factors that affect this parameter in the polar $>C{=}O$ grouping. Maciel[45] has considered the origin of ^{13}C carbonyl shifts in compounds of the general type X.CO.Y in terms of the Karplus and Pople theory for the local paramagnetic contribution δ_p. If the following assumptions are made—

(i) that there is an invariant sigma electron network;
(ii) a constant average excitation energy, ΔE;
(iii) that neighbouring anisotropy and intermolecular dispersion forces may be neglected;

then a formula may be derived relating the ^{13}C chemical shift to the polarity of the carbonyl π-bond. If the ^{13}C carbonyl shifts are further corrected for factors (i) and (iii) above, by a strict comparison with the ^{13}C shifts in symmetrical disubstituted ethylenes, then a correlation of the "corrected" carbonyl shifts with both the C=O π-bond polarity and the substituent parameters is found. The experimental data were additionally found to correlate with Tafts' reactivity parameter σ_I, which is in agreement with the interpretation that the substituents determine the π-bond polarity of the carbonyl group.

Low field ^{13}C carbonyl shifts are generally observed in simple five-membered ring compounds and apparently are not dependent on the ring strain.[46] However, in contrast to the above discussion, variations in the average excitation energy ΔE appear to be significant, and a linear correlation between the ^{13}C carbonyl shifts of some cyclic and bicyclic ketones and the $n \rightarrow \pi^*$ transitions of the carbonyl group have been established. The behaviour of ^{13}C chemical shifts in fused ring ketones (**7–10**) is somewhat different (Table IV). The high-field shift

TABLE IV

Carbonyl carbon chemical shifts, p.p.m. from CS_2 and the $n \rightarrow \pi^*$ absorption of some bicyclic compounds

Compound		Shift	$n \rightarrow \pi^*(\lambda_{max})$
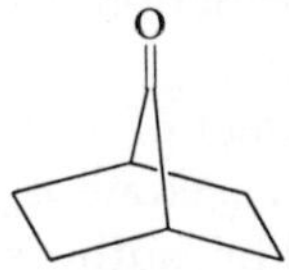	**7**	$-21\cdot5$	293
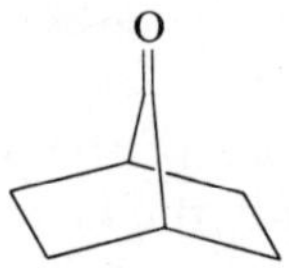	**8**	$-11\cdot5$	274
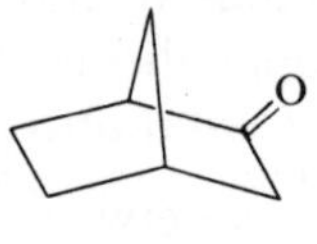	**9**	$-22\cdot4$	293
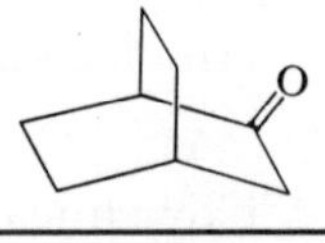	**10**	$-20\cdot0$	298

of (**8**) is due to the strained geometry of the rings, since interaction between the carbonyl π-system and the carbon–carbon double bond π-system is precluded owing to the orthogonality of the two orbital systems.

Conjugation of the carbonyl group with the electrons of the cyclopropyl ring is evident from the ^{13}C shifts of aliphatic and alicyclic ketones that have a three-membered ring α to the carbonyl group.[47]

Similarily conjugation of π-electrons of olefins with the carbonyl bonds have an important effect on the ^{13}C carbonyl resonances of α,β-unsaturated ketones. High-field shifts are observed when there is facile conjugation, whereas steric interference to coplanarity of the carbonyl group results in loss of orbital interaction, with a resultant downfield resonance of the carbonyl carbon resonance. The ^{13}C chemical shifts of the carbonyl group of ortho-substituted acetophenones[48] are also indicative of the existence of steric inhibition to conjugation, and it has been suggested that the value of the carbonyl carbon resonance (Table V) will directly reflect the degree of steric interference in similar ketones[49] and in methyl benzoates.[50] The ^{13}C carbonyl shifts of methyl aryl ketones[49] having polycyclic aryl groups indicate that there is steric interaction between the acetyl group and the

TABLE V

Carbonyl ^{13}C shifts of acetophenones (11), alkyl phenyl ketones (12) and methyl benzoates (13), p.p.m. from CS_2

Substituent, X	11	12			13
		$R'=Et$	$R'=Pr^i$	$R'=Bu^t$	
H	−3·2	−5·6	−10·3	−14·4	26·9
o-Me	−6·5	−9·7	−13·9	−19·2	26·5
m-Me	−2·7	..	..	..	27·2
p-Me	−3·2	..	..	..	27·5
o-OMe	−5·0	..	..	..	..
m-OMe	−3·3	..	..	..	..
p-OMe	−2·9	−4·7	−8·5	−11·0	27·2
o-NO$_2$	−5·5	..	..	..	28·4
m-NO$_2$	−2·8	..	..	..	..
p-NO$_2$	−3·3	..	..	..	27·6
2,3-Me$_2$	−7·8	..	..	..	25·7
2,6-Me$_2$	−12·9	..	..	..	23·6
2,4,6-Me$_3$	−13·4	−15·0	−18·2	−23·0	24·0
2,3,5,6-Me$_4$	−14·2	−16·7	−19·8	..	..
2,3,4,5,6-Me$_5$	−14·1	−16·9	−20·1	..	..
o-Pr^i	−8·0	..	..	..	..
p-Pr^i	−3·4	..	..	..	..
2,6-Pr$^i_2$	−13·5	..	..	..	..
2,4,6-Pr$^i_3$	−13·8	−16·3	−19·5	..	..
o-OH	−11·6	..	..	..	..
p-OH	−4·6	..	..	..	..
2,6-(OH)$_2$	−12·0	..	..	..	..
2,4-(OH)$_2$	−10·1	..	..	..	..

aromatic ring system in those cases in which the *peri* hydrogen atoms could interfere with the rotation of the acetyl group, e.g., 1-naphthyl-, 9-phenanthryl- and 9-anthranyl-methyl ketones. Estimates may be made of the angle of twist, θ, for some of the hindered ketones.

Carbon-13 shifts, measured by the double-resonance technique, of the carbonyl group of *meta*-substituted benzaldehydes correlate with Hammetts' σ_m parameter.[15] In the case of the *para*-substituted benzaldehydes, there was no correlation between the ^{13}C chemical shift and σ_p, presumably because, in contrast to substituted benzenes, resonance contributions for both electron-attracting and releasing groups will not significantly affect the electron density at the carbonyl carbon.

Solvent effects on ^{13}C carbonyl chemical shifts are related to the polarity of the carbonyl π-bond as determined by hydrogen bonding, polar and van der Waals effects of the solvents.[51] The former is frequently the predominant effect, especially in solvents containing a hydrogen that is capable of hydrogen bonding. The sensitivity of the ^{13}C carbonyl shifts to solvent effects is decreased on replacing the alkyl group by the trichloromethyl, CCl_3, group or by an alkoxy group which probably reflects a decrease in the basicity of the carbonyl group. The influence of the above effects on ^{13}C chemical shifts of the carbonyl group are well illustrated from a study[52] of the carbonyl resonances of acetic acid in various solvents at differing concentrations (Fig. 2). In cyclohexane solution, the insensitivity of the carbonyl shift on dilution shows that hydrogen bonding is important over all the

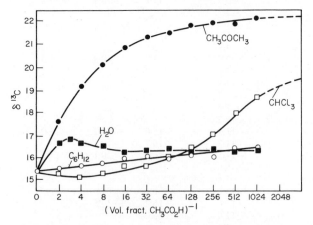

FIG. 2. Concentration and solvent dependence of the ^{13}C shifts of [*carboxy*-^{13}C]-acetic acid in: ●, acetone; ■, water; ○, cyclohexane; □, chloroform. (From Maciel and Traficante.[52])

concentration range. Thus the acid exists as a dimer in both the liquid state and in solution with non-polar solvents. Acetone has a basic centre but no acidic proton, and thus at lower concentrations in this solvent the equilibrium (i) is forced to the right. In chloroform,

$$
CH_3-C\underset{O-H\cdots O}{\overset{O\cdots H-O}{<}}C-CH_3 + O{=}C\underset{CH_3}{\overset{CH_3}{<}} \rightleftharpoons CH_3-C\underset{O-H\cdots O=C}{\overset{O}{<}}CH_3 \quad (i)
$$

which is a weak proton donor, it is apparent that, at infinite dilution some chloroform-bonded acid and some acetic acid dimer co-exist. At low concentrations of the acid in water, there is the possibility of the formation of two hydrogen bonds to the carbonyl and carboxyl centres. This possibility is reflected by the similarity of the chemical shifts at infinite dilution in both cyclohexane and water.

The nature of the species present in solutions of carboxylic acids in strong acidic media has been the subject of several investigations, and ^{13}C resonance studies have been used in this work.[53-56] Maciel and Traficante[53,54] have studied the ^{13}C n.m.r. of the carbonyl group of acetic and benzoic acids and their ethyl esters in solutions of fuming sulphuric acid and in concentrated sulphuric acid. In concentrated sulphuric acid the principal organic species formed is the carbonyl protonated cation $R—\overset{\oplus}{C}OH—OH$. Freshly prepared solutions of the esters show the corresponding protonated cation $R—\overset{\oplus}{C}OH—OC_2H_5$ to be present, but this slowly hydrolyses on standing to $R—\overset{\oplus}{C}OH—OH$. As the concentration of sulphur trioxide is increased, the equilibrium—

$$
R—\overset{\oplus}{C}(OH)_2 + SO_3 \rightleftharpoons R—\overset{\oplus}{C}{=}O + H_2SO_4
$$

is forced to the right, and the concentration of the acylium cation in solution increases. Protonated acids (carboxonium ions) and acyl cations may also be generated by use of antimony pentafluoride, hydrogen fluoride or FSO_3H/SbF_5 solutions,[55,56] thus confirming the pattern of molecular decomposition of acids in strongly protonated media.

E. Cyanides, isocyanides, etc.

The ^{13}C chemical shifts of simple alkyl cyanides, isocyanides, isocyanates and isothiocyanates may be divided into two distinct groups.[57]

Firstly, a group consisting of carbon monoxide, the cyanide ion and alkyl isocyanides, which exhibit ^{13}C chemical shifts in the range 12–37 p.p.m., and secondly a group made up of carbon dioxide, alkyl cyanides, isothiocyanates and the cyanate and thiocyanate ions with ^{13}C chemical shifts in the range 55–76 p.p.m. (from CS_2). The groupings reflect similarities between the valence bond description of each set of compounds with their "parent" molecules, carbon monoxide and carbon dioxide.

F. Aromatic compounds

The ^{13}C resonance of aromatic compounds has been extensively studied,[1,2,3] and factors influencing both the chemical shifts and coupling constants have been investigated.

LaLanchette and Benson[58] have used the characteristic ^{13}C chemical-shift values of aromatic compounds to confirm that the ten π-electron system cyclononatetraenide possesses aromatic character.

The methyl–[13]C chemical shifts of methylbenzenes have been measured using proton decoupling,[59] and attention has been drawn to empirical correlations between shifts and the conformational features of the molecules.[59,60] Three *ortho*-substituent parameters were given together with other additive parameters for *m*- and *p*-methyl groups that reflect hyperconjugative effects. The *p*-^{13}C chemical shifts (δC_p) of several monosubstituted benzenes are linearly related to the total π-electron density at the *para* position.[62] Furthermore, the corrected shifts ($\delta C_p - \delta C_m$) are linearly related to *p*-carbon π-electron density due to resonance interaction with the substituent. These conclusions, based on comparisons with ^{19}F studies in similar compounds, indicate that both ^{13}C shifts in monosubstituted benzenes and ^{19}F shifts of *para*-substituted fluorobenzenes are useful parameters for determining the π-electron density at the *p*-carbon atoms.

Another application of *p*-^{13}C chemical shifts is in the estimation of the effects of twist in substituted acetophenones.[48] In general, the combined substituent effects on the *m*- and *p*-carbon nuclei of substituted acetophenones are additive. However for the 2-mono- and 2,6-di-substituted acetophenones deviations from additivity occur due to twisting with the resultant steric inhibition to conjugation which is reflected in the ^{13}C shifts of the *p*-carbon nuclei. The observed variation of the acetyl methyl shieldings appear to indicate the extent of steric interference of the *ortho*-substituents with the acetyl group (see also effects on the carbonyl ^{13}C-shifts p. 167). Similar trends are observed[49] for alkyl phenyl ketones in which the α-carbon nuclei of the alkyl groups are deshielded and the β-carbons shielded relative to the corresponding alkyl benzenes. The fact that α-carbons are shifted to lower field with increasing *ortho*-substitution in the aromatic ring is consistent with the existence of steric interference to coplanarity of the carbonyl group. Steric inhibition of resonance in substituted methyl benzoates,[50] styrenes[40] and anisoles[61] is also reflected in the shielding of the aromatic carbon nuclei, and the magnitude is directly related to the bulk of the substituent group(s). Conjugation of the methoxy-group of anisoles with the aromatic ring is operative in *ortho*-substituted derivatives, although there may be only one planar conformation (14) where it may be appreciable. In the case of the 2,6-disubstituted anisoles the *p*-carbon resonates at lower field than is expected

14

indicating steric interference of the *ortho*-groups with the methoxy-group such that delocalization of the electrons from the methoxyl oxygen atom is reduced. Confirmation of these results is provided by the value of the molar extinction coefficient of the 260–270 nm. absorption bonds.

G. Heterocyclic compounds

Carbon-13 chemical shifts have been reported for compounds of the general type $X-(CH_2)_n$ with $n = 2, 3, 4$ and 5 for $X = O$ or S and with $n = 2, 3, 4, 5$ or 6 for $X = NMe$ (Table VI).[35] In each series the

TABLE VI

Carbon-13 chemical shifts, p.p.m. from CS_2, of compounds of the type $-X-(CH_2)_n-$

	$X = CH_2$	$X = O$			$X = S$			$X = NCH_3$			
n	δC	δC_α	δC_β	δC_γ	δC_α	δC_β	δC_γ	δC_α	δC_β	δC_γ	δNCH_3
2	196·3	154·0	..	..	174·8	..	..	165·0	..	..	144·9
3	170·4	120·9	170·6	..	166·0	163·8	..	135·8	176·0	..	147·1
4	167·2	125·1	167·0	..	161·0†	161·0†	..	136·8	169·1	..	150·8
5	165·9	124·0	165·8	168·6	164·1‡	164·1‡	164·1‡	136·3	167·1	167·1	145·8
6	164·7	..	..	..	..	..	..	134·6	165·0	165·0	145·5

The subscripts α, β and γ refer to positions relative to the heteroatom.
† Reliable only to ± 1 p.p.m.   ‡ Reliable only to $\pm 2·5$ p.p.m.

largest shielding for the carbon atom adjacent to the heteroatom occurs when $n = 2$, in agreement with the behaviour of cyclopropanes in which the presence of a large ring current has been postulated to account for the large positive ^{13}C and proton shifts in the parent cyclopropane.

Page et al.[63] have measured the ^{13}C n.m.r. of furan, pyrrole, thiophen and some of their methyl derivatives, and the range of ^{13}C chemical shifts confirms the aromaticity of the molecules. Substituent parameters were obtained for the methyl groups and the linearity of the plot of the ^{13}C versus the proton chemical shifts implies that similar shielding effects are operative for both nuclei (Fig. 3), but the scatter of the points suggested that σ-bond charge distributions are important.

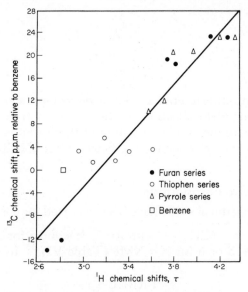

FIG. 3. Plot of ^{13}C chemical shifts (in p.p.m. from benzene), of the ring carbon atoms of heterocyclics, against the chemical shift of the attached proton (in τ values). (From Page et al.[63])

Values of the ^{13}C shifts of some 4-substituted pyridines are shown in Table VII.[64] Substituent effects were generally within ± 3 p.p.m. of those found in the corresponding monosubstituted benzenes, and therefore suggested similar shielding mechanisms for the two classes of compounds. This hypothesis receives support in a more recent study of 2-substituted pyridines.[65] The ^{13}C shift of C_5 is directly dependent upon the σ_p parameters of the 2-substituent and consequently the shielding mechanisms for carbon atoms para to substituents are similar for both the pyridine and benzene systems.

TABLE VII
Carbon-13 chemical shifts, p.p.m. from CS_2, of 4-substituted pyridines

Substituent	Aromatic carbons			Other groups	
	CH-2 and 6	CH-3 and 5	C-4		
H	43·1	69·2	57·3	..	..
NH_2	44·1	83·9	37·4	..	..
Br	41·9	65·9	60·3	..	..
CH_3	43·6	67·9	46·0	(CH_3)	172·2
CH_2CH_3	43·9	70·6	41·4	(CH_2)	165·4
				(CH_3)	179·8
$CH(CH_3)_2$	42·7	71·0	35·9	(CH)	159·7
				(CH_3)	170·1
$C(CH_3)_3$	43·0	72·6	33·9	(C)	158·6
				(CH_3)	162·7
$CH{=}CH_2$	42·8	72·3	48·7	(vinyl CH)	58·2
				(vinyl CH_2)	74·8
CN	42·2	67·0	72·8	(CN)	76·2
$COCH_3$	42·3	71·8	50·6	(C=O)	−4·1
				(CH_3)	166·8
CHO	42·2	70·9	51·8	(C=O)	1·0

Lauterbur[66] has presented values for the ^{13}C chemical shifts of six known azines and some of their methyl derivatives. Calculated π-electron densities have been used in conjunction with the Karplus–Pople theory to predict chemical shifts in the azines with reasonable agreement with experiment. Evidence for σ–π interaction and inductive effects are considered.

Mathias and Gil[14] have attempted to explain the observed high-field shifts of the ^{13}C signals of protonated azines as arising from one of two effects. Either a decrease of the paramagnetic term in Ramseys equation, or a change in bond order of the C_α—C_β bond, results in extra shielding. Parameters, obtained by regressional analysis, may be used to correlate ^{13}C chemical shifts of protonated diazines with those of unprotonated heterocycles.[67] The upfield chemical shifts found in the protonated species may be estimated using extended Hückel MO techniques considering both σ- and π-electron contributions.[67, 68]

By use of both deuterated compounds and proton-spin decoupling, the ^{13}C resonance spectrum of purine has been analysed.[69] A correlation of the ^{13}C data with the theoretical estimates of charge distribution was found in purine, although σ polarization effects may be important especially for the carbon atoms 2 and 8 centred between two nitrogen atoms (15).

Very recently a brief report of the ^{13}C shifts of pyrazole and some three of its derivatives have been reported;[70] the shifts were obtained by direct observation using CAT facilities. These authors state that no correlation between the shifts and the calculated π-electron densities was found.

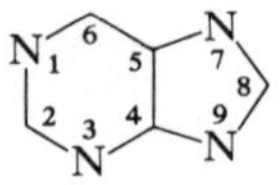

15

H. Organometallic compounds

The ^{13}C shifts of some organolithium compounds have been compared to their parent hydrocarbons, and in each case there is a downfield shift of the α-carbon of the lithium derivative.[71] The downfield shift indicates that extensive rehybridization had occurred at the α-carbon atom. However, opposing this downfield shift there is a shielding contribution that is proportional to the negative charge on the α-carbon atoms; consequently the shifts to low field in the phenyl-methyl series are variable (Table VIII).

TABLE VIII

Carbon-13 chemical shifts, in p.p.m. from CS_2, of the α carbon of phenylmethanes and the lithio-derivatives

	Chemical Shifts	
	X = H	X = Li
$(C_6H_5)_3CX$	+132	+102
$(C_6H_5)_2CHX$	+157	+114
$C_6H_5CH_2X$	+172	+163

Roberts et al.,[72] using a specially constructed spectrometer for ^{13}C resonance measurements, have recorded the ^{13}C chemical shifts, and the relevant coupling constants, of both Group II and Group IV metal alkyls; these results are shown in Table IX.

A linear relationship has been found[73] to exist between ^{13}C shifts of alkanes and the ^{11}B shifts of isoelectronic boron–nitrogen compounds. A least-squares analysis of the available data shows that the ^{13}C chemical shifts may be related to those of ^{11}B in the isoelectronic compounds by the expression—

$$\delta_{13C} = 1 \cdot 44 \delta_{11B} + 86 \cdot 0 \quad \text{(p.p.m. from benzene)}$$

TABLE IX

Carbon-13 parameters of the di- and tetra-methyl derivatives of group II and group IV

	Chemical shift of the methyl group, p.p.m. from CS_2	$J_{^{13}C-M}$, c./sec.	$J_{^{13}C-M-C-^1H}$, c./sec.	$J_{^{13}C-^1H}$, c./sec.
Zn	197·0	..	..	121·6
Cd	191·8	512 (^{111}Cd)	..	126·6
		537·5 (^{113}Cd)		
Hg	169·3	690	1·74	129·6
C	161·4	36·2±1	4·8	124·3
	164·9 (central atom)			
Si	193·0	51	2·1	118·2
Ge	193·6	..	1·9	124·4
Sn	202·1	330±5	1·3	127·7
Pb	196·2	250	1·05	134·2

The correlation was found to be valid for aminoboranes, R_3BNR_3', di-borazanes $H_3BNMe_2BH_2NR_3'$ and cycloborazane $(H_2BNH_2)_2$, where R and R' = H or alkyl.

Retcofsky and Griffin[74] have outlined a method for determining Hammett substituent constants from ^{13}C chemical shift values in phenylphosphorus compounds (Table X). The values of the Hammett functions σ_p and σ_p^+, obtained from the p-^{13}C shieldings show that generally the substituents -PZ_n are weak acceptors.

TABLE X

^{13}C chemical shifts, p.p.m. from CS_2, and the chemical-reactivity parameters for the phenylphosphines $C_6H_5(PZ_n)$

—PZ_n	p-^{13}C shift	σ_p	σ_p^+
—$P(C_6H_5)_2$	59·1	0·68	0·70
—PCl_2	60·1	0·61	0·62
—$P(O)(OC_2H_5)_2$	61·0	0·55	0·54
—$P(O)(C_6H_5)_2$	61·2	0·53	0·52
—$P(Cl)C_6H_5$	62·5	0·44	0·40
—$P(O)Cl_2$	62·7	0·43	0·38
—$P(S)Cl_2$	63·2	0·39	0·33
—$P(OC_2H_5)_2$	64·0	0·33	0·24
—$P(OC_2H_5)C_6H_5$	64·1	0·32	0·23
—$OP(O)(OCH_3)_2$	67·8	0·04	—0·21

The ^{13}C resonance data of metal carbonyl and cyclopentadienyl compounds have been of considerable use in elucidating the nature of these compounds.[75,76] The ^{13}C chemical shifts of irontricarbonyl compounds are shown in Table XI; this data is interpreted[75] as

TABLE XI

Carbon-13 chemical shifts of diene–irontricarbonyl complexes

Diene	Chemical shifts, p.p.m.			Ref.
	C=O	$C_{1,4}$	$C_{2,3}$	
Cyclobutadiene	$-16\cdot2\pm1$	$131\cdot8\pm1$	$131\cdot8\pm1$	74
Butadiene	-16 ± 5	157 ± 5	112 ± 5	74
	$-18\cdot9$	$151\cdot7$	$107\cdot0$	73
Methyl octadecadienoate	..	~129	~108	73

favouring structure (16) rather than (17), since all four carbon atoms have sp^2 characteristics. This conclusion is in agreement with that of Preston and Davis,[76] who, from the magnitude of the $^{13}C–^{1}H$ couplings decided that there was interaction of the iron d orbitals with the

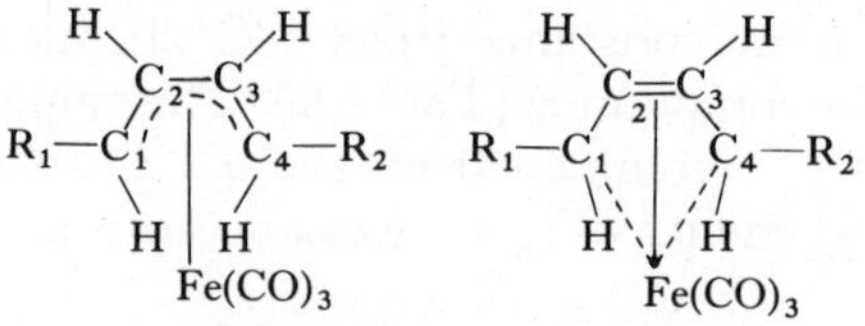

π-electrons rather than formation of Fe—C bonds. A linear correlation between the ^{13}C and the proton chemical shifts has been found[77] for transition metal cyclopentadienyl and carbonyl derivatives, and is colinear with a similar correlation for aromatic compounds. Since the variation in the carbon and hydrogen shieldings in aromatic rings appears to be dependent on local charges, the same explanation would pertain to the cyclopentadienyl systems.

IV. NUCLEAR SPIN–SPIN COUPLING INVOLVING CARBON-13

A. Theoretical considerations

The data available on $^{13}C–^{1}H$ and $^{13}C–F$ coupling constants are more prolific, since these couplings may be measured directly from the more sensitive ^{1}H and ^{19}F resonance spectra. Additionally the availability of CATs has meant that the better signal to noise obtained has greatly assisted in the analysis of the ^{13}C satellite spectra. This in turn has led to the ^{13}C satellite spectra being used to assist in the analysis of the proton or fluorine spectra, especially in those instances where magnetic equivalence is found, as well as being used in structural determination and the study of substituent effects.

The application of quantum mechanical theories to the prediction of the magnitude and sign of coupling involving ^{13}C is now well established. Hiroike[78] has investigated the ^{13}C–^{1}H coupling in hydrocarbons on a theoretical basis. The electron correlation effect on the magnitude of the coupling constants was estimated semi-empirically. The results obtained showed that the coupling constant was inversely proportional to the valence number of the ^{13}C atom and is almost unaffected by substituents at the end of the carbon chain, provided the symmetry is not altered. The general utility of this type of calculation is very limited, and most investigations in this field have used VB or MO methods as the bases for calculation. Yonezawa et al.[79, 80] have used an extended HMO treatment to interpret directly bonded ^{13}C–H coupling constants in both saturated and conjugated molecules. The effect of neighbouring atoms on the coupling constants was taken into account by the use of delocalized molecular orbitals obtained by linear combination of valence atomic orbitals of all the atoms in the molecule. With the added assumption of an average excitation energy, ΔE, the observed values of $J_{^{13}C-^1H}$ were shown to be proportional to the square of the bond order between the 1s atomic orbitals of the hydrogen atom and the 2s orbital of the carbon atom.

The Pople–Santry MO theory[81] of spin–spin coupling constants has found general applicability, since it is capable of predicting the correct signs for long-range couplings. The results obtained by extension of this theory to include orbital overlap are in semi-quantitative agreement with experiment for most types of bonding.[82] For coupling through two bonds, both $J_{^1H-^1H}$ and $J_{^{13}C-^1H}$ are calculated to be negative for saturated hydrocarbons, which is in agreement with experiment. Calculations on hydrocarbons, e.g., CH_4, C_2H_4 and C_2H_2, have suggested that the Pople–Santry theory may overestimate the delocalization in the bonds;[83] the ^{13}C–^{13}C coupling constants calculated for ethylene and acetylene were in reasonable agreement with the observed values. Cowley et al.[84] have shown that EHMO calculations, with complete neglect of differential overlap, are capable of predicting the correct signs for $J_{^{13}C-^1H}$ and $J_{^{13}C-^{19}F}$ in methane and tetrafluoromethane, respectively. The discrepancies between the calculated and observed magnitudes of the coupling constants are however quite large. Murrell *et al.*[85] have further modified the Pople–Santry theory by using the Mulliken-type approximation for evaluating resonance integrals. Small contributions due to orbital and dipolar, as well as the Fermi contact term, were required to improve the agreement between observed and calculated $^{13}C-^{19}F$ couplings in fluoromethanes. Another modification of the Pople–Santry expression, in which the electronegativity of the substituent is introduced by means of the Coulomb integral, has been found to predict satisfactorily the effects of substituents on the $^{13}C-^{1}H$ coupling constants in methane and on the $^{29}Si-^{1}H$ couplings in silane.[86, 87]

The Alternant Molecular Orbital Method (AMO) has been used by Barfield[88] to determine the spin-coupling parameters in alternant systems of $2n$ electrons. For a singlet-state molecular system, the density of spin coupling is proportional to the difference between correlation functions for electrons of same and opposite sign. In the case of directly bonded systems of two electrons, correlations between electrons of antiparallel spins make a significant contribution to the coupling constant. The prediction of negative geminal $^{13}C-^{1}H$ and $^{1}H-^{1}H$ couplings, inherent in the AMO method, may be attributed to the importance of long-range spin correlations.

B. Determination of the signs of carbon-13 coupling constants

Indirect nuclear spin–spin couplings arise from magnetic interactions between nuclei and electrons, and are intrinsic properties of molecules and independent of the n.m.r. experiment. Since theoretical calculations of nuclear spin couplings describe both the magnitude and sign of the interaction, the experimental determination of the signs of coupling will provide information relevant to theories of the electronic structure of molecules. The absolute signs of indirect nuclear spin coupling constants are generally only directly obtained from the n.m.r. spectra of partially orientated molecules, although they may be obtained by consideration of relaxation effects in suitable systems. Relative signs of coupling constants are however more amenable to experimental methods—

   (*i*) Analysis of strongly coupled spectra;
   (*ii*) Double-resonance techniques.

Double resonance "tickling" techniques have been widely used to determine signs of couplings involving ^{13}C. Comprehensive treatments of the theory and experimentation of magnetic double resonance have been given by Baldeschwieler and Randall,[89] Hoffman and Forsen[90] and McFarlane.[17]

The prediction of Karplus and Grant[91] that the ^{13}C–^{1}H coupling constant is absolutely positive has been used by many workers to obtain absolute values for other couplings whose relative signs were known. Bernheim and Lavery[92] have recently confirmed that the prediction is in fact correct by using methyl fluoride partially orientated in liquid crystal solvents. The direct nuclear magnetic dipole–dipole interaction observed in the n.m.r. spectrum confirmed that $J_{^{13}C-^{1}H}$ is positive and $J_{^{13}C-^{19}F}$ is negative, in agreement with theory. Dipole–dipole interaction between protons and ^{13}C in the n.m.r. spectrum of tetramethylsilane oriented by nematic crystal solvents confirms[93] that $J_{^{13}C-^{1}H}$ is positive and is 124·1 c./sec. at 75°C. The value of the ^{13}C–^{1}H coupling constant, at the same temperature, in neopentane was found to be +130·3 c./sec.

Extensive use has been made of the double-resonance technique for determining couplings involving ^{13}C. McLauchlan has shown that both ^{13}C–^{13}C and ^{13}C–^{1}H couplings are both of the same sign in doubly ^{13}C enriched methyl cyanide.[94] The directly bonded ^{13}C–^{13}C coupling ($J_{^{13}C-^{13}C} = 57·6$ c./sec.) may be observed in partially enriched acetic acid by CAT-accumulated scans of the ^{13}C resonance spectrum with simultaneous proton decoupling.[95] The absolute sign of $J_{^{13}C-^{13}C}$ is positive, which indicates that the Fermi contact term dominates the coupling. Using ^{15}N substituted methyl cyanide, heteronuclear "tickling" of ^{15}N and ^{13}C satellite spectra indicates that the sign of the reduced $-^{13}$C≡^{15}N coupling constant is positive.[96] Similar experiments on ^{13}C enriched acetonitrile have confirmed that values obtained for other couplings in the molecule are self consistent. The reduced coupling constants between the singly bonded nitrogen and carbon in methyl isocyanide is also positive;[97] the results are summarized in Table XII. The ^{13}C–^{29}Si coupling constant, determined by heteronuclear "tickling" involving ^{13}C and ^{29}Si satellites, is negative, i.e., opposite in sign to $J_{^{13}C-^{1}H}$.[98, 99] Vicinal coupling of the type $^{13}C-Si-C-H$ could give rise to inner satellites in the proton spectrum, but this was shown to be of very small magnitude, less than 2 c./sec. (Table XII).

The signs of both $J_{^{13}C-^{31}P}$ and $J_{^{31}P-C-H}$ are reversed on quarternization of the phosphorus atom of dimethylphenylphosphine.[100] The change in sign of $J_{^{31}P-C-H}$ is in accord with earlier studies on complexes of trimethylphosphine,[101] and the large difference between the values of $J_{^{13}C-^{31}P}$ of the phosphine and its hydrobromide indicates the extreme sensitivity of this parameter to the nature of groups attached to

TABLE XII

The signs of ^{13}C coupling constants in some selected compounds

Compound	Type of Coupling	J, c./sec.	Reduced coupling constant[†] $K \times 10^{-20}$ cm^{-3}	Ref.
$CH_3{}^{13}CO_2H$	$^{13}C-^{13}C$	$+57\cdot6$	$..$	94
$C_aH_3C_b{}^{15}N$	$^{13}C_a-^{13}C_b$	$+57\cdot3\pm0\cdot3$	$..$	93
	$^{13}C_a-^1H$	$\pm136\cdot0\pm0\cdot2$	$+45\cdot0$	
	$^{13}C_a-^{15}N$	$\pm3\cdot0\pm0\cdot4$	$-9\cdot77$	95
	$^{13}C_b-^{15}N$	$\mp17\cdot5\pm0\cdot4$	$+57\cdot0$	
	$^{13}C_b-^1H$	$\mp10\cdot0\pm0\cdot2$	$-3\cdot31$	
$(CH_3)_4Si$	$^{13}C-^1H$	$+121\pm0\cdot2$	$+40\cdot1$	
	$^{13}C-^{29}Si$	-52 ± 2	$+8\cdot7$	97, 98
	$^{13}C-Si-C-^1H$	<2	$..$	
$(CH_3)_4Pb$	$^{13}C-^1H$	$+135$	$..$	104
	$^{13}C-^{207}Pb$	$+250\pm1$	$+395$	
$(CH_3)_2Se$	$^{13}C-^1H$	$+139$	$..$	105
	$^{13}C-^{77}Se$	-62 ± 1	-108	
$(CH_3)_2Te$	$^{13}C-^1H$	$+139\cdot7$	$..$	105
	$^{13}C-^{125}Te$	$+162\pm1$	-170	
$(CH_3)_3Se^{\oplus}I^{\ominus}$	$^{13}C-^1H$	$+145\cdot8$	$..$	105
	$^{13}C-^{77}Se$	-50 ± 3	$..$	
$(CH_3)_3Te^{\oplus}I^{\ominus}$	$^{13}C-^1H$	$+146\cdot0$	$..$	105
	$^{13}C-^{125}Te$	$..$	$..$	
$(CH_3)_2Se_2$	$^{13}C-^1H$	$+141\cdot7$	$..$	105
	$^{13}C-^{77}Se$	-75	$..$	
$(CH_3)_2Hg$	$^{13}C-^1H$	$+129\cdot6\pm0\cdot1$	$..$	106
	$^{13}C-^{199}Hg$	$+687\cdot4\pm1$	$..$	
	$^{13}C-Hg-C-^1H$	$-1\cdot9\pm0\cdot2$	$..$	

[†] The reduced coupling constant is defined by $K_{AX}=J_{AX}\cdot2\pi/h\gamma_A\gamma_B$.

the phosphorus atom. Tetramethyldiphosphine has a deceptively simple proton spectrum of the type $X_nAA'X_n'$.[102] Additional information regarding the signs and magnitudes of coupling constants in the molecule was obtained by observation of the ^{13}C satellite spectrum. Analysis of the ^{13}C satellite spectrum, in conjunction with "tickling" experiments, indicates that the values of the $^{13}C-^{31}P$ coupling across one and two bonds are small and opposite in sign. A heteronuclear triple resonance experiment is needed[103] in order to determine the relative signs of the coupling constants in dimethyl phosphite (18)

18

owing to the absence of coupling between the two types of hydrogen. The magnitudes and signs of the determined couplings are shown in Table XIII.

TABLE XIII

Coupling constants involving the ^{13}C nucleus in some phosphorus compounds

Compound	Type of coupling	J, c./sec.	Ref.
$Me_2PC_6H_5$	$^{13}C-^1H$	$+130\cdot3 \pm 0\cdot2$	99
	$^{13}C-^{31}P$	$-14\cdot0 \pm 1$	
$Me_2\overset{\oplus}{P}H\,'C_6H_5Br^{\ominus}$	$^{13}C-^1H$	$+134\cdot0 \pm 0\cdot2$	99
	$^{13}C-^{31}P$	$+56 \pm 1$	
	$^{13}C-P-^1H\,'$	$+4 \pm 2$	
$Me_2P.PMe_2$	$^{13}C-^1H$	$+128\cdot9 \pm 0\cdot2$	101
	$^{13}C-^{31}P$	~ -14	
	$^{13}C-P-^{31}P$	$\sim +8$	
$(MeO)_2P(O)H$	$^{13}C-^1H$	$+148\cdot7 \pm 0\cdot2$	102
	$^{13}C-O-^{31}P$	$-6\cdot0 \pm 1$	

McFarlane[104] has determined the signs of $J_{119Sn-13C}$ and $J_{119Sn-1H}$ in a series of methyltin halides. In all cases the reduced coupling constants $K_{119Sn-1H}$ are negative and $K_{119Sn-13C}$ positive. The two couplings are approximately linearly related (Fig. 4). The line, however, does not pass through the origin, indicating that one of the two couplings

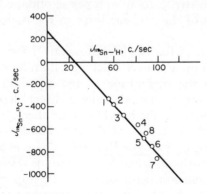

FIG. 4. The relationship between $J_{13C-119Sn}$ and $J_{1H-119Sn}$ in methyltin halides for the compounds: Me_4Sn containing 10% dioxan (1); Me_3SnBr containing 10% benzene (2); Me_3SnBr in water (3); Me_2SnCl_2 in acetone solution (4); Me_2SnCl_2 in acetone + 10% water (5); Me_2SnCl_2 in acetone + 25% water (6); Me_2SnCl_2 in water (7); and $MeSnBr_3$ in benzene solution. (From McFarlane.[104])

involves significant contribution from interactions other than that of the Fermi contact term. A similar situation is indicated for the coupling in tetramethyl-lead,[105] in which heteronuclear "tickling" showed that $J_{^{13}C-^{207}Pb}$ is positive and $J_{^{207}Pb-C-H}$ is negative (Table XII). The coupling involving the carbon nucleus is not dominated by the Fermi term. In contrast to the above observations, the directly bonded couplings of carbon to selenium and tellurium are both negative, whereas the geminal couplings of both elements to the protons are positive.[106] It appears that similar mechanisms dominate the coupling to both the carbon and protons in these compounds, and that changes in hybridization of the metalloid atoms are important (Table XII). Dreeskamp and Stegmeir[107] have also obtained the ^{13}C–metal and the longer-range $^{13}C-M-C-^1H$ coupling constants in ^{13}C–enriched metal alkyls using heteronuclear tickling procedures.

The elegant experiments of McLauchlan et al.[108] and of Dean and McFarlane[109] on dimethylmercury illustrate the general features of heteronuclear tickling and show how coupling constants between two nuclei may be determined when neither is directly observed. The principles involved in this technique have already been described in detail in Volume 1 of this series.[17]

C. Aliphatic compounds and their derivatives

The observation of spin coupling of ^{13}C to protons has been used as the basis of an analytical technique for determining the relative amount of ^{13}C in enriched methane gas. The ratio of the relative abundance of the two carbon isotopes is obtained directly from the ratio of the areas of the ^{13}C-satellites to the main ^{12}C–H resonance signals.[110]

The application of Ramsey's expression[111] for indirect spin coupling shows that, if the Fermi contact term dominates the spin-coupling interaction, then the magnitude of the coupling constant between directly bonded nuclei should show a direct dependence upon the amount of s character in the bond between them. This correlation has been widely used in studies of directly bonded couplings between carbon and hydrogen (e.g., see Ref. 4b). There is no doubt that it has value if used carefully in suitable compounds. However other factors in the coupling-constant expression may be important.[112] Grant and Litchman[113] have shown, by a consideration of charge transfer in some simple aliphatic halides, that changes in the effective nuclear charge of carbon (Z) can account for observed changes in $J_{^{13}C-^1H}$. Changes in hybridization parameters are not necessary to obtain a correlation with the experimental coupling constants. The variability of the coupling constants in these compounds can thus be accounted for in terms of the polarity of the bonds to substituent atoms or groups, other than hydrogen, and reasonable dependence of $J_{^{13}C-^1H}$ is observed on halogen electronegativity.[114] Lunazzi and Taddei[115] have proposed the relationship—

$$J_{^{13}C-^1H} = 3\cdot25dE + 94\cdot9$$

where d is the bond distance in Å and E is the substituent electro-negativity (Mulliken), to account for the variation of $^{13}C-^1H$ coupling constants in monosubstituted methanes. A modification of the above equation is needed[116] for polysubstituted methanes, and takes the form—

$$J_{^{13}C-^1H} = E[3\cdot25nd + 4\cdot6(n-1)] - 68\cdot7n + 163\cdot6$$

where n is the number of substituents attached to the same atom. This latter equation gave a good correlation between the observed and calculated values of the coupling constants.

Douglas[117] has also obtained, for monosubstituted methanes CH_3X, linear plots of $J_{^{13}C^1H}$ against the Pauling electronegativity of the substituent. The slope of the plots depends on the row of the periodic table to which the substituent atom belongs, which in turn reflects that changes in the C—X bond length are important. The attain-ment of maximum orbital overlap via changes in the carbon hybridiza-tion is therefore implied, and consequently changes in s character of the orbitals will contribute to the variation in $J_{^{13}C-^1H}$. The difficulties that arise in interpreting results of this nature are shown in the study of this problem by infrared spectroscopy.[118,119] Linear correlations were found between the C–H stretching frequencies and the $^{13}C-^1H$ coupling constants for the series $(CH_3)_4M$, where $M=C$, Si, Ge, Sn and Pb, and for the series CH_3X, where $X=F$, Cl, Br and I.[118] Similar correlations were found in cases where the hybridization had been changed from sp^3 to sp^2, which is accompanied by both an increase in the value of $J_{^{13}C-^1H}$ and an increase in the frequency of the C–H stretching mode. Brown and Puckett[119] have interpreted similar results for aliphatic derivatives in terms of variation in the electro-negativity of the substituents rather than changes in the fractional s character of the C–H bond. This conclusion was based upon the fact that while the force constant (K_r) could be related to the $^{13}C-^1H$ coupling by the relation—

$$K_r = 4\cdot74 + 8\cdot8(J - 125)10^{-3} \text{ mdyn./Å}$$

the force constant was not significantly altered by small variations in the s character but increased with the increasing ionic character of the C–H bond.

Further complications in the interpretation of the variation in $^{13}C-^{1}H$ coupling constants arise from solvent effects. The existence of molecular association in both methyl chloride and triethylamine in the liquid phase has been demonstrated by observation of directly bonded $^{13}C-^{1}H$ coupling constants;[120] increased coupling is observed for hydrogen-bonded species. Watts and Goldstein[121] have also interpreted the variations in the $^{13}C-^{1}H$ coupling constants of substituted methanes in various solvents in terms of intermolecular hydrogen bonding, e.g., the value of $J_{^{13}C-^{1}H}$ in bromoform tends to increase with the proton-accepting ability of the solvent. In hydrogen-bonded complexes, the electron-rich acceptor repels the charge from the vicinity of the bonded proton towards the carbon atom. This increases the s character of the carbon orbitals bonded to the proton, thus increasing the value of $J_{^{13}C-^{1}H}$. Steric effects may be important for amine solvents, and the large increase for $J_{^{13}C-^{1}H}$ in aromatic solvents, relative to cyclohexane, probably reflects some complexing of the protons with the π charge of the aromatic ring. Some earlier work[122] specifically concerned with the variation of $J_{^{13}C-^{1}H}$ of the chloromethyl group in ethers and ketones of the form $ClCH_2XR$, where $X = O$, S and $C=O$, found an essentially linear relationship between the chemical shift and the $J_{^{13}C-^{1}H}$ of the chloromethyl group. However it was observed that both the shift and $J_{^{13}C-^{1}H}$ varied in a similar manner with the nature of the solvent, and these authors suggested that the protons of the chloromethyl group participated in hydrogen bonding with the basic site of the solvent. Murray and Davis[123] have drawn attention to the difficulties that may arise from ^{13}C satellite interference in studies of hydrogen bonding between cyclohexane and diethylamine by proton n.m.r. Hydrogen bonds between diethylamine and cyclohexane are still formed at concentrations of the amine of less than a mole fraction of 0·11. Unfortunately, the $^{13}C-^{1}H$ satellites of the solvent molecules obscure the NH resonance as the concentration decreases. Confirmation of the above observation is shown by a similar study of piperidine in cyclohexane, since in this case the ^{13}C satellites of cyclohexane and the NH resonance of the amine are easily resolved and differentiated at all concentrations of the solute.

Sackmann and Dreeskamp[124] have presented values for both the magnitude and the signs of direct and two bond $^{13}C-^{1}H$ coupling constants in halogenoethanes (Table XIV). The values for the three bond coupling $^3J_{^{13}C-C-C-H}$ in compounds of the general form

TABLE XIV

The carbon-13–proton coupling constants, c./sec., of halogenoethanes

	$J_{^{13}C_a-^1H}$	$J_{^{13}C_b-^1H}$	$J_{^{13}C_b-C_a-^1H}$
$H_3C_a-C_bH_3$	125	125	$-4\cdot5$
$H_3C_a-C_bH_2I$	127	151	$-5\cdot0$
$H_2ClC_a-C_bClH_2$	154	154	$-3\cdot4$
$H_2BrC_a-C_bBrH_2$	157	157	$-4\cdot2$
$HCl_2C_a-C_bCl_2H$	181	181	$+1\cdot2$
$HBr_2C_a-C_bBr_2H$	181	181	$+1\cdot1$

$(CH_3)_3{}^{13}C$—C were found to be sensitive to non-bonded repulsions between groups attached to the ^{13}C nucleus.[125] Increase in the size of the substituent group R should increase the angles θ and θ' (19)

19

and, by analogy with the behaviour of vicinal $^1H-^1H$ coupling, should decrease the value of $^3J_{^{13}C-C-CH}$, which is in accord with experimental observations. The presence of halogen substituents on the ^{13}C nucleus increases the value of the three-bond coupling, which may be due to some dipolar contribution arising from interaction between the proton magnetic moment and the current induced on the halogen atom by the ^{13}C nucleus. This suggestion is however contrary to earlier theoretical predictions[126] that coupling via currents induced by a third atom will always be negligible. Although the authors[125] are naturally cautious in making this suggestion, it is a point that obviously warrants further investigation. Both $J_{^{13}C-^{13}C}$, in the series $XC(CH_3)_3$, and $J_{^{13}C-^1H}$, in the series XCH_3, increase in a directly proportional manner with increase in the electronegativity of X (Table XV).[127] The value of $J_{^{13}C-^{13}C}$ is found to be less sensitive to the directly

TABLE XV

The effect of polar groups on directly bonded coupling constants

	$J_{^{13}C-^{13}C}$, c./sec., in $XC(CH_3)_3$	$J_{^{13}C-^1H}$, c./sec., in XCH_3
CH_3	36·9	126
NH_2	37·1	133
OH	39·5	141
Cl	40·0	150
Br	40·2	152

bonded polar substituents than is $J_{^{13}C-^1H}$. Consequently more confidence may be placed in the use of $J_{^{13}C-^{13}C}$ values as a criterion for variations of bond hybridization.

The values of the $^{13}C-^{19}F$ coupling constants in hexafluoroethane are $J_{^{13}C-^{19}F}=281\cdot3$ c./sec. and $J_{^{13}C-C-^{19}F}=46\cdot0$ c./sec.[128] The existence of a positive vicinal C–F coupling in this molecule is also discussed. Although the Fermi contact interaction is the most important in explaining $^{13}C-^1H$ coupling constants other terms are important for couplings involving nuclei such as fluorine. Considine[129] has pointed out the limitations of the established theories of spin–spin interaction when applied to coupling between ^{13}C and ^{19}F. Theoretical predictions of coupling between carbon and hydrogen (σ-bonds) should not be expected to apply to molecules such as tetrafluoromethane where stabilization of the molecule is due to considerable π-bonding arising from canonical structures of the form (20).

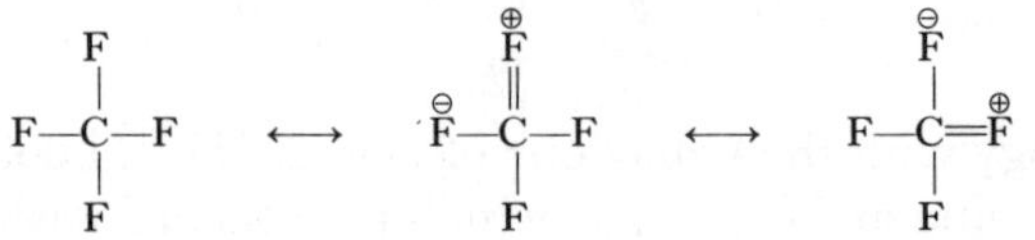

20

Olah and Comisarow[130] have observed the $^{13}C-^1H$ coupling in carbonium ions stabilized in strongly acidic solutions. The values of the spin coupling constants obtained from the secondary isopropyl and diphenylmethyl carbonium ions are shown in Table XVI. The linearity of the $^{13}C-^1H$ coupling constants with the fractional s character of the carbon atom is applicable to both the carbonium ions and their parent hydrocarbons.

TABLE XVI

$^{13}C-^1H$ **Spin–spin coupling constants of primary and secondary carbonium ions and of the parent hydrocarbons**

	$J_{^{13}C-^1H}$, c./sec.	Calc. % s character	State of hybridization
2,4-(Bu^t)$_2$-6-Me-C$_6$H$_2$.$\overset{\oplus}{C}$H$_2$	168	33·8	sp^2
(CH$_3$)$_2$^{13}CH$_2$	128	25·6	sp^3
(CH$_3$)$_2$$^{13}\overset{\oplus}{C}$HSbF$_5Cl^\ominus$	168	33·6	sp^2
(C$_6$H$_5$)$_2$^{13}CH$_2$	126	25·2	sp^3
(C$_6$H$_5$)$_2$$^{13}\overset{\oplus}{C}$HSbF$_5Cl^\ominus$	164	32·8	sp^2

D. Alicyclic hydrocarbons

Watts and Goldstein[131] have provided, by analysis of the ^{13}C satellite spectra, accurate values of proton–proton coupling constants in cyclopropane. The directly bonded $^{13}C-^1H$ coupling constant has a value of 160·45 c./sec.

Carbon-13–proton coupling constants can be useful parameters in providing information regarding the nature of bonding in highly strained carbocyclic rings. In cyclopropanes, for example, the carbon orbitals forming the C—H bonds are expected to have more s character than normal hydrocarbons, whereas the C—C bonds will possess more p character. It is alleged[132] that bonding of this type corresponds to sp^5 hybridization of the carbon with a predicted value of the $^{13}C-^{13}C$ coupling constant, formed between two sp^5 hybrid orbitals, of 15 c./sec. The $^{13}C-^{13}C$ coupling constants for a series of cyclopropane derivatives are in excellent agreement with this theory.[133] The values of some $^{13}C-^1H$ coupling constants found in substituted cyclopropanes are shown in Table XVII.

The deviations that are found in the values of the $^{13}C-^1H$ coupling constants in the three-membered ring fragment of styrene sulphide and styrenimine have led to the suggestion[134] that in many cases the $^{13}C-^1H$ coupling constant does not necessarily measure the percentage s character in the carbon orbitals when the carbon atoms have substituent groups that are capable of additional electronic effects. Deviation from a simple correlation can probably *a priori* be expected for substituents with π-electrons, second and higher row elements and fluorine atoms in close proximity to a set of spin-coupled nuclei. Possibly low-lying excited states and/or d orbital participation contributes to these effects for second and higher row elements.

The available $^{13}C-^1H$ coupling data for four-membered carbocyclic ring systems have been summarised by Fleming and Williams.[135] The values of $^{13}C-^1H$ coupling constants can provide a qualitative measure of angular distortion in these and similar compounds.[136] The value of $J_{^{13}C-^1H}$ increases, for example, in the series cyclohexane, cyclobutane, cyclopropane and the bridgehead position of bicyclobutane (Table XVIII). The difference in magnitude of the $^{13}C-^1H$ coupling constant for the *exo-* and *endo*-methylene hydrogen atoms of bicyclobutane (**21** and **22**; Table XVIII) may be due to bond-angle distortions arising from repulsive interactions between the two *endo* hydrogen atoms. Closs and Larrabee[137] have studied the acidity of various tricyclic hydrocarbons using the ^{13}C satellites of their proton spectra. Values of the $^{13}C-^1H$ coupling constants were correlated with

TABLE XVII

Carbon-13 coupling constants in some cyclopropyl derivatives

	$J_{^{13}C-^1H}$, c./sec., of the cyclopropyl ring		of substituent	$J_{^{13}C-^{13}C}$ c./sec.
	α carbon	β carbon		
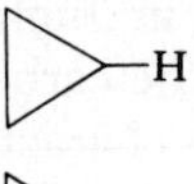 ▷—H	160·45	160·45	..	..
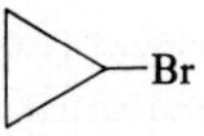 ▷—Br	..	..	..	13·3
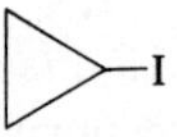 ▷—I	..	..	..	12·9
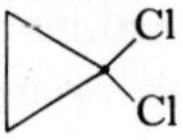 ▷⟨Cl Cl	..	170	..	15·5
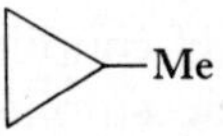 ▷—Me	..	..	..	{ 44·0 (αC-CH₃)
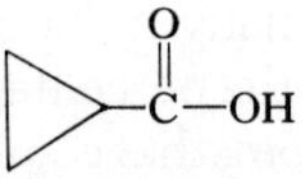 ▷—C(O)—OH	157	153	..	..
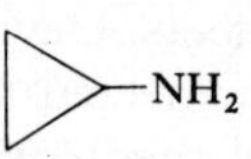 ▷—NH₂	173	161	..	..
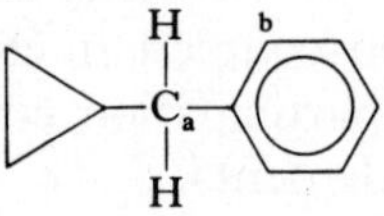 ▷—C$_a$(H)(H)—◯^{b}	165	167	127(a) 155(b)	..
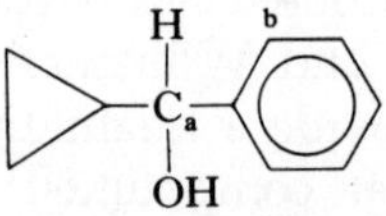 ▷—C$_a$(H)(OH)—◯^{b}	160	161	146(a) 158(b)	..
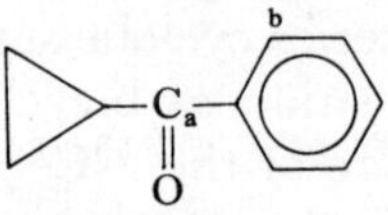 ▷—C$_a$(=O)—◯^{b}	173	173	169(b)	..
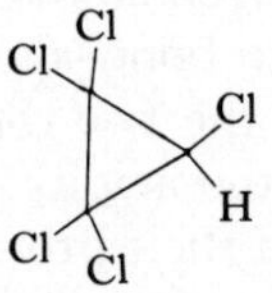 Cl₂C—C(Cl)(Cl)—C(H)(Cl)—Cl₂	193±1	..	..	..

TABLE XVIII

The $^{13}C-^1H$ coupling constants of some cyclic and bicyclic hydrocarbons

	$J_{^{13}C-^1H}$, c./sec.		$J_{^{13}C-^1H}$, c./sec.
Cyclohexane	123	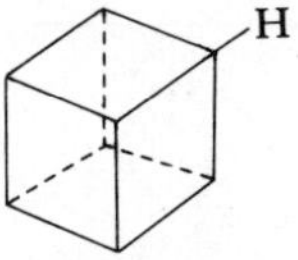	
Cyclobutane	134		160 ± 5
Cyclopropane	161		

144

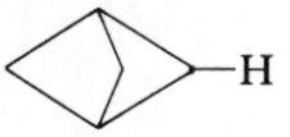

164

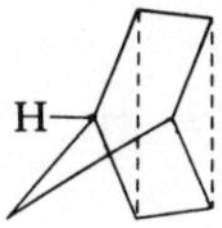

178·5

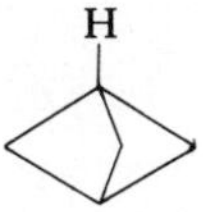

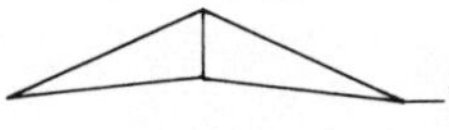

(21) 170

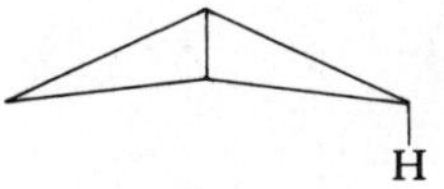

(22) 152

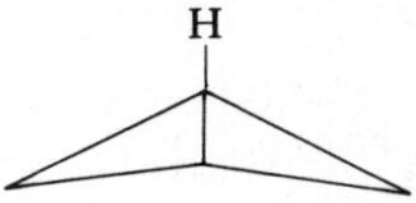

202

the relative rates of metallation of the hydrocarbon with methyllithium in ether at 25°C (Table XIX). Since resonance stabilization of any possible carbanionic intermediate cannot occur in these systems, the observed C–H acidity must be determined by the electronegativity of the carbon atoms and by possible inductive effects of the substituents. An approximately linear relationship exists between $\log K/K_0$ (metallation rate) and the C–H coupling constant, which could serve as a measure of the s character of the C—H bond.

The general problem of the correlation of the $^{13}C-^1H$ coupling, in both carbocyclic and heterocyclic systems, has been considered by Laszlo.[138]

E. Olefins and acetylenes

Vladimiroff,[139] in a study of carbon–proton coupling in ethylene, has considered the familiar Pople–Santry expression for coupling constants in terms of contributions due to symmetric and antisymmetric molecular states. If the symmetric and antisymmetric parts are denoted

7*

TABLE XIX

**The $^{13}C-^{1}H$ coupling constants and the relative metallation rates
of some strained hydrocarbons**

	$J_{^{13}C-^{1}H}$, c./sec.	k/k_0	$\log k/k_0$
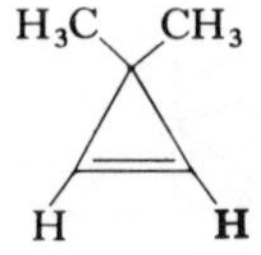	221 ± 0.5	2,500	3·4
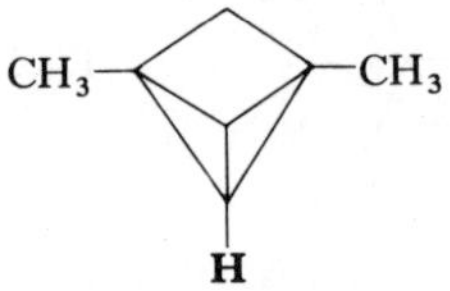	212 ± 2	65	1·8
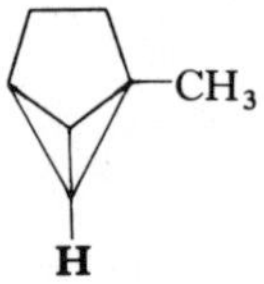	206 ± 1	12	1·1
	200 ± 1	1	0·0

by S and A, respectively, then the Fermi contact term, δ^F, for the direct and the two-bond coupling may be written—

$$\delta^F_{^{13}C-H} = S+A \quad \text{and} \quad \delta^F_{^{13}C-C-H} = S-A$$

The differences in magnitude and relative sign for the directly and non-directly bonded $^{13}C-^{1}H$ coupling can be interpreted as a result of approximately equal contributions from symmetric and antisymmetric states. The *geminal* and the *cis* and *trans* proton–proton couplings and also the $^{13}C-^{1}H$ coupling of the $=CHX$ group of vinyl compounds show similar deviations from an inverse linear relationship between coupling constants and electronegativity of the substituent in mono-substituted ethylenes.[140] It was suggested that there was interaction between the substituent X and the C—H bond which affected the $^{13}C-^{1}H$ coupling constant and not necessarily implying any alteration in the hybridization of the carbon atom. The calculated values of $J_{^{13}C_\beta-^1H}$ for vinyl halides, using the method of maximum overlap orbitals (MOO), depend largely on fractional amounts of polar structure in the vinyl halides, whereas $J_{^{13}C_\alpha-^1H}$ values depend predominantly upon the nature of the C—X bond.[141] The magnitude of $J_{^{13}C_\alpha-^1H}$ thus reflects the s character of the halogen bonding orbital and ionic character of the carbon—halogen bond. The MOO calculations, using pure p orbitals for Cl, Br and I, are sufficient to predict $^{13}C_\alpha-^1H$ couplings that are in agreement with experiment; inclusion of 25% s character is necessary for the fluorine orbitals in order to obtain consistency with the experimental values of $J_{^{13}C_\alpha-^1H}$ for vinyl fluoride. The concept of partial-double-bond character in the C—F bond is necessary to explain the high values of $^{13}C-^{19}F$ coupling constants in some bromofluoroethylenes (Table XV).[142] If in the ethylene (23)

TABLE XX

$^{13}C-^{19}F$ **coupling constants of some halogenofluoroethylenes**

	$J_{^{13}C_a-^{19}F}$, c./sec.	$J_{^{13}C_b-C_a-^{19}F}$, c./sec.
$Br_2C_b=C_aFBr$	323·6	39·9
$Cl_2C_b=C_aFCl$	303·1	44·2
$Br_2C_b=C_aF_2$	289·9	43·1
$Cl_2C_b=C_aF_2$	288·9	43·7
cis-$BrFC_b=C_aFBr$	+324·7	−35·8
trans-$BrFC_b=C_aFBr$	+355·0	−102·5
cis-$ClFC_b=C_aFCl$	+299·3	−38·1
trans-$ClFC_b=C_aFCl$	+289·6	−53·9

$X_1 = F$ and $X_2 = Cl$ or Br then the contribution from the structure (24) is greater than that of (25) when $X_2 = Br$ rather than for $X_2 = Cl$ and thus the observed features of ^{19}F chemical shifts and the $^{13}C-^{19}F$ coupling constants may be rationalized. The large value for $J_{^{13}C-C-F}$ of trans 1,2-dibromodifluoroethylene is, however, anomalous.

Govil[143] and Sackmann and Dreeskamp[124] have used spin "tickling" techniques to determine the magnitude and signs of various $^{13}C-^1H$ coupling constants in olefinic and acetylenic molecules

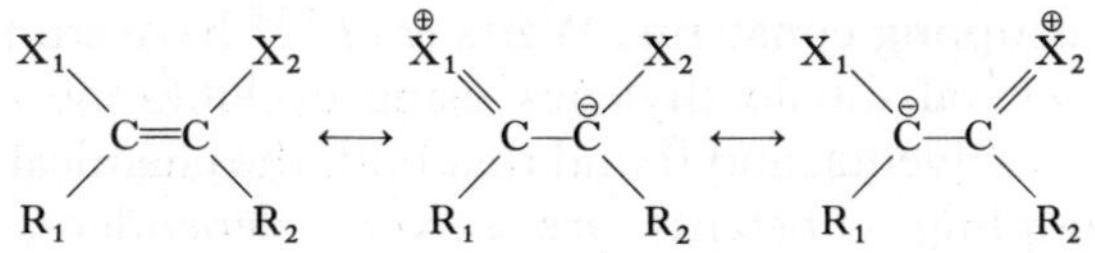

23   24   25

(Table XXI). The principle is demonstrated in Fig. 5, which shows the effect of the "tickling" experiment on *cis* 1,2-dichloroethylene. It should be noted that the value of the ^1H–^1H coupling constant is readily obtained by inspection of the ^{13}C satellites and thus may be used to ascertain the identity of the isomer, since, owing to the magnetic equivalence of the two protons, the value of J_{AB} cannot be obtained directly from the proton resonance spectrum. The values of the two-bond ^{13}C–C–^1H coupling constants are primarily influenced by the

TABLE XXI

^{13}C–^1H **coupling constants of acetylene and ethylene derivatives**

	^{13}C–^1H coupling constant, c./sec.
Acetylene H^a—$C^1{\equiv}C^2$—H^b	$J_{^{13}C_1-H_a} = 249$ $J_{^{13}C_1-H_b} = 49 \cdot 3$
Ethylene	$J_{^{13}C_1-H_a} = 156 \cdot 4$ $J_{^{13}C_1-H_b} = -2 \cdot 4$
trans-**Dichloroethylene**	$J_{^{13}C_1-H_a} = 198 \cdot 0$ $J_{^{13}C_1-H_b} = 0 \cdot 8$
cis-**Dichloroethylene**	$J_{^{13}C_1-H_a} = 197 \cdot 3$ $J_{^{13}C_1-H_b} = 16 \cdot 0$

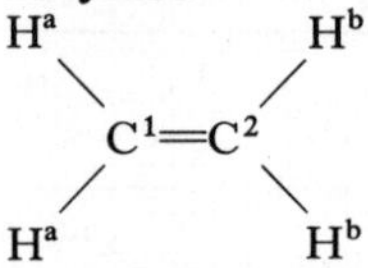

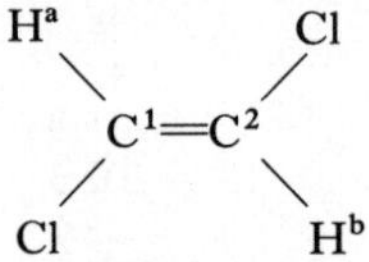

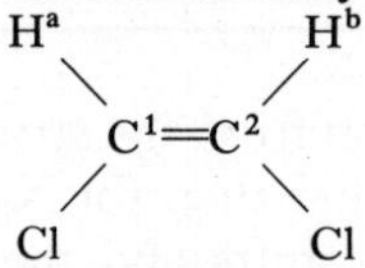

magnitude of the ^{13}C—C—H bond angle, and, as in the case of *gem* proton–proton couplings, tend to zero as the bond angle approaches 120° and are negative below that value of bond angle.

Several workers,[144–146] have investigated the solvent dependence of ^{13}C–^1H coupling constants. Watts *et al.*[144] have studied the n.m.r. spectra of several dihaloethylenes using cyclohexane and dimethyl-formamide as solvents, and found that both the chemical shifts and the ^{13}C–^1H coupling constants are solvent dependent, whereas the *vicinal* ^1H–^1H coupling is invariant. It was additionally observed that

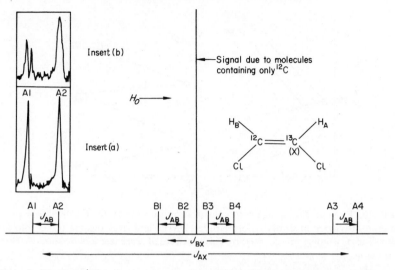

FIG. 5. Typical ^{1}H resonance spectrum for *cis*-dichloroethylene including the inner and outer ^{13}C satellites. The outer satellites are well resolved in the experimental spectrum and those at the lower field are shown in insert (a). Insert (b) shows the splitting of these lines when an r.f. field of about 0·3 c./sec. is applied near B1 which is connected regressively to A1 and progressively to A2. (From Govil.[143])

there was a correspondence of the effects on the n.m.r. parameters with the solvent variation of the C–X stretching frequencies. It was suggested that some specific interaction, affecting the halogen substituent, was the predominant factor in these solvent effects. In both the *cis* and *trans* isomers of 1,2-dichloro- and 1,2-dibromo-ethylenes there was an increase in $J_{^{13}C-^1H}$ on dilution with dimethylformamide, whereas on dilution with cyclohexane, $J_{^{13}C-^1H}$ decreased (Fig. 6). It was found[145] that the proton chemical shift and the *gem* ^{1}H–^{1}H and the *cis* ^{1}H–^{19}F coupling of 1-chloro-1-fluoroethylene were primarily dependent upon the dielectric constant of the solvent. In the case of the *cis*- and *trans*-1,2-dichlorofluoroethylenes it was found[146] that although the ^{13}C–^{1}H coupling constants increase, the ^{13}C–^{19}F coupling constants decrease with the increasing polarity of the solvent. These authors suggest that the variations in chemical shifts and coupling constants arise from the reaction field of the solvent, although specific interactions of the type suggested[144] cannot be completely ruled out. The reaction field acting in the region of the C—F bond will draw the σ-bonding electrons towards the fluorine atom and the increased polarity of the bond results in the ^{13}C–^{19}F coupling becoming more positive. However, since the sign of the ^{13}C–^{19}F coupling is negative, the resultant observed ^{13}C–^{19}F coupling decreases in magnitude.

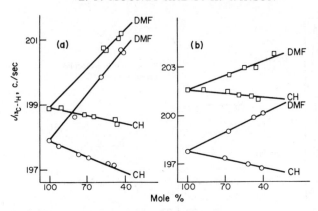

FIG. 6. Plots of $J_{^{13}C-^1H}$ against concentration in mole % for (a) dichloro- and (b) dibromo-ethylenes in dimethylformamide (DMF) and cyclohexane (CH) solutions. Values for *cis* isomers are denoted by circles, those of *trans* isomers by squares. (From Watts *et al.*[144])

The authors draw attention to the possible use of solvent effects to determine the signs of coupling.

The *geminal* proton–proton coupling constant in α-chloroacrylonitrile is both solvent and temperature dependent.[147, 148] Heteronuclear spin "tickling" experiments were used to show that the sign of the *geminal* $^1H–^1H$ coupling constant is of opposite sign to that of

TABLE XXII

$^{13}C–^1H$ **coupling constants of acrolein and its methyl derivatives**

$$R_1 \quad R_3$$
$$C^1{=}C^2$$
$$R_2 \quad C^3{=}O$$
$$R_4$$

	Substituents				Coupling constants, c./sec.			
	R_1	R_2	R_3	R_4	$J_{C_1R_1}$	$J_{C_1R_2}$	$J_{C_2R_3}$	$J_{C_2R_4}$
Acrolein	H	H	H	H	162·3	156·6	162·3	173·2
Crotonaldehyde	CH$_3$	H	H	H	(127·5)	152·7	159·3	170·7
α-Methylacrolein	H	H	CH$_3$	H	160·1	157·4	(127·6)	175·0
Tiglaldehyde	CH$_3$	H	CH$_3$	H	(126·8)	153·6	(127·5)	171·7

The values in parenthesis are the $^{13}C–^1H$ coupling constants of the substituent methyl groups.

the $^{13}C-^1H$ coupling, and therefore negative. The proton and ^{13}C satellite spectra of acrolein, crotonaldehyde, α-methylacrolein and tiglaldehyde at varying concentrations in cyclohexane have been analysed;[149] the $^{13}C-^1H$ couplings of these molecules are shown in Table XXII. Explicit in the analysis of the spectra are the long-range $^{13}C-^1H$ couplings. The ^{13}C satellite spectrum of vinylene carbonate (**26**) showed[150] the presence of both a geminal $^{13}C-C-^1H$ coupling

26

(17·47 ± 0·12 c./sec.) and a three-bond $^{13}C-O-C-^1H$ coupling, through the ring oxygen atom (9·26 ± 0·10 c./sec.), in addition to the direct $^{13}C-^1H$ coupling of 220·15 ± 0·15 c./sec. Double-resonance "tickling" experiments showed that both $J_{^{13}C-^1H}$ and $J_{^{13}C-C-^1H}$ were of the same sign, and correlation of these two coupling constants should be a guide to the existence of hyperconjugation in these and other similar systems. In a recent paper the long-range $^{13}C-C-^1H$ coupling constants of allyl bromide have been determined[151] using a triple-resonance procedure, in which the methylene protons were decoupled completely to afford a first-order AMX spectrum for the olefinic protons accompanied by tickling experiments. The values of the coupling constants found are shown in (**27**).

$J_{C^1-H_A} = 1·0 ± 0·3$ c./sec.

$J_{C^1-H_M} = 2·9 ± 0·2$ c./sec.

27

The proton spectrum of cyclobutene consists of two sharp singlet resonance peaks, but, by analysis of the ^{13}C satellite spectra of cyclobutene and several partially deuterated isomers, Roberts et al.[152,153] have obtained values for the proton–proton and $^{13}C-^1H$ coupling constants of these molecules. Theoretical calculations of the line positions of the ^{13}C satellite resonances indicate that long-range $^{13}C-C-H$ and $^{13}C-C-C-H$ couplings are present and that these in effect make the two CH_2 groups and the two olefinic protons non-equivalent. A similar study[154] of the symmetrical butatriene molecule at −55°C afforded both the cis and trans proton–proton coupling constants as well as the directly bonding $^{13}C-^1H$ coupling $J_{^{13}C-H} = 170·9$ c./sec.

Long-range three-bond ^{13}C–^1H coupling was observed in some acetylene derivatives of the type R_n—M—$(C\equiv C)_m$—CH_3 and R_n—M—$(C\equiv C)_m$—H, where M is an element of Group IVb, Vb or VIb, R = CH_3, C_2H_5 or C_6H_5 and m = 1, 2 or 3.[155] The coupling of the acetylenic proton, or of the methyl protons, to the α-, β- or γ-^{13}C nuclei are shown in Tables XXIII and XXIV. The directly bonded

TABLE XXIII

^{13}C–^1H **coupling constants of substituted acetylenes**
R—C≡C—H

Substituent R	Coupling constants, c./sec.	
	$J_{\equiv^{13}C-^1H}$	$J_{^{13}C\equiv C-^1H}$
Me₃Si—	236	42
Et₃Ge—	236	42
Ph₃Sn—	238	41
Ph₃Si—	239	42·5
Ph₂P—	247	45·8
PhS—	256	51·6
PhMeN—	258	55·2
Ph₂N—	259	55·5
PhO—	269	61
Ph—	252	49·8

TABLE XXIV

^{13}C–^1H **coupling constants of some substituted polyacetylenes**
R—$(C\equiv C)_m$—CH_3

Substituent R	m	Coupling constants, c./sec.		
		$J_{^{13}C-^1H}$	$J_{\equiv^{13}C-C-^1H}$	$J_{^{13}C\equiv C-C-^1H}$
Me₃Sn—	1	130	..	..
Et₃Ge—	1	131	..	..
Ph₂P—	1	132	..	..
PhO—	1	132·1	10·8	4·8
PhS—	1	132·4	..	..
PhSe—	1	132·3	10·4	5·8
Et₂As—	2	132·8	..	..
EtS—	2	132·5	11·4	..
PhS—	2	132·8	11·4	..

^{13}C–^1H couplings of the acetylenic group show considerable variation, and depend on the nature of the substituent R—M, and are in the range 236–269 c./sec.

F. Carbonyl-containing compounds

Hammaker[156, 157] has shown that, in a series of substituted alde-hydes of the form $X \cdot CO \cdot H$, the directly bonded aldehydic proton–carbon-13 coupling constant may be correlated with the electro-negativity of the substituent group X. The increase in J_{13C-H}, with the increasing group electronegativity of the substituent, is caused by an increase in the p character of the aldehydic carbon orbital used in bonding to the substituent and consequent increase in the s character of the orbital forming the aldehydic C—H bond. Values of the directly bonded coupling constants between carbon and the aldehyde proton may be predicted by a modified form of the empirical equations of Malinowski and others.[158–160]

The sign of the two-bond geminal $^{13}C-^{1}H$ coupling in acetaldehyde is positive, and values obtained from the analysis of the proton ^{13}C satellite spectra for this and other aldehydes are shown in Table XXV.[124] The coupling over two bonds depends upon two factors: (*i*), the character of the grouping containing the nuclei; and (*ii*), the s

TABLE XXV

$^{13}C-^{1}H$ coupling constants of the aldehyde group

	Coupling constant, c./sec.	
	$J_{13C-^{1}H}$	$J_{13C-C(O)^{1}H}$
o-HOC$_6$H$_4$CHO	177·0	19·8
o-ClC$_6$H$_4$CHO	182·0	23·6
p-CH$_3$OC$_6$H$_4$CHO	173·0	23·8
C$_6$H$_5$CHO	174·0	24·1
Pyridine-3-aldehyde	178·5	24·8
Pyridine-4-aldehyde	181·0	25·2
Furfuraldehyde	180·5	32·1
CH$_3$-C≡C—CHO	199·0	32·8
CH$_3$CHO	172·0	26·6
CHCl$_2$CHO	198·0	35·8
CCl$_3$.CHO	207·0	46·3

character of the carbon atoms. A correlation of these two-bond coup-lings with the directly bonded aldehydic proton–carbon-13 coupling is obtained. The temperature dependence of the proton spectra of propionaldehyde-3-^{13}C and its oxime indicates[161, 162] that *trans* $J_{13C-C-C-H}$ is greater than the *gauche* coupling (**28–31**) in accordance with the *vicinal* proton–proton coupling. The $^{13}C-^{1}H$ couplings of the N-methylphenylhydrazones (**32**) of several aldehydes have been

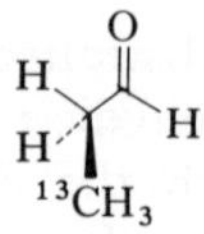

gauche	trans	gauche	trans
28	**29**	**30**	**31**

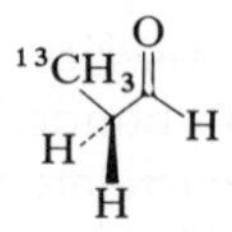

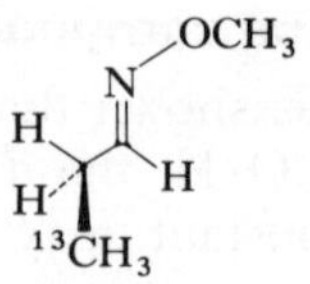

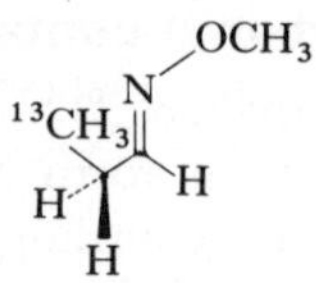

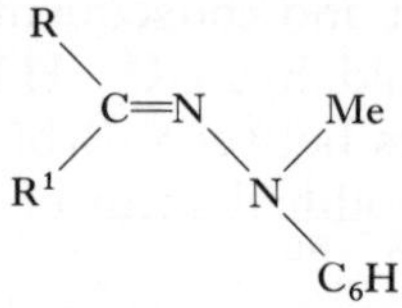

32

recorded, and fall in the range 153–162 c./sec., which are typical values expected for sp^2 hybridized carbon atoms.[163]

The variations of $J_{^{13}C-^1H}$ and $J_{^1H-^1H}$ in acetone and dimethyl sulphoxide in various solvents show an almost linear relationship with the carbonyl-^{13}C and ^{17}O chemical shifts.[164] Hydrogen bonding with the solvent, or the presence of large solvent dipoles, may increase the relative importance of polar resonance structures of the carbonyl or sulphoxide group (**33**), and the electron withdrawl experienced by the methyl group will result in increased values of C–H couplings.

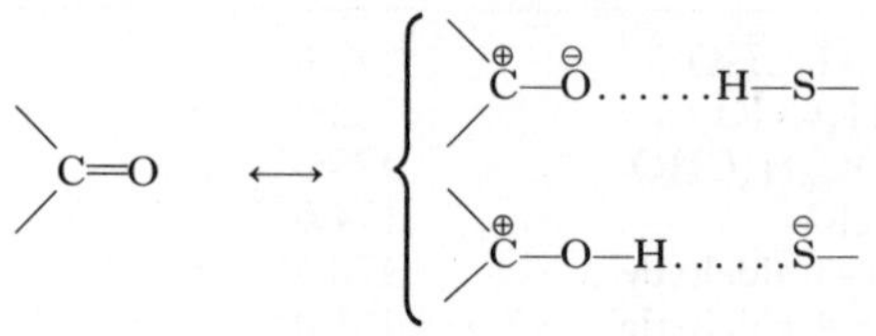

33

The inner satellites of the proton resonance spectra of both acetone and acetic acid are simple doublets arising from long-range coupling through two bonds. Freeman[11] has illustrated the use of the pulsed INDOR technique and obtained the spectrum of the carbonyl group, of both acetone and acetic acid, by monitoring one of the inner ^{13}C satellite lines in the proton spectrum of the methyl group while sweeping through the ^{13}C resonance region. The spectra obtained are a septet and quartet, respectively, and arise from long-range coupling of the ^{13}C nucleus to the methyl group(s), $J_{^{13}C-C-H} = 5 \cdot 9 \pm 0 \cdot 2$ c./sec. for acetic acid. Long-range $^{13}C-O-H$ coupling may also be observed in the ^{13}C and proton resonance spectra of protonated acetic and propionic acids.[165] Oxocarbonium and carboxonium ions are generated from the parent acids in FSO_3H–SbF_5 solution (Table XXV). The existence of two protonated forms of acetic acid was postulated, and in protonated benzoic acid, showing only one two-bond ^{13}C–H coupling, rapid rotation around the C—O bond must occur.

TABLE XXVI

^{13}C–^1H coupling constants of carbonium ions (protonated acids) and oxocarbonium ions (acyl cations) in fluorosulphonic acid–antimony pentafluoride solvent

	Temp. °C	Coupling constants, c./sec.		
		$J_{^{13}C-^1H}$	$J_{^{13}C-C-^1H}$	$J_{^{13}C-C-C-H}$
HCO_2H†	−40	225·1	..	..
$HCO_2H_2^\oplus(1)$	−75	244·8	..	..
(2)	−75	235·8	..	..
$CH_3CO_2H_2^\oplus$	−65	..	6·5	..
$CH_3CO^\oplus$	−10	..	9·3	..
$CH_3CH_2CO_2H_2^\oplus$	−65	..	6·2	6·2
$CH_3CH_2CO^\oplus$	−10	..	9·3	8·2

† In liquid SO_2 solution.

The proton n.m.r. spectra of substituted anhydrides have been analysed and the ^{13}C–^1H coupling constants reported.[166] The values of the ^{13}C–^1H coupling constants in the monosubstituted anhydrides (**34**), which are similar in magnitude to those observed in cyclopropanes, indicate that there is a certain amount of sp^2 hybridization in the C—H bonds. In the disubstituted anhydrides (**35** and **36**) both

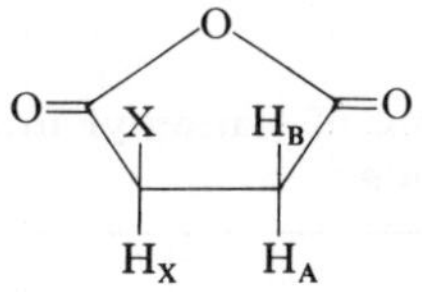

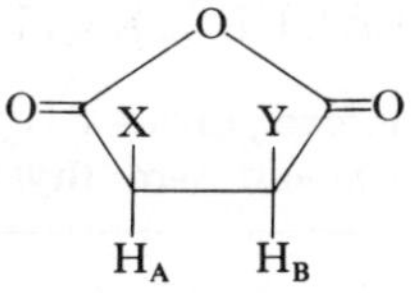

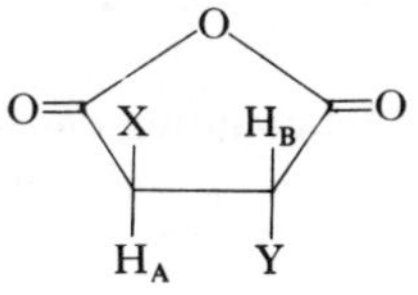

X = Cl, Br, OH and Y = Br, Cl.

J_{AB} and $J_{^{13}C-^1H}$ are strongly solvent dependent. The exact solution of the iterative programme for the analysis of the ^{13}C satellite spectra of acetal required that the ^{13}C–H coupling parameters of the two methylene protons are different.[167] The occurrence of two distinct ^{13}C–H couplings means that the non-equivalence can actually be localized in the two corresponding C—H bonds. Pletcher and Cordes[168] have, in the course of the study of the basic properties and the acid hydrolysis of the acetals, ketals and ortho esters, recorded the $^{13}C-^1H$ coupling constants of methyl t-butyl ether, 2,2-dimethoxypropane, methyl acetate and methyl orthoacetate.

The barrier to rotation about the C—N bond in various NN-dimethyl-amides,-thioamides and -amidinium ions decrease in the order thioamides $>$ amides $\sim$ amidinium ions.[169] The values for the $^{13}C-^1H$ coupling constants of the N-methyl groups are related to the extent of the localization of the positive charge on the nitrogen atom.

$$
\begin{array}{ccc}
\overset{O}{\underset{\underset{R}{\diagup}}{\diagdown}}\!\!C\!\!-\!\!\overset{R'}{\underset{R''}{\diagup}}N & \longleftrightarrow & \overset{\overset{\ominus}{O}}{\underset{\underset{R}{\diagup}}{\diagdown}}\!\!C\!\!=\!\!\overset{R'}{\underset{R''}{\diagup}}\overset{\oplus}{N}
\end{array}
$$

| 37 | 38 |

The contribution of dipolar canonical forms, of the type (38), to the ground-state configuration determines the magnitude of the rotational barrier; those compounds with high barriers would thus be expected to have larger values of $J_{^{13}C-^1H}$ than those with low barriers. The low value of this coupling for NN-dimethylacetimidine is suggested to support the view that the barrier to inversion is very low in this compound; although there is only a variation in the coupling constants of 5 c./sec., between that of NN-dimethylacetamide and the NN-dimethylacetimidine (Table XXVII), this observation is probably valid since the coupling of the latter compound is very similar to that found in trimethylamine.

TABLE XXVII

$^{13}C-^1H$ **coupling constants, c./sec., of** N—CH_3 **protons of** N-**methyl amide derivatives and** N-**methyl lactams**

	$J_{^{13}C-^1H}$		$J_{^{13}C-^1H}$
Dimethylthioacetamide	140	N-Methylpropiolactam	138
Dimethylthioformamide	140	N-Methylbutyrolactam	137
Dimethylacetamide	138	N-Methylvalerolactam	138
Dimethylformamide	138	N-Methylcaprolactam	138
Dimethylacetamidinium			
chloride	141	N-Methylenantholactam	138
		N-Methylcapryllactam	137
Dimethylacetimidine	135		
		Trimethylamine	134

Solvent-induced chemical shifts are observed in the proton spectra of *N*-methyl lactams, which are attributed to the formation of a collision complex (**39**); for a full discussion of these effects see p. 113.

39

The orientation of the solvent molecules with respect to the lactam is non-random, the aromatic solvent is attracted to the partial positive charge on the nitrogen atom, but is repelled by the partial negative charge on oxygen.[170] The $^{13}C-^1H$ coupling constants of these compounds are shown in Table XXVII. As in the case of the amides above, the partial charge on the nitrogen tends to increase the electronegativity of the nitrogen atom, relative to the uncharged state. This in turn induces greater p character in the C—N bond and greater s character in the C—H bond of the methyl group. Generally, the values of the $^{13}C-^1H$ coupling constants are similar to those found for *NN*-dimethylacetamide, and this suggests about 40% double-bond character for the C—N bond of the amido-group.

The large $^{13}C-^1H$ coupling constants for carbonium ions (see above) are due to the increased s character in the C—H bond relative to the parent molecule. Extension of this principle to negatively charged ions leads to the prediction that $J_{^{13}C-^1H}$ should be smaller for the ion than for the neutral species. Experimental results are in accord with this idea.[157] The direct $^{13}C-^1H$ coupling in the formate ion (194·8 c./sec.) is smaller than that in formic acid or the methyl or ethyl ester (218–220 c./sec.) and similarly that of the methoxide ion (130·8 c./sec.) is smaller than that of methanol (141·5 c./sec.).

G. Aromatic compounds

The ^{13}C spectrum of benzene, measured in natural abundance, under high resolution shows long-range $^{13}C-^1H$ coupling through two, three and four bonds. By analysis of benzene and its deuterated isomers, using iterative techniques, Weigert and Roberts[10] have shown that the values of the long-range couplings are $^2J_{^{13}C-^1H}=$ $+1·0$ c./sec., $^3J_{^{13}C-C-C-^1H} = +7·4$ c./sec. and $^4J_{^{13}C-C-C-C-^1H} = -1·1$ c./sec. Analysis of the ^{13}C satellite spectrum of the proton n.m.r. of benzene affords a value for the directly bonded C–H coupling constant, but only difference values

$$(^3J_{^{13}C-^1H} - {}^2J_{^{13}C-^1H}) \text{ and } (^4J_{^{13}C-^1H} - {}^2J_{^{13}C-^1H})$$

for the long-range couplings;[171, 172] this method, however, affords accurate values for the proton–proton couplings in the molecule.

Spin–spin coupling involving ^{13}C and proton and fluorine is observed in the ^{13}C satellite spectrum of fluorobenzene.[173] Values of the directly bonded ^{13}C–H and ^{13}C–F coupling constants are shown in Table XXVIII. The dispersion mode ^{13}C n.m.r. spectrum of fluorobenzene (Fig. 7) also exhibits a two-bond ^{13}C–^{19}F coupling, not

TABLE XXVIII

^{13}C–^{1}H **and** ^{13}C–^{19}F **coupling constants of fluorobenzene**

Coupling	Ref. 174	Ref. 175
$^{13}C_2$–$^{1}H_2 \equiv {}^{13}C_6$–$^{1}H_6$	$160\cdot0\pm2\cdot0$	$155\pm2\cdot0$
$^{13}C_3$–$^{1}H_3 \equiv {}^{13}C_5$–$^{1}H_5$	$160\cdot0\pm2\cdot0$	$163\pm2\cdot0$
$^{13}C_4$–$^{1}H_4$	$160\cdot0\pm2\cdot0$	$161\pm2\cdot0$
$^{13}C_1$–$^{19}F_1$	$265\cdot5\pm2\cdot0$	$252\pm2\cdot0$
$^{13}C_2$–C_1–$^{19}F_1$	..	$17\cdot5\pm3\cdot0$

obtainable from satellite analysis.[174] The average directly bonded ^{13}C–^{1}H coupling constants for some substituted fluorobenzenes, obtained from ^{13}C satellite analysis are shown in Table XXIX[175–177] The ^{13}C–^{1}H coupling constants for a particular position show regular increase with increase of the electron-withdrawing power (Hammett σ parameters) of the substituent. However, for a given substituent, the values of the ^{13}C–^{1}H coupling constants increase with decreasing σ values of the second substituent of the disubstituted fluorobenzene and additionally change with the position of the substitution. No similar correlations were found for the ^{13}C–^{19}F coupling constants, which suggests that other contributions to the Fermi term affect these couplings. Dhingra et al.[177] have however shown that the ^{13}C–^{19}F coupling constants in p-substituted fluorobenzenes vary linearly with the Hammetts' constant σ_p; the change in the ionic character of the C—F bond, calculated on the basis of the change in the coupling constants, agrees well with that calculated from ^{19}F chemical-shift data. The ^{13}C–^{19}F coupling constants are solvent dependent and in trifluoroacetic acid solution exhibit large variations, which are ascribed to hydrogen bonding and dipolar interaction of the solvent molecules with the C—F bonds of the solute. The analysis of the ^{13}C

satellite spectra of the proton n.m.r. of symmetrical *p*-dihalogeno-benzene[178] afforded values of proton–proton, directly bonded $^{13}C–^1H$ and difference values for long-range $^{13}C–^1H$ coupling constants. The existence of a ^{13}C isotope effect is postulated to account for observed

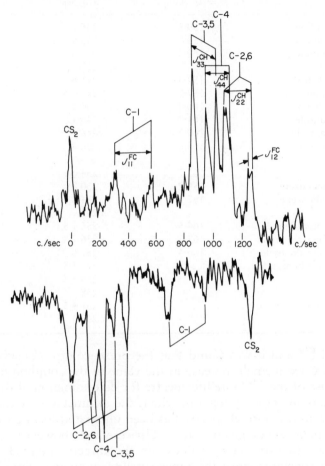

Fig. 7. The observed 15·085 Mc./sec. ^{13}C n.m.r. spectrum of fluorobenzene. Top spectrum scanned from low to high field and bottom spectrum scanned from high to low field. (From Page.[174])

differences between the low- and high-field satellite multiplets. Successful analysis of the observed spectra is obtained by treating the molecule as an ABCDX (X = ^{13}C) case rather than as a symmetrical AA′A″A‴X spin system. The values for the directly bonded $^{13}C–^1H$ couplings of the methyl group of some substituted toluenes have been

TABLE XXIX

$^{13}C-^{1}H$ and $^{13}C-^{19}F$ coupling constants, c./sec., of some substituted fluorobenzenes

	$J_{^{13}C-^{1}H}$	$J_{^{13}C-^{19}F}$	Ref.
o-Fluoroaniline	159·5	236·7	176
m-Fluoroaniline	158·8	243·9	176
p-Fluoroaniline	162·3	233·3	176
		237	178
o-Fluorophenol	157·3	241·6	176
m-Fluorophenol	157·2	245±4	176
p-Fluorophenol	160·2	240·7	176
o-Fluoroanisole	161·3	246±5	176
m-Fluoroanisole	160·7	246±5	176
p-Fluoroanisole	165·6	236·8	176
		240	178
o-Difluorobenzene	162·7	254±3	176
m-Difluorobenzene	159·2	250·8	176
p-Difluorobenzene	167·2	234·3	176
		243	178
o-Fluorobenzaldehyde	164·5	256±5	176
m-Fluorobenzaldehyde	163·3	236·7	176
p-Fluorobenzaldehyde	166·4	251·6	176
p-Fluoronitrobenzene	..	271±5	177
		259±5	177
		258	178
p-Fluorochlorobenzene	..	261±5	177
		249	178

reported,[179] and it was found that the presence of *ortho* substituent groups caused a small increase in the value of the coupling constant.

The use of the ^{13}C satellite spectra for determination of the n.m.r. parameters in those systems in which the symmetry precludes their detection in the normal spectra has been illustrated for the case of *p*-dihalogenobenzenes given above. This method, however, generally only leads to satisfactory values for the directly bonded $^{13}C-^{1}H$ coupling constants since the inner satellite resonances are obscured by the main proton signal(s). Recourse to the homonuclear double-resonance techniques[11,143] is necessary in order to obtain absolute rather than difference values for long-range couplings involving ^{13}C. Values obtained, by application of these techniques, in some chlorinated benzenes are shown in Table XXX. The three-bond $^{13}C-^{1}H$ coupling constant, $^{3}J_{^{13}C-C-C-^{1}H}$ has a comparable, if not larger, magnitude than that across two bonds ($^{2}J_{^{13}C-C-^{1}H}$), and a positive sign in accord with the majority of proton–proton couplings across the same

TABLE XXX

**Long-range $^{13}C\cdots^{1}H$ coupling constants, c./sec.,
in some polychlorobenzene derivatives**

H_b [ring: 1-Cl, 2-Cl, 3-Cl, 4-Cl, positions 5,6 with H_a] $\quad J_{^{13}C_5-H_a}=171\cdot9$
$\quad J_{^{13}C_5-H_b}=0\cdot4$

[ring with NH$_2$ at 1, Cl at 2, Cl at 6, Cl at 4, H_b at 5, H_a at 3] $\quad J_{^{13}C_3-H_a}=170\cdot1$
$\quad J_{^{13}C_3-H_b}=4\cdot3$

[ring with H_a at 1, Cl at 6, Cl at 2, Cl at 4, H_b at 5, H_b at 3] $\quad J_{^{13}C_1-H_a}=172\cdot2$
$\quad J_{^{13}C_1-H_b}=5\cdot4$

[ring with NO$_2$ at 1, Cl at 6, Cl at 2, Cl at 5, Cl at 3, H_a at 4] $\quad J_{^{13}C_4-H_a}=175\cdot0$
$\quad J_{^{13}C_2-H_a}=+4\cdot9$

[ring with NO$_2$ at 1, H_b at 6, Cl at 2, Cl at 5, H_a at 4, Cl at 3] $\quad J_{^{13}C_3-H_a}=164\cdot0;\ J_{^{13}C_3-H_b}=2\cdot2$
$\quad J_{^{13}C_6-H_b}=165\cdot4;\ J_{^{13}C_6-H_a}=0\cdot6$

number of bonds. The coupling constant $^4J_{^{13}C-C-C-C-^1H}$ is very sensitive to the position of the ^{13}C and ^1H nuclei with respect to other substituents in the molecule. Although there are but a few values available for long–range $^{13}C-^1H$, couplings their inclusion in the data for the analysis of ^{13}C satellite spectra is essential. This feature has been emphasized by Govil[180] in a study of some substituted p-benzo-quinones. The data obtained from double-resonance experiments on chlorobenzoquinone and toluquinone were used in the iterative analysis of the ^{13}C satellite n.m.r. spectrum of p-benzoquinone. Considerable deviation in the values of the long-range coupling constants was found from that reported in earlier work, but are in close agreement with those predicted from theoretical considerations.[181]

The directly bonded $^{13}C-^1H$ coupling constants have been used to give a measure of aromaticity in mono- and polycyclic hydrocarbon ring systems.[134, 182, 183] Cyclo-octatetraene reacts with methylene dichloride and methyl-lithium to afford a mixture of syn and anti-9-chlorobicyclo[6,1,0]nona-2,4,6-triene (**40** and **41**) which, on treatment with a 30% lithium dispersion in tetrahydrofuran, gives cyclonona-tetraenide, which is isolated as the tetraethylammonium salt.[58] The ^{13}C chemical shift and the coupling constant ($J_{^{13}C-^1H}=137$ c./sec.) observed for the lithio-salt (**42**) are indicative of the aromatic character of the ring, in accord with the predictions of Hückel's Aromaticity rule.

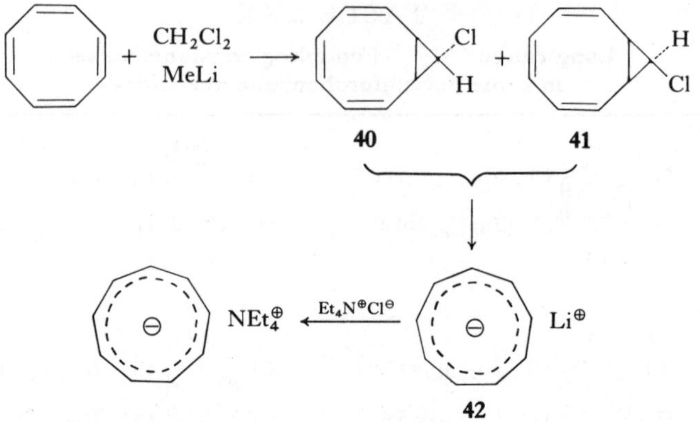

The values $(145 \pm 1$ c./sec.) of the $^{13}C-^{1}H$ coupling constant of the bridgehead proton in triptycene $(43)^{182, 183}$ is similar to those obtained for bicycloheptanols and other compounds containing the bicyclo-[2,2,1]heptyl ring system. The value reflects enhanced s character of the tertiary C—H bond and resultant π character in the strained ring system.

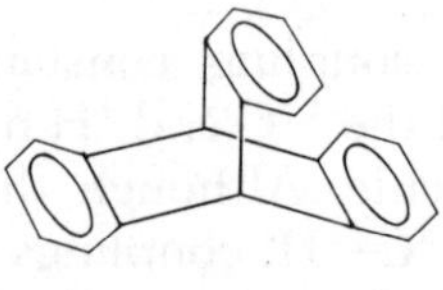

43

H. Heterocyclic compounds

Radeglia[184] has presented values for the $^{13}C-^{1}H$ coupling constants of the methylene groups in diaziridin and oxaziridin derivatives, 178 and 173 c./sec., respectively, and compared these values with those of cyclopropane (161), ethylenimine (168) and ethyleneoxide (176 c./sec.). These results were discussed in the terms of the electronegativity of the ring substituents. In an investigation[138] of some similar three-membered ring systems of the form (44), the magnitude of the $^{13}C-^{1}H$

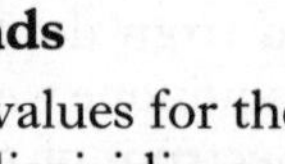

44

coupling constants was dependent upon the endocyclic XCY bond angle and upon the electronegative properties of the atoms X and Y. This latter effect appears to be only operative for heteroatoms in the

α-position; in the β- and γ-positions the heteroatoms do not appreciably alter the value of the coupling constant. This feature is well illustrated by the $^{13}C-^{1}H$ coupling constants of thiophene (45) and thiazole (46) and 2-methylthiophene (47) and 5-methylthiazole (48)

45   46   47   48

The values in parentheses are the $^{13}C-^{1}H$ coupling constants.

where it is seen that the coupling constants of the β-C—H are approximately 20 c./sec. smaller than for the α-C—H bond. Introduction of the second heteroatom causes about a 20 c./sec. increase in the $^{13}C-^{1}H$ coupling constants; such observations could prove useful in making assignments in more complex molecules. Values of the $^{13}C-^{1}H$ couplings at positions 2,4 and 5 in thiazole and its derivatives (Table XXXI) have been found[185] to show dependence upon both the bond length and the bond angle involving the heteroatom.

TABLE XXXI

$^{13}C-^{1}H$ **coupling constants, c./sec., in thiazole derivatives**

	J_{C_2-H}	J_{C_4-H}	J_{C_5-H}		J_{C_2-H}	J_{C_4-H}	J_{C_5-H}
Thiazole	210·0	184·2	189·0	2-Cl	..	189·0	189·0
2-Me	..	183·8	187·5	4-Cl	214·0	..	194·0
4-Me	212·0	..	185·5	5-Cl	214·5	190·0	..
2,4-Me$_2$	..	..	183·0	2-Br	..	191·2	192·2
2,5-Me$_2$	..	179·5	..	5-Br	212·0	190·2	..
4,5-Me$_2$	208·0	..	..	2,4-Cl$_2$	..	..	193·0
2-Pr^i,4-Bu^t	..	..	182·0	2,4-Br$_2$	..	..	194·0
2,4-(Bu^t)$_2$	..	..	181·0	2,5-Br$_2$	..	192·5	..
2-NH$_2$	..	183·2	190·0	2-Cl,5-Br	..	191·5	..
2-NMe$_2$	..	182·0	190·0				
2-Piperidino	..	184·6	190·0				

Page et al.[63] have re-determined the values of directly bonded $^{13}C-^{1}H$ couplings in furan, pyrrole, thiophen and some of the methyl derivatives. Values for the $^{13}C_\alpha-^{1}H$ couplings of bromo-substituted thiophens are generally larger than those of the $^{13}C_\beta-^{1}H$ coupling constants by about 15 c./sec.[186] The results, shown in Table XXXII, reflect a larger s character of the C_α–H bond, which is consequently shorter than the C_β–H bond in thiophen and its derivatives.

TABLE XXXII

^{13}C–^{1}H coupling constants, c./sec., in bromothiophens

	$J_{C_\alpha–H}$	$J_{C_\beta–H}$
2,3-dibromo-	190	176
2,4-dibromo-	195	178
2,5-dibromo-	..	174
3,4-dibromo-	194	..
2,3,4-tribromo-	195	..
2,3,5-tribromo-	..	181

Read et al.[187] have analysed the proton and ^{13}C satellite spectra of selenophen and several mono- and di-halogenated derivatives. Values of the directly bonded ^{13}C–^{1}H coupling constants are given in Table XXXIII. It will be observed that introduction of an halogen atom,

TABLE XXXIII

^{13}C–^{1}H coupling constants, c./sec., in selenophen and some of its derivatives

	$J_{C_2–H}$	$J_{C_3–H}$	$J_{C_4–H}$	$J_{C_5–H}$
Selenophen	187·23	164·62	164·62	187·23
2-chloro-	..	169·15	167·17	189·96
2-bromo-	..	169·69	167·32	189·58
2,5-dichloro-	..	171·61	171·61	..
2,5-dibromo-	..	171·42	171·42	..

either chlorine or bromine, results in an increase in the ^{13}C–^{1}H coupling of the C—H bond α to the halogen. Information regarding the conformational properties of six-membered heterocyclic ring compounds may be obtained from analysis of the proton and ^{13}C satellite spectra.[188,189] The proton n.m.r. evidence shows that in trans-2,3-dichloro- and trans-2,3-dibromo-1,4-dioxans, the chair form of the dioxan ring is deformed. Analysis of the satellite spectrum arising from the C(2) and C(3) protons show that $J_{^{13}C–^1H}$ is 184 c./sec.; this high value, relative to that observed in dioxan itself $J_{^{13}C–^1H} = 142·2$ c./sec., may indicate partial double-bond character in the C_2–C_3 bond. Mayo and Goldstein[190] have re-analysed the proton and ^{13}C–^{1}H satellite spectra of 4-pyrone in an effort to resolve disagreements concerning two of the proton–proton couplings. An iterative least-squares analysis of all four satellites showed that the values of the directly bonded ^{13}C–^1H couplings were: $J_{^{13}C_2\text{-}^1H} = 199.52$ c./sec. and $J_{^{13}C_3\text{-}^1H} = 168.82$ c./sec. and, as has already been stated, only difference values for the long-range ^{13}C–^1H couplings could be obtained.

The directly bonded ^{13}C–^1H coupling constants of six azines, namely pyridine, pyridazine, pyrimidine, pyrazine, s-triazine and s-tetrazine and their methyl derivatives have been obtained by the analysis of their ^{13}C satellite spectra;[191] the electronic implications of the variation of these coupling constants has been considered.[138] Generally speaking, the directly bonded ^{13}C–^1H couplings are of a similar value to those in other six-membered rings. The C–H couplings are larger at less shielded carbon atoms, possibly reflecting in part an increase in the contact (Fermi) interaction with increasing effective nuclear charge. The proton resonance spectrum of pyridazine (49) has been the subject of several studies.[192, 193] The spectrum is of the AA'XX' type and each of the two satellite ^{13}C spectra may be treated as ABMX (X = ^{13}C) spin systems. Values of the ^{13}C–^1H coupling constants are shown in (49).

$$J_{^{13}C_3\text{-}^1H} \equiv J_{^{13}C_6\text{-}^1H} = 183 \text{ c./sec.}$$
$$J_{^{13}C_4\text{-}^1H} \equiv J_{^{13}C_5\text{-}^1H} = 168 \text{ c./sec.}$$

49

The directly bonded ^{13}C–^1H coupling constant observed in the cyclobutane ring of the photodimer of thymine (50) is 153 ± 2 c./sec.[194] The behaviour of purine in acid media has been studied by n.m.r.,[195] and both the proton chemical shifts and the ^{13}C–^1H coupling constants

R = H or Me   **50**

demonstrate similar response to changes in pH values, which suggests a simple acid–base equilibrium. Tanabe and Detre[196] have demonstrated an unusual application of ^{13}C–^1H coupling constants in the determination of molecular structure. Generally, radioactive ^{14}C labelling techniques have been used to test and verify proposed biosynthetic pathways. These authors, however, used ^{13}C labelled acetate in the study of the biosynthesis of microbial metabolites, in this instance griseofulvin (51). The location of incorporated ^{13}C labelled atoms in excess of those in natural abundance was determined by p.m.r. The ^{13}C–^{1}H coupling constants are shown in (51), and the increase in value expected with increase in the s character of the carbon orbital was of considerable value in the assignment of specific carbon atoms.

* Denotes ^{13}C-labelled atoms.

$J_{^{13}C–^{1}H}$ of $C_{6'}$—CH_3 $\quad = 120$

$\left.\begin{array}{l} \text{of } C_4\text{—}OCH_3 \\ \text{of } C_6\text{—}OCH_3 \end{array}\right\} = 140$

of $C_{3'}$—H $\quad = 160$

of C_5—H $\quad = 160$

51

I. Organometallic and inorganic compounds

Substituent effects on $J_{^{13}C–^{1}H}$ in silyl compounds may be used to predict the ^{13}C–^{1}H coupling constants in related compounds.[197, 198] The application of a general relationship of the form—

$$J_{MH}(MHXYZ) = \zeta X + \zeta Y + \zeta Z,$$

where M = magnetically active isotope of a group IV element and $\zeta X = J_{MH}(MH_3X) - \frac{2}{3}J_{MH}(MH_4)$ to di- and tri-substituted derivatives of the methyl silanes shows that additive properties, of not very electronegative α substituents (e.g., CH_3, SR, I, Br), are sufficient to account for the variation of the directly bonded C–H coupling constants. Significant deviations are however found for highly electronegative substituents (F, OR). There is little correlation between $J_{^{13}C–^{1}H}$ and $J_{^{29}Si–^{1}H}$ in compounds of the form CH_3SiXHY, which is only to be expected if changes in both coupling constants are determined by changes in σ-bond polarization.[199]

Roberts et al.[72] have recently measured the ^{13}C coupling constants of both Group II and Group IV metal alkyls using the ^{13}C spectra. These coupling constants, together with the ^{13}C chemical shifts are shown in Table IX (p. 175). There was fairly good agreement between the experimental values, of the direct ^{13}C–metal coupling, with those calculated using the method of Karabatsos[200] and Smith[201] (their treatment was essentially based upon the Fermi contact term and related the metal–carbon coupling to that of the carbon–carbon coupling in neopentane).

Fluck et al.[202] have determined the directly bonded ^{13}C–^{1}H coupling constants in trimethylsilylphosphines, $[Me_3Si]_nPH_{3-n}$, which all fall in the range 120·2–120·9 c./sec. A linear relationship was obtained between the $^{13}C-^{1}H$ coupling constant and the methyl chemical shift in compounds of the form $M(CH_3)_4$, where M is an element of Group IV.[203] The values of the $^{13}C-^{1}H$ coupling constants indicate that the hybridization of the methyl carbon atom in the derivatives changes with the effectiveness of the central element–carbon overlap. Cumper et al.[204] have indicated that measurements of proton chemical shifts and directly bonded $^{13}C-^{1}H$ coupling constants can give information regarding the existence of $p_{\pi}-d_{\pi}$ bonding in compounds of the type $Me_{4-n}X(OMe)_n$, where $n = 1 - 4$ and $X = C$, Si, Ge and $Me_{4-n}X(SMe)_n$ where $X = C$ and Si. By comparing the values of proton chemical shifts and $J_{^{13}C-^{1}H}$ values for silicon- and germanium-containing compounds relative to the corresponding hydrocarbons, where $p_{\pi}-d_{\pi}$ delocalization is absent, the authors presented evidence for this type of bonding between silicon and oxygen. For the series $Me_{4-n}Si(OMe)_n$ the $^{13}C-^{1}H$ couplings are larger than those in the corresponding $Me_{4-n}C(OMe)_n$ series when $n = 1$ and 2, but are smaller when $n = 3$ and 4. This implies that, although the total electronic charge around the silicon atom is increased by $p_{\pi}-d_{\pi}$ delocalization from the oxygen, the π-bond character decreases with increasing values of n. The $^{13}C-^{1}H$ coupling constants for some methylgermanium halides are shown in Table XXXIV.[205]

TABLE XXXIV

$^{13}C-^{1}H$ **coupling constants, c./sec., in methylgermanium halides**

	$J_{^{13}C-^{1}H}$
CH_3GeCl_3	138
$(CH_3)_2GeCl_2$	132
$(CH_3)_3GeCl$	128·5
$(CH_3)_4Ge$	124·5
GH_3GeH_3	127·8
$(CH_3)_2GeH_2$	126·8
$(CH_3)_3GeH$	126·2

The $^{13}C-^{1}H$ coupling constants for (trimethylsilyl)methylamino-stannanes $[(CH_3)_3Si-N(CH_3)]_nSn(CH_3)_{4-n}$, where $n = 1-4$, have been reported[206] and are shown in Table XXXV. Clark et al.[207] have presented values for the various couplings in fluorinated organotin compounds. The $^{13}C-^{1}H$ coupling constant for the methyltin groups in several fluoroalkyl trimethyltin derivatives are in the range 130·0–131·0 c./sec. The values of the $^{13}C-^{1}H$ coupling constants of the

TABLE XXXV

^{13}C–^{1}H coupling constants, c./sec., in
[(Trimethylsilyl)methylamino]stannanes $[(CH_3)_3SiN(CH_3)]_nSn(CH_3)_{4-n}$

	$J_{^{13}C-^1H}$			
	$n=1$	$n=2$	$n=3$	$n=4$
Sn–^{13}C–^{1}H	129·5	129·5	131·0	..
Si–^{13}C–^{1}H	118·0	117·5	117·5	118·0
N–^{13}C–^{1}H	133·0	133·0	133·5	134·5

methylene groups of benzyltin derivatives are in a similar range, 131–133 c./sec.[208]

The preparation of various ^{13}C isotopically enriched acetylacetonate complexes of Li, Na, K, Be, Mg, Al, Cu and Pd have been described.[209] Long-range ^{13}C····^{1}H coupling over two or three bonds are observed in the p.m.r. spectra of the enol and keto forms of the acetylacetonates and their corresponding metal complexes (Table XXXVI).

TABLE XXXVI

^{13}C–^{1}H coupling constants, c./sec., of acetylacetone, keto and enol form, and metal complexes (acac)

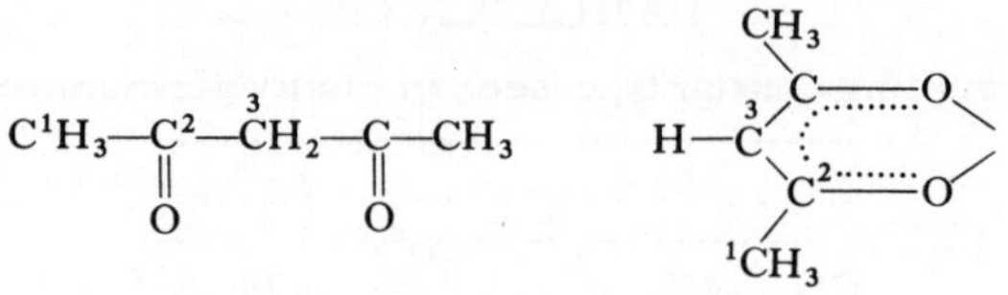

Coupling	Keto	Enol	Be(acac)$_2$	Al(acac)$_3$	Pd(acac)$_2$
C^1–H	129·5	129·0	129·0	128·0	129·3
C^3–H	129·0	167·5	166·0	161·8	160·8
C^3–C–C^1–H	<0·5	3·0	~2·0	..	2·4
C^1–C–C^3–H	<0·5	~2	~2	..	2·2

It is clear from the Table that the directly bonded ^{13}C–^{1}H coupling of the =C—H or —CH$_2$ group of the enol and keto forms are, as expected, markedly different. It is also of interest to note that the long-range $^3J_{^{13}C-C-C-^1H}$ coupling is greater in the enol than in the keto form.

The application of the observation of the ^{13}C chemical shifts to determine the structure of diene–irontricarbonyl complexes has been mentioned above (p. 176).[75, 76] The ^{13}C–^{1}H coupling constants, obtained from the ^{13}C resonance studies on butadiene- and methyl-octadecadienoate-iron tricarbonyls (16 and 17), indicate that all the C—H bonds in the diene complexes are essentially sp^2 hybridized. The bonding of the iron atom at C_2, C_3 is very similar to that in ferrocene. However steric effects at the terminal CH_2 or CHR groups cause twisting about the C_1—C_2 and C_3—C_4 bonds and this leads to smaller rotational displacement in the substituted butadiene of the octadecadieneoate complex. The rotation of the $C_{1,4}$ p_z orbitals leads to differences in the bonding of iron to $C_{1,2}$ and $C_{3,4}$ and that to $C_{2,3}$.

Thus the ^{13}C spectra of these two diene–irontricarbonyl complexes support a structure approaching (16), in which all four carbon atoms of the butadiene system have essentially sp^2 hybrids. Similar conclusions were reached by Preston and Davis[76] in a study of the cyclobutadiene complex in which the high value of the ^{13}C–^1H coupling constant of 191 c./sec. indicates that hybridization of the carbon orbital is between sp^2 and sp, consistent with a strained butadiene structure. In both this and the butadiene–irontricarbonyl complex the magnitude of J_{13C-1H} is a reflection of the interaction of iron d orbitals with π-electrons rather than the result of Fe—C bond formation.

The measurement of the ^{13}C coupling constants to nuclei other than proton or fluorine are rare. Loewenstein and Shporer[210] have measured the ^{59}Co–^{13}C coupling constant and the ^{59}C isotope shifts in $K_3Co(CN)_6$, prepared from potassium cyanide enriched to 15 atom per cent. with ^{13}C. The value of $J_{13C-59Co}$ is 128 ± 0.5 c./sec.

REFERENCES

1. P. C. Lauterbur, *J. Chem. Phys.*, 1957, **26**, 217.
2. P. C. Lauterbur, "Nuclear Magnetic Resonance Spectra of Elements Other than Hydrogen and Fluorine", Chapter 7 *in* "Determination of Organic Structures by Physical Methods", Ed. F. C. Nachod and W. D. Phillips. Academic Press, New York, 1962.
3. J. B. Stothers, *Quart. Rev.*, 1965, **19**, 144.
4. J. W. Emsley, J. Feeney and L. H. Sutcliffe, "High Resolution Nuclear Magnetic Resonance Spectroscopy". Vol. 2. (a) p. 988; (b) p. 1011. Pergamon Press, London, 1966.
5. D. F. S. Natusch and R. E. Richards, *Chem. Comm.*, 1966, 579.
6. J-P. Imband, *Compt. rend.*, 1965, **261**, 5442.
7. R. R. Ernst, *J. Chem. Phys.*, 1966, **45**, 3845.
8. D. C. Dehlsen and A. V. Robertson, *Austral. J. Chem.*, 1966, **19**, 269.
9. J. M. Read and J. H. Goldstein, *Analyt. Chem.*, 1965, **37**, 1609.
10. F. J. Weigert and J. D. Roberts, *J. Amer. Chem. Soc.*, 1967, **89**, 2967.
11. R. Freeman, *J. Chem. Phys.*, 1965, **43**, 3087.
12. R. Freeman and W. A. Anderson, *J. Chem. Phys.*, 1965, **42**, 1199.
13. J. K. Becconsall and P. Hampson, *Mol. Phys.*, 1965, **10**, 21.

14. A. Mathias and V. M. S. Gil, *Tetrahedron Letters*, 1965, 3163.
15. A. Mathias, *Tetrahedron*, 1966, **22**, 217.
16. G. E. Hall, *Ann. Review of N.M.R. Spectroscopy*, 1968, **1**, 227.
17. W. McFarlane, *Ann. Review of N.M.R. Spectroscopy*, 1968, **1**, 135.
18. A. Saika and W. P. Slichter, *J. Chem. Phys.*, 1954, **22**, 26.
19. T. Yonezawa, I. Morishima and H. Kato, *Bull. Chem. Soc. Japan*, 1966, **39**, 1398.
20. J. M. Sichel and M. A. Whitehead, *Theor. Chim. Acta*, 1966, **5**, 35.
21. B. V. Cheney and D. M. Grant, *J. Amer. Chem. Soc.*, 1967, **89**, 5319.
22. J. Feeney, L. H. Sutcliffe and S. M. Walker, *Mol. Phys.*, 1966, **11**, 117.
23. M. A. Whitehead, N. C. Baird and M. Kaplansky, *Theor. Chim. Acta*, 1965, **3**, 135.
24. M. Karplus and J. A. Pople, *J. Chem. Phys.*, 1963, **38**, 2803.
25. H. L. Retcofsky, J. M. Hoffmann and R. A. Friedel, *J. Chem. Phys.*, 1967, **46**, 4545.
26. T. D. Alger, D. M. Grant and E. G. Paul, *J. Amer. Chem. Soc.*, 1966, **88**, 5397.
27. D. T. Clark, *Chem. Comm.*, 1966, 390.
28. D. T. Clark and J. W. Emsley, *Mol. Phys.*, 1967, **12**, 365.
29. G. B. Savitsky and K. Namikawa, *J. Phys. Chem.*, 1964, **68**, 1956.
30. G. B. Savitsky, R. M. Pearson and K. Namikawa, *J. Phys. Chem.*, 1965, **69**, 1425.
31. E. R. Malinowski, T. Vladimiroff and R. F. Tavares, *J. Phys. Chem.*, 1966, **70**, 2046.
32. W. M. Litchman and D. M. Grant, *J. Amer. Chem. Soc.*, 1968, **90**, 1400.
33. P. Bucci, *J. Chem. Soc.*, 1968, **90**, 252.
34. J. J. Burke and P. C. Lauterbur, *J. Amer. Chem. Soc.*, 1964, **86**, 1870.
35. G. E. Maciel and G. B. Savitsky, *J. Phys. Chem.*, 1965, **69**, 3925.
36. P. H. Weiner and E. R. Malinowski, *J. Phys. Chem.*, 1967, **71**, 2791.
37. G. W. Buchanan, D. A. Ross and J. B. Stothers, *J. Amer. Chem. Soc.*, 1966, **88**, 4301.
38. D. K. Dalling and D. M. Grant, *J. Amer. Chem. Soc.*, 1967, **89**, 6612.
39. G. E. Maciel, *J. Phys. Chem.*, 1965, **69**, 1947.
40. K. S. Dhami and J. B. Stothers, *Canad. J. Chem.*, 1965, **43**, 510.
41. D. H. Marr and J. B. Stothers, *Canad. J. Chem.*, 1965, **43**, 596.
42. T. Lippmaa, V. I. Sokolov, A. I. Olivson and Ya. O. Past, *Doklady Akad. Nauk S.S.S.R.*, 1967, **173**, 358.
43. D. D. Traficante and G. E. Maciel, *J. Phys. Chem.*, 1965, **69**, 1348.
44. G. E. Maciel, P. D. Ellis and D. C. Hofer, *J. Phys. Chem.*, 1967, **71**, 2160.
45. G. E. Maciel, *J. Chem. Phys.*, 1965, **42**, 2746.
46. G. B. Savitsky, K. Namikawa and G. Zweifel, *J. Phys. Chem.*, 1965, **69**, 3105.
47. D. H. Marr and J. B. Stothers, *Canad. J. Chem.*, 1967, **45**, 226.
48. K. S. Dhami and J. B. Stothers, *Canad. J. Chem.*, 1965, **43**, 479.
49. K. S. Dhami and J. B. Stothers, *Canad. J. Chem.*, 1965, **43**, 499.
50. K. S. Dhami and J. B. Stothers, *Canad. J. Chem.*, 1967, **45**, 233.
51. G. E. Maciel and J. J. Natterstad, *J. Chem. Phys.*, 1965, **42**, 2752.
52. G. E. Maciel and D. D. Traficante, *J. Amer. Chem. Soc.*, 1966, **88**, 220.
53. G. E. Maciel and D. D. Traficante, *J. Phys. Chem.*, 1965, **69**, 1030.
54. D. D. Traficante and G. E. Maciel, *J. Phys. Chem.*, 1966, **70**, 1314.
55. G. A. Olah and M. B. Comisarow, *J. Amer. Chem. Soc.*, 1966, **88**, 4442.
56. G. A. Olah and A. M. White, *J. Amer. Chem. Soc.*, 1967, **89**, 7072.
57. G. E. Maciel and D. A. Beatty, *J. Phys. Chem.*, 1965, **69**, 3920.
58. E. A. LaLanchette and R. E. Benson, *J. Amer. Chem. Soc.*, 1965, **87**, 1941.

59. W. R. Woolfender and D. M. Grant, *J. Amer. Chem. Soc.*, 1966, **88**, 1497.
60. D. M. Grant and B. V. Cheney, *J. Amer. Chem. Soc.*, 1967, **89**, 5315.
61. K. S. Dhami and J. B. Stothers, *Canad. J. Chem.*, 1966, **44**, 2855.
62. G. E. Maciel and J. J. Natterstad, *J. Chem. Phys.*, 1965, **42**, 2427.
63. T. F. Page, T. D. Alger and D. M. Grant, *J. Amer. Chem. Soc.*, 1965, **87**, 5333.
64. H. L. Retcofsky and R. A. Friedel, *J. Phys. Chem.*, 1967, **71**, 3592.
65. H. L. Retcofsky and F. R. McDonald, *Tetrahedron Letters*, 1968, 2575.
66. P. C. Lauterbur, *J. Chem. Phys.*, 1965, **43**, 360.
67. R. J. Pugmire and D. M. Grant, *J. Amer. Chem. Soc.*, 1968, **90**, 697.
68. W. Adam, A. Grimison and G. Rodriguez, *Tetrahedron*, 1967, **23**, 2513.
69. R. J. Pugmire, D. M. Grant, R. K. Robins and G. W. Rhodes, *J. Amer. Chem. Soc.*, 1965, **87**, 2225.
70. R. G. Rees and M. J. Green, *J. Chem. Soc. B*, 1968, 387.
71. R. Waack, M. A. Doran, E. B. Baker and G. A. Olah, *J. Amer. Chem. Soc.*, 1966, **88**, 1272.
72. F. J. Weigert, M. Winokur and J. D. Roberts, *J. Amer. Chem. Soc.*, 1968, **90**, 566.
73. B. F. Spielvogel and J. M. Purser, *J. Amer. Chem. Soc.*, 1967, **89**, 5294.
74. H. L. Retcofsky and C. E. Griffin, *Tetrahedron Letters*, 1966, 1975.
75. H. L. Retcofsky, E. N. Frankel and H. S. Gutowsky, *J. Amer. Chem. Soc.*, 1966, **88**, 2711.
76. H. G. Preston and J. C. Davis, *J. Amer. Chem. Soc.*, 1966, **88**, 1585.
77. P. C. Lauterbur and R. B. King, *J. Amer. Chem. Soc.*, 1965, **87**, 3266.
78. E. Hiroike, *J. Phys. Soc. Japan*, 1967, **23**, 1079.
79. T. Yonezawa, I. Morishima, M. Fujii and K. Fukui, *Bull. Chem. Soc. Japan*, 1965, **38**, 1224.
80. T. Yonezawa, I. Morishima and M. Fujii, *Bull. Chem. Soc. Japan*, 1967, **39**, 2110.
81. J. A. Pople and D. P. Santry, *Mol. Phys.*, 1964, **8**, 1.
82. R. C. Fahey, G. C. Graham and R. L. Piccioni, *J. Amer. Chem. Soc.*, 1966, **88**, 193.
83. F. B. van Duijneveldt, V. M. S. Gil and J. N. Murrell, *Theoret. Chim. Acta*, 1966, **4**, 85.
84. A. H. Cowley, W. D. White and S. L. Manatt, *J. Amer. Chem. Soc.*, 1967, **89**, 6433.
85. J. N. Murrell, P. E. Stevenson and G. T. Jones, *Mol. Phys.*, 1967, **12**, 265.
86. R. Ditchfield, M. A. Jensen and J. N. Murrell, *J. Chem. Soc. A*, 1967, 1674.
87. T. Vladimiroff and E. R. Malinowski, *J. Chem. Phys.*, 1967, **46**, 1830.
88. M. Barfield, *J. Chem. Phys.*, 1966, **44**, 1836.
89. J. D. Baldeschwieler and E. W. Randall, *Chem. Rev.*, 1963, **63**, 81.
90. R. A. Hoffman and S. Forsen, *Progress in Nuclear Magnetic Resonance Spectroscopy*, 1966, **1**, 15.
91. M. Karplus and D. M. Grant, *Proc. Natl. Acad. Sci.*, 1959, **45**, 1269.
92. R. A. Bernheim and B. J. Lavery, *J. Amer. Chem. Soc.*, 1967, **88**, 1279.
93. L. C. Snyder and S. Meiboom, *J. Chem. Phys.*, 1966, **44**, 4057.
94. K. A. McLauchlan, *Chem. Comm.*, 1965, 105.
95. D. M. Grant, *J. Amer. Chem. Soc.*, 1967, **89**, 2228.
96. W. McFarlane, *Mol. Phys.*, 1966, **10**, 603.
97. W. McFarlane, *J. Chem. Soc. A*, 1967, 1660.
98. K. A. McLauchlan, *Mol. Phys.*, 1966, **11**, 303; 503.
99. R. R. Dean and W. McFarlane, *Mol. Phys.*, 1967, **12**, 289, 364.

100. W. McFarlane, *Chem. Comm.*, 1967, 58.
101. A. R. Cunningham, A. Pidcock and J. D. Smith, *Chem. Comm.*, 1966, 89.
102. E. G. Finer and R. K. Harris, *Mol. Phys.*, 1967, **13**, 65.
103. W. McFarlane, *J. Chem. Soc. A*, 1967, 1148.
104. W. McFarlane, *J. Chem. Soc. A*, 1967, 528.
105. W. McFarlane, *Mol. Phys.*, 1967, **13**, 587.
106. W. McFarlane, *Mol. Phys.*, 1967, **12**, 243.
107. H. Dreeskamp and G. Stegmeir, *Z. Naturforsch.*, 1967, **22A**, 1458.
108. K. A. McLauchlan, D. H. Whiffen and L. W. Reeves, *Mol. Phys.*, 1966, **10**, 131.
109. R. R. Dean and W. McFarlane, *Mol. Phys.*, 1967, **13**, 343.
110. R. E. Eckstein and A. Attalla, *Analyt. Chem.*, 1966, **38**, 1965.
111. N. F. Ramsey, *Phys. Rev.*, 1953, **91**, 301.
112. G. W. Smith, *J. Chem. Phys.*, 1965, **42**, 435.
113. D. M. Grant and W. M. Litchman, *J. Amer. Chem. Soc.*, 1965, **87**, 3994.
114. J. E. Huckley, *J. Chem. Phys.*, 1966, **45**, 405.
115. L. Lunazzi and F. Taddei, *Boll. sci. della Fac. Chem. ind. Bologna*, 1965, **23**, 358.
116. L. Lunazzi and F. Taddei, *Spectrochim. Acta*, 1967, **23A**, 841.
117. A. W. Douglas, *J. Chem. Phys.*, 1966, **45**, 3465.
118. P. Jouve, *Compt. rend.*, 1966, **262B**, 815.
119. T. L. Brown and J. C. Puckett, *J. Chem. Phys.*, 1966, **44**, 2238.
120. A. W. Douglas and D. Dietz, *J. Chem. Phys.*, 1967, **46**, 1214.
121. V. S. Watts and J. H. Goldstein, *J. Phys. Chem.*, 1966, **70**, 3887.
122. G. J. Martin, B. Castro and M. Martin, *Compt. rend.*, 1965, **261**, 395.
123. R. A. Murray and J. C. Davis, *J. Phys. Chem.*, 1967, **71**, 3361.
124. E. Sackmann and H. Dreeskamp, *Spectrochim. Acta*, 1965, **21**, 2005.
125. G. J. Karabatsos and C. E. Orzech, *J. Amer. Chem. Soc.*, 1965, **87**, 560.
126. J. A. Pople, *Mol. Phys.*, 1958, **1**, 216.
127. W. M. Litchman and D. M. Grant, *J. Amer. Chem. Soc.*, 1967, **89**, 6775.
128. R. E. Graves and R. A. Newmark, *J. Chem. Phys.*, 1967, **47**, 3681.
129. W. J. Considine, *Tetrahedron Letters*, 1966, 4923.
130. G. A. Olah and M. B. Comisarow, *J. Amer. Chem. Soc.*, 1966, **88**, 1818.
131. V. S. Watts and J. H. Goldstein, *J. Chem. Phys.*, 1967, **46**, 4165.
132. W. A. Bernett, *J. Chem. Educ.*, 1967, **44**, 17.
133. F. J. Weigert and J. D. Roberts, *J. Amer. Chem. Soc.*, 1967, **89**, 5962.
134. S. L. Manatt, D. D. Elleman and S. J. Brois, *J. Amer. Chem. Soc.*, 1965, **87**, 2220.
135. I. Fleming and D. H. Williams, *Tetrahedron*, 1967, **23**, 2747.
136. K. B. Wiberg, G. M. Lampman, R. P. Ciula, D. S. Connor, P. Schertler and J. Lavanish, *Tetrahedron*, 1965, **21**, 2749.
137. G. L. Closs and R. B. Larrabee, *Tetrahedron Letters*, 1965, 287.
138. P. Laszlo, *Bull. Soc. chim. France*, 1966, 558.
139. T. Vladimiroff, *J. Phys. Chem.*, 1965, **69**, 3197.
140. F. Hruska, G. Kotowycz and T. Schaefer, *Canad. J. Chem.*, 1965, **43**, 2827.
141. V. S. Watts and J. H. Goldstein, *Theor. Chim. Acta.*, 1966, **4**, 265.
142. J. Reuben and A. Demiel, *J. Chem. Phys.*, 1966, **44**, 2216.
143. G. Govil, *J. Chem. Soc. A*, 1967, 1420.
144. V. S. Watts, J. Loemaker and J. H. Goldstein, *J. Mol. Spectroscopy*, 1965, **17**, 348.
145. H. M. Hutton and T. Schaefer, *Canad. J. Chem.*, 1967, **45**, 1111.
146. C. L. Bell and S. S. Danyluk, *J. Amer. Chem. Soc.*, 1966, **88**, 2344.
147. K. A. McLauchlan, L. W. Reeves and T. Schaefer, *Canad. J. Chem.*, 1966, **44**, 1473.

148. E. B. Whipple, M. Ruta, V. S. Watts and J. H. Goldstein, *J. Chem. Phys.*, 1966, **45**, 4372.
149. A. W. Douglas and J. H. Goldstein, *J. Mol. Spectroscopy*, 1965, **16**, 1.
150. K. A. McLauchlan and T. Schaefer, *Canad. J. Chem.*, 1966, **44**, 321.
151. J. Feeney and P. J. S. Pauwels, *Mol. Phys.*, 1968, **14**, 209.
152. S. Borčić and J. D. Roberts, *J. Amer. Chem. Soc.*, 1965, **87**, 1056.
153. E. A. Hill and J. D. Roberts, *J. Amer. Chem. Soc.*, 1967, **89**, 2047.
154. S. G. Frankiss and I. Matsubara, *J. Phys. Chem.*, 1966, **70**, 1543.
155. M-P. Simonnin, *Bull. Soc. chim. France*, 1966, 1774.
156. R. M. Hammaker, *J. Chem. Phys.*, 1965, **43**, 1843.
157. R. M. Hammaker, *J. Mol. Spectroscopy*, 1965, **15**, 506.
158. E. R. Malinowski, L. Z. Pollara and J. P. Larmann, *J. Amer. Chem. Soc.*, 1962, **84**, 2649.
159. C. S. Juan and H. S. Gutowsky, *J. Chem. Phys.*, 1962, **37**, 2198.
160. R. M. Hammaker, *Canad. J. Chem.*, 1965, **43**, 2916.
161. G. J. Karabatsos and N. Hsi, *J. Amer. Chem. Soc.*, 1965, **87**, 2864.
162. G. J. Karabatsos, C. E. Orzech and N. Hsi, *J. Amer. Chem. Soc.*, 1966, **88**, 1817.
163. G. J. Karabatsos and K. L. Krumel, *Tetrahedron*, 1967, **23**, 1097.
164. W. H. DeJeu, H. A. Gaur and J. Smidt, *Rec. Trav. Chim.*, 1965, **84**, 1621.
165. G. A. Olah and A. M. White, *J. Amer. Chem. Soc.*, 1967, **89**, 7072.
166. L. E. Erickson, *J. Amer. Chem. Soc.*, 1965, **87**, 1867.
167. L. S. Rattet, L. Mandell and J. H. Goldstein, *J. Amer. Chem. Soc.*, 1967, **89**, 2253.
168. T. Pletcher and E. H. Cordes, *J. Org. Chem.*, 1967, **32**, 2294.
169. R. C. Neuman and L. Brewster Young, *J. Phys. Chem.*, 1965, **69**, 2570.
170. R. M. Moriarty and J. M. Kliegman, *Tetrahedron Letters*, 1966, 891.
171. J. M. Read, R. E. Mayo and J. H. Goldstein, *J. Mol. Spectroscopy*, 1966, **21**, 235.
172. J. M. Read, R. E. Mayo and J. H. Goldstein, *J. Mol. Spectroscopy*, 1967, **22**, 419.
173. S. Mohanty and P. Venkateswarlu, *Mol. Phys.*, 1966, **11**, 329.
174. T. F. Page, *Mol. Phys.*, 1967, **13**, 523.
175. S. Mohanty and P. Venkateswarlu, *Mol. Phys.*, 1967, **12**, 277.
176. G. Aruldhas, *Proc. Indian Acad. Sci.*, 1966, **63A**, 349.
177. M. M. Dhingra, G. Govil and C. L. Khetrapal, *Proc. Indian Acad. Sci.*, 1966, **64A**, 91.
178. J. M. Read, R. W. Crecely and J. H. Goldstein, *J. Mol. Spectroscopy*, 1968, **25**, 107.
179. N. Muller, *J. Chem. Phys.*, 1965, **42**, 4309.
180. G. Govil, *J. Chem. Soc. A*, 1967, 1416.
181. G. T. Jones and J. N. Murrell, *J. Chem. Soc. A*, 1966, 1421.
182. W. B. Smith and B. A. Shoulders, *J. Phys. Chem.*, 1965, **69**, 2022.
183. K. G. Kidd, G. Kotowycz and T. Schaefer, *Canad. J. Chem.*, 1967, **45**, 2156.
184. R. Radeglia, *Spectrochim. Acta*, 1967, **23A**, 1677.
185. E-J. Vincent and J. Metzger, *Comptes rend.*, 1964, **66**, 261.
186. K. Takahashi, T. Sone, Y. Matsuki and G. Hazato, *Bull. Chem. Soc. Japan*, 1965, **38**, 1041.
187. J. M. Read, C. T. Mathis and J. H. Goldstein, *Spectrochim. Acta.*, 1965, **21**, 85.
188. W. B. Smith and B. A. Shoulders, *J. Phys. Chem.*, 1965, **69**, 579.
189. C.-Y. Chen and R. J. W. LeFevre, *J. Chem. Soc. B*, 1966, 544.
190. R. E. Mayo and J. H. Goldstein, *Spectrochim. Acta.*, 1967, **23A**, 55.
191. P. C. Lauterbur, *J. Chem. Phys.*, 1965, **43**, 360.
192. V. M. S. Gil, *Mol. Phys.*, 1965, **9**, 443.

193. J. A. Elvidge and P. D. Ralph, *J. Chem. Soc. B*, 1966, 249.
194. R. Anet, *Tetrahedron Letters*, 1965, 3713.
195. J. M. Read and J. H. Goldstein, *J. Amer. Chem. Soc.*, 1965, **87**, 3440.
196. M. Tanabe and G. Detre, *J. Amer. Chem. Soc.*, 1966, **88**, 4515.
197. T. Yoshioka and A. G. MacDiarmid, *J. Mol. Spectroscopy*, 1966, **21**, 103.
198. H. J. Campbell-Ferguson, E. A. V. Ebsworth, A. G. MacDiarmid and T. Yoshioka, *J. Phys. Chem.*, 1967, **71**, 723.
199. E. A. V. Ebsworth and S. G. Frankiss, *Trans. Farad. Soc.*, 1967, **63**, 1574.
200. G. J. Karabatsos, F. D. Graham and F. M. Vane, *J. Amer. Chem. Soc.*, 1962, **84**, 37.
201. G. W. Smith, *J. Chem. Phys.*, 1963, **39**, 2031.
202. E. Fluck, H. Burger and U. Goetze, *Z. Naturforsch.*, 1967, **22b**, 912.
203. R. S. Drago and N. A. Matwiyoff, *J. Organometallic Chem.*, 1965, **3**, 62.
204. C. W. N. Cumper, A. Melnikoff, E. F. Mooney and A. I. Vogel, *J. Chem. Soc. B*, 1966, 874.
205. D. F. Van de Vondel, *J. Organometallic Chem.*, 1965, **3**, 400.
206. O. J. Scherer and P. Hornig, *J. Organometallic Chem.*, 1967, **8**, 465.
207. H. C. Clark, N. Cyr and J. H. Tsai, *Canad. J. Chem.*, 1967, **45**, 1073.
208. L. Verdonck and G. P. Van der Kelen, *J. Organometallic Chem.*, 1966, **5**, 532.
209. H. Junge, H. Musso and U. I. Zahorszky, *Chem. Ber.*, 1968, **101**, 793.
210. A. Loewenstein and M. Shporer, *Mol. Phys.*, 1965, **9**, 289.

Boron-11 Nuclear Magnetic Resonance Spectroscopy

W. G. HENDERSON AND E. F. MOONEY

University of Birmingham, P.O. Box 363, Birmingham 15, England

I. INTRODUCTION

THE DEVELOPMENT of boron chemistry, especially that of the organic chemistry of boron, grew at an alarming rate particularly in the period

1956–60. This initial growth was a little too early for ^{11}B n.m.r. to establish itself in the same way as it would have done had the development been delayed for 10 years. The unfortunate consequence of this is that the ^{11}B data available on many of the simple derivatives are rather scattered, and very few systematic studies have been undertaken; most of the work tends to be centred around an isolated number of related compounds. The same situation is not the case with the carboranes, in which the study of the ^{11}B resonance spectra have been used to ascertain the symmetry of the insertion of the carbon atoms; this is amply illustrated by reference to the *Annual Reports* of the Chemical Society for 1965 and 1966.[1,2] However in most studies of carboranes, the ^{11}B spectra are very complex at the lower frequencies and the powerful applications of the high-field superconducting magnets have been amply demonstrated in this work. Unfortunately, these facilities are not available to many workers, and so assignments of the resonance signals of complex carborane derivatives are by no means as complete as would be desired.

Much of the early work on the ^{11}B shifts of simple ter- and tetra-covalent boron compounds, complexes, and some simple borane derivatives, has been reviewed by Emsley *et al.*[3] The review of ^{11}B shifts by Schaeffer,[4] although published earlier, is a more comprehensive account of this particular subject, although the text is primarily concerned with borane derivatives. Since the last review, there have been only very brief articles dealing with some particular aspect of the ^{11}B resonance investigations; these articles are mentioned in the appropriate sections of the accompanying text.

Although *Annual Reviews of N.M.R. Spectroscopy* are primarily intended to cover specific years and, for the purpose of the written account, 1965 to the early months of 1968 are covered; we are tabulating the available data on the simple ter- and tetra-covalent boron compounds and of the boron complexes with Lewis bases. Our purpose for doing this is twofold; firstly to bring together much of this scattered information, and secondly to correct some mistakes, or draw attention to anomalous results that have appeared in separate accounts.

In the general text, the reference standard used for measuring the chemical shift will be cited, but in the Tables all shifts will be corrected to those of diethyl ether–boron trifluoride. This, in our opinion, is not the best standard to use as the reference resonance signal, and in our laboratories we have used dimethyl ether–boron trifluoride for many years. However, the possible advantage of using diethyl ether–boron trifluoride is that it is commercially available and we have decided to refer all data in the Tables to that of diethyl ether–boron trifluoride.

The conversions from other reference standards were obtained by the following adjustments—

$$\delta(Et_2O,BF_3) = \delta[(MeO)_3B] \quad -18\cdot3\dagger$$
$$\delta(Et_2O,BF_3) = \delta(Me_2O,BF_3) \quad +\ 0\cdot3$$
$$\delta(Et_2O,BF_3) = \delta(BCl_3) \quad\quad -47\cdot5$$
$$\delta(Et_2O,BF_3) = \delta(NaBH_4) \quad\ +42\cdot6$$

II. THEORETICAL CONSIDERATIONS OF BORON-11 CHEMICAL SHIFTS

Rather surprisingly, little attention has been given to the calculation of ^{11}B chemical shifts. Although the shifts have often been considered in a qualitative manner, the theory is by no means as well advanced as that of ^{13}C or ^{14}N shifts.

One of the most useful attempts to relate the ^{11}B shifts qualitatively to the nature of the substituent groups has been made by Nöth and Vahrenkamp.[5] This work clearly showed that the ^{11}B shift was dependent upon the type and number of substituent groups, although the incremental increase or decrease, on progressively replacing a group X by a group Y, was not necessarily uniform. These authors also attempted to relate the chemical shift of the tetra covalent anions $[BX_4]^{\ominus}$ with electronegativity of the group X. The correlation was certainly linear in the cases where X was hydrogen, alkyl or aryl, but considerable discrepancies were found for the tetramethoxy, tetra-(methylamino)- and tetrafluoro-borate ions.

Thompson and Davis[6] have also considered the effects of electro-negativity on the ^{11}B chemical shift of tetraborate ions $[BX_4]^{\ominus}$. No direct correlation was found between the measured chemical shift and the electronegativity of X; although the shift of the tetraiodo-, tetra-bromo- and tetrachloro-borate ions were in the expected order, the shift of the tetrafluoro- and tetra(phenylacetylene)-borates were un-usually high. For the boron trihalides, BX_3, Good and Ritter[7] had suggested that the ^{11}B chemical shift was given by—

$$\delta = \delta_{\sigma} + \delta_{\pi}$$

where δ_{σ} is the linear function of valence state electronegativity of the atoms directly bonded to boron and δ_{π} was proportional to the electron delocalization.

† In Emsley et al.[3] this conversion is given as $\delta[(MeO)_3B] = \delta(Et_2O,BF_3) + 17\cdot4$, whereas in their Table 12·3 the shift of $(MeO)_3B$ is given as $-18\cdot1$ p.p.m. with respect to Et_2O,BF_3.

8*

Although this expression was an over simplification of the situation it was nevertheless found to give good estimates of the π-bonding in the boron trihalides. The correlation of the chemical shifts of the tetraborate ions is more complicated because of the absence of π-bonding.[6] The observed shifts of the tetraborates could be represented by the expression—

$$\delta = A - BE_X + \delta_{para}$$

where $(A - BE_X)$ corresponds to δ_σ for the $[BX_4]^\ominus$ ion and depends upon the electronegativity E_X of the atoms bonded to the boron atom. It was further assumed that δ_{para} was proportional to the trigonal boron π-bond shifts of Good and Ritter, i.e., $\delta_{para} = C\delta_\pi$. Therefore δ can be written in the form—

$$\delta = A - BE_X + C\delta_\pi$$

The authors[6] found the values of A, B and C by substitution of the observed shifts of the tetrafluoro-, tetrachloro- and tetrabromo-borate ions. Consequently the equation for the observed shift in p.p.m. is given by the expression—

$$\delta = 480 - 201{\cdot}5E_X + 1{\cdot}79\delta_\pi$$

A plot of $\delta_\sigma = \delta_{obs} - 1{\cdot}79\delta_\pi$ against E_X was linear (Fig. 1), thus substantiating this treatment for the compounds considered. It seemed likely that the substituent electronegativity contributes to both the diamagnetic and paramagnetic shielding effects of the $[BX_4]^\ominus$ ions; the greatest deviation from the direct correlation with substituent electronegativity occurred where there was a large π-contribution in the trigonal compounds.

Armstrong and Perkins[8] have calculated the [11]B chemical shifts of mixed fluoroboron halides using different values of ΔE, the average electronic excitation energy. The correlation between the calculated and observed values are discussed but the best agreement was found using higher values of ΔE.

The correlation of both the [11]B chemical shifts and the [11]B coupling constants in boron compounds have been considered by Williams et al.[9] Chakrabarty et al.[10] have related the [11]B shifts of a series of amino-boranes of the type (1), using the values given in the literature,[5] to the

$$R \diagdown \qquad \diagup R''$$
$$N = B$$
$$R' \diagup \qquad \diagdown R'''$$

1

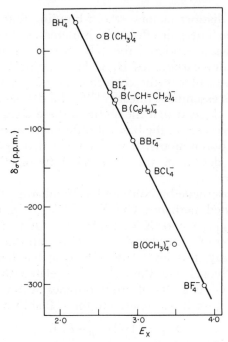

FIG. 1. Dependence of the calculated σ contribution to the ^{11}B chemical shift ($\delta_\sigma = \delta_{obs} - 1 \cdot 79 \delta_\pi$) upon the electronegativity of the substituents in $[BX_4]^\ominus$ ions. (From Thompson and Davis.[6])

calculated electron densities on the boron atom. It was found that the increasing shift to high field corresponds with an increase in the electron density on boron.

Dewar et al.,[11] in a study of the ^{11}B chemical shifts of heteroaromatic boron compounds, have referred to the work on the ^{19}F shifts of aryl fluorides in which, by using the treatment of Karplus and Goodman for the chemical shifts of π-systems, it was shown that the chemical shift of the nucleus i was given by—

$$\delta v_i = Aq_i + \sum_{j \neq i} Bq_j / r_{ij}^3$$

where q_i is the π-electron density of atom i, r_{ij} is the internuclear distance between atoms i and j and A and B are constants.

Thus atoms with unshared pairs of electrons adjacent to the boron atom will make a large contribution of the chemical shift since q_j will be large and r_{ij} small. On this basis the authors[11] attempted to account for the observed pattern of shifts in the series—

B(NMe$_2$)$_3$	B(OMe)$_3$	BF$_3$	BCl$_3$	BBr$_3$	BI$_3$
$-27 \cdot 3$	$-18 \cdot 3$	$-11 \cdot 6$	$-46 \cdot 5$	$-39 \cdot 4$	$+7 \cdot 1$

in terms of two distinct factors—the π-bonding that decreases along the series and the lone-pair effect which increases along the series.

Lipscomb[12] has considered the ^{11}B chemical shifts of the three isomeric icosahedral carboranes, $B_{10}C_2H_{12}$. Using the Pople notation it was found that a plot of the corrected shift $\delta^{(p)} = \delta_{obs} - \sigma^{(d)}$ against $Q_{AA} + \Sigma Q_{AB}$ was essentially linear ($\sigma^{(d)}$ is the diamagnetic shielding). It was therefore claimed that the shifts in these compounds could be satisfactorily explained on the basis of differences in the paramagnetic shielding of the boron atoms. It was thought that local paramagnetic effects probably determine the chemical shifts of other boron compounds.

An attempt was made by Nöth and Vahrenkamp[5] to relate the ^{13}C shifts of substituted methanes, CH_3X and CY_4, with the ^{11}B shifts of the anions $[BX_4]^{\ominus}$, where X=H, CH_3 and OCH_3; the correlation with the ^{13}C shifts of tetrasubstituted methane appeared to be promising. More recently, this line of development has been further considered by Spielvogel and Purser[13] who related the ^{13}C shifts of alkanes with the ^{11}B shifts of aminoboranes. From a least-squares treatment, the ^{13}C shift was related to the ^{11}B shift by—

$$\delta_{^{13}C} = 1 \cdot 71 \delta_{^{11}B} + 81 \cdot 0$$

where ^{13}C shifts are in p.p.m. from benzene and those of ^{11}B are in p.p.m. from diethyl ether–boron trifluoride.

III. TERCOVALENT BORON COMPOUNDS

A. Substituted boron halides

Nöth and Vahrenkamp,[14] using an extension of a method previously described,[15, 16] have prepared a range of alkyl- and dialkyl-boron halides and recorded the ^{11}B shifts (Table I). The shifts of the methyl and dimethyl boron halides have also been given by DeMoor and Van der Kelen,[17] and in addition included data for the methyl boronic and borinic acids (Table II). The shifts of the two parent chloroboranes $ClBH_2$ and Cl_2BH (Table III) have also been measured,[18] the ^{11}B–^{1}H coupling constants in these two compounds were found to be 131 and 162 c./sec., respectively. A rather unusual tetrachloride has been prepared[19] by treating the product obtained on dehydration of o-anisylboronic acid with boron trichloride, which has been shown to be the o-(oxyboron dichloride)phenylboron dichloride (2). This compound showed two ^{11}B resonance peaks at -25 and -40 p.p.m. from Et_2O,BF_3. The lower-field signal, which is broad, is assigned to the aryl-BCl_2 group by comparison with the data for other arylboron dichlorides having ^{11}B shifts between -54 and -56 p.p.m. These authors state that the boron shift of arylboron difluorides occur in the range 6–7·5 p.p.m. with respect to trimethyl borate, without stating whether to high or low field. However, it must be to low field, since this gives a range of values of -24 to $-25\cdot3$ p.p.m. with respect to Et_2O,BF_3; the shift for phenylboron difluoride is $-24\cdot8$.[14]

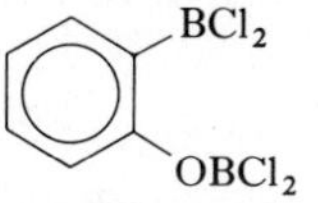

2

The shift of the $-OBCl_2$ group of (2), viz -25, is at higher field than is found in a series of alkyl dichloroborinite compounds ($ROBCl_2$), which occur at about -31 to -33 p.p.m.[17, 20] (Table IV). From these results it seems to us probable that there is either intermolecular or intramolecular co-ordination in (2) of the type (3 or 4), since both shifts are at higher field than would be expected.

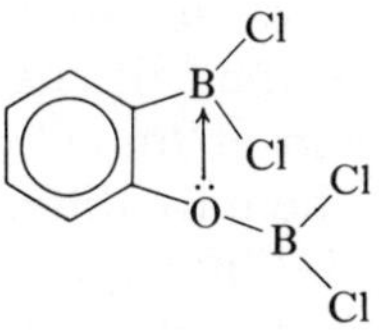

3 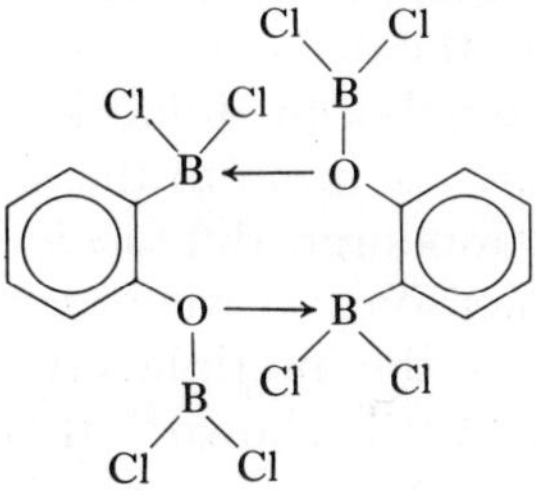   4

The ^{11}B shift of alkylboron difluorides occur at about -29 p.p.m. from Et_2O,BF_3 (Table I) and the ^{11}B–^{19}F coupling constant is approximately 80 c./sec. in each case.[21] n-Butylboron dichloride and difluoride undergo mutual exchange to give n-butylboron chloride fluoride, nBuBClF, in equilibrium with the two parent halides. Three distinct signals are observed, so that exchange is slow; the shift of the mixed halide is $-45\cdot9$ p.p.m. from Me_2O,BF_3 with a ^{11}B–^{19}F coupling constant of 105 c./sec.[22] The stability of the mixed halide is in contrast to the instability of the alkylboron chloride bromides and

chloride iodides, $RB\overset{\displaystyle Cl}{\underset{\displaystyle Br}{\big<}}$ and $RB\overset{\displaystyle Cl}{\underset{\displaystyle I}{\big<}}$, which were prepared by

interaction of the boron trihalide with the alkylboron dichloride.[23] Although the signals of the individual mixed boron trihalides were observed, only a single broad signal was observed for the alkylboron halides.

B. Aminoboranes

Considerable interest has been aroused in the monomer–dimer equilibrium of aminoboranes (5–6). As is to be expected in the dimers, where the boron is tetracovalent by co-ordination from nitrogen to boron (6), the resonance of the boron nucleus occurs to higher field

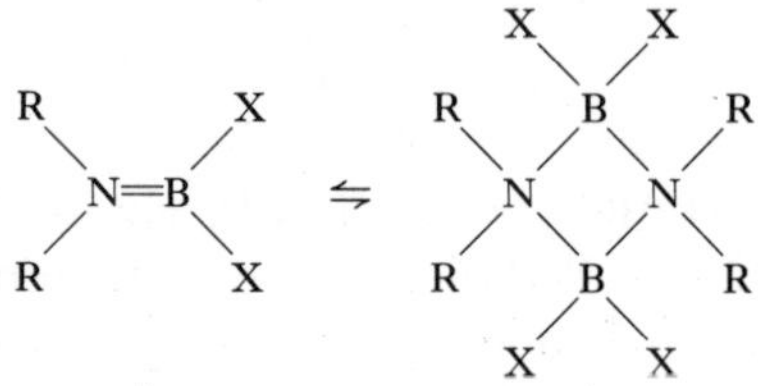

5   6

(Table V). This problem has been considered in some detail by Nöth and Vahrenkamp,[24] and Greenwood et al.[25,26,27] have also been interested in the occurrence of dimers in dialkylaminoboron dihalides and alkylaminoboron difluorides. In one of the latter papers,[25] the authors draw attention to the similarity of the [11]B chemical shifts of the alkylaminoboron difluoride (-0.3) and of the alkylamine-boron trifluoride complex of the order of ~ 0; the only differentiation is in observation of the multiplets from the [11]B–[19]F coupling. Using these correlations it was shown[26] that the bis(trifluoromethyl)aminoboron dibromide existed as a dimer (shift of -11.3); it is of interest that the dialkylamine–boron tribromide complexes have a chemical shift of $+6.7$; this difference reflecting the greater acceptor strength of boron tribromide (see later). However in the case of the B-bromo aminoboranes no ambiguity can occur between the monomers, dimers and the 1:1 complexes. Using a similar argument, Chatt et al.[28] have used the [11]B shifts to show that the aminoboranes (7), formed by addition of boron trihalides to the trifluoromethyl nitrile, are dimeric.

$$[X_2B-N=C(X)CF_3]_2$$
7

Using the [11]B resonance spectrum Nöth and Vahrenkamp[29] have studied the formation of the mixed monomeric and dimeric diethyl-aminoboron dihalides by reaction of bis(diethylamino)boron fluoride and hydrogen chloride; the shifts and the [11]B–[19]F coupling constants are shown in scheme (1)—

$$[Et_2N]_2BF + 2HCl \rightarrow Et_2NBCl_2 + Et_2NBFCl$$
$$\delta = -30 \cdot 3 \quad \delta = -24 \cdot 6$$

$$+ [Et_2NBFCl]_2 + [Et_2NBF_2]_2$$
$$\delta = -6 \qquad \delta = -3 \cdot 8$$
$$J_{^{11}B-^{19}F} = 67 \text{ c./sec.} \quad J_{^{11}B-^{19}F} = 45 \text{ c./sec.}$$

Scheme (1)

Greenwood and Walker[30] have similarly investigated the formation of mixed halogeno-dialkylaminoboranes and have found that the ^{11}B spectrum showed no scrambling of the dimethylaminoboron di-halides; only on heating to 100°C was the mixed halide (scheme 2) formed. The shifts of the monomeric compounds are shown. The behaviour of diethylaminoboron halides was different and scrambling (scheme 3) occurred spontaneously at room temperature.

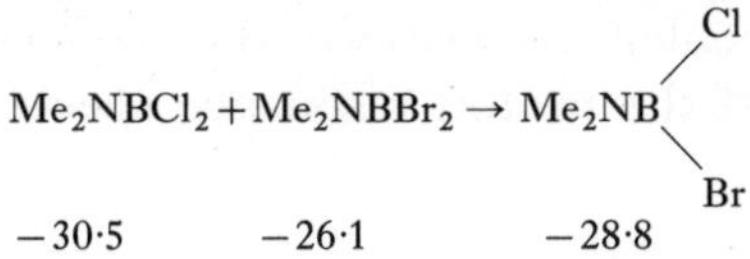

$$Me_2NBCl_2 + Me_2NBBr_2 \rightarrow Me_2NB\begin{smallmatrix} Cl \\ \\ Br \end{smallmatrix}$$

$$-30 \cdot 5 \qquad\qquad -26 \cdot 1 \qquad\qquad -28 \cdot 8$$

Scheme (2)

$$Et_2NBCl_2 + Et_2NBBr_2 \rightleftharpoons Et_2NB\begin{smallmatrix} Cl \\ \\ Br \end{smallmatrix}$$

$$-31 \cdot 8 \qquad\qquad -26 \cdot 9 \qquad\qquad -29 \cdot 6$$

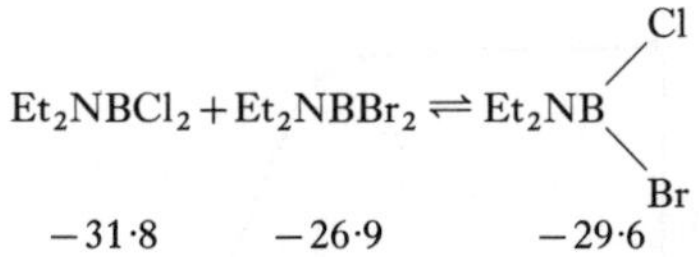

Scheme (3)

The ^{11}B shift of both the monomeric (8) and dimeric (9) form of the methylbis(trifluoromethyl)phosphinylaminoboron dichloride have also been recorded and are at $-31 \cdot 5$ and $-20 \cdot 0$ p.p.m. [with respect to $(MeO)_3B]$, respectively.[31] Dimerization of the form (10) was excluded due to the lack of ^{11}B–^{31}P coupling (see p. 241).

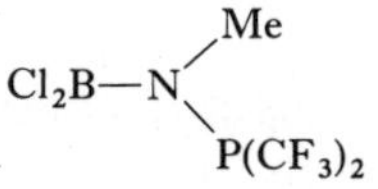

8

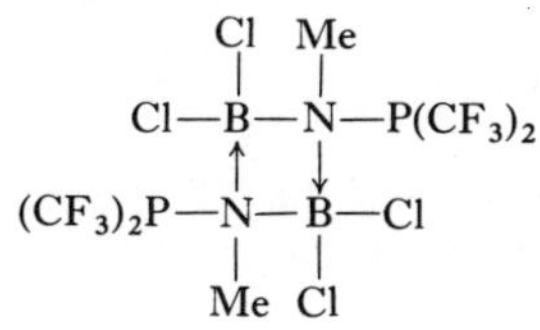

9

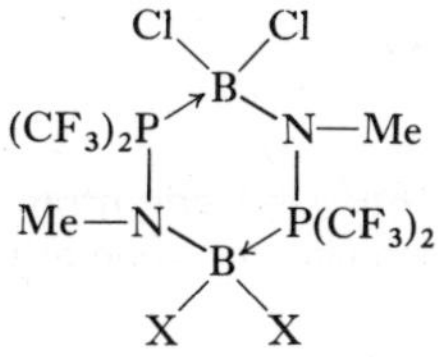

10

The reaction of aliphatic secondary amines with diborane afforded only the dialkylaminoborane, R_2NBH_2, and not the expected com-plex.[32] The ^{11}B resonance signals were in each case triplets with

^{11}B–^1H coupling constants of ~ 100 c./sec. The shifts of these compounds would imply that dimerization had occurred (Table V).

The shifts of aminoboranes R_2NBXY and $BXYZ$ (X and Y=Hal, OMe, R_2N etc.) are shown in Tables V and VI respectively.

C. Association of tercovalent boron compounds

The tendency for dialkylaminoboranes to dimerize has been discussed above. However it has been believed for some time that many boron compounds tend to associate and attempts have been made to confirm this idea. Probably the most extensive investigations have been made in the study of the cyclic boronates and thiaboronates,[33] but no definite evidence was obtained. The presence of two ^{11}B resonance signals in the spectrum of dimethylborazide Me_2BN_2 has been ascribed[34] to molecular association; the association was apparent from examination of the proton resonance spectrum over a range of temperatures.

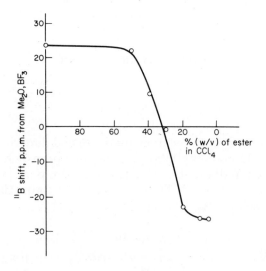

FIG. 2. Concentration dependence of the ^{11}B chemical shift of dibenzyl phenylboronate in carbon tetrachloride solution. (From Mooney and Winson.[35])

Similarly the self-association in dibenzyl phenylboronate has been demonstrated.[35] On dilution with carbon tetrachloride there was a shift of nearly 50 p.p.m. to low field corresponding to the formation of a tercovalent species (Fig. 2).

IV. TETRA-COVALENT BORON COMPOUNDS

The structure of the alkoxyboron difluorides has recently aroused some interest, and the historical consideration of the structure of these compounds has been outlined.[20] Although the [11]B chemical shifts of these compounds are comparatively high[17,20] (+0·1 to +0·8) this does not imply quadricovalency (see above discussion); however, the formation of the pyridine co-ordination complexes of the alkoxy-boron difluorides (11) did not give appreciably higher [11]B chemical shifts, and it was concluded that the boron atom in alkoxyboron difluorides was already tetracovalent.[20] Molecular-weight determination confirmed the trimeric structure similar to the boroxole ring system.

The [11]B shifts of the tetraco-ordinate compounds formed by reaction of the boron derivatives of β-diketones (12) have been considered in some detail.[36] Although the number of compounds investigated is relatively few, the generalization that the increasing σ^* function, i.e., increasing $-I$ effect, of the group R corresponds to a shift to higher field was made. It was further noted that the greater the [11]B shift then the more resistant is the compound to hydrolysis. 2-Diethyl-aminobenzo-1,3-dioxa-2-borole reacted with diketone to give the tetracovalent compound (13) with a [11]B shift of −8·63 (from Et_2O,BF_3).[37]

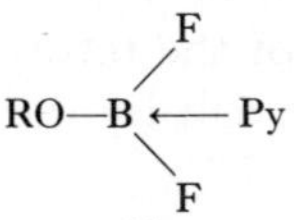

11 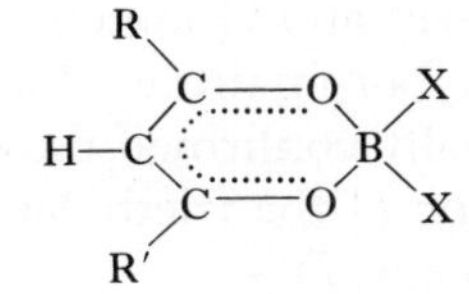   12 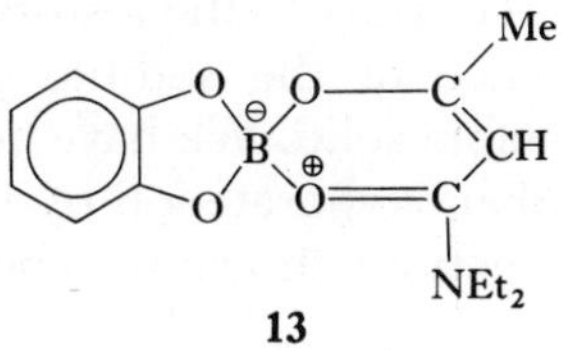   13

A. Borohydride derivatives

The [11]B shifts of hafnium and aluminium borohydride have been recorded.[38] There was both a big difference in the chemical shift and in the general appearance of the [11]B signals of these two borohydrides. It was suggested that in the case of the aluminium borohydride a rapid exchange process was occurring through a single bridge atom species (scheme 4)—

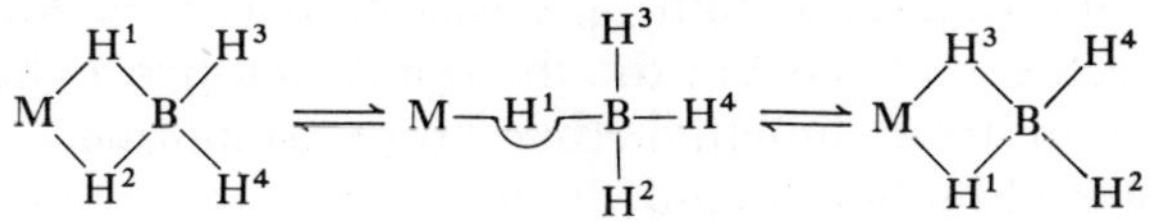

Scheme (4)

The π-cyclopentadienyl zirconium borohydride **(14)** has a ^{11}B chemical shift of $+32\cdot5$ p.p.m. from trimethyl borate and is a quintet with a ^{11}B–^{1}H coupling constant of 86 c./sec.[38, 39] In contrast to this, the π-cyclopentadienyl zirconium hydride borohydride **(15)** shows only a very broad signal at $+30\cdot5$ p.p.m. from trimethyl borate.[39]

$$(\pi\text{-C}_5\text{H}_5)_2\text{Zr(BH}_4)_2 \qquad (\pi\text{-C}_5\text{H}_5)_2\text{Zr(H)BH}_4$$
$$\textbf{14} \qquad\qquad\qquad \textbf{15}$$

The reaction of hydrogen sulphide with lithium borohydride afforded the compound $\text{Li}^{\oplus}[\text{HSBH}_3]^{\ominus}$. The ^{11}B spectrum consisted of a $1:3:3:1$ quartet at $+25\cdot0$ (from $\text{Et}_2\text{O},\text{BF}_3$) with ^{11}B–^{1}H coupling constant of 94 c./sec.[40] There was in addition two further signals of very low intensity, a pentet at $+32\cdot2$ due to the borohydride ion and a triplet at $+14\cdot5$ arising from a $>\text{BH}_2$ species, probably the $[(\text{HS})_2\text{BH}_2]^{\ominus}$ ion.

Recent work in our laboratory, using the ^{11}B spectra to monitor the reactions, has shown[41] that sodium borohydride and phenol reacted to form the sodium tetraphenoxyborate **(16, scheme 5)** with a shift of

$$\text{Na}^{\oplus}[\text{BH}_4]^{\ominus} + \text{PhOH} \longrightarrow \text{Na}^{\oplus}[\text{B(OPh)}_4]^{\ominus} + \text{H}_2$$
$$\textbf{16}$$

Scheme (5)

$-2\cdot8$ p.p.m. from dimethyl ether–boron trifluoride. This observation is contrary to the results of Dessey and Grannen,[42] who claim the existence of the sodium phenoxyborohydride, $\text{Na}^{\oplus}[\text{PhOBH}_3]^{\ominus}$, as a stable solid. We have additionally confirmed the identity of the tetraphenoxyborate ion by formation of the triethylammonium salt by the reactions shown in schemes (6 and 7)—

$$\text{Et}_3\text{N} + \text{B(OPh)}_3 + \text{PhOH} \rightarrow \text{Et}_3\text{NH}^{\oplus}[\text{B(OPh)}_4]^{\ominus}$$

Scheme (6)

$$\text{Et}_3\text{N},\text{BH}_3 + \text{PhOH} \rightarrow \text{H}_2 + \text{Et}_3\text{NH}^{\oplus}[\text{B(OPh)}_4]^{\ominus}$$

Scheme (7)

In the three reaction schemes given above no other anionic species of lower symmetry was detected. The triethylammonium tetrathiophenoxyborate, $\text{Et}_3\overset{\oplus}{\text{NH}}[\text{B(SPh)}_4]^{\ominus}$, was prepared by the analogous reaction to scheme (6) above; the thioborate ion has a chemical shift of $-6\cdot82$ p.p.m. from dimethyl ether–boron trifluoride.

The triphenylthioborate and diborane gave the monomeric compound bis(phenylthio)borane, $(\text{PhS})_2\text{BH}$, with a shift of -24 (p.p.m.

from Et_2O,BF_3) and $^{11}B-^1H$ coupling constant of 140 c./sec.[43] However thiophenol and sodium borohydride gave the ionic compound $\overset{\oplus}{Na}[(PhS)_2BH_2]^{\ominus}$ the ^{11}B resonance signal of which was a poorly resolved triplet at $+26$ and $^{11}B-^1H$ coupling constant of 134 c./sec.

The shift of the sodium boronocarbonate $Na_2^{\oplus}[H_3BCO_2]^{2\ominus}$ has been found[44] to be $+50$[from $(MeO)_3B$] with a coupling constant of 81 c./sec. Attempts to obtain the ^{11}B spectrum of the ion $[HB(OH)_3]^{\ominus}$ have been unsuccessful; only signals from the two symmetrical borohydride $[BH_4]^{\ominus}$ and tetrahydroxyborate $[B(OH)_4]^{\ominus}$ ions were observed.[45] It was claimed that the ion $BH_2^{\oplus}$ was formed from the ionic species $K^{\oplus}[HB(OH)_3]^{\ominus}$ and gave a broad signal at $+29$ p.p.m. from boron trichloride.

B. Tetraborates of the form $[BX_4]^{\ominus}$

(1) Tetrahalogenoborates

The ^{11}B chemical shifts of the tetrahalogenoborate ions have been considered in some detail and in some cases a limiting value of the ^{11}B chemical shift was obtained, being dependent upon the concentration of the halide ion.[6] The shift of tetramethylammonium tetrachloroborate in dimethyl sulphoxide solution was -6.84, but was -6.58 (from Et_2O,BF_3) in liquid hydrogen chloride at $-100°C$. The addition of excess tetramethylammonium chloride affected this latter shift. The gradual addition of triphenylmethyl chloride to boron trichloride gave a limiting shift of -6.74.

Pyridinium tetrabromoborate in dimethyl sulphoxide has a ^{11}B shift of $+2.07$, and addition of pyridinium bromide increases the shift to a limiting value of $+13.0$. The shift of pyridinium tetrabromoborate in liquid hydrogen bromide at $-75°C$ was $+23.6$ p.p.m. and was invariant of the addition of further amounts of bromide ion. The addition of tetraethylammonium bromide to boron tribromide in methylene dichloride caused a shift to a limiting value of $+23.8$ p.p.m.

The shift of the tetraiodoborate, prepared by the addition of tetrabutylammonium iodide to boron tri-iodide in methylene dichloride solution, varied from $+66.0$ when the reactants were mixed in $1:1$ proportions to $+127.5$ in the presence of excess of tetrabutylammonium iodide. Boron tri-iodide in liquid hydrogen iodide at $-43°C$ has a ^{11}B shift of $+128$ p.p.m.

Triphenylmethyl tetrafluoroborate in methylene dichloride has a shift of $+1.55$ and is not affected by addition of tetrabutylammonium fluoride. Potassium tetrafluoroborate dissolved in liquid hydrogen fluoride at $-5°C$ had a shift of $+1.81$, whereas boron trifluoride in liquid hydrogen fluoride at $-80°C$ showed a shift of $+1·76$ p.p.m. The limiting shifts of tetrahalogenoborates and the shifts of other tetraborates are shown in Table VII.

(2) *Tetra-alkylborons*

The shifts for several lithium tetra-alkylboron salts were also given by these same authors[6] and occur in the range of $+16$ to $+20$ p.p.m. to high field of diethyl ether–boron trifluoride. In the presence of excess of trialkylboron with the lithium alkyl, two distinct [11]B signals are observed, indicating there is no exchange between the species.

(3) *Tetraborates*

The tetramethylammonium tetranitratoborate, formed by reaction of nitrogen dioxide on the corresponding tetrachloroborate (reaction scheme 8), showed a shift of $+44·0$ p.p.m. from sodium borohydride[46]

$$Me_4N^\oplus[BCl_4]^\ominus + N_2O_4 \rightarrow Me_4N^\oplus[B(NO_3)_4]^\ominus$$

Scheme (8)

The borate–polyborate equilibria in aqueous solution has been thoroughly investigated.[47] Sodium pentaborate NaB_5O_8 showed two [11]B resonance signals, the relative intensities depending upon the concentration of the borate. The low field signal at $1·1$ p.p.m. relative to boric acid arises from equilibrium between $B(OH)_3$, $[B(OH)_4]^\ominus$ and $[B_3O_3(OH)_4]^\ominus$, whereas the high-field signal at $15·0$ is assigned to the complex ion $[B_5O_6(OH)_4]^\ominus$, the structure of which is shown in (**17**), indicating the ion is of a spiro-boroxole structure. The pH dependence of the [11]B chemical shift of borate–boric acid solutions, resulting

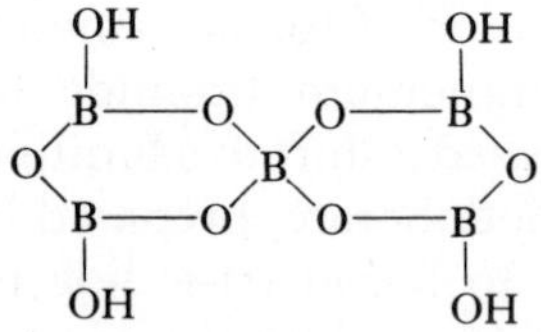

17

in the formation of the tetrahydroxyborate ion $[B(OH)_4]^\ominus$ at high pH, has been studied in our laboratories in relationship to the effect of borate buffers on the stereospecific formation of carbohydrate derivatives.[48] It will be observed from Fig. 3 that the pH at which transition, from the tercovalent boric acid to the tetravalent tetrahydroxyborate ion, occurs is very sharp.

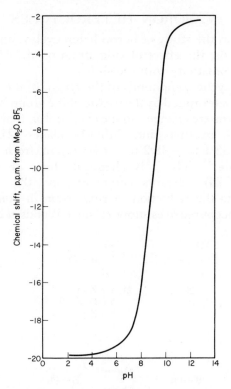

FIG. 3. The pH dependence of the ^{11}B chemical shifts of sodium tetraborate $(Na_2B_4O_7 \cdot 10H_2O)$ solutions (50 mg./ml.) at 33°C. (From How et al.[48])

C. Boronium ions

The ^{11}B data on boronium ions are very sparse, but two interesting examples, which are additionally optically active, have been recorded.[49] The shift of the ion (18; X=H) is $17 \cdot 8 \pm 0 \cdot 5$ p.p.m. (from trimethyl borate) with a coupling constant of 90 ± 5 c./sec., and that of (18; X=Cl), the shift is $9 \cdot 3 \pm 0 \cdot 8$ p.p.m. with ^{11}B–^{1}H coupling constant of 140 ± 15 c./sec. The shift of the boronium perchlorate (19) has been reported[50] at -5 p.p.m. (from Et_2O,BF_3), which is intermediate between the shifts quoted in the previous two examples; the ^{11}B–^{1}H coupling constant was 95 ± 15 c./sec.

V. BORON HETEROCYCLES

The interest in the study of boron heterocycles can be divided into two distinct fields, the effect of ring strain on the ^{11}B shift and the correlation of aromaticity with the shift.

In the heterocyclic compounds of the type (20) the chemical shift is predominantly determined by the nature of the group X, and, naturally, as the heteroatoms are changed so the chemical shift alters. Thus in the 2-phenyl-dioxa-, oxathia- and dithia-borolanes (21) the shift decreases from $-33\cdot1$ to $-48\cdot2$ to $-64\cdot5$ p.p.m. from dimethyl ether–boron trifluoride.[51] The ^{11}B chemical shifts of the 2-B-phenyl derivatives (22–24) warrants comment, and the decreasing shift probably reflects the reduction in ring strain in going from (22) to (24).[51] This concept receives support, since Woods *et al.*[52] have shown

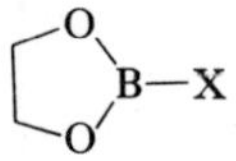

20

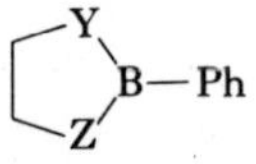

21, Y = Z = O
Y = O, Z = S
Y = Z = S

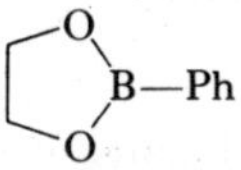

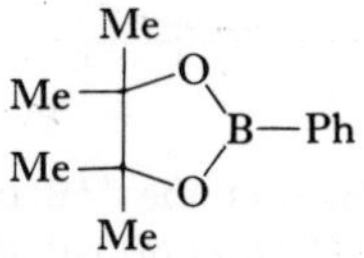

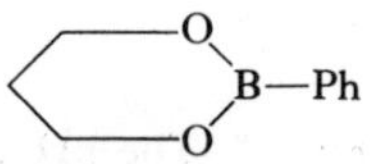

Shifts, p.p.m.
from Me_2O,BF_3

22	23	24
$-33\cdot1$	$-30\cdot7$	$-28\cdot0$

that the shifts of (25; X = CH=CH$_2$) is similar to that of di-n-butyl vinylboronate (26) and that of (25); X = C≡CH) is similar to the dimethyl etherylboronate 27 (the shifts are shown in p.p.m. from diethyl ether–boron trifluoride). Similarly the shift of (25; X = OC$_4$H$_9$) is very similar to that of tributyl borate.

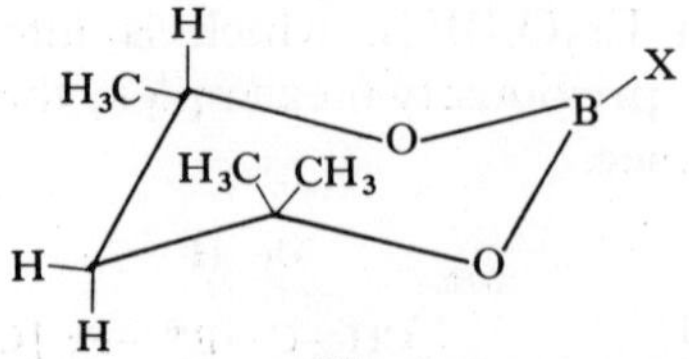

25

X = —CH=CH$_2$, $-25\cdot5$ p.p.m.
= —C≡C—H, $-20\cdot9$ p.p.m.

$(Bu^nO)_2B$—CH=CH$_2$
26, $-25\cdot4$ p.p.m.

$(MeO)_2B$—C≡C—H
27, -21.6 p.p.m.

The boron heterocycles of the general type (20) have been investigated by Laurent and Bonnet,[53] who found that the 2-chloro-1,3,2-dioxaborolane (20; X = Cl) showed a complex set of ^{11}B resonance signals; our own investigation of this compound has tended to confirm these results. To rationalize the observation on the spectrum of the 2-chloro-1,3,2-dioxaborolane, it seems probable that disproportionation by some elaborate mechanism will have to be invoked. The complexes of the 2-chloro-1,3-dithioborolane (20; X = Cl and O = S) have been reported by Young et al.,[54] and only one resonance signal was reported (see p. 240).

The shifts of some cyclic boroles and borolanes are given in Table VIII.

Boron–sulphur ring compounds are not as commonly occurring as those of oxygen. The chemical shifts of a four- and six-membered ring compound of the type $(R_2NBS)_n$ have been reported by Forstner and Muetterties.[55] The two compounds and their shifts [p.p.m. from $(MeO)_3B$] are shown in (28) and (29). Rather interestingly, the ethylthioborane $EtSBH_2$ exists as a trimer and has a shift of $+14.5$ (p.p.m.

28

Shift = −18·5 p.p.m.

29

Shift = −20·1 p.p.m.

from Et_2O,BF_3) with ^{11}B–^{1}H coupling of 116 c./sec., while the benzylthioborane $PhCH_2SBH_2$ exists as a polymer and shows a very broad resonance signal at $+14.7$.[43] This is in complete contrast to the behaviour of the phenylthioborane $PhSBH_2$, which is claimed to exist as a monomer with a shift of -3.3 and a ^{11}B–^{1}H coupling constant of 122 c./sec.

The ^{11}B chemical shift of borazoles has been investigated by several groups of workers, and some of the shifts have been discussed in a review on boron–nitrogen compounds.[56] However the shift of the borazoles are not as meaningful as might have been anticipated. This is probably due to the fact that irrespective of the B or N substituent the electron density on the boron atom is essentially constant due to contributions from either of the structures (30) or (31). The ^{11}B chemical shifts of borazole and substituted borazoles are shown in Table IX. Hensen and Messer[57] have considered the ^{14}N and ^{11}B shifts of B-trifluoro-, B-trichloro- and B-tribromo-borazole with respect to those of the parent borazole molecule; these shifts are not included in Table IX, but there was shift to high field in the order Br($+2 \cdot 1$) < Cl($+3 \cdot 3$) < F($4 \cdot 8$).

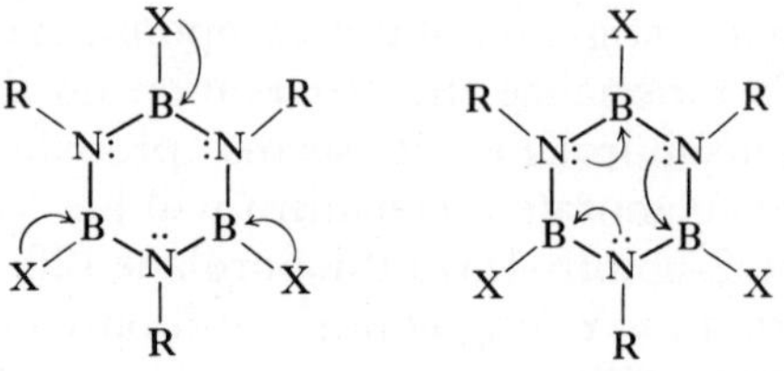

30   31

The general observation of the invariance of the ^{11}B shifts in the borazole ring systems made above is further borne out by the condensed ring systems. Boone and Willcockson[58] found that there was no marked difference in the shift of the B-trimethylborazole ($-34 \cdot 7$ p.p.m. from Et$_2$O,BF$_3$) and that of the condensed ring system (32) ($-34 \cdot 5$ p.p.m.); there was however a marked difference in the half-width of the resonance signal. A study[59] of the fused five-membered ring system of the NN'-diboryloxamidines (33) has shown that the ^{11}B shift is markedly dependent upon the nature of the N-substituent.

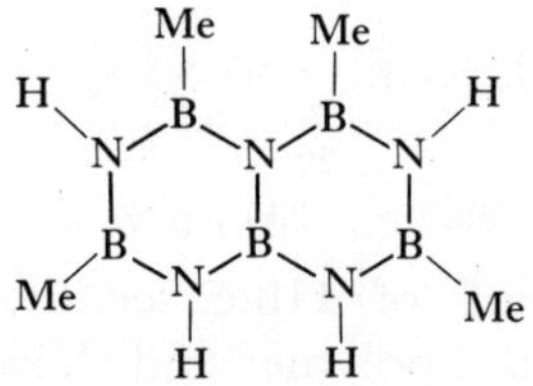

32 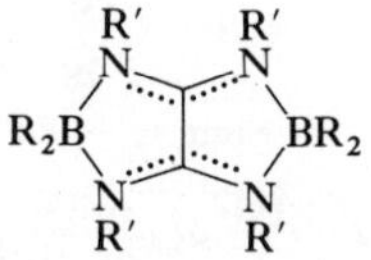   33

Thus when R' is a phenyl group, irrespective whether R is alkyl or phenyl, the shift is $+2$ p.p.m. [from (MeO)$_3$B] whereas when R' is an alkyl group the shift is 11 ± 1 p.p.m.

The derivatives of 1,3,2,4,5-diazatriborols (34) exhibit a ^{11}B resonance shift in the region of -37 p.p.m. (from Et$_2$O,BF$_3$).[60] However if the fused-ring system (35) is formed, two ^{11}B signals are

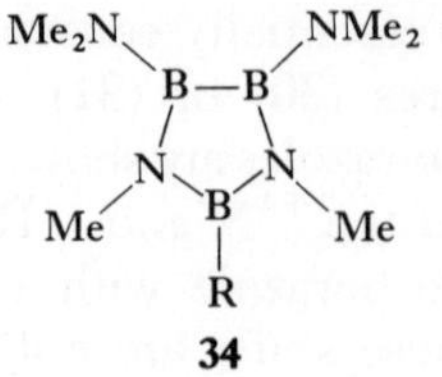

34 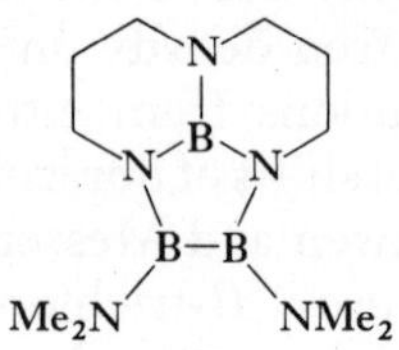   35

found. One, at -35 p.p.m., corresponds to the $>$B—B$<$ entity and is similar to the shift of the diazatriborols, and the second, at -28.4 p.p.m., corresponds to the N—B$\underset{\diagdown N}{\overset{\diagup N}{}}$ unit and is similar in value to that of the trisaminoborons $B(NR_2)_3$. However the shift of a closely related molecule (36), which contains the BN_3 grouping to form a fused bicyclic system having a five- and a six-membered ring, occurs at a higher field of -22 p.p.m.[61]

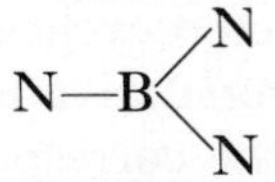

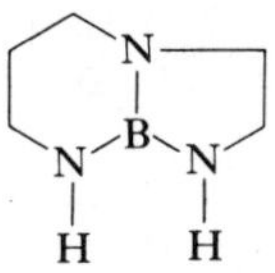

36

The study of boron–pyrazole chemistry by Trofimenko[62,63] has produced some rather interesting heterocyclic boron ring systems. The pyrazaboles of the form (37) all show a ^{11}B shift in the region of $+27$ p.p.m. [from $(MeO)_3B$] and, in those instances where the signal was resolved, showed a ^{11}B–^{1}H coupling in the range 103–108 c./sec. The reaction of pyrazole with potassium borohydride resulted in the formation of the three poly(1-pyrazolyl) borates (38), $n=2,3$ and 4) and the shifts [with respect to $(MeO)_3B$] were $+25.7$, $+19.6$ and $+17.3$ respectively.[64] The derivatives of cyclotetrazenoborane (39) also show little variation of the ^{11}B chemical shift on varying the nature of substituents from methyl to phenyl, and occur in the range $+26$ to $+30$ p.p.m. (with respect to BCl_3).[65,66]

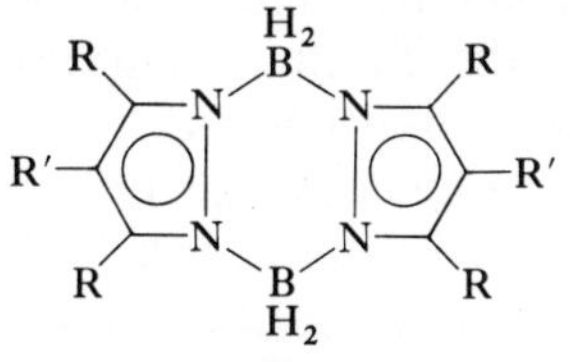

37 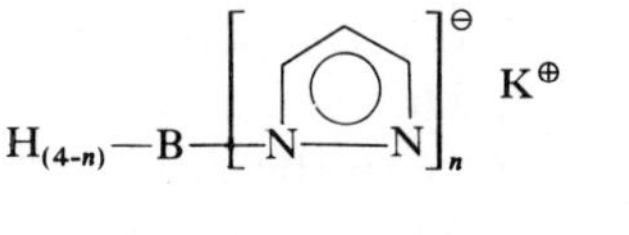   **38** 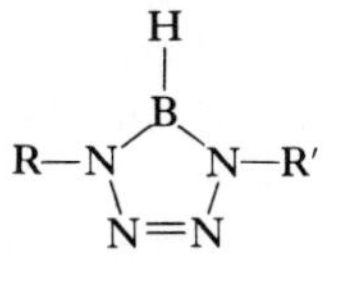   **39**

Dewar et al.[11] have examined the ^{11}B shifts of several heteroaromatic boron compounds and suggested that the results yielded additional evidence of the aromaticity of the compounds. From the order of the chemical shifts, it was inferred that the π-bonding between the boron and the adjacent heteroatom was more important than in the open-chain analogues; this of course is as expected if the former compounds possess aromatic character.

The six-membered ring heterocyclics containing two adjacent boron atoms, and are thus diboron derivatives, have been prepared and the ^{11}B shifts compared with the corresponding five-membered ring borolanes.[67] There was a surprising degree of similarity between the pairs of compounds (**40** and **41**; X$=$O or S and Y$=$Cl or NMe$_2$). The shifts of these and other diboron compounds are shown in Table X.

VI. CO-ORDINATION COMPOUNDS OF BORON

It is in the field of the co-ordination compounds of boron that some of the most conflicting results have been obtained. It is however generally recognized that the transformation of the sp^2 hybridization of the boron atom to an sp^3 hybridized state on complex formation results in a shift to high field. In our laboratories, we have designated this chemical-shift difference between the free and complexed boron acceptor molecule as the Δ value. We have found it very convenient to use this Δ value although it is not always applicable, e.g., in borane BH$_3$, which exists as the dimer, diborane, and in phenylborane, PhBH$_2$, which we have not yet isolated in the free state.

In our preliminary work on ketone–boron trihalide complexes it was found[68] that there was a correlation between the Δ value and the displacement of the carbonyl stretching frequency; this carbonyl displacement has previously been used in both ketones and esters to establish the acceptor strengths of Lewis acids. Similarly, in the triethylamine complexes it was found that the proton chemical shift values $[\delta_{CH_3} - \delta_{CH_2}]$, which can be related to the electron density on the nitrogen atom, were in the same order as the Δ values of the ^{11}B shifts and both were in the established order of the acceptor strengths of the boron halides. Thus by using a standard base (for convenience we have used pyridine), the acceptor strengths of the various boron compounds have been determined and are given by the Δ value. In a similar manner, *provided the same boron acceptor molecule is used for the comparison*, the donor strengths of various bases may be determined.[68–73]

The one major difficulty in all this work is the solvent. In all our work we have used either methylene dichloride or chloroform, which we consider to be relatively inert. However in much of the early work on the thermochemical investigation of donor–acceptor interaction nitrobenzene was used as the solvent. We have recently measured the Δ values of the nitrobenzene–boron halide systems and shown that nitrobenzene is a particularly good donor molecule.[72] The data that have so far been advanced to criticize our use of the Δ value have involved the use of either nitrobenzene or acetonitrile as solvents, and both being strong donors, equilibria of the type $L_1 + L_2 \rightarrow B \rightleftharpoons L_1 \rightarrow B + L_2$ were involved. Heitsch[74] suggested that the ^{11}B chemical shift was a poor criterion of complex stability; however most of the data on which this statement depends were obtained with acetonitrile or 1,4-dioxan as the solvent.

Heitsch,[74] using the ^{11}B chemical-shift data for a series of borane complexes, has suggested that the basic strength increases in the order—

$$Me_3N < Me_2NH \approx Et_3N < MeNH_2 < NH_3 < Me_3P$$

It was observed that the shift of the boron trifluoride adducts were all essentially similar, and no conclusions could be drawn; a similar situation was found in our study of ketone–boron trifluoride complexes.[75] A different order of basic strength was found for the trimethylborane adducts, the order being—

$$Me_3N < Me_2NH < MeNH_2 < NH_3 < Et_3N \ll Me_3P$$

the author[74] stated that in this instance the shifts could not be rationalized in terms of the basic strength. The shifts of the 1:1 and 1:2 complexes of borane with both $NNN'N'$-tetramethylethylenediamine and NN'-dimethylpiperazine have been measured;[76,77] in both cases that of the 2:1 complex is to higher field.

Greenwood et al.[78] have measured the ^{11}B shifts of the substituted borane complexes of triethylamine $Et_3N \rightarrow BH_2X$ (where X = Cl, Br, I and Ph). The ^{11}B shifts of the complexes of pyridine and substituted pyridine with both borane and phenylborane have been compared;[71] the order of the basic strengths was explained in terms of steric strain on the introduction of the phenyl group.

The complexes of urea and thiourea with boron trifluoride have been studied[79] and, as with other boron trifluoride complexes, the shifts are very similar namely $19 \cdot 2 \pm 0 \cdot 3$ p.p.m. [with respect to $(MeO)_3B$]. A similar shift was observed for the more complex adducts with cadmium chloride or nickel bromide. It was found that dimethyl ether–boron trifluoride (shift of $17 \cdot 6$) and di-t-butylthiourea–boron trifluoride (shift of 19·5) gave only a single signal, indicating rapid exchange with an average life-time of less than 6 msec. The boron trifluoride complex of the methiodide of sym-ethylthiourea $[(EtNH)_2\overset{\oplus}{C}\text{-S-Me, BF}_3]I^{\ominus}$ has a shift of $+18·5$, slightly lower than the thiourea complex. The disproportionation of the sym-dimethyl-urea–boron trichloride complex was followed by means of the ^{11}B spectra, and the formation of the tetrachloroborate ion and of a cyclic compound was suggested from the shift data.

The acid–base properties of the five-membered heterocyclic dioxa– and dithia–boron systems (similar to **20**) with trimethylamine and tri-methylphosphine have been considered,[54, 80] and it was claimed[54] that there was a reversal of base strength. In this work Shore et al. did not make use of the ΔB values, although these did in fact correspond to the relative acid–base strengths found from the study of homogenous displacement reactions and from dissociation tendencies. Similarily, from dissociation pressures it was concluded[80] that the five-membered dioxaborolane (**42**) was a stronger Lewis acid than the corresponding six-membered compound (**43**); the ΔB values obtained for the com-plexes of (**42**; $\Delta B = +21·2$) and (**43**; $\Delta B = +9·3$) are in agreement with this conclusion.

42   43

A rather unique use of the ^{11}B chemical shifts is in the differentiation between boronic acids acting as acceptor molecules or participating as protic acids (schemes 9 and 10, respectively)[81]—

$$R_2BOH + OH^{\ominus} \rightarrow [R_2B(OH)_2]^{\ominus}$$
Scheme (9)

$$R_2BOH + OH^{\ominus} \rightarrow R_2BO^{\ominus} + H_2O$$
Scheme (10)

The range of chemical-shifts differences, $\Delta\delta$, between those recorded in neutral and alkaline solutions fall into two distinct groups. If the $\Delta\delta$ value is greater than $+13$, then the acid is behaving as a Lewis acid (scheme 9), but if the shift is to low field and is in the range of -3 to -7 then the acid behaves as a protic acid and salt formation has occurred (scheme 10). Consequently, phenyl and tolyl boronic acids with $\Delta\delta$ of $+25$ and $+19$, respectively, behave as acceptor molecules whereas

2-hydroxy-2,1-borazaronaphthalene (**44**) and 4-hydroxy-4,3-bora-zaroisoquinoline (**45**) with $\Delta\delta$ of $\sim -3\cdot3$ behave as protic acids.

The ^{11}B chemical shifts of various complexes are shown in Table XI.

44   **45**

VII. PHOSPHORUS COMPLEXES

The complexes of boranes and boron trihalides with simple phosphorus compounds have been extensively investigated, possibly because of the presence of ^{11}B–^{31}P coupling. Reaction of phosphine with diborane gave[82] the monomeric complex H_3P,BH_3 with a ^{11}B signal $+60\cdot8$ p.p.m. [from $(MeO)_3B$] which was a quartet of doublets with ^{11}B–^{31}P coupling of 27 c./sec. and the ^{11}B–^{1}H coupling of 103 c./sec. These authors also refer to some unpublished work by Gilje and Parry[83] on the methylphosphine borane complex.

The difluorophosphine borane complex F_2PH,BH_3 has a ^{11}B shift of $+60\cdot4$ [from $(MeO)_3B$] and the signal again consists of a quartet of doublets with ^{11}B–^{31}P coupling of 48·6 c./sec. and ^{11}B–^{1}H coupling of 102 c./sec.[84] The trifluorophosphine borane complex F_3P,BH_3 has a shift of $+66\cdot6$ [from $(MeO)_3B$] with ^{11}B–^{31}P coupling of 39 c./sec. and ^{11}B–^{1}H coupling of 106 c./sec.; the ^{11}B–^{19}F coupling was 6 c./sec.[84] The tetrafluorodiphosphine borane complex P_2F_4,BH_3 had a ^{11}B shift of $+60$ [from $(MeO)_3B$] at $-80°C$ with a ^{11}B–^{1}H coupling of 101 c./sec.; no coupling of the ^{11}B nucleus to the phosphorus atom was observed.[85] It was suggested by these authors that tetrafluorodiphosphine was a stronger Lewis base than trifluorophosphine; however the evidence for this conclusion was not very clear, especially since the tetrafluorodiphosphine complex decomposes into the trifluorophosphine borane complex.

The ^{11}B resonance data of the phosphorus trioxide, P_4O_6, diborane complexes have been discussed by Riess and Van Wazer.[86] It was concluded that the cage structure of the P_4O_6 was retained intact (see p. 350). The ^{11}B shift was $+40$ p.p.m. (from Et_2O,BF_3) and the ^{11}B–^{31}P coupling of 47 c./sec. and ^{11}B–^{1}H coupling of 102 c./sec. was observed. Although the crystalline complexes of phosphorus triiodide and tetraiododiphosphine with boron tribromide have been isolated the ^{11}B shifts of the complexes in carbon disulphide solution are very similar to that of boron tribromide in the same solvent.[87] It was therefore suggested that the complexes are dissociated in solution.

The $^{11}B-^{31}P$ coupling constant in the trialkyl phosphite-boranes are of same magnitude as the $^{11}B-^{1}H$ coupling constants.[88] The ^{11}B spectrum of the trimethyl phosphite–borane is a simple quintet, owing to the equality of the $^{11}B-^{1}H$ and $^{11}B-^{31}P$ coupling constants.

The reaction of ammonia or dimethylamine with the phosphine diborane affords ionic compounds of the form (46).[89] The ^{11}B spectra

$$[R_2NH_2]^{\oplus}[H_2P(BH_3)_2]^{\ominus}$$

46

of the compounds recorded in aqueous solution were a quartet of doublets with the $^{11}B-^{1}H$ coupling of about 92 c./sec. and a $^{11}B-^{31}P$ coupling of 60–61 c./sec. The ^{11}B chemical shifts [in p.p.m. from $(MeO)_3B$] were 59·8 (**46**; R = H) and 57·3 (**46**; R = Me).

VIII. BORANES

A. Diborane

There has been some controversy over the structure of the complexes of diborane. Shore and Hall[90] suggested that the reaction of ammonia, methylamine or trimethylamine resulted in asymmetric cleavage of diborane, with the resultant formation of the complex with structure (47) having a single hydrogen-bridged borane structure. The spectrum, recorded at −65°C in methylene dichloride solution, consisted of an overlapping quartet, from the BH_3 group, and a triplet from the BH_2 group. Eastman[91] later pointed out that the nine-line pattern found in the spectrum of (47; L = Me₃N) could be interpreted as the triplet of triplets previously reported in Ogg's[92] spectrum of diborane. He concluded that the spectrum could not be a singly hydrogen-bridged borane, and therefore suggested the structure as shown in (48). Shore and Hall[93] have further commented on this and point out that Ogg's spectrum of diborane, recorded at 6 Mc./sec. was a well resolved triplet of triplets, whereas the spectrum of (48), recorded at 19·25

$$\begin{matrix} H_2B\text{—}H\text{—}BH_3 \\ | \\ L \end{matrix}$$

47

$$H_2B \underset{H}{\overset{H}{\diagup\hspace{-0.3em}\diagdown}} \underset{}{\overset{:NR_3}{BH_2}}$$

48

$$L = NH_3, MeNH_2 \text{ or } Me_3N$$

Mc./sec., was poorly resolved. They additionally point out that in the ion $B_2H_7^{\ominus}$ the ^{11}B spectrum is not ambiguous and the only reasonable interpretation is a single hydrogen-bridged structure $[H_3B—H—BH_3]^{\ominus}$.

Linder and Onak[94] have investigated the ^{11}B spectra of a whole series of alkyl substituted diboranes. The shifts of groups occur in the ranges indicated (given in p.p.m. from Et_2O,BF_3): BH_2 (-10 to -3), BHR (-30 to -20) and BR_2 (-40 to -36). These results are given in Table XII, and it is evident that the chemical-shift ranges are of diagnostic use.

B. Polyboranes

The application of the ^{11}B resonance spectra to the study of the structure of polyboranes has been one of the most prolific areas of development of ^{11}B n.m.r. However, a complete assignment of the spectrum is not always possible, but the general appearance and chemical-shift data are often sufficient to give support to proposed structures. Because of the complex nature of the polyboranes, readers who are not familiar with this field of work are advised to refer to the paper by Adams[95] on the nomenclature of cage boranes. The ^{11}B spectra of many of the parent polyboranes have been described and discussed by Lipscomb.[96] The spectra of boranes have also been extensively reviewed by Schaeffer.[4]

1. Triborane

Ring et al.[97] have studied complexes of triborane B_3H_7,L, where $L=Me_3N$ and tetrahydrofuran. It was concluded that in the trimethylamine complex, no base exchange was occurring but only hydrogen tautomerism, whereas in the tetrahydrofuran complex, both base exchange and hydrogen tautomerism occurred.

2. Tetraborane

The ^{11}B resonance spectra have been used to follow the deuteration of tetraborane by fully deuterated diborane.[98] The spectra of the two deuterated tetraboranes $B_4H_8D_2$ and $B_4D_8H_2$ have been discussed;[99] it was reported that the former compound quickly reverted to normal tetraborane. The spectra of the two complexes of tetraborane with carbon monoxide and phosphorus trifluoride were described by the same authors.[99] The ^{11}B spectrum confirmed the structure of the μ-deuterotetraborane-10 with a bridging deuterium atom.[100]

3. *Pentaborane*

The ^{10}B-labelled pentaborane, $^{10}BB_4H_{11}$, prepared by reaction of diborane with ^{10}B- labelled tetraborane–carbonyl complexes, showed only a very small high-field triplet.[99] However on warming to room temperature the intensity of the high-field triplet increases, thus indicating facile interchange between the apical and basal positions. The ^{11}B chemical shifts of several pentaborane derivatives have been tabulated Table XIII.[101] A substituent at the apical or basal position generally results in a downfield shift of the attached boron atom; however, the corresponding upfield shift of the boron atom diagonally opposite the substituent was a little surprising, and no rational reason

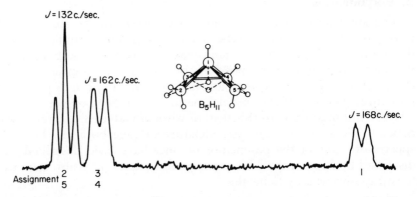

Fig. 4. The 64·2 Mc./sec. ^{11}B resonance spectrum of pentaborane–11. (From Williams, *et al.*[103])

could be given. The identity of the 1-chloropentaborane was also confirmed from the ^{11}B resonance spectrum with the four basal boron atoms resonating at 11·9 p.p.m. (from Et_2O,BF_3) and a single resonance signal at 29·3 p.p.m. from the apical B–Cl group.[102]

The application of high-field n.m.r. studies has been elegantly illustrated in the investigation of the ^{11}B resonance spectrum of pentaborane at 64·2 Mc./sec. This is possible using a superconducting selenoid magnet and these studies have the advantage that the high resolution normally required in proton resonance studies is not as important because of the quadrupole moment of the ^{11}B nucleus. This study on pentaborane was carried out because of the earlier confusion in the interpretation of the ^{11}B spectrum; however, at this high frequency the three boron signals are completely separated (Fig. 4).[103]

The lithium salt of the octahydropentaborate(-1) anion $B_5H_8^{\ominus}$ has been prepared, and the ^{11}B spectrum recorded, showing a poorly resolved group of signals at low field, from the four basal boron atoms, and a high field doublet.[104] However the anion is not very stable, and within 10 min. the spectrum of the borohydride, $BH_4^\ominus$, ion is obtained. The sodium, potassium and lithium salts of the octahydropentaborate-(-1) ion have also been independently investigated.[105] The basal boron atoms occurred in the range $+17$ to $+18$, and the apical boron was at approximately $+53 \pm 1$ p.p.m. (from Et_2O,BF_3). It was found that the low-field doublet of the lithium salt was temperature dependent and the apparent equivalence of the basal boron atoms at ambient temperature was ascribed to tautomerism.

The [11]B resonance spectrum showed that 1,2-dimethylpenta-borane(9) had rearranged under basic conditions, but the spectrum of the rearranged product, with a singlet and two doublets at $+1·2$, $+19·6$ and $+50·4$ p.p.m. (from Et_2O,BF_3) and of relative intensity $2:2:1$, was consistent with either the 2,3- or the 2,4-dimethyl derivative.[106] X-ray structural investigation showed that the 2,3-dimethyl isomer had been formed.

4. Hexa-, hepta- and octaboranes

The [11]B spectra of the caesium salts of the three new polyhedral borane anions, $B_6H_6^{2\ominus}$, $B_7H_7^{2\ominus}$ and $B_8H_8^{2\ominus}$, have been described.[107] The hexa- and octa-borane anions showed single [11]B resonance signals at $+31·7$ and $+24·1$ p.p.m. [relative to $(MeO)_3B$], respectively, with [11]B–[1]H coupling of 122 and 128 c./sec., respectively, thus indicating a very symmetric structure. The heptaborate ion showed two resonance signals at $+18·3$ and $+40·7$, in the ratio of $5:2$, with a [11]B–[1]H coupling of about 120 c./sec.

The spectrum of octaborane-12 (**49**) recorded in pentane at $-30°C$

49   50

consists of two doublets at $-6·8$ [$J_{11B-1H} = 168$ c./sec.] and $+20·5$ p.p.m. [$J_{11B-1H} = 153$ c./sec.] (from Et_2O,BF_3) of equal relative intensity; the spectrum in diethyl ether is very similar.[108] However, the spectra recorded in trimethylamine or in acetonitrile are more complicated, indicating that complex formation has occurred (**50**). The [11]B spectrum of octaborane-14 in pentane at $-30°C$ consists of three sets

9

of doublets at $-24 \cdot 1$ $[J_{^{11}B-^1H} = 161]$, $+21 \cdot 4$ $[J_{^{11}B-^1H} = 153]$ and $+38 \cdot 9$ p.p.m. $[J_{^{11}B-^1H} = 154$ c./sec.] in the relative intensity of $2:4:2$. The structure of octaborane-14 is probably a hybrid of structures (51) and (52).[108]

5. *Nonaborane*

The ^{11}B resonance spectra were used to investigate the formation of isotopically substituted nonaborane-15,[109] in which both ^{10}B and deuterium were introduced. Muetterties *et al.*[110, 111] have investigated the ^{11}B spectra of several new nonaborate ions. The trimethylsulphonium nonaborate, $[Me_3S^{\oplus}]_2B_9H_9^{2\ominus}$, showed two doublets at $+21 \cdot 5$ $[J_{^{11}B-^1H} = 133 \pm 3$ c./sec.] and $+39 \cdot 6$ p.p.m. [relative to $(MeO)_3B]$ $[J_{^{11}B-^1H} = 124$ c./sec.] in relative intensities of $1:2$.[110] The remaining ions, although containing nine boron atoms, have, in addition, a sulphur atom in the cage and thus are considered by the authors[111] to be derivatives of decaborane, and thus, to avoid further confusion, will be considered under this heading. Addition of acid to $CsB_{10}H_{13}NH_3$ did not yield the $B_9H_{14}^{\ominus}$ ion but the compound $B_9H_{13}NH_3$, ^{11}B spectrum of which was very similar to other members of this class of compounds.[112]

6. *Decaborane*

The advantage of studying ^{11}B n.m.r. spectra at high fields has been amply demonstrated with the prototype superconducting spectrometer made by Varian Associates. In some relatively early work (1964), Pier *et al.*[113] clarified the spectrum of decaborane. The resonance frequency of the ^{11}B nucleus at the high field used was 60 Mc./sec.

Using a similar magnet, but working at a slightly higher field strength, to give the resonance frequency of ^{11}B at $64 \cdot 2$ Mc./sec., Williams and Pier[114] again looked at the spectrum of decaborane, which was not different from that at 60 Mc./sec. They have also examined the spectrum of 1-chlorodecaborane, the low field B-1 resonance signal being readily recognized by its singlet character. (Fig. 5).

The deuteration of decaborane-14 has been followed by ^{11}B resonance spectroscopy.[109] Similarly the ^{11}B resonance spectra have been used to confirm the position of ^{10}B substitution in the decaborane molecule. The 19·3 and 32·1 Mc./sec. spectra of $^{11}B^{10}B_9H_{14}$ and the 19·3 Mc./sec. spectrum of 1,2,3,4-$^{11}B^{10}B_9H_{10}D_4$ are shown in the paper.[115] The 64·2 Mc./sec. ^{11}B spectra of decaborane in carbon disulphide shows clearly resolved structure; however, in dry cineole the low-field resonances are poorly resolved[116] and the situation is even worse in wet cineole. This behaviour is explained in terms

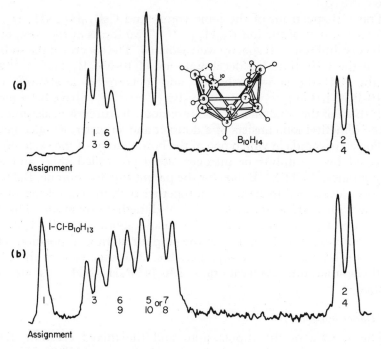

FIG. 5. The 64·2 Mc./sec. ^{11}B resonance spectra of (a) decaborane and (b) 1-chlorodecaborane. (From Williams and Pier.[114])

of hydrogen exchange. The 12·8 Mc./sec. spectrum of the ethoxy derivative, $EtOB_{10}H_{13}$, is interpreted by these same authors as being consistent with the 5,6-μ-$C_2H_5OB_{10}H_{13}$ structure.[116]

The ^{11}B spectra of some 1,10-disubstituted decaborane derivatives have been discussed by Knoth.[117] A high field doublet is usually found for the equatorial boron atoms and a broad singlet at low field due to the apical boron atoms. Several octachloro-derivatives (1,10-$B_{10}Cl_8X_2$) are also discussed by these authors. The ^{11}B chemical shifts of some complexes of decaborane of the form $B_{10}H_{12}L_2$ have been tabulated;[118] a generalization was made that the doublet arising from B-6 and 9 moves to higher field with the increasing basic strength of the ligand.

The metallic derivatives of decaborane have been considered. The ^{11}B spectra of the zinc derivatives $ZnB_{10}H_{12}$, xL (where $L = Et_2O$ or C_4H_8O) are very similar to that of decaborane;[119] these ionize in aqueous solution to give the ion $[(B_{10}H_{12})_2Zn]^{2\ominus}$. The ^{11}B spectral data of the closely related ion $[(B_{10}H_{12})_2Hg]^{2\ominus}$ have also been given.[120]

The ^{11}B spectrum of the ionic compound $CsB_{10}H_{13}NH_3$ is very different to that of the ion $B_{10}H_{13}{}^{\ominus}$.[112] Two forms of the compound with very different ^{11}B spectra were isolated. The spectra of the sodium salt of the 1,10-dimethyl decaborate ion $(1,10\text{-}Me_2B_{10}H_8{}^{2\ominus})$[121] and of the 1,10-dicyano-octachloro- and octabromo-decaborate ions $[1,10\text{-}B_{10}Cl_8(CN)_2{}^{2\ominus}$ and $1,10\text{-}B_{10}Br_8(CN)_2{}^{2\ominus}]$[122] have been recorded; those of the octahalogeno ions are single featureless peaks and that of the dimethyl ion consists of a doublet and singlet resonance peaks.

The compounds in which one of the boron atoms of the skeleton are replaced by a sulphur or nitrogen atom are called thia- and aza-decaboranes.[111] The ^{11}B data for the parent thiadecaborane, $B_9H_{11}S$, has been described in some detail together with the complexes of this borane with both acetonitrile and NN-dimethylformamide. The ^{11}B spectrum of the caesium salt of the thiadecaborate ion, $B_9H_{12}S^{\ominus}$, is very complex; it is thought that the sulphur atom is at position 6 but there are alternative structures possible. The spectrum of the tetra-methylammonium azadecaborate, $Me_4N^{\oplus}B_9H_{12}NH^{\ominus}$, is also described.

7. Higher boranes

The spectra of the dipotassium and the mixed caesium, tetra-methylammonium salts of the undecaborate ions, $K_2^{\oplus}B_{11}H_{11}^{2\ominus}$ and $CsMe_4^{\oplus}NB_{11}H_{11}^{2\ominus}$, are very simple, consisting of two doublets in the ratio of $10:1$.[110] The spectra permit an unambiguous structure to be assigned to the ion.

The ^{11}B spectrum of the thiaundecaborane, $B_{10}H_{12}S$, is fairly complex and consists of four doublets and a triplet, and that of the cor-responding caesium salt, $\overset{\oplus}{Cs}B_{10}H_{11}S^{\ominus}$, consists of four doublets in the relative intensities of $2:3:4:1$.[111] This latter ion forms a complex ion with cobalt ions, in which the cobalt is sandwiched between two of the cage structures, $(B_{10}H_{10}S)_2Co^{\ominus}$; the structure of this ion and that of the $B_{10}H_{11}S^{\ominus}$ ion are shown in Fig. 6. The spectra of the parent thiaundecaborane, and the two ions are shown in Fig. 7 and are perhaps rather good illustrations of the use of ^{11}B spectra in the determination of the structure of boranes.

The ^{11}B resonance data of the 1,7 and 1,12 carbonyl and carboxyl derivatives of dodecaborane have been recorded.[121] The three ions

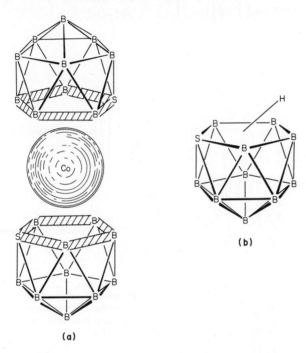

(b)

(a)

FIG. 6. Proposed structures of (a) the $(B_{10}H_{10}S)_2Co^{\ominus}$ ion and (b) the $B_{10}H_{11}S^{\ominus}$ ion. (From Hertler *et al.*[111])

derived from the brominated dodecaborane $[B_{12}Br_{11}(OCN)^{2\ominus}$, $B_{12}Br_{11}N_3^{2\ominus}$ and $B_{12}Br_{11}(OC_6H_5)^{2\ominus}]$ show only one peak in the ^{11}B resonance spectrum at $+31$ p.p.m. [from $(MeO)_3B$], which is identical to the shift of the parent dodecabromododecaborane ion $[B_{12}Br_{12}]^{2\ominus}$.[122] It was found that the ^{11}B spectra were more helpful for the polycyano-derivatives as boron atoms attached to the cyano-group are shifted to high field. Thus, although dodecachlorododeca-borate ion $[B_{12}Cl_{12}]^{2\ominus}$ exhibits a single resonance at $+31$ p.p.m. that of the pentachloroheptacyanododecaborate ion $[B_{12}Cl_5(CN)_7]^{2\ominus}$ shows two distinct resonance signals at $+28.6$ and $+40.6$ p.p.m. in the relative intensities of $5:7$. Data for the nonacyanododecaborate ions, $[B_{12}Br(CN)_9H_2]^{2\ominus}$ and $[B_{12}Br_3(CN)_9]^{2\ominus}$ are also given.[122] The reaction of thiaundecaborane with butyl-lithium and phenylboron dichloride afforded the 2-phenylthiadodecaborane(11), whose spectrum is included in Fig. 7.[111]

The spectra of the ions of some higher boranes have also been reported, namely $[Et_3NH]_2^{\oplus}$ $[B_{20}H_{18}]^{2\ominus}$,[123] $[Et_3NH]_3^{\oplus}$ $[B_{20}H_{19}]^{3\ominus}$[124] and $Cs_3^{\oplus}[B_{24}H_{23}]^{3\ominus} \cdot 3H_2O$.[125]

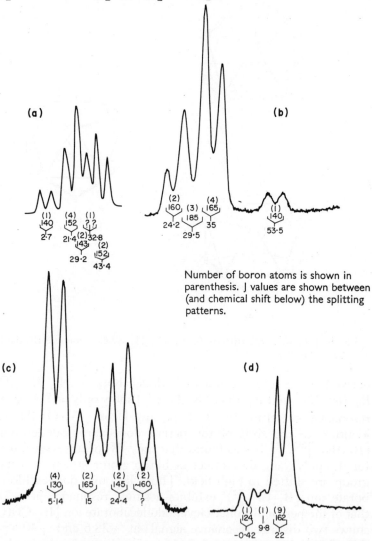

Number of boron atoms is shown in parenthesis. J values are shown between (and chemical shift below) the splitting patterns.

FIG. 7. The [11]B resonance spectra of (a) thiaundecaborane(12), $B_{10}H_{12}S$, (b) caesium thiaundecaborate, $Cs^{\oplus}[B_{10}H_{11}S]^{\ominus}$, (c) caesium cobalt thiaundecaborate, $Cs^{\oplus}[(B_{10}H_{10}S)_2Co]^{\ominus}$ (see Fig. 6a for structure) and (d) 2-phenylthiadodecaborane-(11), $C_6H_5B_{11}H_{10}S$. (From Hertler et al.[111])

IX. CARBORANES

Readers who are not completely familiar with the nomenclature are again urged to refer to the article by Adams.[95] It has been agreed that the term carborane should be used for *clovo* or near-*clovo* boron–carbon hydrides in which carbon atoms are in the main skeleton. The alkyl-substituted borons, e.g., ethyldecaborane are not covered by the generic name carboranes. There is still some confusion concerning those carboranes with *C*-alkyl substituents; it has been suggested that the *C* substituents should be indicated separately, e.g., a carborane with an ethyl and propyl substituent may be named *C*-ethyl,*C*'-propyl-carborane.

A. Dicarba *clovo* pentaboranes

The dimethyl derivatives of the second of the three possible isomers of carborane $C_2B_3H_5$, having a trigonal bipyramidal structure, has been isolated and characterized by the [11]B spectrum, which shows two doublets at $-7\cdot8$ ($J=174$ c./sec.) and $-34\cdot9$ ($J=184$ c./sec.) and a singlet at $-6\cdot2$ p.p.m. [from $(EtO)_3B$] of relative intensities of $1:1:1$.[126] The high-field singlet and doublet were assigned to the equatorial boron atoms and the low-field doublet to an apical boron atom. Consequently the structure of this isomer is a trigonal bipyramid with one of the carbon atoms equatorial and the other in the apical position. In the isomer isolated earlier, both carbon atoms occupied apical positions.[127] In some related work, Grimes[128] has also isolated several similar compounds and reported the [11]B chemical shifts of 1,5-dicarba*clovo*pentaborane(5) and of 2-methyl-1,5-dicarba*clovo*-pentaborane(5). The structure of the *C*-3-dimethyl-1,2-dicarba*clovo*-pentaborane(5) mentioned above[126] was also discussed further.

B. Carba *clovo* hexaboranes

In the work described above, Grimes[128] also isolated the 2-methyl-1,6-dicarba*clovo*hexaborane(6); the [11]B shifts of this and the 1,6-di-carba*clovo*hexaborane, which had previously been described,[129] were given. Although the dicarborane derivatives are well known there are far fewer examples of the mono- and tri-carboranes. The structure of the compound obtained from ethyldiborane and acetylene was shown[130] to be the *C*-methyl-*B*-pentaethyl-2-carbahexaborane (**53**) and the [11]B spectrum consisted of three broadish signals at $-23\cdot2$, $-5\cdot7$ and $+36\cdot5$ p.p.m. (from Et_2O,BF_3). It is perhaps of interest to note that the proton spectrum is by no means as simple as might have been expected (Fig. 8). Onak *et al.*[131] earlier published the [11]B spectra of the 2-,3- and

4-methyl-2-carbahexaboranes(9); in each case the high-field signal from the apical boron atom occurred in the range 49·5–52 p.p.m. to high field of Et_2O,BF_3.

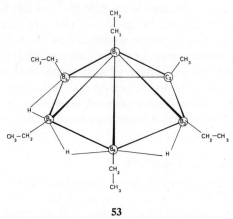

53

(a)

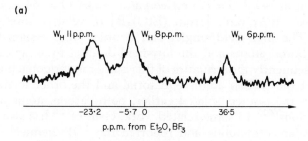

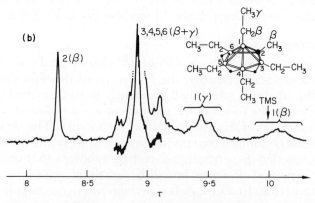

FIG. 8. The n.m.r. spectra of C-methyl-B-pentaethyl-2-carbahexaborane(9); (a) [11]B spectrum; (b) ^{1}H spectrum. (From Koster et al.[130]).

The [11]B spectra of the 2-methyl-, 2,3-dimethyl- and 2,4-dimethyl-2,3,4-tricarbahexaborane(7) (54) have been shown in a paper by Bramlett and Grimes,[132] although the precise chemical shifts were, in

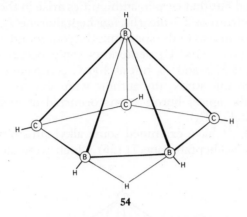

54

point of fact, not determined. The chemical shifts of a tetracarbahexaborane(6) have been given by Binger.[133] The shifts were measured relative to the signal of calcium bis(tetraethylboron) $[Ca(BEt_4)_2]$ and two signals of relative intensity 1:1 were obtained; the compound was identified as the C-tetraalkyl-B-diethyl-3,4,5,6-tetracarbahexaborane-(6) (55).

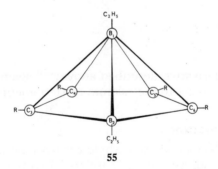

55

[11]B resonance spectroscopy has been used to follow the deuteration of 2,3-dicarbahexaborane(8) and its C-dimethyl derivative.[134,135] Treatment of the parent compound with sodium hydride gave the 2,3-dicarbaheptahydrohexaborate(-1) ion.[134] Treatment of this ion with deuterium chloride gave the dideutero-derivatives, whose [11]B spectrum showed the loss of the small coupling (44 c./sec.) of the resonance signal of B-4 and -6, thus clearly indicating that the bridging hydrogens had been replaced.

9*

C. Dicarbaheptaboranes

The ^{11}B chemical shifts of the 1-methyl-, 3-methyl- and 5-methyl-2,4-dicarba*clovo*heptaborane(7) have been given by Grimes.[128] Onak *et al.*[136] pointed out that certain ambiguities arise in the interpretation of the ^{11}B spectrum of 2,3-dicarba*clovo*heptaborane(7). In an attempt to assist the assignment of the spectrum the compound was deuterated; at low temperature (100°C) deuteration only occurred at the basal positions, i.e., B-3,-5 and -6, but at 400°C complete deuteration was achieved. From this study, the authors were able to confirm that the resonance of the apical boron atoms occurred at high field (+23·5 p.p.m. from Et_2O,BF_3).

Köster *et al.*[137] have examined some alkyl substituted derivatives of 2,4-dicarba*clovo*heptaborane(7) (**56**) which were closely related to

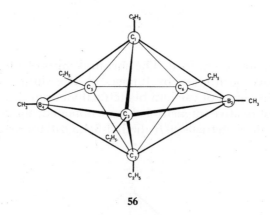

56

the hexaborane derivative described above;[130] again the boron shifts were given with respect to the calcium bis(tetramethyl)boron.

D. Dicarbaoctaboranes

Tebbe *et al.*[138] obtained a dimethyldicarbaoctaborane that was identical to the compound previously isolated by other workers,[139] but discrepancies were observed in the ^{11}B spectrum recorded at 19·3 Mc./sec. with that previously recorded at 12·8 Mc./sec. From the spectrum, which consisted of two doublets in the ratio 4:2, an Archimedean antiprism structure with the carbon atoms at positions 1 and 3 (**57**) was preferred. However it was pointed out that if, at higher field, the doublet of intensity four was revealed to be two doublets, then a distorted antiprism or bisdispheroid structure would be correct; this is obtained by compression along the dotted lines shown in (**57**).

Tebbe *et al.*[140] have more recently examined the spectrum at 32 Mc./ sec., and again found only two doublets. Although this is as expected for the antiprism structures, the authors have reverted to the dodecahedron structure **(58)** originally proposed by Williams and Gerhart.[139]

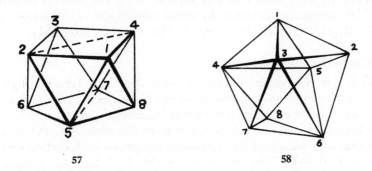

57   58

The structure has been confirmed by X-ray studies[141] to be that of a distorted dodecahedron with the carbon atoms at positions 1 and 6. This is perhaps an excellent example of the care that must be exercised in the interpretation of the apparently simple [11]B spectra of carboranes.

E. Carbanonaboranes

Tebbe *et al.*,[138, 140] have similarily twice investigated the [11]B spectrum of C,C'-dimethyl-dicarbanonaborane. In the earlier paper[138] it was suggested that the structure of this carborane was that of a tricapped trigonal prism with the carbon atoms at positions 1 and 7 **(59)**; the same data and conclusions were presented in the latter paper.[140] The structure has been confirmed by X-ray analysis.[141] Another isomer, the 1,3-dimethyl-1,3-dicarbanonaborane(13) **(60)**, obtained by degradation of the 1,8-dimethyl-1,8-dicarba*clovo*undecaborane(11),

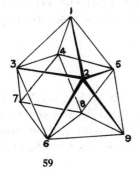

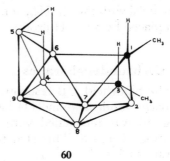

59   60

was obtained by these authors, and the ^{11}B spectrum, recorded at 32 Mc./sec., was examined in detail, although the conclusions reached did not differ from the earlier study made at 19·3 Mc./sec.[142]

Knoth[143] has isolated the 1-$B_9H_9CH^\ominus$ ion, which is isostructural with the $B_{10}H_{10}^{2\ominus}$ ion; this was supported by the general features of the ^{11}B resonance spectrum in which one of the apical boron atoms of the $B_{10}H_{11}^{2\ominus}$ ion had been replaced by a carbon atom (61).

F. Carbadecaboranes

The ^{11}B resonance spectra of both the C,C' 1,6-dimethyl- and C,C' 1,10-dimethyl-carbadecaboranes have been examined at 19·3 Mc./sec., and the results have again been reported twice;[138, 140] the conclusions drawn on each occasion were the same, *viz.*, the structure was that of a bicapped Archimedean antiprism with carbon atoms at 1,6 or 1,10 (62). The spectrum of the 1,10-dimethyl isomer was especially simple, consisting of one doublet $[J_{^{11}B-^1H} = 162$ c./sec. and a shift of $+103$ p.p.m. (from Et_2O,BF_3)] since in (62: 1 and 10 = C—Me) all the remaining boron atoms are equivalent.

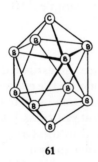

61

62

Knoth,[143] from consideration of the ^{11}B spectrum of the salt $Cs^\oplus(1-B_9H_9CH)^\ominus$ concluded that the ion $(1-B_9H_9CH)^\ominus$ was isostructural with the $B_{10}H_{10}^{2\ominus}$ ion in which one of the apical boron atoms is replaced by a C—H group.

G. Carbaundecaboranes

The high-field ^{11}B resonance spectrum (at 60 Mc./sec.) of 1,8-di-carba*clovo*undecaborane(11) has been recorded[140] and the spectrum (Fig. 9) was reconciled with structure (63) with carbon atoms at positions 1 and 8. This structure has recently been confirmed from X-ray studies.[144]

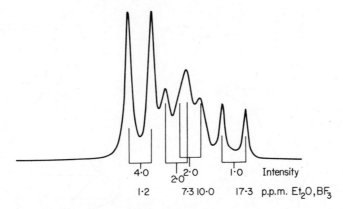

FIG. 9. The ^{11}B spectrum of 1,8-dicarba*clovo*undecaborane(11) in carbon disulphide at 60 Mc./sec. (From Tebbe *et al.*[140])

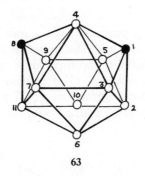

63

Decaborane-14 reacts with alkyl isocyanides to afford products that are considered to have a zwitterionic structure $RNH_2^{\oplus}[-CB_{10}H_{12}]^{\ominus}$ (**64**).[145] The ^{11}B spectrum, at 32·1 Mc./sec., of the trimethyl derivative $Me_3NCB_{10}H_{12}$ is shown in the paper, but this is clearly one case in which studies at higher fields would be profitable. Some closely related ions have also been investigated by Hyatt *et al.*[146] The spectrum of the tetramethylammonium salt of the $B_{10}H_{12}CH^{\ominus}$ ion was very similar to that of the compound (**64**; $RNH_2 = Me_3N$) above. It was considered that the structure of the ion was a nearly regular isosahedron with one vertex missing. The ^{11}B spectra of $B_{10}H_{10}CN(Me)_3$ and the salt $Na^{\oplus}[B_{10}H_{10}CH]^{\ominus}$ were essentially similar and the structure was rationalized in terms of a "*clovo*" octadecahedral structure of C_{2v} symmetry (**65**). The ^{11}B spectra of the halogenated products were also discussed.

Olsen and Hawthorne[147] have compared the ^{11}B spectra of the iododicarbaundecaborate(11) ion and the iododicarbaundecaborane

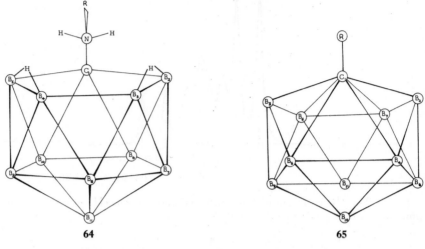

64   65

$(B_9C_2H_{12}I)$ formed by protonation of the ion. The ^{11}B spectrum was considered to be consistent with the structure **(66)**.

The ^{11}B chemical shifts of the 6-phenyl-, 6-phenyl-1,2-dimethyl- and the 6-ethyl-derivatives of (3)-1,2-dicarbadodecahydroundeca-borate(-1) were generally uninformative;[148] the singlet boron signal from the B-phenyl or B-ethyl group could not even be distinguished.

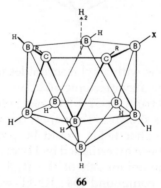

66

1,2-Dicarba*clovo*dodecaborane(12) and piperidine react to give the piperidinium salt of the dodecahydrodicarbaundecaborate in which one additional molecule of piperidine was associated, possibly in-volving B–N co-ordination.[149] The ^{11}B resonance spectrum of the piperidinium salt has been investigated by Hawthorne et al.[150] in both 95% ethanol and in piperidine solution. Since the spectra were essen-tially identical, it was concluded that the additional molecule of piperi-dine was only loosely associated, possibly by hydrogen bonding.

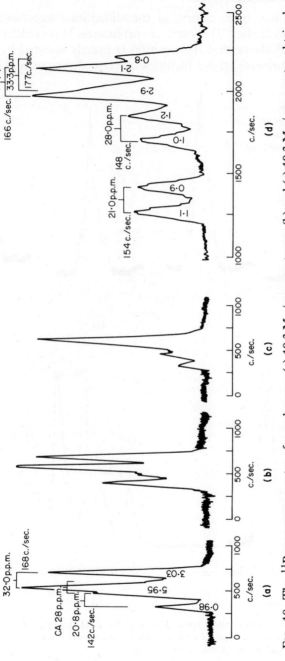

Fig. 10. The ^{11}B resonance spectra of *o*-carborane: (a) 19·3 Mc./sec. spectrum; (b) and (c) 19·3 Mc./sec. spectra obtained while irradicating protons at 60 Mc./sec.; (d) 64·16 Mc./sec. spectrum. (From Vickers *et al.*[151])

H. Carbadodecaboranes

Attention has been drawn to the difficulties experienced in the interpretation of the ^{11}B spectra of carboranes. It is evident from what has been said above that the position is greatly assisted by studies at high field; however, these facilities are not always available. Vickers

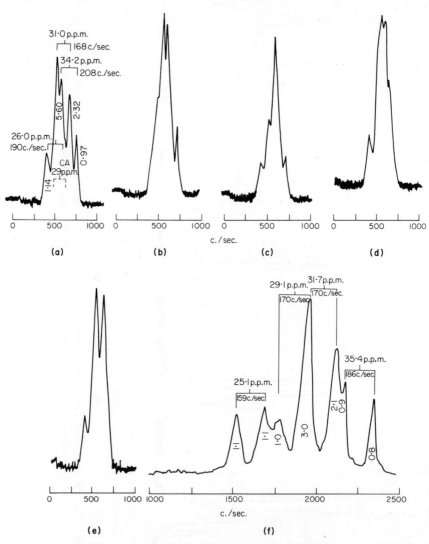

FIG. 11. The ^{11}B resonance spectra of m-carborane: (a) 19·3 Mc./sec. spectrum; (b)–(e) 19·3 Mc./sec. spectra obtained while irradicating protons at 60 Mc./sec.; (f) 64·16 Mc./sec. spectrum. (From Vickers et $al.$[151])

et al.[151] have investigated the ^{11}B–{^{1}H} heteronuclear decoupled spectra of the three dicarba*clovo*dodecaborane(12) isomers; the ^{11}B spectra of two had not previously been assigned. The heteronuclear decoupling certainly assisted in the analysis, but there can be no denying the advantage of the high-field spectra (Figs. 10–12). ^{11}B–{^{1}H} heteronuclear double resonance has also been used to elucidate the

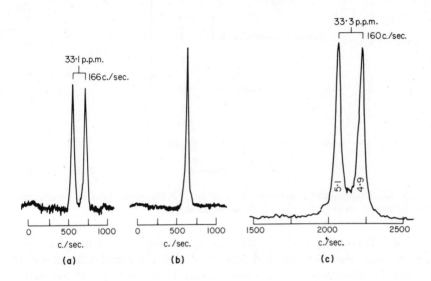

FIG. 12. The ^{11}B resonance spectra of *p*-carborane: (a) 19·3 Mc./sec. spectrum; (b) 19·3 Mc./sec. spectrum obtained while irradicating protons at 60 Mc./sec.; (c) 64·12 Mc./sec. spectrum. (From Vickers *et al.*[151])

spectra of the 9-bromo-, 9,12-dibromo- and 8,9,12-tribromo-*o*-carborane derivatives.[152] The effect on the chemical shifts by the introduction of bromine atoms is tabulated in Fig. 13. The ^{11}B spectrum of the 9,10-dibromo-*m*-carborane have also been given,[153] and the spectrum of this compound is compared with that of the parent *m*-carborane and of the decachloro-*m*-carborane (*m*-$B_{10}Cl_{10}C_2H_2$).

The ^{11}B chemical shifts of several salts of (3)-1,2-and (3)-1,7-dicarbadodecahydroundecaborate ions have been tabulated.[154] The ^{11}B spectrum of the potassium (3)-1,2-dicarbadodecahydroundecaborate-(-1) at 60 Mc./sec. (Fig. 14) showed additional small proton coupling in the high-field doublet, which was ascribed as due to coupling to the "extra" hydrogen atom; the structure of the ions are shown schematically in **(67)**.

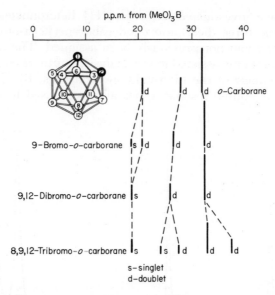

FIG. 13. Diagrammatic representation of the ^{11}B chemical shifts of o-carborane and the bromo-derivatives. (From Lipscomb *et al.*[152])

The ^{11}B spectra of the 3-phenyl-, 1,3-diphenyl-, 3-phenyl-1,2-dimethyl and the 3-ethyl derivatives of the 1,2-dicarba*clovo*dodecaborane(12) derivatives were insufficiently resolved to be of any assistance in the structural determination.[148]

The ^{11}B spectrum of the caesium tropenylium undecahydro*clovo*dodecaborate consisted of an unsymmetrical doublet at 13·7 p.p.m. (from Et_2O,BF_3) compared to the symmetrical doublet of the $B_{12}H_{12}^{2\ominus}$

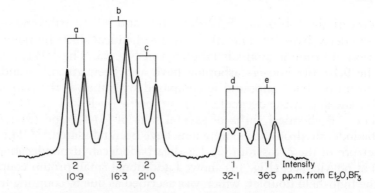

FIG. 14. The 60 Mc./sec. ^{11}B spectrum of the (3)-1,2-$B_9C_2H_{12}^{\ominus}$ ion showing the secondary splitting of doublet d. (From Hawthorne *et al.*[154])

ion. The data for the corresponding caesium tropenylium nonohydro-*clovo*decaborate is also discussed, and in this case it was possible to demonstrate that the substituent is in the equatorial position.[155]

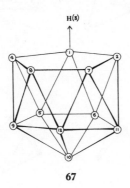

67

X. METALLIC DERIVATIVES OF CARBORANES

Pentacarbonylmanganese bromide and the dicarboundecahydro-nonaborate reacts to give the complex ion $B_6C_2H_8Mn(CO)_3^{\ominus}$, which was isolated as the tetramethylammonium salt.[156] The ^1H resonance spectrum showed that the two C—H groups were equivalent and the ^{11}B spectrum also substantiated the symmetrical structure of the complex ion shown in (68).

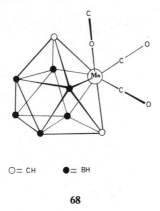

$O = CH \qquad \bullet = BH$

68

The dicarboundecahydrononaborate ion and cobalt chloride gave the complex ion $(B_7C_2H_9)_2Co^{\ominus}$.[157] The ^{11}B spectrum showed a low-field doublet and six overlapping, but distinct, doublets, indicating seven distinct types of boron atoms in the complex ion (69). X-ray

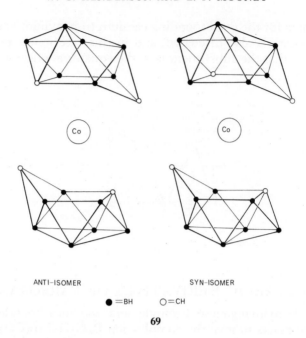

ANTI-ISOMER   SYN-ISOMER

● =BH   ○=CH

69

data have confirmed that the structure is that of the *anti*-isomer. A similar spectrum was obtained for the cyclopentadienyl derivative $(C_5H_5)Co(B_7C_2H_9)$ (**70**).

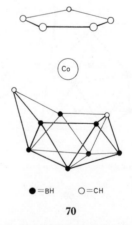

●=BH   ○=CH

70

The "dicarbollide" ions $(3)\text{-}1,2\text{-}B_9C_2H_{11}^{2\ominus}$ and $(3)\text{-}1,7\text{-}B_9C_2H_{11}^{2\ominus}$ act as ligands in the formation of transition-metal complexes which resemble the metallocenes.[158] However the ^{11}B spectra of the iron(II) complexes were generally uninformative, and at the best showed broad, poorly resolved, doublets. The spectra of the iron(III) complexes, which are paramagnetic, afford the first examples of paramagnetic contact shifts found in ^{11}B resonance spectroscopy. Some examples of the spectra are shown in Fig. 15; it should be noted that no ^{11}B–^{1}H coupling is observed in the spectra. The structure of the bis-π-(3)-1,2-dicarbollyl–iron(III) complex is shown in (71). The nickel(II) and (III)

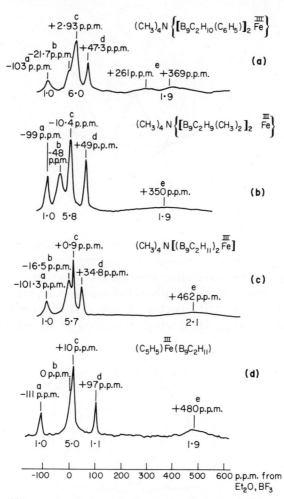

FIG. 15. The ^{11}B resonance spectra of some iron(III) dicarbollyl derivatives: (a) $Me_4N^{\oplus}\{[B_9C_2H_{10}(C_6H_5)]_2Fe^{III}\}$; (b) $Me_4N^{\oplus}\{[B_9C_2H_9Me]_2Fe^{III}\}$; (c) $Me_4N^{\oplus}-[B_9C_2H_{11})_2Fe^{III}]$; (d) $(C_5H_5)Fe^{III}(B_9C_2H_{11})$. Shifts shown in p.p.m. from Et_2O,BF_3. (From Hawthorne et al.[158])

complexes also exhibit paramagnetic shifts. It would appear that in these sandwich complexes, the ^{11}B spectra are either essentially worthless or exhibit large paramagnetic shifts, although even in this latter case the spectra have not been completely interpreted.

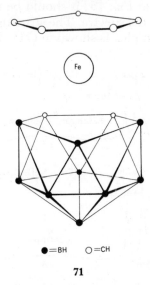

●=BH   ○=CH

71

Hyatt et al.[159] also found that in the cobalt(III), iron(III) and nickel(IV) complexes of carbadecaborane the ^{11}B resonance were very broad in some cases extending over some 300 p.p.m.

Relatively few examples of phosphaboranes exist, but Little et al.[160] have reported the ^{11}B spectra of the carbadecahydrophosphaundecaborane ($B_{10}H_{10}CHP$), which consisted of six signals of relative

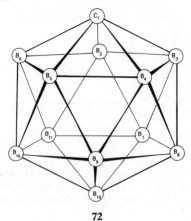

72

intensity $1:1:2:2:2:2$, which was consistent with the 1,2- or 1,7-isomer; the structure of the 1,7-isomer is shown in **(72)**. The spectrum of the P-phenyl-undecahydrophosphaundecaborane, which consisted of three overlapping doublets of relative intensity $1:5:5$, was consistent with an icosahedral cage structure.

XI. OTHER METALLO-BORON SYSTEMS

The octahydrotriborane ion $(B_3H_8)^\ominus$ reacts with chromium, molybdenum and tungsten hexacarbonyls to give the complex ion $[(OC)_4MB_3H_8]^\ominus$, which shows two broad ^{11}B-resonance signals at $23\cdot0$ and $61\cdot3$ p.p.m. [from $B(OMe)_3$] of relative intensity $1:2$.[161]

Gaines and Iorns[162] have prepared the μ-trimethylsilylpentaborane(9), and the ^{11}B spectra, at both $32\cdot1$ and $9\cdot2$ Mc./sec., are shown in the paper. The trimethylsilyl group forms a bridge between B_2 and B_3 **(73)** and is the first example of a compound containing a B–Si–B three-centre bond.

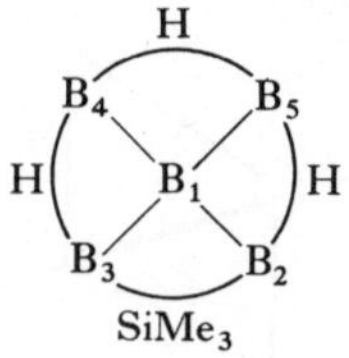

73

The ^{11}B shifts of a series of metal complexes of poly(1-pyrazolyl)-borates, $M[H_{2-n}B(pz)_{2+n}]_2$, where $pz = 1$-pyrazolyl group, have been discussed.[163] A rather different type of complex of iron with the 1,3,4-triaza-2,5-diborine system has been described by Nöth and Regnet.[164] Two ^{11}B resonance signals were observed at $-29\cdot7$ and $-26\cdot8$ p.p.m. (from Et_2O,BF_3) and the complex was considered to have a metallocene structure.

Nöth and co-workers[165–167] have considered the ^{11}B shifts of several metal derivatives of bis(dimethlamino)boranes; these shifts are, for convenience of comparison, shown in Table XIV. Nöth and Schmid[168] have discussed co-ordination compounds containing metal-boron bonds and the ^{11}B shifts are also reproduced in Table XIV.

Tetraphenylarsonium trichloro-stannate(II) and germanate(II) react[169] with boron trifluoride to give a complex anion in which the tin or germanium is co-ordinated to boron trifluoride **(74)**. The anions had a ^{11}B shift of $19\cdot0\pm1$ p.p.m. [from $(MeO)_3B$].

$$Ph_4As^{\oplus}[MCl_3]^{\ominus} + BF_3 \longrightarrow Ph_4As^{\oplus}[Cl_3MBF_3]^{\ominus}$$

M = Sn or Ge   **74**

Two other references are included here for completeness of compounds containing both boron and another metal, but which are not directly bonded. The [11]B shifts of the mixed B-trimethylsilylaminobis(trimethylsilyl)aminoboranes (**75**) have been recorded.[170] The [11]B

$$[Me_3Si]_2-N-B-NHSiMe_3$$
$$\overset{|}{X}$$

X = NH$_2$, NHR, NR$_2$, NHSiMe$_3$ or OMe

75

shift of the complex compound Al$_4$B[N(Me$_2$)$_3$]Me$_6$ was found to be −44·6 p.p.m. (from Me$_2$O,BF$_3$);[171] the proposed structure of the compound is shown in (**76**).

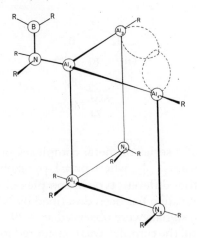

76

TABLE I

^{11}B shifts of alkyl and aryl boron halides, RBXY p.p.m. from Et_2O,BF_3

R	X	Y	δ	Ref.
Me	F	F	−28.2	14, 17
Me	Cl	Cl	−62.3	5, 14
			−61.6	17
Me	Br	Br	−62.5	14
Me	I	I	−50.5	14
Et	F	F	−28.7	5, 14
			−29.9	21
Et	Cl	Cl	−63.4	14
Et	Br	Br	−65.6	14
Et	I	I	−55.9	14
Pr^n	Cl	Cl	−63.1	16
Bu^n	F	F	−29.0	21
Bu^n	Cl	Cl	−63.4	16
$n\text{-}C_5H_{11}$	F	F	−29.0	21
$n\text{-}C_6H_{13}$	F	F	−29.0	21
$n\text{-}C_8H_{17}$	Cl	Cl	−63.6	16
$CH_2{=}CH{-}$	Cl	Cl	−54.5	23
			−53.7	172
$CH_2{=}CH{-}$	F	F	−23.3	172
Et	F	Cl	−45.8	172
Bu^n	F	Cl	−45.6	22
Me	Me	F	−59.0	14
		Cl	−60.3	17
Me	Me	Br	−77.2	14
		I	−75.7	17
Me	Me	Br	−78.8	14
Me	Me	I	−79.1	14
Et	Et	F	−59.6	5, 14
Et	Et	Cl	−78.0	5, 14
Et	Et	Br	−81.9	14
Et	Et	I	−84.4	14
Ph	F	F	−24.8	14
Ph	Cl	Cl	−54.8	5, 14
Ph	Br	Br	−57.9	14
Ph	I	I	−48.2	14
$p\text{-}MeOC_6H_4{-}$	Cl	Cl	−53.9	19
$m\text{-}CH_3C_6H_4{-}$	Cl	Cl	−55.8	23
Ph	Ph	F	−47.4	14
Ph	Ph	Cl	−61.0	5
Ph	Ph	Br	−66.7	14
Ph	Ph	I	−69.1	14

TABLE II

^{11}B shifts of alkyl and aryl boron derivatives, RBXY, p.p.m. from Et_2O,BF_3

R	X	Y	δ	Ref.
Me	Me	Me	−86·0	5
Et	Et	Et	−86·5	5
Ph	Ph	Ph	−60·0	173
Me	Me	OMe	−53·0	5
Et	Et	OMe	−53·6	5
Et	Et	$O \cdot CMe_3$	−52·0	5
Me	OMe	OMe	−29·5	5
Et	OMe	OMe	−31·5	5
Et	$O \cdot CMe_3$	$O \cdot CMe_3$	−29·5	5
Ph	OEt	OEt	−28·6	71
Ph	OCH_2Ph	OCH_2Ph	†	35
Me	Me	OH	−54·8	17
Me	OH	OH	−32·1	17
$o\text{-}CH_3C_6H_4$	OH	OH	−32·2	81
Bu^n	OH	OH	−32·4	175
$n\text{-}C_9H_{19}$	OH	OH	−29·3	173
Ph	OH	OH	−33·6‡	174
			−32·7§	174
	OH	OH	−28·4	81
$CH_2{=}CH$	OBu^n	OBu^n	−25·6	52a
$HC{\equiv}C$	OMe	OMe	−21·6	52b
Bu^n	SBu^n	SBu^n	−69·7	175
Bu^i	$-SCH_2-CH_2S-$		−70·3	175
Me	Me	N_3	−62·5(a) / −4·9(b)	5¶
Ph	Ph	N_3	−50·5	5
Me	NMe_2	NMe_2	−33·5	5

R	X	Y	δ	Ref.
Et	NMe_2	NMe_2	−34·2	5
Bu^n	NMe_2	NMe_2	−34·2	176
Bu^n	NEt_2	NEt_2	−39·3	177
Ph	NMe_2	NMe_2	−32·4	5
Et	$NHMe$	$NHMe$	−32·1	5
Bu^n	$NHMe$	$NHMe$	−32·2	5
Me	NMe_2	Cl	−38·5	5
Et	NMe_2	F	−30·8	5
Et	NMe_2	Cl	−39·3	5
Et	NPr^i_2	Cl	−39·5	5
Bu^n	NMe_2	Cl	−39·1	5
Pr^n	OEt	OEt	−31·0	23
Bu^n	OCH_2CH_2Cl	OCH_2CH_2Cl	−31·7	23
Bu^n	OCH_2CH_2F	OCH_2CH_2F	−30·7	23
Bu^n	OCH_2CF_3	OCH_2CF_3	−32·7	23
Bu^n	Bu^n	OCH_2CF_3	−30·7	23
Et	OMe	Cl	−42·0	5
Et	$O \cdot CMe_3$	F	−25·9	5
Et	Et	NMe_2	−45·7	5
Et	Et	NEt_2	−45·9	5
Bu^n	Bu^n	NMe_2	−45·5	5
Et	Et	$NHMe$	−46·8	5
Ph	Ph	NEt_2	−41·8	5
Me	NMe_2	OMe	−31·8	5
Et	NMe_2	OMe	−31·8	5
Me	Me	NMe_2	−44·6	5
Me	Me	NEt_2	−44·9	5

† The shift is concentration and solvent dependent (see p. 228).

‡ In pyridine solution.

§ In acetone solution.

¶ See also ref. 34, which also reports the presence of molecular association in this compound (p. 228); (a) value for

TABLE III

^{11}B shifts of boron halides, BXYZ, p.p.m. from Et$_2$O,BF$_3$

X	Y	Z	δ	Ref.	X	Y	Z	δ	Ref.
F	F	F	−9.4	178	F	Cl	Br	−31.1	181
Cl	Cl	Cl	−47.5 / −46.4	178 / 41†	F	Br	Br	−29.6	181
Br	Br	Br	−40.1 / −38.8	178 / 41†	Cl	Cl	H	−7.0	18
I	I	I	+5.5 / +7.4	179 / 41†	Cl	Cl	Br	−46.1	182
F	F	H	−23.6	180	Cl	Cl	I	−37.3	182
F	F	Cl	−20.0	181	Cl	H	H	−4.3	18
F	F	Br	−19.5	181	Cl	Br	Br	−43.4	182
F	Cl	Cl	−31.2	181	Cl	Br	I	−32.8	182
					Cl	I	I	−19.0	182
					Br	I	I	−12.5	182
					Br	Br	I	−27.7	182

† The shifts of the boron trihalides as reported are rather variable and tend to be dependent upon the solvent and degree of purity.

TABLE IV

^{11}B shifts of derivatives of boric acid, BXYZ, p.p.m. from $Et_2O.BF_3$

X	Y	Z	δ	Ref.
OH	OH	OH	−18·8	178†
OMe	OMe	OMe	−18·3	5
OEt	OEt	OEt	−18·3	23
OPr^n	OPr^n	OPr^n	−18·2	23
OPr^i	OPr^i	OPr^i	−17·6	23
OBu^n	OBu^n	OBu^n	−18·1	5
OBu^s	OBu^s	OBu^s	−18·2	23
OBu^i	OBu^i	OBu^i	−18·4	23
OBu^t	OBu^t	OBu^t	−15·5	5
O.Allyl	O.Allyl	O.Allyl	−17·5	23
ClCH$_2$CH$_2$O	ClCH$_2$CH$_2$O	ClCH$_2$CH$_2$O	−17·1	23
Bu^{n}S	Bu^{n}S	Bu^{n}S	−66·2	22
PhO	PhO	PhO	−16·5	41
o-ClC$_6$H$_4$O—	o-ClC$_6$H$_4$O—	o-ClC$_6$H$_4$O—	−14·0	178
o-CH$_3$C$_6$H$_4$O—	o-CH$_3$C$_6$H$_4$O—	o-CH$_3$C$_6$H$_4$O—	−15·0	178
PhS—	PhS—	PhS—	−61·6	41
MeO	MeO	H	−26·1	178
MeO	MeO	Cl	−23·7	5
EtO	EtO	F	−15·0	17
MeO	MeO	F	−15·8	17
MeO	F	F	+0·4‡	20
EtO	F	F	+0·3‡	20
Pr^{n}O	F	F	+0·1‡	20
Bu^{n}O	F	F	−16·2	5
Bu^{n}O	F	F	+0·25‡	20
MeO	Cl	Cl	−31·9	5
EtO	Cl	Cl	−31·8	20
Pr^{n}O	Cl	Cl	−30·9	20
Bu^{n}O	Cl	Cl	−30·9	20
ClCH$_2$CH$_2$O—	Cl	Cl	−30·9	20
PhO	Cl	Cl	−31·1	41
PhS	Br	Br	−27·3	41
C$_6$F$_5$O—	Br	Cl	−47·2	41
C$_6$F$_5$O—	Cl	I—	−33·6	41
PhS—	I—	Cl	−12·0	41
PhO	PhO	Cl	−21·7	41
PhO	PhO	Br	−21·4	41

† Shift in pH dependent (see p. 232).   ‡ Trimers.

TABLE V

^{11}B shifts of aminoboranes, $\begin{smallmatrix} R \\ \\ R' \end{smallmatrix} N{-}B \begin{smallmatrix} X \\ \\ Y \end{smallmatrix}$, p.p.m. from Et_2O,BF_3

R'	X	Y	δ	Ref.
Me	Me	Me	−44·6	5
Et	Me	Me	−44·9	5
Me	Et	Et	−45·7	5
Et	Et	Et	−45·9	5
Me	Bu^n	Bu^n	−45·5	5
H	Et	Et	−46·8† , −2·1‡	5 , 5
Et	Ph	Ph	−41·8	5
Me	CMe$_3$	H	−43·7† , −4·5‡	5 , 5
Me	Me	Me	−46·1	10
Me	Ph	Me	−44·6	10
Me	Ph	CH=CH$_2$	−40·2	10
Me	Me	CH=CH$_2$	−39·7	10
CH$_2$Ph	Ph	CH$_2$Ph	−49·4	10
Me	H	H	−37·9† , −5·4‡	24 , 24
Et	H	H	−37·3† , −1·9‡	24 , 24
−(CH$_2$)$_5$−	H	H	−37·5† , −2·3‡	24 , 24
Bu^n	H	H	−37·8† , −3·0‡	24 , 24
Pr^i	H	H	−36·0	32
Bu^s	H	H	−36·6	32
H	Me	Me	−47·1† , +3·0‡	24 , 24
H	Et	Et	−48·7† , +0·4‡	24 , 24
H	Me	Me	−45·7† , +1·0‡	24 , 24
Me	H	Me	−42·1† , −5·4‡	24 , 24
Me	F	Me	−31·6† , −7·0‡	24 , 24
Me	Cl	Me	−38·5† , −10·1‡	24 , 24
Me	Br	Me	−37·8† , −10·5‡	24 , 24
Me	Cl	Cl	−30·8† , −10·4‡ , −30·5	5, 24 , 5, 24 , 30

R	R'	X	Y	δ	Ref.
Me	Me	Br	Br	−25·7† , −6·1‡ , −26·1	5, 24 , 5, 24 , 30
Me	Me	Et	F	−30·8† , −6·5‡	24 , 24
Me	Me	Me	Cl	−38·5† , −10·1‡	24 , 24
Me	Me	Et	Cl	−39·3† , −10·2‡	24 , 24
Me	Me	Cl	Br	−28·8	30
Et	Et	F	F	−17·5† , −1·1‡ , −3·8‡	24 , 24 , 29
	Et	F	Cl	−24·6† , −6·0‡	29 , 29
Et	Et	Cl	Cl	−31·8 , −30·3	30 , 29
Et	Et	Br	Br	−26·9	30
Et	Et	Cl	Br	−29·6	30
Bu^n	Bu^n	F	F	−17·6† , −0·9‡	5, 24 , 5, 24
CF$_3$	CF$_3$	Br	Br	−11·3‡	26
Et	H	F	F	+0·4	25
Pr^i	H	F	F	−0·3	25
Bu^t	H	Cl	Cl	−30·6	23
Me	P(CF$_3$)$_2$	Cl	Cl	−38·3	31
Bu^t	P(CF$_3$)$_2$	Cl	Cl	−49·8†	31
	=C(Cl)CF$_3$	Cl	Cl	−5·6‡	28
	=C(Br)CF$_3$	Br	Br	+2·3‡	28
Me	Me	I	I	−4·9	5
Et	Et	Bu^t	H	−42·4	177
Bu^n	Bu^n	Bu^t	H	−42·8	177
Et	Et	Bu^i	H	−42·8	177
Pr^i	Pr^i	Bu^t	H	−42·9	177
Et	Et	Bu^s	H	−43·2	177
Me	Me	Bu^t	H	−43·6	177
Bu^i	Bu^i	Bu^t	H	−43·9	177
Me	H	Bu^t	H	−4·0	177

† Monomer.   ‡ Dimer.

TABLE VI

^{11}B shifts of aminoboranes, BXYZ, p.p.m. from Et_2O,BF_3

X	Y	Z	δ	Ref.
Me_2N	Me_2N	Me_2N	-27.3	5
Et_2N	Et_2N	Et_2N	-28.7	5
$Bu^n{}_2N$	$Bu^n{}_2N$	$Bu^n{}_2N$	-28.8	5
MeNH	MeNH	MeNH	-24.6	5
$—NHNMe_2$	$—NHNMe_2$	$—NHNMe_2$	-23.3	5
Me_2N	Me_2N	H	-28.6	5
Me_2N	Me_2N	F	-21.8	5
Et_2N	Et_2N	F	-22.6	5
$Bu^n{}_2N$	$Bu^n{}_2N$	F	-22.5	5
Me_2N	Me_2N	Cl	-27.9	5
Et_2N	Et_2N	Cl	-28.4	5
Me_2N	Me_2N	Br	-27.6	5
Me_2N	Me_2N	I	-25.0	5
Me_2N	Me_2N	OMe	-25.1	5
Me_2N	OMe	OMe	-21.3	5
Me_2N	OMe	Cl	-24.9	5
$(Me_3Si)_2N$	Me_3SiNH	NH_2	-28.5	170
$(Me_3Si)_2N$	Me_3SiNH	NMe_2	-28.0	170
$(Me_3Si)_2N$	Me_3SiNH	NHMe	-26.7	170
$(Me_3Si)_2N$	Me_3SiNH	$NHBu^t$	-25.4	170
$(Me_3Si)_2N$	Me_3SiNH	NHEt	-27.2	170
$(Me_3Si)_2N$	Me_3SiNH	NEt_2	-25.0	170
$(Me_3Si)_2N$	Me_3SiNH	$NHSiMe_3$	-28.0	170
$(Me_3Si)_2N$	Me_3SiNH	OMe	-23.5	170

TABLE VII

^{11}B shifts of tetravalent ions, p.p.m. from Et_2O,BF_3

Ion	δ	Ref.	Ion	δ	Ref.
$Al(BH_4)_3$	$+36.7$	174	$Bu_4^n\overset{\oplus}{N}BI_4^{\ominus}$	$+127.5\dagger$	6
$NaBH_4$	$\left.\begin{array}{c}\\ +42.6\pm3 \\ \end{array}\right.$	174	$Pr_4^n\overset{\oplus}{N}BI_4^{\ominus}$	$+128.0\dagger$	6
$LiBH_4$		179	$Na_2^{\oplus}[H_3BCO_2]^{2\ominus}$	$+32.0$	44
$Na[B(OMe)_4]$	-3.2	183	$Me_4\overset{\oplus}{N}[B(NO_3)_4]^{\ominus}$	$+86.6$	46
$Li[B(OMe)_4]$	-2.9	178	$Li^{\oplus}[HSBH_3]^{\ominus}$	$+25.0$	40
$Na[B(OH)_4]$	-1.1	5	$Li^{\oplus}[(HS)_2BH_2]^{\ominus}$	$+14.5$	40
$Li[B(C{\equiv}CPh)_4]$	$+31.3$	174	$Na^{\oplus}[B(OPh)_4]^{\ominus}$	-2.5	41
$Li[B(CH{=}CH_2)_4]$	$+16.1$	6	$Et_3\overset{\oplus}{N}H[B(OPh)_4]^{\ominus}$	-2.5	41
$Li[B(CH_2{-}CH{=}CH_2)_4]$	$+16.8$	6	$Et_3\overset{\oplus}{N}H[B(SPh)_4]^{\ominus}$	-6.3	41
$Li[BMe_4]$	$+20.2$	6	$Et_3\overset{\oplus}{N}H[C_6F_5OBF_3]^{\ominus}$	$+0.8$	41
$Li[BEt_4]$	$+17.5$	6	$Et_3\overset{\oplus}{N}H[PhOBF_3]^{\ominus}$	$+1.3$	41
$Na[BEt_4]$	$+16.6$	5			
$Li[BPr^n_4]$	$+17.5$	6	$K^{\oplus}\left[\left(\underset{N-\!-N}{\text{pz}}\right)_2\!\!-BH_2\right]^{\ominus}$	$+7.4$	64
$Li[BBu^n_4]$	$+17.6$	6			
$Na[BPh_4]$	$+6.3$	5			
$Bu_3^n\overset{\oplus}{N}H[BPh_4]^{\ominus}$	$+6.5$	173	$K^{\oplus}\left[\left(\underset{N-\!-N}{\text{pz}}\right)_3\!\!-BH\right]^{\ominus}$	$+1.3$	64
$AgBF_4$	$+2.2$	174			
$NaBF_4$	$+2.3$	178			
KBF_4 in liq HF	$+1.81$	6			
$Ph_3C\overset{\oplus}{B}F_4^{\ominus}$	$+1.55\dagger$	6	$K^{\oplus}\left[\left(\underset{N-\!-N}{\text{pz}}\right)_4\!\!-B\right]^{\ominus}$	-1.0	64
$Me_4\overset{\oplus}{N}BCl_4^{\ominus}$	$-6.6\dagger$	6			
$Ph_3\overset{\oplus}{C}BCl_4^{\ominus}$	$-6.7\dagger$	6			
$C_5H_5\overset{\oplus}{N}HBBr_4^{\ominus}$	$+24.1\dagger$	6			
$Me_4\overset{\oplus}{N}BBr_4^{\ominus}$	$-23.8\dagger$	6			
$Ph_3\overset{\oplus}{C}BBr_4^{\ominus}$	$+23.9\dagger$	6			

$\dagger$ Limiting values of chemical shift, i.e. in the presence of excess halide ion, $X^{\ominus}$ in $BX_4^{\ominus}$.

TABLE VIII

^{11}B shifts of heterocyclic boron compounds, p.p.m. from Et_2O,BF_3

Compound	R	R'	R''	X	δ	Ref.
	H	Me	Me	F	-2.0	36
	H	Ph	Ph	F	-2.7	36
	H	Me	Me	$-C{\equiv}C{-}Ph$	$+1.2$	36
	H	Me	Me	Ph	-10.8	36
	H	Me	Me	Et	-14.7	36
	H	Me	OEt	Et	-14.4	36
	H	Ph	Ph	Et	-14.5	36
	H	CF_3	CF_3	Et	-20.3	36

TABLE VIII—*cont.*

Compound		R	X	δ	Ref.
		Me_2N	S	$-38\cdot4$	55
		H_2	SEt	$+14\cdot5$	43
		Me	O	$-33\cdot4$	17
		MeO	O	$-17\cdot3$	178
		F_2	OMe	$+0\cdot5$	17, 20
		F_2	OEt	$\begin{cases} +0\cdot8 \\ +0\cdot3 \end{cases}$	17 20
		F_2	OPr^n	$+0\cdot1$	20
		F_2	OBu^n	$+0\cdot25$	20

Compound	n	R	X	Y	δ	Ref.
	2	H	O	O	$-28\cdot7$	80
	3	H	O	O	$-25\cdot9$	80
	2	Cl	O	O	$-31\cdot4$†	67
	3	Cl	O	O	$-24\cdot1$	51
	2	OPr^n, OBu^n and OC_5H_{11}	O	O	$\begin{cases} -23‡ \\ -18 \end{cases}$	53
	3	OEt	O	O	$-18\cdot1$	51
	2	Et	O	O	-34	53
	2	Bu^n	O	O	-34	53
	2	Ph	O	O	$-31\cdot9$	51
	3	Ph	O	O	$-27\cdot7$	51
	2	NMe_2	O	O	-11	184
	2	NEt_2	O	O	-11	184
	2	NHMe	O	O	-11	184
	2	$NHPr^i$	O	O	-11	184
	2	$NHBu^t$	O	O	-11	184
	2	Bu^n	O	CH_2	$-56\cdot5$	53
	2	Ph	O	S	$-47\cdot7$	51
	2	H	S	S	$-61\cdot3$	80
	2	Cl	S	S	$\begin{cases} -62\cdot7 \\ -61\cdot7 \end{cases}$	67 51
	3	Cl	S	S	$-54\cdot8$	51
	2	Bu^i	S	S	$-70\cdot0$	80
	2	Ph	S	S	$-64\cdot1$	51
	3	Ph	S	S	$-57\cdot0$	51
	2	NMe_2	S	S	$-45\cdot3$	67
	3	$CH{=}CH_2$	NH	NH	$-27\cdot2$	52a

† See discussion on p. 235.
‡ Two signals due to possible exchange reactions (see p. 235).

TABLE VIII—*cont.*

Compound	R	δ	Ref.
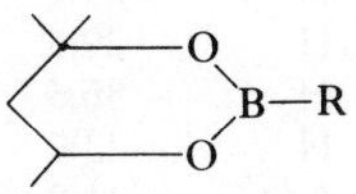	OBu^n	$-18\cdot7$	52a
	—CH=CH$_2$	$-25\cdot5$	52a
	—C≡CH	$-20\cdot9$	52b
	OEt	$-18\cdot9$	51
	Cl	$-18\cdot3$	51
	Ph	$-31\cdot1$	51

Compound	X	δ	Ref.
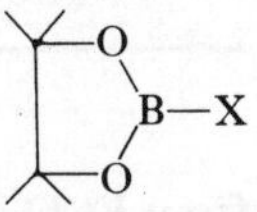	OEt	$-22\cdot5$	51
	Ph	$-29\cdot4$	51

Compound	R	X	Y	δ	Ref.
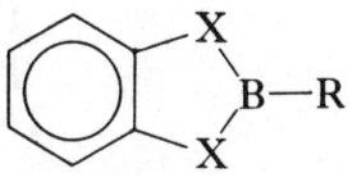	Cl	O	O	$-29\cdot0$	51
	Br	O	O	$-26\cdot9$	23
	Ph	O	O	$\begin{cases} -28\cdot5 \\ -33\cdot0 \end{cases}$	23 / 51
	m-CH$_3$C$_6$H$_4$—	O	O	$-28\cdot6$	23
	OEt	O	O	$-23\cdot0$	51
	OCH$_2$CH$_2$Cl	O	O	$-22\cdot2$	23
	Ph	NH	NH	$-27\cdot7$	11
	OH	O	—	$-29\cdot1$	81
	Ph	O	—CH$_2$O—	$-26\cdot8$	51
	Ph	—CH$_2$O—	—CH$_2$O—	$-27\cdot0$	51

Compound	R	δ	Ref.
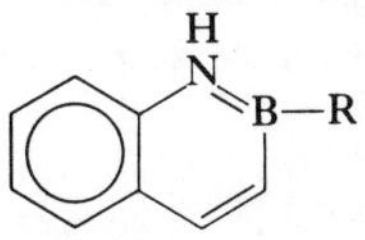	CH$_3$	$-37\cdot5$	11
	OEt	$-29\cdot7$	11
	OH	$-29\cdot7$	81

Compound	R	X	Y	δ	Ref.
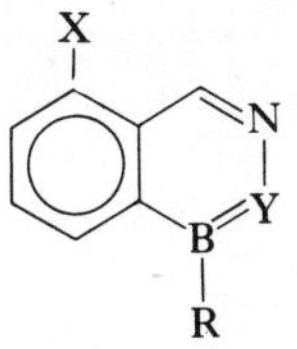	CH$_3$	H	NH	$-36\cdot5$	11
	OEt	H	NH	$-30\cdot0$	11
	OH	H	NH	$-29\cdot8$	81
	CH$_3$	Br	NH	$-37\cdot5$	11
	OEt	H	O	$-30\cdot0$	11
	OH	H	O	$-30\cdot0$	81

TABLE VIII—*cont.*

Compound	R	Y	X	δ	Ref.
	CH_3	NH	H	-39.0	11
	OEt	NH	H	-29.3	11
	Ph	NH	H	-36.5	11
	Cl	NH	H	-33.7	11
	CH_3	NH ·	NO_2	-41.9	11
	OEt	O	H	-28.8	11
	Cl	O	H	-36.9	11
	$-CH_2(CH_2)_2-CH_2-N$		H	-38.1	11
	$-CH=CH-CH=CH-N$		H	-31.0	11

TABLE IX

^{11}B **shifts of borazole derivatives,** $(RBNR')_3$ **p.p.m. from** Et_2O,BF_3

R	R'	δ	Ref.
H	H	-30.4	174
H	Me	-32.4	174
F	H	-25.1	185
F	Me	-24.3	185
F	Pr^n	-23.1	185
Cl	H	-29.6	23, 186
Cl	Me	-31.2	5
Cl	Et	-31.7	23
Cl	Pr^n	-32.5	23
Cl	Pr^i	-32.7	23
Br	H	-27.8	23
Br	Me	-31.6	23
Br	Et	-31.8	23
Br	Pr^n	-32.6	23
Br	Pr^i	-32.8	23
Me	H	-34.5	186
Me	Me	$\begin{cases} -35.8 \\ -36.4 \end{cases}$	5 23
Me	Et	-36.2	23
Et	Me	$\begin{cases} -36.6 \\ -35.7 \end{cases}$	5 23
Et	Et	-35.7	23
$CF_2=CF-$	Me	-18	187
Cl	$o-CH_3C_6H_4-$	-30.6	188
Me_2N	$o-CH_3C_6H_4-$	-30.8	188
OH	$o-CH_3C_6H_4-$	-20.7	188
Cl	Bu^t	$\begin{cases} -30.1† \\ -31.1 \end{cases}$	183 23
Br	Bu^t	$\begin{cases} -30.3† \\ -30.0 \end{cases}$	183 23

† Tetramer structures.

TABLE X

^{11}B shifts of diboron compounds, p.p.m. from Et_2O,BF_3

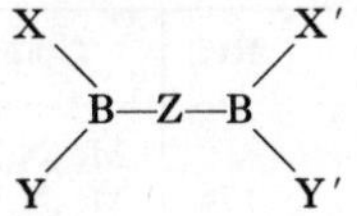

$$\begin{array}{c} X \qquad\qquad X' \\ \diagdown \qquad\quad \diagup \\ B{-}Z{-}B \\ \diagup \qquad\quad \diagdown \\ Y \qquad\qquad Y' \end{array}$$

X	X'	Y	Y'	Z	δ	Ref.
OMe	OMe	OMe	OMe	..	$-30\cdot5$	5
NMe_2	NMe_2	NMe_2	NMe_2	..	$-36\cdot6$	5
$NHBu^n$	$NHBu^n$	$NHBu^n$	$NHBu^n$	..	$-33\cdot0$	5
$NHNMe_2$	$NHNMe_2$	$NHNMe_2$	$NHNMe_2$	..	$-28\cdot5$	5
OMe	NMe_2	OMe	NMe_2	..	$-34\cdot5$	5
OMe	NMe_2	NMe_2	NMe_2	..	$-35\cdot4$	5
Cl	NMe_2	NMe_2	NMe_2	..	$-37\cdot4$	5
Me	NMe_2	Me	NMe_2	..	$-51\cdot1$	5
Et	NMe_2	Et	NMe_2	..	$-52\cdot9$	5
Bu^n	NMe_2	Bu^n	NMe_2	..	$-50\cdot9$	5
$-O{-}CH_2{-}CH_2{-}O-$		Cl	Cl	..	$-30\cdot8$	67
$-S{-}CH_2{-}CH_2{-}S-$		Cl	Cl	..	$-67\cdot8$	67
$-S{-}CH_2{-}CH_2{-}S-$		NMe	NMe	..	$-43\cdot7$	67
$-S{-}CH_2{-}CH_2{-}S-$		NHMe	NHMe	..	$-11\cdot8$	67
AcO	AcO	AcO	AcO	O	-1	178
Et	Et	Et	Et	NH	$-57\cdot4$	5
Et	Et	Et	Et	O	$-52\cdot6$	5
Ph	Ph	Ph	Ph	NH	$-40\cdot8$	5
Ph	Ph	Ph	Ph	NHNH	$-38\cdot0$	5
Ph	Ph	Ph	Ph	O	$-28\cdot5$	5
Me	Me	NMe_2	NMe_2	NH	$-33\cdot8$	5
Ph	Ph	NMe_2	NMe_2	NH	$-32\cdot5$	5

TABLE XI

^{11}B shifts of complexes, p.p.m. from Et_2O,BF_3

Compound	δ	Ref.	Compound	δ	Ref.
Ethers			Me_3N,Me_2BN_3	−4·6	5
C_4H_8O,BH_3	0·9	174	$Me_3N,EtBF_2$	−6·7	5
Me_2O,BH_3	−2·5	54	Me_3EtBCl_2	−12·4	5
Me_2O,BF_3	+0·28	189	Me_3N,BF_3	−0·6	5
Pr^n_2O,BF_3	+0·03	189	Me_3N,BCl_3	−10·2	5
Pr^i_2O,BF_3	−0·4	189	Me_3N,BBr_3	+3·1	5
Bu^n_2O,BF_3	0·0	174	Me_3N,BI_3	+54·4	5
Bu^nOEt,BF_3	−0·07	189	Et_3N,BH_3	+13·3	78
Bu^iOEt,BF_3	−0·05	189	Et_3N,BF_3	+0·1	68
Me_2O,BCl_3	−11·5	54	Et_3N,BCl_3	−9·7	68
Et_2O,BCl_3	−10·5	178	Et_3N,BBr_3	+5·4	68
Bu_2O,BCl_3	−20·7	23	Et_3N,BI_3	+60·1	68
C_4H_8O,BF_3	0·9	179	Et_3N,BH_2Cl	+1·7	78
$Et_2O,HBCl_2$	−7·9	178	Et_3N,BH_2Br	+6·7	78
$Et_2O,DBCl_2$	−8·0	178	Et_3N,BH_2I	+16·7	78
C_4H_8O,BCl_3	−10·4	54	Et_3N,BH_2Ph	+6·7	78
C_6H_5OMe,BF_3	−1·3	41	Et_3N,BMe_3	+13·5	74
C_6H_5OMe,BCl_3	−19·3	41	Me_2NH,BEt_3	−4·0	173
			Me_2NH,BF_3	+0·3	74
Sulphides			Me_2NH,BMe_3	+4·0	74
Me_2S,BH_3	+20·1	54	$Et_2NH,BFCl_2$	−7·1	29
Et_2S,BF_3	−2·60	189	$MeNH_2,BF_3$	−0·5	74
Me_2S,BF_3	−2·8	54	$MeNH_2,BMe_3$	+6·6	74
Pr^n_2S,BF_3	−2·62	189	Bu^tNH_2,BH_3	+22·1	190
Pr^i_2S,BF_3	−3·42	189	Bu^tNH_2,BF_3	−0·2	31
Bu^sSEt,BF_3	−2·57	189	$Pyridine,BH_3$	+13·2	71
Bu^iSEt,BF_3	−2·65	189	$Pyridine,BF_3$	+0·6	68
Bu^nSEt,BF_3	−2·53	189	$Pyridine,BCl_3$	−7·7	68
Pr^nSPr^i,BF_3	−2·78	189	$Pyridine,BBr_3$	+7·4	68
Me_2S,BCl_3	−7·5	54	$Pyridine,BI_3$	+60·0	173
C_4H_8S,BH_3	+20·1	54	$Pyridine,PhBH_2$	+3·6	71
C_4H_8S,BF_3	−3·5	54	$Pyridine,Bu^nBCl_2$	−11·6	72
C_4H_8S,BCl_3	−8·1	54	$Pyridine,PhBCl_2$	−10·3	72
			$Pyridine,PhBBr_2$	−57·4	189
Alcohols and phenols			$Pyridine,PhBF_2$	−22·7	22
H_2O,BF_3	−0·2	173	$Pyridine,Bu^n,BCl$	−77·7	189
$MeOH,BF_3$	1·0	179	$Pyridine,PhB(OEt)_2$	−28·5	71
$2PhOH,BF_3$	−1·9	41	$Pyridine,MeOBCl_2$	−8·0	20
$2(4-FC_6H_4OH),BF_3$	−1·4	41	$Pyridine,EtOBCl_2$	−7·1	20
			$Pyridine,Pr^nOBCl_2$	−8·2	20
Amines			$Pyridine,ClCH_2CH_2OBCl_2$	−7·3	20
$MeNH_2BH_3$	+18·2	5	$Pyridine,MeOBF_2$	+1·1	20
Me_2NH,BH_3	+14·2	5	$Pyridine,EtOBF_2$	+0·8	20
Me_3N,BH_3	+8·2	5	$Pyridine,Pr^nOBF_2$	−0·3	20
Me_3N,BMe_3	−0·1	74	$2-Me—Py,BH_3$	+14·7	71
Me_3N,BEt_3	−4·3	5	$2-Me—Py,BF_3$	+2·1	70
Me_3N,Et_2BOMe	−50·7	5	$2-Me—Py,BCl_3$	−7·9	70
Me_3N,Me_2BOMe	−32·9	5	$2-Me—Py,BBr_3$	+9·2	70
Me_3N,Et_2BF	−10·3	5	$2-Me—Py,Bu^nBCl_2$	−7·3	72
Me_3N,Et_2BCl	−11·7	5	$2-Me—Py,PhBCl_2$	−10·5	72

TABLE XI—*cont.*

Compound	δ	Ref.	Compound	δ	Ref.
2-Me—Py,PhBH$_2$	+6·1	71			
3-Me—Py,BH$_3$	+12·6	71			
3-Me—Py,Bu^{n}BCl$_2$	−8·8	72			
3-Me—Py,PhBCl$_2$	−10·0	72			
3-Me—Py,PhBH$_2$	+3·9	71			
4-Me—Py,BH$_3$	+13·5	71			
4-Me—Py,BF$_3$	+0·71	70			
4-Me—Py,BCl$_3$	−7·7	70			
4-Me—Py,BBr$_3$	+7·7	70			
4-Me—Py,Bu^{n}BCl$_2$	−11·2	72			
4-Me—Py,PhBCl$_2$	−10·0	72			
4-Me—Py,PhBH$_2$	+4·3	71			
2-Et—Py,BH$_3$	+15·1	71			
2-Et—Py,BF$_3$	+2·1	70			
2-Et—Py,BBr$_3$	+9·5	70			
2-Et—Py,Bu^{n}BCl$_2$	−8·7	72			
2-Et—Py,PhBCl$_2$	−11·4	72			
2-Et—Py,PhBH$_2$	+6·4	71	**Esters**		
2-Et—Py,PhB(OEt)$_2$	−28·2	71	CH$_3$CO$_2$Et,BF$_3$	−0·3	69
3-Et—Py,BH$_3$	+12·8	71	CH$_3$CO$_2$Et,BCl$_3$	−12·6	69
3-Et—Py,Bu^{n}BCl$_2$	−8·5	72	CH$_3$CO$_2$Et,BBr$_3$	+9·6	69
3-Et—Py,PhBCl$_2$	−10·5	72	CH$_3$CH$_2$CO$_2$Et,BF$_3$	+0·4	69
3-Et—Py,PhBH$_2$	+4·0	71	CH$_3$CH$_2$CO$_2$Et,BCl$_3$	−9·3	69
3-Et—Py,PhB(OEt)$_2$	−26·1	71	Me$_2$CHCO$_2$Et,BF$_3$	+0·2	69
4-Et—Py,BH$_3$	+13·5	71	Me$_2$CHCO$_2$Et,BCl$_3$	−16·2	69
4-Et—Py,BF$_3$	+0·9	70	ClCH$_2$CO$_2$Et,BF$_3$	−0·6	69
4-Et—Py,BCl$_3$	−7·8	70	ClCH$_2$CO$_2$Et,BCl$_3$	−14·1	69
4-Et—Py,BBr$_3$	+8·1	70	ClCH$_2$CO$_2$Et,BBr$_3$	−24·0	69
4-Et—Py,Bu^{n}BCl$_2$	−8·8	72	Cl$_2$CHCO$_2$Et,BF$_3$	−1·5	69
4-Et—Py,PhBCl$_2$	−10·4	72	Cl$_2$CHCO$_2$Et,BCl$_3$	−42·8	69
4-EtPy,PhBH$_2$	+4·9	71	Cl$_2$CHCO$_2$,Et,BBr$_3$	−32·3	69
4-EtPy,PhB(OEt)$_2$	−23·9	71	Cl$_3$C.CO$_2$Et,BF$_3$	−2·4	69
2-Pr^n—Py,BH$_3$	+14·7	71	Cl$_3$C.CO$_2$Et,BCl$_3$	−47·1	69
2-Pr^n—Py,PhBH$_2$	+7·1	71	Cl$_3$C.CO$_2$Et,BBr$_3$	−38·2	69
2-Bu^n—Py,BH$_3$	+14·7	71	BrCH$_2$CO$_2$Et,BF$_3$	−1·1	69
2-Ph—Py,BH$_3$	+14·2	71	BrCH$_2$CO$_2$Et,BCl$_3$	−19·4	69
4-Ph—Py,BH$_3$	+14·1	71	BrCH$_2$CO$_2$Et,BBr$_3$	−8·0	69
2,6-Me$_2$—Py,BH$_3$	+19·3	71	Br$_2$CHCO$_2$Et,BF$_3$	−1·4	69
2,6-Me$_2$—Py,Bu^{n}BCl$_2$	−7·5	72	Br$_2$CHCO$_2$Et,BCl$_3$	−39·5	69
2,6-Me$_2$—Py,PhBCl$_2$	−13·6	72	Br$_2$CHCO$_2$Et,BBr$_3$	−18·4	69
2,4,6-Me$_3$—Py,BH$_3$	+19·8	71			
2,4,6-Me$_3$—Py,Bu^{n}BCl$_2$	−7·5	72	**Acid halides**		
2,4,6-Me$_3$—Py,PhBCl$_2$	−11·1	72	CH$_3$COCl,BCl$_3$	−45·8	69
Me$_2$NCH$_2$CH$_2$NMe$_2$,BH$_3$	+8·0	76	CH$_3$COCl,EtOBCl$_2$	−10·5	69
Me$_2$NCH$_2$CH$_2$NMe$_2$,2BH$_3$	+10·1	76			
			Amides		
			HCO.NMe$_2$,BF$_3$	+0·4	22
			HCO.NMe$_2$,BCl$_3$	−8·3	22
			HCONMe$_2$,BBr$_3$	+9·0	22
			HCONMe$_2$,BuBF$_2$	−8·8	22

Structures in left column (between table entries):

$$\text{MeN}\begin{array}{c} \diagup \text{CH}_2-\text{CH}_2 \diagdown \\ \diagdown \text{Ch}_2-\text{CH}_2 \diagup \end{array}\text{NMe,BH}_3 \quad +9\cdot4 \quad 77$$

Structures in right column:

$$\text{MeN}\begin{array}{c} \diagup \text{CH}_2-\text{CH}_2 \diagdown \\ \diagdown \text{CH}_2-\text{CH}_2 \diagup \end{array}\text{NMe,2BH}_3 \quad +12\cdot1 \quad 77$$

$$\text{N}\begin{array}{c} \diagup \text{CH}_2-\text{CH}_2 \diagdown \\ -\text{CH}_2-\text{CH}_2- \\ \diagdown \text{CH}_2-\text{CH}_2 \diagup \end{array}\text{N,2BH}_3 \quad +10\cdot9 \quad 77$$

$$\text{N}\begin{array}{c} \diagup \text{CH}_2-\text{CH}_2 \diagdown \\ -\text{CH}_2-\text{CH}_2- \\ \diagdown \text{CH}_2-\text{CH}_2 \diagup \end{array}\text{N,2BBr}_3 \quad +4\cdot6 \quad 70$$

TABLE XI—*cont.*

Compound	δ	Ref.	Compound	δ	Ref.
Ketones			**Sulphones and sulphoxides**		
$PhCOPh,BF_3$	} $-1\cdot2$	68	(cyclic sulphone), BF_3	$+0\cdot9$	191
$PhCOCHMe_2,BF_3$		68		$-0\cdot18$	22
$PhCOPh,BCl_3$	$-9\cdot8$	68			
$PhCOPh,BBr_3$	$+10\cdot7$	68	(cyclic sulphone), BCl_3	$-9\cdot2$	22
$PhCOCHMe_2,BCl_3$	$-10\cdot8$	68			
Nitriles			(cyclic sulphone), BBr_3	$+12\cdot35$	22
$CH_3CH_2C\equiv N,BF_3$	$+1\cdot8$	32			
$CH_3CH_2C\equiv N,BCl_3$	$-1\cdot4$	32	Me_2SO_2,BF_3	$0\cdot0$	22
$CH_3CH_2C\equiv N,BBr_3$	$+20\cdot5$	32	Me_2SO_2,BCl_3	$-7\cdot8$	22
$C_6H_5CH_2C\equiv N,BF_3$	$+1\cdot5$	32	**Phosphorus complexes**		
$C_6H_5CH_2C\equiv N,BCl_3$	$-1\cdot7$	32	H_3P,BH_3	$+42\cdot5$	82
$C_6H_5CH_2C\equiv N,BBr_3$	$+20\cdot0$	32	Me_2PH,BH_3	$+37\cdot4$	179
$C_6H_5C\equiv N,BF_3$	$+0\cdot9$	41	Me_3P,BH_3	$+36\cdot2$	54
$C_6H_5C\equiv N,BCl_3$	$-2\cdot1$	32	Me_3P,BF_3	$-1\cdot0$	54
$C_6H_5C\equiv N,BBr_3$	$+20\cdot1$	32	Me_3P,BCl_3	$-3\cdot0$	54
$C_6F_5C\equiv N,BF_3$	$-4\cdot3$	192	Me_3P,BBr_3	$+14\cdot5$	54
$C_6F_5C\equiv N,BCl_3$	$-19\cdot3$	192	F_2PH,BH_3	$+42\cdot1$	84
$C_6F_5C\equiv N,BBr_3$	{ $+10\cdot8$	28	F_3P,BH_3	$+48\cdot3$	84
	$+3\cdot4$	192	F_2PPF_2,BH_3	$+41\cdot7$	85
$C_6F_5C\equiv N,BI_3$	$+35\cdot1$	192	Ph_3P,BF_3	$-0\cdot4$	178
			Cl_3P,BI_3	$+65\cdot0$	173
Ureas and thioureas			Cl_3P,BF_3	$0\cdot0$	173
$(MeNH)_2C=O,BF_3$	$+0\cdot9$	79	$(Me_2N)_3P,BH_3$	$+43\cdot0$	5
$(MeNH)_2C=S,BF_3$	$+0\cdot9$	79	$(MeO)_3P,BH_3$	{ $+45\cdot1$	5
$(Bu^tNH)_2C=S,BF_3$	$+1\cdot2$	79		$+48\cdot8$	88
			$(Pr^iO)_3P,BH_3$	$+44\cdot7$	88
$[(EtNH)_2\overset{\oplus}{C}-S-Me,BF_3]I^{\ominus}$	$+0\cdot2$	79	P_4O_6,xBH_3	$+40\cdot0$	86
			$Me_3P, ClB(S-S)$	$-3\cdot8$	54
Nitrobenzenes					
$C_6H_5NO_2,BF_3$	$-3\cdot0$	73			
$C_6H_5NO_2,BCl_3$	$-32\cdot7$	73	$Me_3P, HB(S-S)$	$+11\cdot3$	54
$C_6H_5NO_2,BBr_3$	$+10\cdot3$	73			
$C_6H_5NO_2,PhBCl_2$	$-53\cdot7$	73			
$C_6H_5NO_2,Bu^nBCl_2$	$-64\cdot1$	73			
$C_6F_5NO_2,BF_3$	$+0\cdot6$	73			
$C_6F_5NO_2,BCl_3$	$-46\cdot1$	73			
$C_6F_5NO_2,BBr_3$	$39\cdot5$	73			
$C_6F_5NO_2,PhBCl_2$	$-55\cdot0$	73			

TABLE XII

^{11}B shifts of alkyl diborons, p.p.m. from Et_2O,BF_3

Compound	δBH_2	δBHR	δBR_2	J_{B-H_t}	J_{B-H_b}
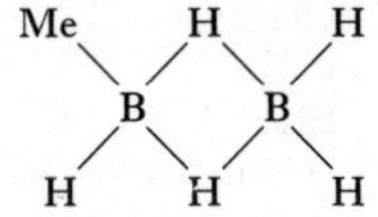 Me, H, H / B—B / H, H, H	$-8\cdot8$	$-26\cdot7$	..	127	48
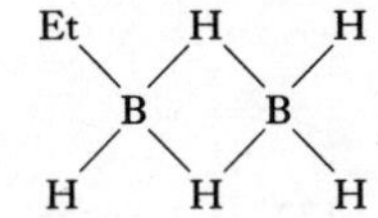 Et, H, H / B—B / H, H, H	$-10\cdot0$	$-29\cdot5$	..	133	45
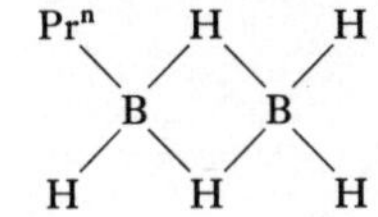 Pr^n, H, H / B—B / H, H, H	$-9\cdot4$	$-28\cdot7$	..	$\left\{\begin{array}{l}128\\134\end{array}\right.$	$\left\{\begin{array}{l}43\\46\end{array}\right.$
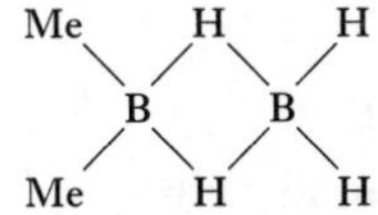 Me, H, H / B—B / Me, H, H	$-3\cdot6$	..	$-36\cdot4$	125·5	$\left\{\begin{array}{l}36\\50\end{array}\right.$
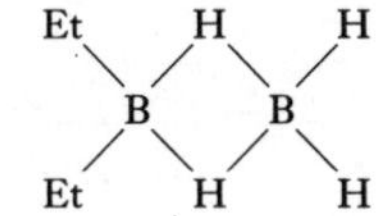 Et, H, H / B—B / Et, H, H	$-3\cdot9$	..	$-40\cdot8$	123	$\left\{\begin{array}{l}37\\48\end{array}\right.$
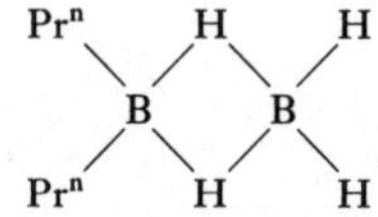 Pr^n, H, H / B—B / Pr^n, H, H	$-4\cdot5$	..	$-38\cdot8$	125	46
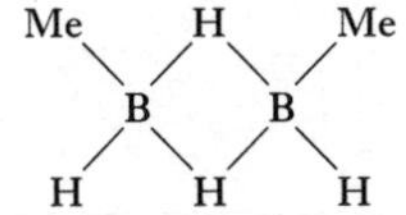 Me, H, Me / B—B / H, H, H	..	$-20\cdot5$	..	131·2	47·5
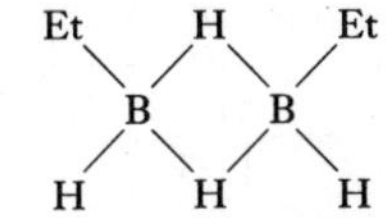 Et, H, Et / B—B / H, H, H	..	$-22\cdot7$	..	125·5	42
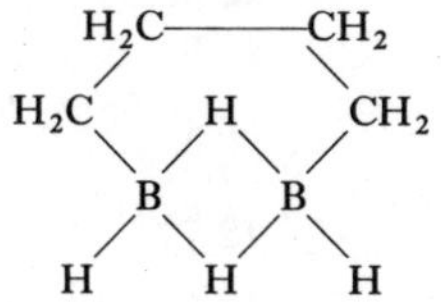 H_2C—CH_2 / H_2C, H, CH_2 / B—B / H, H, H	..	$-22\cdot1$	..	129	40

TABLE XII—*cont.*

Compound	δBH_2	δBHR	δBR_2	J_{B-Ht}	J_{B-Hb}
H₂C H₂C H CH₂ B B H H H	..	−21·8	..	131	41
H₂C Me H₂C H CH B B H H H	..	−22·4	..	132	45

From Linder and Onak.[94]

TABLE XIII

^{11}B **shifts of pentaborane derivatives, p.p.m. from** Et_2O,BF_3

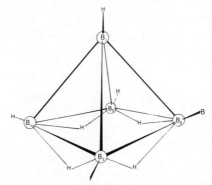

	Assignment	δ
Pentaborane	B(1)	51·8
	B(2,3,4,5)	12·5
1-Me pentaborane	B-Me	44·5
	B(2,3,4,5)	13·8
2-Me pentaborane	B(1)	50·4
	B-Me	−2·2
	B(3,5)	12·7
	B(4)	18·1

TABLE XIII—*cont.*

	Assignment	δ
1-Et pentaborane	B-Et	42·5
	B(2,3,4,5)	14·2
2-Et pentaborane	B(1)	51·4
	B-Et	−4·2
	B(3,5)	13·4
	B(4)	18·1
1-Chloropentaborane	B-Cl	30·6
	B(2,3,4,5)	14·5
2-Chloropentaborane	B(1)	51·0
	B-Cl	−0·5
	B(3,5)	12·5
	B(4)	22·0
1-Bromopentaborane	B-Br	36·4
	B(2,3,4,5)	12·5
2-Bromopentaborane	B(1)	53·5
	B-Br	∼11
	B(3,5)	∼15
	B(4)	∼20
1-Iodopentaborane	B-I	55·0
	B(2,3,4,5)	11·8
1,2-Me$_2$pentaborane	B(1)-Me	44·3
	B(2)-Me	0·8
	B(3,5) $\Big\}$	15·3
	B(4)	
2,3-Me$_2$pentaborane	B(1)	50·4
	B(2,3)-Me	1·2
	B(4,5)	19·6
1-Bromo-2-methyl pentaborane	B(1)-Br	34·0
	B(2)-Me	0·4
	B(3,5) $\Big\}$	13·6
	B(4)	
1,2,3-Me$_3$pentaborane	B(1)-Me	43·6
	B(2,4 or 2,3)-Me	2·3
	B(3,5 or 4,5)	17·7

From Onak *et al.*[101]

10*

TABLE XIV

^{11}B shifts of compounds containing metal—boron bonds, p.p.m. from Et_2O,BF_3

Compound	δ	Ref.
$(Me_2N)_2B$—$SnMe_3$	-39	168
$(Me_2N)_2B$—$Mn(CO)_5$	$-27\cdot1$	166–168
Ph_2B—$Mn(CO)_5$	$-42\cdot8$	168
$(Me_2N)_2B$—$Mn(CO)_4PPh_3$	$-20\cdot0$	166–168
Ph_2B—$Mn(CO)_4PPh_3$	$-28\cdot5$	167, 168
Cl_2B—$Mn(CO)_4PPh_3$	$-16\cdot0$	167, 168
Ph_2B—$Fe(CO)_2\pi$–C_5H_5	$-43\cdot5$	168
$(Me_2N)_2B$—$Fe(CO)_2\pi$–C_5H_5	$+25\cdot0$	168
Ph_2B—$Co(CO)_4$	$-34\cdot2$	168
Ph_2B—$Co(CO)_3PPh_3$	$-21\cdot6$	168
Ph_2B—$Co(CO)_3P(OPh)_3$	$-42\cdot5$	168
Ph_2B—$Co(CO)_3PBu_3^n$	$-29\cdot8$	168
Ph_2B—$Co[o\text{-}C_6H_4(PMe_2)_2]_2$	$+23\cdot5$	168
Ph_2B—$Co(PF_3)_4$	$-44\cdot9$	168
$(Me_2N)_2B$—$Co(PF_3)_4$	$-21\cdot4$	168
$(Ph_3P)_2Rh(CO)Cl,BCl_3$	$-3\cdot6$	168
$(Ph_3P)_2Rh(CO)Br,BBr_3$	$+14\cdot4$	168
Ph_2B—$PtCl(PEt_3)_2$	$-29\cdot2$	168
$(Ph_2B)_2$—$Pt(PPh_3)_2$	$-30\cdot0$	168
$(Me_2N)_2B$—$SiPh_3$	$-35\cdot0$	165
$(Me_2N)_2B$—$SiMe_3$	$-36\cdot1$	165, 166
$(Me_2N)_2B$—PEt_2	$-35\cdot9$	165, 166
$(Me_2N)_2B$—$SnMe_3$	$-39\cdot0$	166

REFERENCES

1. B. F. G. Johnson, N. L. Paddock and M. J. Ware, *Ann. Reports*, The Chemical Society, London, 1965, p. 132.
2. A. J. Downes, E. A. V. Ebsworth and J. J. Turner, *Ann. Reports*, The Chemical Society, London, 1966, p. 138.
3. J. W. Emsley, J. Feeney and L. H. Sutcliffe, "High Resolution Nuclear Magnetic Resonance Spectroscopy", Vol. 2, p. 970, Pergamon Press, 1966.
4. R. Schaeffer, In "Progress in Boron Chemistry" (H. Steinberg and A. L. McCloskey, Eds.), Pergamon Press, 1964.
5. H. Nöth and H. Vahrenkamp, *Chem. Ber.*, 1966, **99**, 1049.
6. R. J. Thompson and J. C. Davis, *Inorg. Chem.*, 1965, **4**, 1464.
7. C. D. Good and D. M. Ritter, *J. Amer. Chem. Soc.*, 1962, **84**, 1162.
8. D. R. Armstrong and P. G. Perkins, *Chem. Comm.*, 1965, 337.
9. R. E. Williams, K. M. Harman and J. R. Spielman, *U.S. Govt. Res. Report* AD 603782, 1964.
10. M. R. Chakrabarty, C. C. Thompson and W. S. Brey, *Inorg. Chem.*, 1967, **6**, 518.
11. F. A. Davis, M. J. S. Dewar and R. Jones, *J. Amer. Chem. Soc.*, 1968, **90**, 706.

12. W. N. Lipscomb, *J. Amer. Chem. Soc.*, 1966, **88**, 5340.
13. B. F. Spielvogel and J. M. Purser, *J. Amer. Chem. Soc.*, 1967, **89**, 5294.
14. H. Nöth and H. Vahrenkamp, *J. Organometallic Chem.*, 1968, **11**, 399.
15. F. E. Brinckman and F. G. A. Stone, *Chem. and Ind.*, 1959, 254; *J. Amer. Chem. Soc.*, 1960, **82**, 6218.
16. W. Gerrard, E. F. Mooney and R. G. Rees, *J. Chem. Soc.*, 1964, 740.
17. J. E. DeMoor and G. P. Van der Kelen, *J. Organometallic Chem.*, 1966, **6**, 235.
18. D. J. Pasto and P. Balasubramaniyan, *J. Amer. Chem. Soc.*, 1967, **89**, 295.
19. C. A. Eggers and S. F. A. Kettle, *Inorg. Chem.*, 1967, **6**, 160.
20. W. Gerrard, E. F. Mooney and W. G. Peterson, *J. Inorg. Nuc. Chem.*, 1967, **29**, 943.
21. J. P. Tuchaques and J.-P. Laurent, *Bull. Soc. chim. France*, 1967, 4160.
22. E. F. Mooney and W. G. Peterson, unpublished work.
23. E. F. Mooney, unpublished work.
24. H. Nöth and H. Vahrenkamp, *Chem. Ber.*, 1967, **100**, 3353.
25. N. N. Greenwood, K. A. Hooton and J. Walker, *J. Chem. Soc. A*, 1966, 21.
26. N. N. Greenwood and K. A. Hooton, *J. Chem. Soc. A*, 1966, 751.
27. N. N. Greenwood and J. Walker, *J. Chem. Soc. A*, 1967, 959.
28. J. Chatt, R. L. Richards and D. J. Newman, *J. Chem. Soc. A*, 1968, 128.
29. H. Nöth and H. Vahrenkamp, *Chem. Ber.*, 1966, **99**, 2757.
30. N. N. Greenwood and J. Walker, *Inorg. Nuc. Chem. Letters*, 1965, **1**, 65.
31. N. N. Greenwood and B. H. Robinson, *J. Chem. Soc. A*, 1968, 226.
32. E. F. Mooney and B. S. Thornhill, unpublished work.
33. A. Finch and D. Steele, *Trans. Faraday Soc.*, 1964, **60**, 2125.
34. P. I. Paetzold and H.-J. Hansen, *Z. anorg. Chem.*, 1966, **345**, 79.
35. E. F. Mooney and P. H. Winson, *Chem. Comm.*, 1967, 341.
36. L. H. Toporcer, R. E. Dessy and S. I. E. Green, *Inorg. Chem.*, 1965, **4**, 1649.
37. J. R. Horder and M. F. Lappert, *Chem. Comm.*, 1967, 485.
38. B. D. James, R. K. Nanda and M. G. H. Wallbridge, *J. Chem. Soc. A*, 1966, 182.
39. B. D. James, R. K. Nanda and M. G. H. Wallbridge, *Inorg. Chem.*, 1967, **6**, 1979.
40. B. F. Spielvogel and E. F. Rothgery, *Chem. Comm.*, 1966, 765.
41. K. Jones and E. F. Mooney, unpublished work.
42. R. E. Dessey and E. Grannen, *J. Amer. Chem. Soc.*, 1961, **83**, 3953.
43. D. J. Pasto, C. C. Cumbo and P. Balasubramaniyan, *J. Amer. Chem. Soc.*, 1966, **88**, 2187.
44. L. J. Malone and R. W. Parry, *Inorg. Chem.*, 1967, **6**, 817.
45. W. L. Jolly and T. Schmitt, *J. Amer. Chem. Soc.*, 1966, **88**, 4282.
46. C. R. Guibert and M. D. Marshall, *J. Amer. Chem. Soc.*, 1966, **88**, 189.
47. R. K. Momii and N. H. Nachtrieb, *Inorg. Chem.*, 1967, **6**, 1189.
48. M. J. How, G. Kennedy and E. F. Mooney, unpublished work.
49. G. E. Ryschkewitsch and J. M. Garrett, *J. Amer. Chem. Soc.*, 1967, **89**, 4240.
50. J. E. Douglass, G. E. Rochrig and O-H. Ma, *J. Organometallic Chem.*, 1967, **8**, 421.
51. W. G. Henderson and E. F. Mooney, unpublished work.
52a. W. G. Woods, I. S. Bengelsdorf and D. L. Hunter, *J. Org. Chem.*, 1966, **31**, 2766.
52b. W. G. Woods and P. L. Strong, *J. Organometallic Chem.*, 1967, **7**, 371.
53. J.-P. Laurent and J.-P. Bonnet, *Bull. Soc. chim. France*, 1967, 2702.
54. D. E. Young, G. E. McAchran and S. G. Shore, *J. Amer. Chem. Soc.*, 1966, **88**, 4390.

55. J. A. Forstner and E. L. Muetterties, *Inorg. Chem.*, 1966, **5**, 164.
56. K. Niedenzu and J. W. Dawson, "Boron-Nitrogen Compounds", p. 154. Academic Press, New York, 1965.
57. K. Henson and K. P. Messer, *Theoret. Chim. Acta*, 1967, **9**, 17.
58. J. L. Boone and G. W. Willcockson, *Inorg. Chem.*, 1966, **5**, 311.
59. S. Trofimenko, *J. Amer. Chem. Soc.*, 1967, **89**, 7014.
60. H. Nöth and G. Abeler, *Chem. Ber.*, 1968, **101**, 969.
61. K. Niedenzu and W. Weber, *Z. Naturforsch.*, 1966, **21B**, 811.
62. S. Trofimenko, *J. Amer. Chem. Soc.*, 1966, **88**, 1842.
63. S. Trofimenko, *J. Amer. Chem. Soc.*, 1967, **89**, 3165.
64. S. Trofimenko, *J. Amer. Chem. Soc.*, 1967, **89**, 3170.
65. N. N. Greenwood and J. H. Morris, *J. Chem. Soc.*, 1965, 6205.
66. J. H. Morris and P. G. Perkins, *J. Chem. Soc. A*, 1966, 576; 580.
67. C. N. Welch and S. G. Shore, *Inorg. Chem.*, 1968, **7**, 225.
68. P. N. Gates, E. J. McLauchlan and E. F. Mooney, *Spectrochim. Acta*, 1965, **21**, 1445.
69. P. G. Davies and E. F. Mooney, *Spectrochim. Acta*, 1966, **22**, 953.
70. E. J. McLauchlan and E. F. Mooney, *Spectrochim. Acta*, 1967, **23A**, 1227.
71. E. F. Mooney and M. A. Qaseem, *J. Inorg. Nuc. Chem.*, 1968, **30**, 1439.
72. E. F. Mooney and M. A. Qaseem, *Spectrochim. Acta*, 1968, **24A**, 969.
73. E. F. Mooney, M. A. Qaseem and P. H. Winson, *J. Chem. Soc. B*, 1968, 224.
74. C. W. Heitsch, *Inorg. Chem.*, 1965, **4**, 1019.
75. P. N. Gates and E. F. Mooney, *J. Inorg. Nuc. Chem.*, 1968, **30**, 839.
76. A. R. Gatti and T. Wartik, *Inorg. Chem.*, 1966, **5**, 329.
77. A. R. Gatti and T. Wartik, *Inorg. Chem.*, 1966, **5**, 2075.
78. J. N. G. Faulks, N. N. Greenwood and J. H. Morris, *J. Inorg. Nuc. Chem.*, 1967, **29**, 329.
79. N. N. Greenwood and B. H. Robinson, *J. Chem. Soc., A*, 1967, 511.
80. G. E. McAchran and S. G. Shore, *Inorg. Chem.*, 1966, **5**, 2044.
81. M. J. S. Dewar and R. Jones, *J. Amer. Chem. Soc.*, 1967, **89**, 2408.
82. R. W. Rudolph, R. W. Parry and C. F. Farran, *Inorg. Chem.*, 1966, **5**, 723.
83. G. W. Gilje and R. W. Parry, unpublished work cited in ref. 82.
84. R. W. Rudolph and R. W. Parry, *J. Amer. Chem. Soc.*, 1967, **89**, 1621.
85. K. W. Morse and R. W. Parry, *J. Amer. Chem. Soc.*, 1967, **89**, 172.
86. J. G. Riess and J. R. Van Wazer, *J. Amer. Chem. Soc.*, 1967, **89**, 851.
87. A. H. Cowley and S. T. Cohen, *Inorg. Chem.*, 1965, **4**, 1200.
88. E. F. Mooney and B. S. Thornhill, *J. Inorg. Nuc. Chem.*, 1966, **28**, 2225.
89. J. W. Gilje, K. W. Morse and R. W. Parry, *Inorg. Chem.*, 1967, **6**, 1761.
90. S. G. Shore and C. L. Hall, *J. Amer. Chem. Soc.*, 1966, **88**, 5346.
91. J. F. Eastman, *J. Amer. Chem. Soc.*, 1967, **89**, 2237.
92. R. A. Ogg, *J. Chem. Phys.*, 1954, **22**, 1933.
93. S. G. Shore and C. L. Hall, *J. Amer. Chem. Soc.*, 1967, **89**, 3947.
94. H. H. Linder and T. Onak, *J. Amer. Chem. Soc.*, 1966, **88**, 1890.
95. R. Adams, *Inorg. Chem.*, 1963, **2**, 1087.
96. W. N. Lipscomb, "Boron Hybrides", Benjamin, New York, 1963.
97. M. A. Ring, E. F. Witucki and R. C. Greenough, *Inorg. Chem.*, 1967, **6**, 395.
98. A. D. Norman, R. Schaeffer, A. B. Boylis, G. A. Pressley and F. E. Stafford, *J. Amer. Chem. Soc.*, 1966, **88**, 2151.
99. A. D. Norman and R. Schaeffer, *J. Amer. Chem. Soc.*, 1966, **88**, 1143.
100. A. D. Norman and R. Schaeffer, *Inorg. Chem.*, 1965, **4**, 1225.

101. T. Onak, G. B. Dunks, I. W. Searcy and J. R. Spielman, *Inorg. Chem.*, 1967, **6**, 1465.
102. D. F. Gaines, *J. Amer. Chem. Soc.*, 1966, **88**, 4528.
103. R. E. Williams, F. J. Gerhart and E. Pier, *Inorg. Chem.*, 1965, **4**, 1239.
104. D. F. Gaines and T. V. Iorns, *J. Amer. Chem. Soc.*, 1967, **89**, 3375.
105. R. A. Geanangel and S. G. Shore, *J. Amer. Chem. Soc.*, 1967, **89**, 6771.
106. T. Onak, L. B. Friedman, J. A. Hartsuck and W. N. Lipscomb, *J. Amer. Chem. Soc.*, 1966, **88**, 3439.
107. F. Klanberg, D. R. Eaton, L. J. Guggenberger and E. L. Muetterties, *Inorg. Chem.*, 1967, **6**, 1271.
108. J. Dobson and R. Schaeffer, *Inorg. Chem.*, 1968, **7**, 402.
109. R. Maruca, J. D. Odom and R. Schaeffer, *Inorg. Chem.*, 1968, **7**, 412.
110. F. Klanberg and E. L. Muetterties, *Inorg. Chem.*, 1966, **5**, 1955.
111. W. R. Hertler, F. Klanberg and E. L. Muetterties, *Inorg. Chem.*, 1967, **6**, 1696.
112. E. L. Muetterties and F. Klanberg, *Inorg. Chem.*, 1966, **5**, 316.
113. R. L. Pilling, F. N. Tebbe, M. F. Hawthorne and E. A. Pier, *Proc. Chem. Soc.*, 1964, 402.
114. R. E. Williams and E. A. Pier, *Inorg. Chem.*, 1965, **4**, 1357.
115. D. B. MacLean, J. D. Odom and R. Schaeffer, *Inorg. Chem.*, 1968, **7**, 408.
116. R. E. Williams, *Inorg. Chem.*, 1965, **4**, 1504.
117. W. H. Knoth, *J. Amer. Chem. Soc.*, 1966, **88**, 935.
118. D. E. Hyatt, F. R. Scholer and L. J. Todd, *Inorg. Chem.*, 1967, **6**, 630.
119. N. N. Greenwood and N. F. Travers, *J. Chem. Soc. A*, 1968, 15.
120. N. N. Greenwood and N. F. Travers, *Chem. Comm.*, 1967, 216.
121. W. H. Knoth, J. C. Sauer, J. H. Balthis, H. C. Miller and E. L. Muetterties, *J. Amer. Chem. Soc.*, 1967, **89**, 4842.
122. S. Trofimenko, *J. Amer. Chem. Soc.*, 1966, **88**, 1899.
123. M. F. Hawthorne and R. L. Pilling, *J. Amer. Chem. Soc.*, 1966, **88**, 3873.
124. A. Kaczmarczyk, *Inorg. Chem.*, 1968, **7**, 164.
125. R. J. Wiersema and R. L. Middaugh, *J. Amer. Chem. Soc.*, 1967, **89**, 5078.
126. R. N. Grimes, *J. Amer. Chem. Soc.*, 1966, **88**, 1070.
127. I. Shapiro, C. D. Good and R. E. Williams, *J. Amer. Chem. Soc.*, 1962, **84**, 3837.
128. R. N. Grimes, *J. Amer. Chem. Soc.*, 1966, **88**, 1895.
129. I. Shapiro, B. Keilin, R. E. Williams and C. D. Good, *J. Amer. Chem. Soc.*, 1963, **85**, 3167.
130. M. A. Grassberger, E. G. Hoffmann, G. Schomburg and R. Köster, *J. Amer. Chem. Soc.*, 1968, **90**, 56.
131. T. P. Onak, G. B. Dunks, J. R. Spielman, F. J. Gerhart and R. E. Williams. *J. Amer. Chem. Soc.*, 1966, **88**, 2061.
132. C. L. Bramlett and R. N. Grimes, *J. Amer. Chem. Soc.*, 1966, **88**, 4269.
133. P. Binger, *Tetrahedron Letters*, 1966, 2675.
134. T. Onak and G. E. Dunks, *Inorg. Chem.*, 1966, **5**, 439.
135. J. R. Spielman, R. Warren, G. B. Dunks, J. E. Scott and T. Onak, *Inorg. Chem.*, 1968, **7**, 216.
136. T. Onak, G. B. Dunks, R. A. Beaudet and R. L. Poynter, *J. Amer. Chem. Soc.*, 1966, **88**, 4622.
137. R. Köster, M. A. Grassberger, E. G. Hoffmann and G. W. Rotermund, *Tetrahedron Letters*, 1966, 905.
138. F. N. Tebbe, P. M. Garrett, D. C. Young and M. F. Hawthorne, *J. Amer. Chem. Soc.*, 1966, **88**, 609.

139. R. E. Williams and F. J. Gerhart, *J. Amer. Chem. Soc.*, 1965, **87**, 3513.
140. F. N. Tebbe, P. M. Garrett and M. F. Hawthorne, *J. Amer. Chem. Soc.*, 1968, **90**, 869.
141. H. V. Hart and W. N. Lipscomb, *J. Amer. Chem. Soc.*, 1967, **89**, 4220.
142. F. N. Tebbe, P. M. Garrett and M. F. Hawthorne, *J. Amer. Chem. Soc.*, 1966, **88**, 607.
143. W. H. Knoth, *J. Amer. Chem. Soc.*, 1967, **89**, 1274.
144. C. D. Tsai and W. E. Streib, *J. Amer. Chem. Soc.*, 1966, **88**, 4513.
145. D. E. Hyatt, D. A. Owen and L. J. Todd, *Inorg. Chem.*, 1966, **5**, 1749.
146. D. E. Hyatt, F. R. Scholer, L. J. Todd and J. L. Warner, *Inorg. Chem.*, 1967, **6**, 2229.
147. F. P. Olsen and M. F. Hawthorne, *Inorg. Chem.*, 1965, **4**, 1839.
148. M. F. Hawthorne and P. A. Wegner, *J. Amer. Chem. Soc.*, 1968, **90**, 896.
149. L. I. Zakharin and V. N. Kalnin, *Tetrahedron Letters*, 1965, 407.
150. M. F. Hawthorne, P. A. Wegner and R. C. Stafford, *Inorg. Chem.*, 1965, **4**, 1675.
151. G. D. Vickers, H. Agahigian, E. A. Pier and H. Schroeder, *Inorg. Chem.*, 1966, **5**, 693.
152. J. A. Potenza, W. N. Lipscomb, G. D. Vickers and H. Schroeder, *J. Amer. Chem. Soc.*, 1966, **88**, 628.
153. H. Beall and W. N. Lipscomb, *Inorg. Chem.*, 1967, **6**, 874.
154. M. F. Hawthorne, D. C. Young, P. M. Garrett, D. A. Owen, S. G. Schwerin, F. N. Tebbe and P. A. Wegner, *J. Amer. Chem. Soc.*, 1968, **90**, 862.
155. A. B. Harmon and K. M. Harmon, *J. Amer. Chem. Soc.*, 1966, **88**, 4093.
156. M. F. Hawthorne and T. A. George, *J. Amer Chem. Soc.*, 1967, **89**, 7115.
157. M. F. Hawthorne and T. A. George, *J. Amer. Chem. Soc.*, 1967, **89**, 7114.
158. M. F. Hawthorne, D. C. Young, T. D. Andrews, D. V. Howe, R. L. Pilling, A. D. Pitts, M. Reintjes, L. F. Warren and P. A. Wegner, *J. Amer. Chem. Soc.*, 1968, **90**, 879.
159. D. E. Hyatt, J. L. Little, J. T. Moran, F. R. Scholer and L. J. Todd, *J. Amer. Chem. Soc.*, 1967, **89**, 3342.
160. J. L. Little, J. T. Moran and L. J. Todd, *J. Amer. Chem. Soc.*, 1967, **89**, 5495.
161. F. Klanberg and L. J. Guggenberger, *Chem. Comm.*, 1967, 1293.
162. D. F. Gaines and T. V. Iorns, *J. Amer. Chem. Soc.*, 1967, **89**, 4249.
163. J. P. Jesson, S. Trofimenko and D. R. Eaton, *J. Amer. Chem. Soc.*, 1967, **89**, 3148.
164. H. Nöth and W. Regnet, *Z. anorg. Chem.*, 1967, **352**, 1.
165. H. Nöth and G. Höllerer, *Chem. Ber.*, 1966, **99**, 2197.
166. H. Nöth and G. Schmid, *J. Organometallic Chem.*, 1966, **5**, 109.
167. H. Nöth and G. Schmid, *Z. anorg. Chem.*, 1966, **345**, 69.
168. H. Nöth and G. Schmid, *Allg. prackt. Chem.*, 1966, 613.
169. M. P. Johnson, D. F. Shriver and S. A. Shriver, *J. Amer. Chem. Soc.*, 1966, **88**, 1588.
170. R. L. Wells and A. L. Collins, *Inorg. Chem.*, 1968, **7**, 419.
171. E. P. Schram, *Inorg. Chem.*, 1966, **5**, 1291.
172. T. D. Coyle, S. L. Stafford and F. G. A. Stone, *J. Chem. Soc.*, 1963, 3103.
173. H. Landesman and R. E. Williams, *J. Amer. Chem. Soc.*, 1961, **83**, 2663.
174. W. D. Phillips, H. C. Miller and E. L. Muetterties, *J. Amer. Chem. Soc.*, 1959, **81**, 4496.
175. M. F. Hawthorne, *J. Amer. Chem. Soc.*, 1961, **83**, 1345.
176. J. K. Ruff, *J. Org. Chem.*, 1962, **27**, 1020.
177. M. F. Hawthorne, *J. Amer. Chem. Soc.*, 1961, **83**, 2671.

178. T. P. Onak, H. Landesman, R. E. Williams and I. Shapiro, *J. Phys. Chem.*, 1959, **63**, 1533.
179. T. P. Onak, *J. Amer. Chem. Soc.*, 1961, **83**, 2584.
180. T. C. Farrar and T. D. Coyle, *J. Chem. Phys.*, 1964, **41**, 2612.
181. T. D. Coyle and F. G. A. Stone, *J. Chem. Phys.*, 1960, **32**, 1892.
182. P. N. Gates, E. F. Mooney and D. C. Smith, *J. Chem. Soc.*, 1964, 3511.
183. H. S. Turner and R. J. Warne, *Proc. Chem. Soc.*, 1962, 69.
184. R. H. Cragg, *J. Inorg. Nuc. Chem.*, 1968, **30**, 395.
185. K. Niedenzu, H. Beyer and H. Jenne, *Chem. Ber.*, 1963, **96**, 2649.
186. P. C. Moews, Ph.D. Thesis, Cornell University (1960), cited by R. Schaeffer in ref. 4.
187. A. J. Klanica, J. P. Faust and C. S. King, *Inorg. Chem.*, 1967, **6**, 840.
188. R. K. Bartlett, H. S. Turner, R. J. Warne, M. A. Young and I. J. Lawrenson, *J. Chem. Soc. A*, 1966, 479.
189. E. F. Mooney and M. A. Qaseem, unpublished results.
190. D. F. Gaines, unpublished results cited by R. Schaeffer in ref. 4.
191. J. G. Jones, *Inorg. Chem.*, 1966, **5**, 1229.
192. E. F. Mooney and P. H. Winson, unpublished results.

Nuclear Electron Double Resonance in Liquids

R. A. DWEK, R. E. RICHARDS AND D. TAYLOR

Physical Chemistry Laboratory, University of Oxford, England

I. INTRODUCTION

THE TERM nuclear electron double resonance is used to describe experiments in which the effect on a nuclear resonance is observed during simultaneous irradiation of an electron resonance in the same sample. If the electron resonance is saturated, then dramatic changes in the intensities of the nuclear resonance may occur. In favourable cases the resonance may be enhanced or inverted by up to three orders of magnitude.

The magnitude and sign of the enhancement in liquids depend upon the spin lattice relaxation processes in the solution, and these are dependent upon the molecular motions and interactions present in the solution. In order to understand the spin lattice relaxation processes in these systems it is first convenient to consider the mechanism for a diamagnetic system of nuclei of spin quantum number $I = \frac{1}{2}$.

When nuclei of spin $\frac{1}{2}$, are placed in an applied magnetic field H_0, the nuclei are distributed between two energy levels, corresponding to the allowed orientations of the nuclear magnets in H_0.

If radiation of angular frequency ω_I is applied to the system, transitions are induced between these two energy levels. Since the probability of a quantum of radiation inducing an upward transition is the same as that for a downward transition, a net exchange of energy between the nuclear spins and the applied radiation will only occur if the populations of the two levels are unequal. If the lower energy level has an excess population (such as it has at thermal equilibrium) then energy is absorbed from the radiation, but if the upper level were more highly populated, then an emission signal would be induced. The probability that a nucleus will undergo a spontaneous jump from one energy level to another is vanishingly small, and for nuclei of spin $\frac{1}{2}$ there is thus no mechanism other than the oscillating field at ω_I, for the particular field H_0, which can cause transitions. (The angular frequency ω_I is equal to $\gamma_I H_0$ where γ_I is the nuclear magnetogyric ratio and when $H_0 \sim 10^4$ gauss, $\omega_I \sim 10^7$ sec.$^{-1}$).

When a sample containing nuclei of spin $\frac{1}{2}$ is placed suddenly in the magnetic field H_0, the initial population of the two nuclear energy levels must be equal, since the nuclear spins have random orientations in zero field. The nuclei "relax" to the populations corresponding to thermal equilibrium values, predicted by the Maxwell–Boltzmann distribution law, with a characteristic time T_1, the spin lattice relaxation time. The oscillating magnetic fields at ω_I needed to induce these transitions are derived from the random Brownian motions of the molecules in the liquid. The nuclear magnetic moments, μ_I, set up local magnetic fields that fluctuate according to the molecular motion. For example, relative diffusion of molecules causes the local fields at the nuclei of one molecule, due to those of another, to change. The variation of the interaction caused by the molecular motion is referred to as "modulation" of the coupling, a term we shall use frequently, and is characterized by a correlation time, τ, which sets a time scale to the random motion.

Since the magnetic interactions between the nuclei are fluctuating in step with the random molecular motions, the frequencies of the magnetic interactions are related to the frequencies of the molecular motion. For any random motion there is a whole spectrum of frequencies, and the variation of the intensity of the fluctuations with frequency (referred to as the spectral density J_ω) must depend on the type of motion concerned. In most cases, the variation of J_ω with ω is of general form shown in Fig. 1.

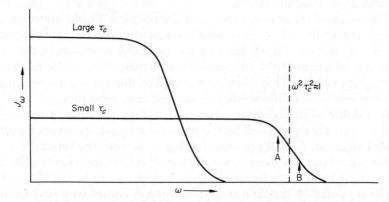

FIG. 1. Spectrum of frequencies of molecular motion in a liquid. ω_I lies on the flat part of the curve. ω_S may lie near A or B at magnetic fields in the range 1–10 kgauss. (From Ehrenberg, Malström and Vänngård (Eds.), "Magnetic Resonance in Biological Systems", Vol. 9, p. 55, Pergamon Press, 1967.)

J_ω is independent of ω until $\omega\tau$ approaches unity, and then falls to zero as ω increases. When τ is small, J_ω is low and extends to high values of ω; when τ is large J_ω is greater, but falls to zero at a lower frequency.

The relaxation times are thus dependent on the values of J_ω at the particular value of ω. J_ω may be written—

$$J_\omega = \int\limits_{-\infty}^{+\infty} g(\tau) \exp{(-i\omega\tau)}$$

where $g(\tau)$ is called the *correlation function*, the form of which must be postulated if correlation times are to be calculated.

For most liquids, τ is $\sim 10^{-10}$ sec. and ω_I is usually 10^7 sec.$^{-1}$; consequently $\omega_I\tau$ is therefore much less than unity (Fig. 1) and the value of J_ω is more or less independent of ω and hence of the applied magnetic field strength. This region of the correlation spectrum is called the "*white spectrum*".

In addition to the spin lattice relaxation time, T_1, there is a further relaxation time, T_2, which is referred to as the spin–spin relaxation time. Whereas T_1 measures the time required for nuclei to exchange energy with their surroundings, T_2 measures the time taken for nuclei to exchange energy among themselves by an adiabatic process. T_2 is sometimes referred to as the transverse relaxation time, because it is concerned with the relaxation of the nuclear magnetization in the transverse (XY) plane at right angles to H_0. For diamagnetic liquids, T_1 and T_2 are usually equal.

The nuclear relaxation times in a diamagnetic liquid are often reduced markedly when very small concentrations of paramagnetic solutes are added. This is because the magnetic moments of the electrons are of the order of 10^3 times greater than those of the nuclei, so that the intensities of local fields generated by them are correspondingly greater, resulting in more efficient nuclear spin relaxation.

In a dilute solution of a paramagnetic solute, the nuclear relaxation is often entirely dominated by the pairwise interaction between an unpaired electron, S, and nucleus, I. This is because the rapid diffusion of the solute in the solvent ensures that all nuclei are equally affected. The strong local fields produced by the electron can be coupled to the nuclei by a dipole–dipole interaction and sometimes by a scalar interaction as well. The scalar interaction is transmitted to the nucleus by similar mechanism to that producing spin–spin multiplets in n.m.r. spectra and the hyperfine structure in e.s.r. spectra.

The Zeeman levels for a nuclear magnetic dipole I and an electron magnetic dipole S in a magnetic field are shown in Fig. 2, where the levels are labelled according to their value of the spin quantum numbers

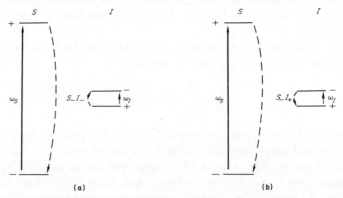

FIG. 2. Zeeman energy levels for electron spin S and nuclear spin I: (a) scalar coupling, dominant relaxation transition $S_- I_-$; (b) dipolar coupling, dominant relaxation transition $S_- I_+$.

$I_z, S_z = \pm \frac{1}{2}$. The lowest nuclear magnetic energy level is by convention labelled + (plus), and because the magnetic moment of the electron has the opposite sign to that of the proton (and most other nuclei of interest), the lower electron magnetic level is labelled − (minus). The random magnetic field fluctuations can induce nuclear spin transitions involving changes in the I_z spin quantum number of $-\frac{1}{2}$ to $+\frac{1}{2}$ and of $+\frac{1}{2}$ to $-\frac{1}{2}$, which are conveniently denoted by I_+ and I_-, respectively. The strong pairwise interaction between the electron and nuclear magnetic dipoles can also induce coupled two spin transitions such as $S_+ I_- (S_- I_+)$ in which the electron and nucleus make simultaneous flips (Fig. 2). The probability of any of the transitions shown in Fig. 2 occurring depends on the nature of the interaction between the electron and the nucleus. It turns out that for dipolar coupling, the $S_- I_-$ and $S_+ I_+$ transitions are the most important, whereas for the scalar interactions the most important are $S_- I_+$ and $S_+ I_-$. Since simultaneous nuclear–electron spin transitions can occur, the nuclear relaxation processes will depend not only on the spectral density function J_{ω_I}, but also on the spectral density function $J_{\omega_S \pm \omega_I}$ which characterize the double-spin transitions. Since $\omega_S \gg \omega_I$, the spectral density functions $J_{\omega_S \pm \omega_I}$, which turn out to be important for nuclear spin relaxation processes, can be approximated by those at J_{ω_S}.

Although in most liquids $\omega_I \tau$ is generally less than unity, this is not so for $\omega_S \tau$. For example, if $\tau \sim 10^{-10}$ sec., then at 10^4 gauss $\omega_S \sim 1.8 \times 10^{10}$ and thus $\omega_S \tau = 1.8$. In terms of correlation spectrum for molecular motion we are no longer in the white spectrum region, and J_ω is then dependent on the applied field, H_0. Thus measurement of relaxation phenomena at high fields provides a sensitive test of the shape of the correlation function and the model postulated for the molecular motion. In the double-resonance experiment, the electron resonance of the free radical present in the solution is strongly irradiated, so that the populations of the electron energy levels are more or less equalized. The spin lattice relaxation processes attempt to restore the populations of these energy levels to their thermal equilibrium values, in which there are more electron spins in the lower level than in the upper level by S_- transitions. For electron nuclear dipolar coupling the dominant $S_- I_-$ transition will cause the nucleus to perform an I_- transition simultaneously, with the result that nuclei originally in the lower nuclei energy level are transferred to the upper level (Fig. 2a). Under optimum conditions, the population of the two nuclear levels may be changed by a factor of $-\frac{1}{2} |\gamma_S| / \gamma_I$ for dipolar coupling, which, for protons, is −330. Thus the population of the

upper nuclear level becomes greatly increased and the nuclear resonance becomes an emission signal, i.e., the signal is inverted. If there is
also scalar coupling present between the electrons and the nuclei, then
there is an additional relaxation mechanism $S_- I_+$. If this mechanism
dominates, then saturation of the electron resonance will lead to an
increase in the intensity of the nuclear resonance absorption signal
(Fig. 2b).

In this review we have attempted to give a concise account of the
basic principles and applications of nuclear electron double resonance,
or as it is sometimes called the nuclear electron Overhauser effect. We
have also tried to illustrate to the non-specialist the progress that has
been made in this subject and indicate what remains to be done.

II. SIMPLE THEORY

The essential features of the Overhauser effect and related relaxation phenomena can be seen by considering the transitions between
the energy levels of a two-spin system consisting of a nuclear spin I
and an electron spin S.[1] Although this may appear to be a drastic over-
simplification for describing the interactions in a solution containing
free radicals, the rapid random diffusion of the molecules ensures that
the solvent molecules are near a free radical many times during the
nuclear relaxation time, and therefore any nucleus in solution may be
considered to be in continuous interaction with an electron.

The general form of the spin Hamiltonian for a nuclear-electron
two spin system is—

$$\mathcal{H} = \mathcal{H}_0 + \mathcal{H}_{IS}(t) + \mathcal{H}_I(t) + \mathcal{H}_S(t) \tag{1}$$

where $\mathcal{H}_0 = -\omega_I I_z + \omega_S S_z$ is the Zeeman energy for the system in an
external magnetic field H_0, i.e., the magnetic interaction between the
nuclear and electron dipole moments and the applied field. $\omega_I = \gamma_I H_0$
and $\omega_S = |\gamma_S| H_0$ are the nuclear and electron Larmor frequencies,
respectively, and γ_I and $|\gamma_S|$ are the magnetogyric ratios of the nucleus
I and the electron S.

$\mathcal{H}_{IS}(t)$ represents the time-dependent nuclear–electron interactions
that give rise to relaxation processes involving both spins and which
are responsible for the Overhauser effect.

$\mathcal{H}_I(t)$ represents the remaining interactions, not involving electron
spins, S, which contribute to relaxation of the nuclear spins I.

$\mathcal{H}_S(t)$ represents similar interactions for the electron spins S. The
unperturbed eigenstates of $\mathcal{H}_0$ are $|-+\rangle$, $|++\rangle$, $|--\rangle$ and $|+-\rangle$
with populations N_{-+}, N_{++}, N_{--} and N_{+-} where the first sign

represents the orientation in the magnetic field of the nuclear spin I, and the second sign that of electron spin S. Figure 3 shows these four energy levels and the continuous lines represent the transitions between

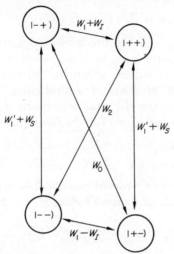

FIG. 3. Eigenstates $|I_z S_z\rangle$ of the unperturbed Zeeman Hamiltonian $H_0 = -\omega_I I_z + \omega_S S_z$, connected by transitions W.

them. We shall denote the transition probabilities between these levels as W_I [which arises from the interactions $\mathscr{H}_I(t)$], W_S [from the interaction $H_S(t)$] and W_0, W_2, W_1, W_1' [from the interactions $\mathscr{H}_{IS}(t)$]. Considering the rate of the populations N_{ij}, it can be seen from detailed balances that—

$$\frac{dN_{-+}}{dt} = \{(W_1 + W_0 + W_1') + W_I + W_S\}(N_{-+} - N_{-+,0})$$

$$+ \{W_1 + W_I\}(N_{++} - N_{++,0}) + \{W_1' + W_S\}(N_{--} - N_{--,0})$$

$$+ \{W_0\}(N_{+-} - N_{+-,0}) \tag{2a}$$

$$\frac{dN_{++}}{dt} = \{W_1 + W_I\}(N_{-+} - N_{-+,0})$$

$$- \{(W_1 + W_2 + W_1') + W_I + W_S\}(N_{++} - N_{++,0})$$

$$+ \{W_2\}(N_{--} - N_{--,0}) + \{W_1' + W_S\}(N_{+-} - N_{+,0}) \tag{2b}$$

$$\frac{dN_{--}}{dt} = \{W_1' + W_S\}(N_{-+} - N_{-+,0}) + \{W_2\}(N_{++} - N_{++,0})$$

$$- \{(W_1 + W_0 + W_1') + W_I + W_S\}(N_{--} - N_{--,0})$$

$$+ \{W_1 + W_I\}(N_{--} - N_{--,0}) \tag{2c}$$

$$\frac{dN_{+-}}{dt} = \{W_0\}(N_{-+} - N_{-+,0}) + \{W_1' + W_S\}(N_{++} - N_{++,0})$$
$$+ \{W_1 + W_I\}(N_{--} - N_{--,0})$$
$$- \{(W_1 + W_2 + W_1') + W_I + W_S\}(N_{+-} - N_{+-,0}) \qquad (2d)$$

where the terms $N_{ij,0}$ refer to the level populations for the system at thermal equilibrium and have been included so that the populations will have their correct values, given by the Boltzmann distribution, when the system is in thermal equilibrium. The experimentally observable quantities are the magnetizations I_z and S_z, which are related to the level populations for the two-spin system by—

$$I_z = K\gamma_I\{(N_{-+} + N_{--}) - (N_{++} + N_{+-})\}$$
$$S_z = K|\gamma_s|\{(N_{-+} + N_{++}) - (N_{--} + N_{+-})\} \qquad (3)$$

where K is a constant of proportionality. Using equation (3) and re-grouping equations (2), the rates of change of I_z and S_z are given by—

$$\frac{dI_z}{dt} = -\{(W_0 + 2W_1 + W_2) + 2W_I\}(I_z - I_0)$$
$$- \frac{\gamma_I}{|\gamma_s|}\{W_2 - W_0\}(S_z - S_0) \qquad (4a)$$

$$\frac{dS_z}{dt} = -\frac{|\gamma_s|}{\gamma_I}\{W_2 - W_0\}(I_z - I_0)$$
$$- \{(W_0 + 2W_1' + W_2) + 2W_S\}(S_z - S_0) \qquad (4b)$$

It follows immediately from equations (4) that, because of the time-dependent interaction $\mathscr{H}_{IS}(t)$, the magnetizations I_z and S_z are no longer independent of each other, but are coupled. When S refers to an electron spin, then equation (4b) can be further simplified. Relaxation of the electron spin will be almost wholly due to the term $\mathscr{H}_s(t)$ which refers to such relaxation mechanisms as electron–electron dipolar interactions, etc., whereas the term $\mathscr{H}_{IS}(t)$, referring to nuclear–electron interactions, will make only a small contribution to the relaxation of the electron spin S. Thus, equations (4) become—

$$\frac{dI_z}{dt} = -\{(W_0 + 2W_1 + W_2) + 2W_I\}(I_z - I_0)$$
$$- \frac{\gamma_I}{|\gamma_s|}\{W_2 - W_0\}(S_z - S_0) \qquad (5a)$$

$$\frac{dS_z}{dt} = -2W_s(S_z - S_0) \qquad (5b)$$

In the double-resonance experiment, the n.m.r. signal, which is proportional to I_z, may be observed under steady-state conditions. Thus putting $dI_z/dt = 0$, equations (5) yields—

$$I_z - I_0 = -\frac{W_2 - W_0}{\{(W_0 + 2W_1 + W_2) + 2W_I\}} \frac{\gamma_I}{|\gamma_S|} (S_z - S_0) \qquad (6)$$

The e.s.r. signal, proportional to S_z, is irradiated with a large oscillating magnetic field at ω_S sufficient to cause partial saturation of the electron transitions. The dependence of S_z on the strength H_{1S} of an oscillating magnetic field applied exactly at resonance is found[2] from the Bloch equations to be—

$$S_z = S_0 \left(\frac{1}{1 + \gamma_S^2 H_{1S}^2 T_{1S} T_{2S}} \right) \qquad (7)$$

where T_{1S}, T_{2S} are the spin–lattice and spin–spin relaxation times of the e.s.r. line. Combining equations (6) and (7) we obtain—

$$(I_z - I_0) = -\left\{ \frac{W_0 + 2W_1 + W_2}{(W_0 + 2W_1 + W_2) + 2W_I} \right\} \left\{ \frac{W_2 - W_0}{W_0 + 2W_1 + W_2} \right\}$$
$$\times \frac{\gamma_I}{|\gamma_S|} S_0 \frac{\gamma_S^2 H_{1S}^2 T_{1S} T_{2S}}{1 + \gamma_S^2 H_{1S}^2 T_{1S} T_{2S}} \qquad (8)$$

If an enhancement, A, of the n.m.r. signal is now defined as $A = (I_z - I_0)/I_0$, equation (7) gives—

$$A = -\frac{|\gamma_S|}{\gamma_I} \left\{ \frac{W_0 + 2W_1 + W_2}{(W_0 + 2W_1 + W_2) + 2W_I} \right\} \left\{ \frac{W_2 - W_0}{W_0 + 2W_1 + W_2} \right\}$$
$$\times \frac{\gamma_S^2 H_{1S}^2 T_{1S} T_{2S}}{1 + \gamma_S^2 H_{1S}^2 T_{1S} T_{2S}} \qquad (9)$$

where the thermal equilibrium values of S_0 and I_0, given by the Curie Law, have been used. In these experiments we are interested in phenomena arising from the nuclear–electron interactions $\mathscr{H}_{IS}(t)$. Since the transition probabilities W_0, W_1 and W_2 are due to the nuclear–electron interaction, it is convenient to define a nuclear–electron coupling parameter ρ, where—

$$\rho = \frac{W_2 - W_0}{W_0 + 2W_1 + W_2} \qquad (10)$$

which is a measurable quantity and depends only on these interactions $\mathscr{H}_{IS}(t)$. The other term in equation (9) depending on the transition probabilities, W_i, is called a *leakage factor*, usually denoted by f, where—

$$f = \frac{W_0 + 2W_1 + W_2}{(W_0 + 2W_1 + W_2) + W_I} \tag{11}$$

The significance of f can be seen by considering equation (5). Since the relaxation time of the electron spins is very much shorter than that of the nuclear spins ($\leqslant 10^{-6}$ sec. cf. $> 10^{-3}$ sec.), any changes in the polarization of the electron spins will appear on the time scale of the nuclear spins to be occurring almost instantaneously. Therefore in equation (5a) the term with $(S_z - S_0)$ may be taken to be constant on the n.m.r. time scale.

Since $(W_0 + 2W_1 + W_2)$ represents that part of the nuclear relaxation rate that arises from interaction with the electrons, and W_I represents contributions to the nuclear relaxation rate from other interactions, such as are normally present in diamagnetic systems (and usually written as $1/T_{1,0}$), the leakage factor f may then be written as

$$f = \frac{1/T_1 - 1/T_{1,0}}{1/T_1} \tag{12}$$

Thus f measures the fraction of the total relaxation rate due to nuclear–electron interactions; when nuclear–electron interactions are negligible, $f = 0$, and when they are dominant $f = 1$. With these definitions for the coupling parameter ρ and leakage factor f equation (10) becomes—

$$A = \frac{I_z - I_0}{I_0} = -\frac{|\gamma_S|}{\gamma_I} f \rho \frac{\gamma_S^2 H_{1S}^2 T_{1S} T_{2S}}{1 + \gamma_S^2 H_{1S}^2 T_{1S} T_{2S}} \tag{13}$$

which is the form usually employed to describe the experimental data. For example, in an experiment performed at a magnetic field of 3300 gauss with corresponding e.s.r. frequency 9250 Mc./sec. (X band) the n.m.r. signal is measured in the absence of microwave irradiation in order to obtain the I_0 value, and then measured as a function of applied microwave power when the e.s.r. signal is being excited to obtain values for I_z. For microwave frequencies, it is not easy to measure directly the applied microwave field H_{1S}, but by assuming that H_{1S}^2 is proportional to the applied microwave power, P, equation (13) can be rewritten as—

$$A^{-1} = -\left(\frac{|\gamma_S|}{\gamma_I} f \rho\right)^{-1} \left\{ 1 + \frac{1}{\alpha P T_{1S} T_{2S}} \right\} \tag{14}$$

where α is a constant. Therefore a plot of reciprocal enhancement, A^{-1}, against reciprocal power, P^{-1}, should give a straight line with intercept

$A_{\infty}^{-1} = -\left[(|\gamma_S|/\gamma_I)f.\rho\right]^{-1}$ corresponding to the value of the enhancement for complete saturation of the e.s.r. signal. The leakage factor f can then be found by measuring the nuclear relaxation time for the solution in the presence of the radical T_1, and in its absence $T_{1,0}$. Alternatively $T_{1,0}$ can be obtained by measuring the nuclear relaxation times of the solutions as a function of radical concentration and extrapolating to zero concentration. In practice, it is often easier to use radical concentrations of around 10^{-1} M when the predominant nuclear relaxation mechanism will be by interaction with the electron spin, in which case $1/T_{1,0}$ is negligible compared with $1/T_1$, and f is almost unity. In this way the nuclear–electron coupling parameter ρ can be found. ρ is a sensitive test of the form and the time dependence of the nuclear–electron interaction $\mathscr{H}_{IS}(t)$ which determines the various transitions probabilities W_0, W_1 and W_2. The experimental observations can usually be explained in terms of two types of interaction, viz, a dipole–dipole interaction with Hamiltonian $\mathscr{H}_{IS}^{D}$, which is analogous to the classical interaction between two magnetic dipoles, and a scalar interaction, with Hamiltonian $\mathscr{H}_{IS}^{s}$, which has no classical counterpart, but which can occur if there is any unpaired electron density produced at the nucleus I by the electron spin S.

When an oscillating magnetic field is applied at the e.s.r. frequency, the transitions $\Delta m_S = \pm 1, \Delta m_I = 0$ are excited (Fig. 3). The populations of the $|-+\rangle$, $|++\rangle$ levels will be increased at the expense of the $|--\rangle$, $|+-\rangle$ levels, respectively, until in the case of complete saturation of the e.s.r. signal, the populations of the levels connected by the oscillating field H_{1S} would be equal. The levels $|-+\rangle$ and $|+-\rangle$ are connected by the interaction $\mathscr{H}_{IS}^{s}$, with the result that their populations approach the equilibrium values given by the Boltzmann distribution. The net result is that the n.m.r. signal, which is proportional to the differences $(N_{--}-N_{+-})$ and $(N_{-+}-N_{++})$ is increased. Although the applied field H_{1S} is tending to equalize the populations of the electron spin levels, the relaxation processes are tending to restore Boltzmann distribution between the levels. For scalar coupling, the dominant term $I_{+}S_{-}$ connects the levels $|-+\rangle$ and $|+-\rangle$, with the result that their populations approach their thermal equilibrium values. The net result is that the n.m.r. signal, which is proportional to the differences $(N_{--}-N_{+-})$ and $(N_{-+}-N_{--})$ is increased. In terms of the transition probabilities among the energy levels, it turns out that the only allowed transition is $W_0(2)$. Thus from equation (10)—

$$\rho = \frac{W_2 - W_0}{W_0 + 2W_1 + W_2}$$

has the value $\rho = 1$ for this particular interaction. Hence the maximum enhancement attainable is—

$$A = \frac{-\rho|\gamma_S|}{\gamma_I} = +\frac{|\gamma_S|}{\gamma_I} \quad \text{(cf. eq. 14)}$$

In the case of dipolar coupling, the transitions W_0, W_2 and W_1 are all allowed. However it can be shown[2] that the nuclear–electron coupling parameter ρ is always positive. Under optimum conditions (white spectrum) the ratios of $W_0 : W_1 : W_2$ are $\frac{1}{2}:\frac{3}{4}:3$, and thus ρ has a value of $+\frac{1}{2}$.[2] Hence the maximum observable enhancement for pure dipolar coupling is $-\frac{1}{2}(|\gamma_S|/\gamma_I)$. In practice, both scalar and dipolar interactions may be present and the observed enhancement will then lie between $-\frac{1}{2}(|\gamma_S|/\gamma_I)$ and $|\gamma_S|/\gamma_I$.

III. MODELS FOR THE NUCLEAR–ELECTRON INTERACTIONS

We have already seen that the coupled relaxation transitions between the nuclei and electrons, which give rise to the Overhauser effect, are stimulated by fluctuations in the local magnetic fields at frequencies ω_I and ω_S. The intensities of these fluctuations (denoted by J_ω, where ω is the appropriate frequency) depends critically on the correlation time for, and the nature of, the nuclear electron interactions, which may be either dipolar or scalar (see above).

A. Dipole–Dipole Interactions

These arise from the interaction of the nuclear and electron magnetic dipoles, and may be treated by starting from the classical Hamiltonian for two interacting dipoles, which can be written as—

$$\mathcal{H}_{IS}^D = \gamma_S^2\gamma_I^2\left[\frac{3(\mathbf{S}.\mathbf{r})(\mathbf{I}.\mathbf{r})}{r^5} - \frac{\mathbf{I}.\mathbf{S}}{r^3}\right] \tag{15}$$

The time dependence of the interaction can arise from variations in the interspin vector, r, due to the relative translational motions of the I and S spins. It can be shown[3] that if the spins I and S are in different molecules and can be treated as diffusing independently, an expression for the reduced spectral density $j_{d,\omega} = J_{d,\omega}/J_{d,0}$ can be obtained. The result is—

$$j_{d,\omega} = \frac{15}{2}I(u) \tag{16}$$

where $u = |\omega\tau_t|^{\frac{1}{2}}$, and τ_t is the dipolar correlation time for translational motion, and $I(u)$ is given by—

$$I(u) = u^{-5}\{u^2 - 2 + e^{-u}[(u^2 - 2)\sin u + (u^2 + 4u + 2)\cos u]\} \quad (17)$$

Under certain circumstances (see Section IV.A) it may be necessary to take into account the contribution of rotational motion to the relaxation behaviour of the system. This would, for example, be when I and S were stuck together for a time comparable with τ_t. Under these circumstances $j_{d,\omega}$ is given by—

$$j_{d,\omega} = \frac{1}{1 + \omega^2 \tau_r^2}$$

where τ_R is the rotational correlation time for this dipolar interaction. Figure 4 shows a plot of $j_{d,\omega}$ as a function of $|\omega\tau|^{\frac{1}{2}}$ for these two cases.

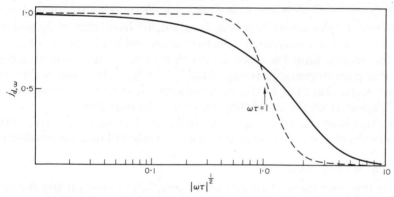

FIG. 4. Reduced spectral densities $j_{d,\omega}$ versus $|\omega\tau|^{\frac{1}{2}}$ for dipolar coupling; continuous curve is translational diffusion and broken curve is rotational diffusion.

B. Scalar interactions

When there is unpaired electron density produced at the nucleus being studied, a so-called scalar interaction between the electron and the nucleus can occur. This unpaired electron density is transmitted from the free radical to the nucleus by a similar mechanism to that giving rise to the nuclear hyperfine structure in normal e.s.r. spectra. Since the unpaired electron and the nucleus are usually in different molecules, the rapid molecular motion means that the scalar inter-action, which of necessity can only occur when the unpaired electron and the nucleus are close to one another, will be varying rapidly. This rapid switching on and off of the scalar interaction means that although any intermolecular nuclear hyperfine structure in the e.s.r. signal is averaged to zero, the scalar interactions may now provide an efficient nuclear relaxation mechanism in addition to the ever present dipolar interaction. However one difference does exist between this scalar and dipolar interaction. As in the case of an unpaired electron and nuclear spin in the same molecule, where the intramolecular nuclear electron dipole interaction is averaged to zero whereas the scalar interaction is not, so also in the case of intermolecular spin–spin interactions. Thus for intermolecular spin–spin interactions, the static dipolar coupling is again averaged to zero but for scalar coupling, although the hyperfine splitting is averaged out, the unpaired electron density produced at the nucleus can manifest itself as a shift in the n.m.r. frequency.[4]

The Hamiltonian for the scalar interaction is—

$$\mathscr{H}^S_{IS} = B_{IS}\mathbf{I}.\mathbf{S} \tag{19}$$

and the time dependence may now arise either from the time dependence of B, the scalar coupling constant, or from that of S, and are denoted as scalar coupling of the first or second kind.[2] Scalar coupling of the second kind has been found to be important in systems containing paromagnetic ions e.g., Mn^{2+},[5,6] where, because of the very short relaxation time of the electron spin, S, the time dependence of $\mathscr{H}^S_{IS}$ arises from the rapid flipping of the electron spin.

In much of our discussion we shall only be concerned with scalar relaxation of the first kind and various models will now be considered.

1. The sticking model[3]

In this case there is a finite scalar interaction only during the time that the spins I and S are "stuck" together. When the spins are stuck together, the scalar interaction is characterized by a coupling constant B, which is zero under all other conditions. The time dependence of B arises because the time of sticking is assumed to be a random variable.

2. The diffusion model[3]

The scalar interaction is assumed here to be a function of the distance between the I and S spins. As in the dipolar case, the variation of r with time is responsible for the time dependence of the interaction. Thus, unlike the sticking model, the unpaired electron density produced at the nucleus is not at one instant finite and then zero (i.e., switched on and then off), but it approaches its maximum value as the radical and solvent molecules collide and then decays to zero again as the molecules recede. Since scalar interaction could arise from the electron–orbital overlap with the nucleus, the interaction is assumed to be of very short range and thus a steep function of the internuclear distance. It is therefore postulated that the overlap varies exponentially with the internuclear distance, and B is then assumed to have the form—

$$B_{IS} = \hbar B \, \frac{d}{r_{IS}} \, \exp\left[-\lambda(r_{IS}-d)\right] \qquad (20)$$

B and λ are constants, r_{IS} is the distance between the I and S spins and d is their distance of closest approach. The interaction is short range and so it follows that $\lambda d \gg 1$. Because this condition is assumed to be true, the factor (d/r_{IS}) has little effect on the functional dependence of B_{IS} and is included only to facilitate the computation of the spectral density function for scalar coupling, J_{e,ω_S}. A plot of j_{e,ω_S} as a function of $(\omega_S \tau)^{\frac{1}{2}}$ is shown in Fig. 5.

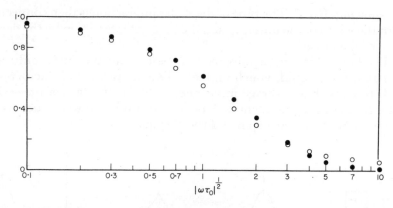

FIG. 5. Reduced spectral density: $\bullet$, $j_{d,\omega}$, dipolar coupling, diffusion model; $\bigcirc$, $j_{e,\omega}$: Scalar coupling, diffusion model. (From Hubbard.[3])

3. The pulse model[7]

In the pulse model, as in the previous models, it is assumed that the time between the radical–solvent collisions, during which the scalar interaction can occur, is a random variable. Thus the variation of the scalar interaction experienced by a nucleus as a function of time will have the generalized form illustrated in Fig. 6. The rate of change of this scalar interaction will depend on the geometry of the interaction between the I and the S spins. For example, different radicals (S) may approach different I spins with preferred orientations with the result that the electron orbital overlap with the nucleus may be described by different functions in each case, so that the existence of different functions for the scalar interaction seems justifiable on a purely physical basis. Several pictorial examples of different pulses

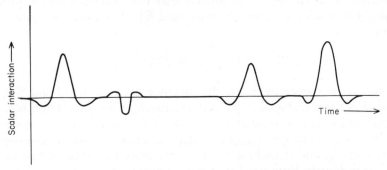

Fig. 6. Scalar interaction experienced by a nucleus as a function of time.

are shown in Fig. 7. The time of the scalar interaction is then connected with the width of the pulse, τ_w and the range of interaction by the decay time of the pulse.

The validity of using a pulse model is based upon the simple diffusion equation for a liquid, which implies a Poisson process of fluctuations with time, with an average jump rate, τ_p^{-1}. For the case of the scalar interaction τ_p may be identified as the mean time between successive encounters of a given I spin and the S spins.

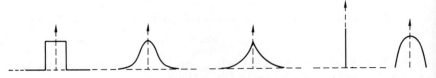

Fig. 7. Types of pulse used to describe scalar interaction. (From Nöack et al.[7])

The difference between this model and the diffusion model above is that the latter explicitly assumes a definite function for the scalar coupling which is invariant in all systems. More specifically, the diffusion model is just one special case of this model. However, for the interested reader it should be pointed out that the calculations for this model are performed using time averages rather than the more cumbersome ensemble averages used in computation of the diffusion model, i.e., the scalar interaction is evaluated as a function of time rather than distance.

The merit of the pulse model is that it is capable of yielding quite different forms of the scalar interaction from the same physical concept. Undoubtedly other stochastic processes that can be explained on a statistical basis would yield models that could equally well explain the experimental results, but in so doing, may well obscure the physical concepts involved.

C. Models for mixed scalar and dipolar interactions

Since dipolar interactions are always present between the electrons and nuclei, additional complications will arise when there are also scalar interactions. When both interactions are present it is necessary to combine the above model for the dipolar interaction with one of the several models for the scalar interaction. Obviously, there are many combinations and it is not the intention of this review to discuss each one in detail. However, the relevant principles involved can best be illustrated by considering one or two of the combinations in detail and referring to the others where necessary. We shall also refer to the combined model by the name given to the scalar interaction.

1. The diffusion model[3]

The dipolar interaction is considered to be modulated by the random translational diffusion of the I and S spins and the scalar interaction is described by the above diffusion model. The relative importance of scalar and dipolar interactions is described by a quantity, ξ, defined as—

$$\xi = J_{e,0}/J_{d,0} \tag{21}$$

$J_{e,0}$ and $J_{d,0}$ being the spectral density functions for scalar and dipolar interactions at zero frequency. If $\xi = 0$, the interaction is only dipolar; if $\xi \gg 1$, the scalar interaction is dominant.

When both dipolar and scalar interactions are present, ρ, the nuclear–electron coupling parameter, has to be calculated as a function of ξ. Because ρ depends also on the spectral density near the electron Larmor frequency, ρ can be plotted as a function of frequency for various values of ξ. In practice, it proves to be convenient to present ρ as a function of $(\omega_S \tau_t)^{\frac{1}{2}}$ where τ_t, the *diffusional correlation time*, is given by—

$$\tau_t = \frac{d^2}{\frac{1}{2}(D_I + D_S)} \tag{22}$$

d being the distance of closest approach of an I and S spin and D_I and D_S, the appropriate self-diffusion coefficients.

11

In order to obtain these plots for ρ, it is necessary to calculate the spectral-density functions for both the scalar and dipolar interactions, i.e.—

$$J_{d,\omega_S} = \frac{J_{d,\omega_S}}{J_{d,0}}$$

$$J_{e,\omega_S} = \frac{J_{e,\omega_S}}{J_{e,0}}$$

where the letters d and e refer to the dipolar and scalar interactions, respectively.

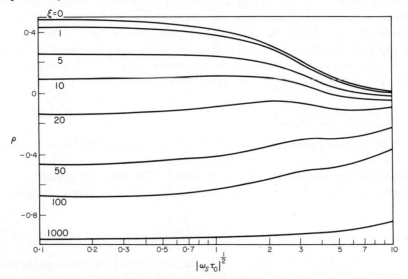

FIG. 8. Mixed scalar and dipolar coupling; diffusion model. ρ versus $|\omega_S\tau|^{\frac{1}{2}}$ for different ξ values. (From Hubbard.[3])

The expression for ρ is then found to be (cf. equation 15)—

$$\rho = \frac{40j_{d,\omega_S\tau_t} - 3\xi j_{e,\omega_S\tau_t}}{50j_{d,\omega_S\tau_t} + 24 + 3\xi j_{e,\omega_S\tau_t}} \tag{23}$$

where the fact that $\omega_S \gg \omega_I$ has been used to simplify the expression. Plots of ρ for different values of ξ for this model are shown in Fig. 8. Note that when $\xi = 0$, (i.e., the interaction is dipolar)—

$$\rho = \frac{40j_{d,\omega_S\tau_t}}{50j_{d,\omega_S\tau_t} + 24} \tag{24}$$

When scalar interactions are present, additional information can be obtained from the field and temperature dependence of T_1 and T_2. Any interaction that affects T_1 must also affect T_2, but scalar interactions can shorten T_2 by a mechanism that does not affect T_1. T_2 measures the time taken for the nuclear magnetization in the xy plane to decay by the loss of phase of the processing nuclei. This phase loss may be induced by any static component of a local field which may cause some nuclei to precess at different frequencies from others. The scalar interaction produces such a component that does not vary as the complex rotates. When scalar interactions are important $T_1 \neq T_2$ and thus measurement of the relaxation times, in addition to the signal enhancement factor, allows further parameters to be determined, which provides a more rigorous test of any theory for the scalar interactions.

For this particular model, T_1 and T_2 are given by[3, 8]—

$$\frac{1}{T_1} - \frac{1}{T_{10}} = N_S J_{d,0}\left[\tfrac{28}{3}j_{d,\omega s \tau_t} + 4 + \tfrac{1}{2}\xi j_{e,\omega s \tau_t}\right] \tag{25}$$

$$\frac{1}{T_2} - \frac{1}{T_{20}} = N_S J_{d,0}\left[\tfrac{26}{3}j_{d,\omega s \tau_t} + \tfrac{14}{3} + \tfrac{1}{4}\xi(1 + j_{e,\omega s \tau_t})\right] \tag{26}$$

where N_S is the number of unpaired electron spins/c.c. of liquid.

One other equation that we shall use later and is relevant to this model is—

$$Dd = \frac{\gamma_I^2 \gamma_S^2 \hbar^2}{50 J_{d,0}} \tag{27}$$

where $D = \tfrac{1}{2}(D_I + D_S)$.

Thus both D and d can be found from experimental results.

2. The sticking model

This is obtained by combining the sticking model for the scalar interaction with that of translational diffusion for the dipolar interaction. However, in order to consider only the translational motion for the dipolar interaction, it is necessary to postulate that the time of sticking, τ_w, is very short compared with τ_t. If this is not so, then there will be an additional contribution to the modulation of the dipolar interaction when $\tau_w \sim \tau_t$ arising from rotation.

In a further model postulated by Hubbard,[3] $\tau_w \ll \tau_t$ and the above equations for ρ apply. Figure 9 shows ρ plotted as a function of $(\omega_S \tau_t)^{\frac{1}{2}}$ for various values of ξ using this model. Again τ_t and ξ are the only variable parameters.

One variation of this model is obtained by relaxing the condition that $\tau_w \ll \tau_t$, but the dipolar interaction is still only assumed to be modulated by translational motion.[9] The shortcomings of this approach have been pointed out above, but can be overcome by using another variation that includes the contribution to the dipolar inter-action during the sticking time. The correlation time for this inter-action is designated τ_R, and it is assumed that $\tau_R = \tau_w$.[10] One of the difficulties in using this model is that there are at least three parameters to consider, and the experimental proof of any basic theory becomes more difficult the greater the number of parameters required.

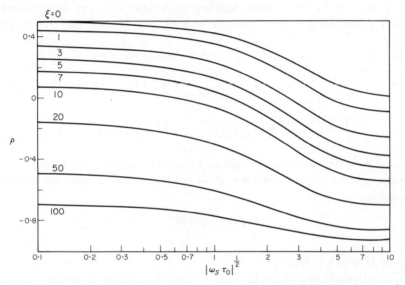

FIG. 9. Mixed scalar and dipolar coupling: sticking models, ρ versus $|\omega_S \tau_t|^{\frac{1}{2}}$ for different ξ values. (From Hubbard.[3])

Further variations of the sticking models have been postulated, and for a comprehensive account the reader is referred to a review by Hausser and Stehlik,[10] in which these are discussed. For example one obvious extension is to allow scalar interaction to occur during the translational phase as well as when the spins I and S are stuck together. However, this introduces yet more parameters into the theory.

3. *Pulse model*[7]

This again uses the random translational diffusion model for the dipolar interaction and the pulse model for the scalar interaction.

On this model ρ is given by—

$$\rho = \frac{40[j_{d,\,\omega_S\tau_t} - Kj_{e,\,\omega_S\tau_w}]}{56j_{d,\,\omega_S\tau_t} + 24 + 40Kj_{e,\,\omega_S\tau_w}} \tag{28}$$

where—

$$K = \frac{5d^3\tau_w^2(B/\hbar)^2}{4\pi N_S\tau_p\tau_t} \tag{29}$$

τ_t characterizes the time of a single diffusion step. Since the same process of molecular diffusion governs the fluctuations of both scalar and dipolar coupling $\tau_{t,}\,\tau_p$ and τ_w are assumed to be related, in that all three correlation times have an equal temperature dependence.

In the absence of scalar coupling, the above equation reduces to the form, already noted, for pure dipolar coupling. When scalar coupling is present, the explicit form of $j_{e,\,\omega_S\tau_w}$ must be evaluated for each particular system, and this may limit the use of this model. The advantage is that the scalar interaction function is not the same for all systems and only one phase of motion, i.e., translation, is considered. The diffusion and sticking models mentioned above may be considered to be special cases of this model.

D. Protocol for extracting parameters from the various models

The experimentally measurable quantities are the radical concentration, ρ, T_1 and T_2. The last three can be measured as a function of frequency (magnetic field) and/or temperature.

The procedure generally involves measuring the nuclear–electron coupling parameter, ρ, as a function of $\omega_S\tau_t$. This can be done by performing the experiment in different magnetic fields thus altering ω_S, or by altering the temperature (or viscosity), thus changing the translational correlation time τ_t. The results are then fitted to a model. For example, for the diffusion model, this would involve fitting the experimental ρ values measured at different frequencies to a curve similar to those shown in Figs. 8 and 9, thus allowing ξ and τ_t to be calculated. Further verification of the fit can often be obtained by measuring ρ at different temperatures.

Most of the models involve many more adjustable parameters than in the case of the relatively simple sticking and diffusion models. For example, in the case of the pulse model it may be necessary to assume that the scalar interaction is described by a combination of the pulses shown in Fig. 7. Thus finding a unique fit to the experimental results is tedious and requires the use of a computer.

A similar treatment of the relaxation-time data is also possible and full details can be found in the literature.[8, 15]

IV. QUANTITATIVE TEST OF THEORIES

A. Protons

Most work on protons has been concerned with solutions of organic liquids containing dissolved organic free radicals (the commonest of which are shown in Table I). The measurement of the Overhauser

TABLE I

Some commonly used free radicals

Name	Formula
Tri-t-butyl-phenoxyl, TTBP	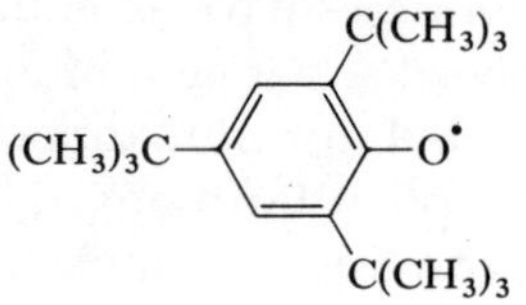
Galvinoxyl (Coppinger's Radical)	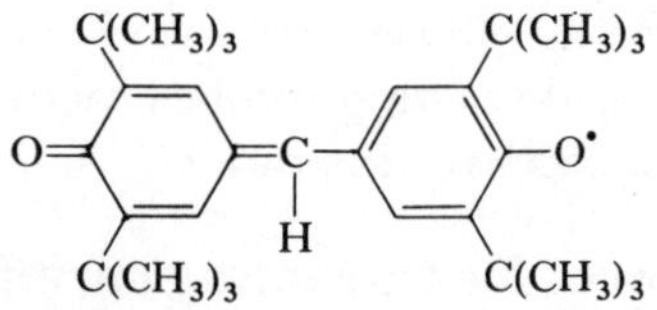
Diphenyl picryl hydrazyl DPPH	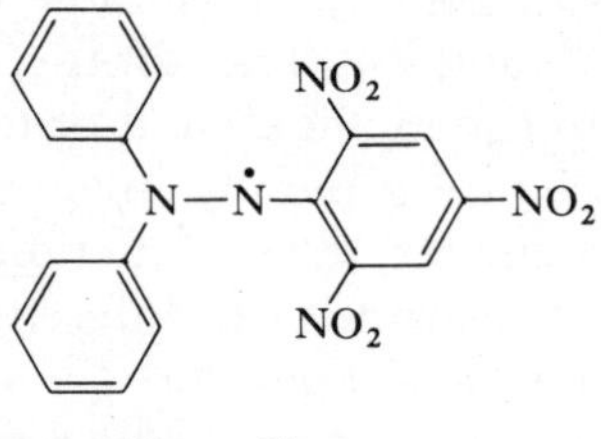
Tetrachloro-semiquinone TCSQ	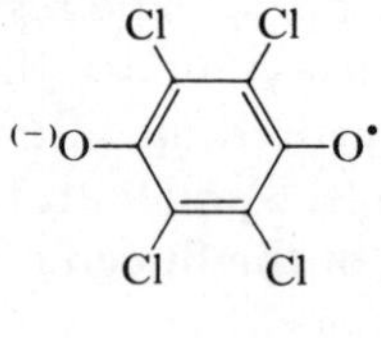
Wursters Blue	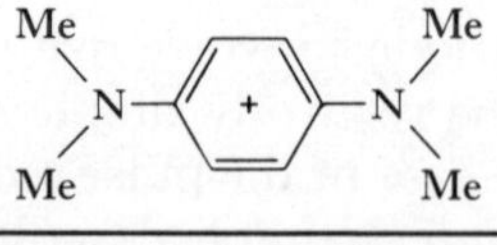

The ideal free radical should be soluble and stable, and also possess an e.s.r. signal that is easy to saturate, i.e., narrow line and long T_{IS}.

Other radicals used have been the anion radicals formed by alkali metal reduction of polycyclic aromatics.[14, 15]

For a more complete list, see reference 23.

effect in magnetic fields ranging from 15 to 12,500 gauss and over almost the complete range of the liquid states has indicated that the results can be described in terms of a dipolar interaction between the radical and the protons modulated by the random relative translational motion of the molecules.[11-14] The absence of the need to consider a rotational motion to describe the results indicates that the lifetimes of the solvent molecules in any solvation sphere is extremely short compared to the correlation time for translational motion, which is of the order of 10^{-11} sec. [One exception however is for solutions of BPA (1,3-bisdiphenylenephenylallyl) in toluene at low temperatures ($< -50°C$) where it was found[15] necessary to include the effect of rotation of a very weak radical solvent complex to describe completely the experimental data.] A study of the temperature dependence of the translational correlation times, obtained by these experiments, allows calculation of the activation energies for the translational motion processes in these systems and the results for several systems are shown in Table II. It is interesting that data on the temperature dependence

TABLE II

Activation energies (kcal./mole.)

Solvent	From n.m.r. correlation times	From plots of $\ln(\eta/T)$ versus $1/T$
Dimethoxyethane	2·8	2·6
Diethoxymethane	2·1	2·2
Dimethoxymethane	1·6	1·9
Benzene	2·9	3·2

of the viscosity, where available, and very similar to those of the translational correlation time, which is as expected if both processes depend on the translational motion of the molecules (Table II).

B. Mixed scalar and dipolar interactions

Although scalar interactions have been observed with several different nuclei (see below) quantitative measurements have mainly been confined to molecules containing ^{19}F nuclei. The sign and magnitude of the observed enhancements has been shown to vary with (a) magnetic-field strength, (b) temperature and viscosity and (c) the radical used. It is convenient to discuss each of these separately.

1. *Field dependence of mixed interactions*

Ideally, measurements should be made at as many magnetic field strengths as possible, so that a unique fit of the experimental data to a particular model, may be obtained. As already mentioned, in addition to measuring the ρ values, measurement of relaxation times will help to substantiate the model chosen.

Although fluorine chemical shifts are approximately an order of magnitude greater than proton chemical shifts, they may still not be sufficiently large to distinguish between chemically shifted fluorine nuclei at very low fields. Accordingly, much of the quantitative work has been confined to C_6F_6 and molecules containing only one type of fluorine nuclei.

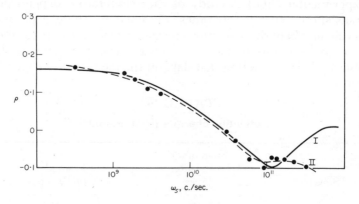

FIG. 10. Plot of ρ versus ω_S for C_6F_6/TTBP: I, generalized sticking model[10]; II, pulse model.[16]

Figure 10 shows the variation of ρ for solutions of 2-4-6-tri-t-butyl-phenoxyl in C_6F_6 with ω_S; the scalar interaction is assumed to be represented in I by a generalized sticking model[10] and II by the pulse model.[16] In fitting the data to the generalized sticking model it has been assumed that there is no scalar interaction during the translational phase of motion and that the correlation times for scalar and dipolar interaction during the sticking time are equal. For the pulse model, the scalar interaction is assumed to be adequately described by a composite pulse (see Fig. 17a, p. 327). The parameters obtained from these models are given in Table III. Although these two models yield the best agreement with experiment, it should be pointed out that they represent the two extremes of thought. On the one hand, there is a scalar interaction during the time of sticking, which is assumed to be finite, while the other case assumes that the scalar interaction varies continuously with the relative translational motion of the molecules and no sticking is assumed.

The fact that a fit to the experimental results can be obtained is hardly surprising when one considers the large number of possible variable parameters that can be used. Despite this, the distances of closest approach and the correlation times for translational motion, calculated for each model, seem very reasonable in comparison with the parameters calculated for benzene.[17]

TABLE III
Parameters for C_6F_6/TTBP

Model	Translational correlation time, τ_t	Scalar correlation time	Ref.
Modified sticking model	$0 \cdot 9 \times 10^{-11}$	$0 \cdot 7 \, \tau_t$	9
Pulse model	$2 \cdot 4 \times 10^{-11}$	$\tau_t / 0 \cdot 95$	16

Note: These correlation times are defined by $\tau_t = d^2/6D$; cf. Dwek et al.,[11] who use $\tau_t = d^2/D$ where $D = \frac{1}{2}(D_I + D_S)$.

Systems containing both proton and fluorine nuclei provide a good test of theory. If the proton data are interpreted in terms of pure dipolar coupling, then a diffusion coefficient can be calculated for the protons. This may be then compared with that obtained from the fluorine data, when scalar interaction is present. As both nuclei are on the same molecule the results should be identical. Unfortunately, diffusion coefficients have only been calculated on a few occasions, but this is a point to be borne in mind for future testing of theories.[11,17]

2. Temperature and viscosity dependence of mixed interactions

The experimental results for solutions of the radical TTBP in benzene can be interpreted in terms of pure dipolar coupling modulated by translational diffusion of the molecules. If however, the viscosity of the solution is changed the measured ρ values are different from those quoted. At 3300 gauss the fluorine resonance spectra of methyl penta-fluorobenzene consists of a low field peak, arising from the ortho-fluorines and an unresolved high-field multiplet. If a solution of the radical TTBP in this solvent is allowed to warm in the microwave cavity, then the initial enhancement of the low-field peak, which is positive, becomes negative. On applying cooling air to the sample, the enhancement becomes, once again, positive. This is illustrated in

Fig. 11. Similarly the qualitative effects of altering viscosity are shown in Fig. 12 where the enhancements for C_6F_6/TTBP solutions with CS_2 added to decrease the viscosity are compared with that for neat C_6F_6/TTBP. The above experiments have been interpreted in terms of changes in the translational correlation time, τ_t.[11, 18, 19]

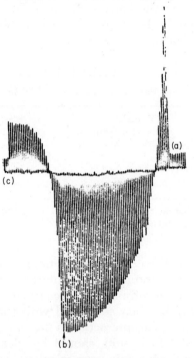

FIG. 11. The behaviour of the *ortho*-fluorine enhancement of methyl penta-fluorotoluene: (a), microwave power applied; (b), cooling air applied; (c), microwave irradiation removed. (From Dwek et al.[11])

Since from equation (22) $\tau_t \propto 1/D$, changes in temperature, by altering the diffusion coefficient D, will affect τ_t proportionally. Further, if it is assumed that the Stokes–Einstein relationship is valid in these systems, then D is proportional to the viscosity, η. Thus η is also proportional to τ_t, so that changes in τ_t may be accomplished by either of these methods.

In order to interpret the temperature-dependent experiments it is necessary to assume an activation energy for the diffusion process. Assigning a value of 3·5 kcal./mole (which is reasonable in comparison with other measured activation energies for diffusion processes[20, 21]), then the correlation time dependence of the ρ values obtained by the

FIG. 12. Unenhanced (*i*) and enhanced (*ii*) ^{19}F resonance signal of (a) C_6F_6 and (b) C_6F_6/CS_2 (50% v/v).

two methods are similar; this is illustrated in Fig. 13. For the system $C_6F_6/TTBP$ at 3300 gauss, the viscosity was altered either by addition of Cereclor S45, a 45% chlorinated C_{14}–C_{19} hydrocarbon, which increased it, or by CS_2, which decreased it.

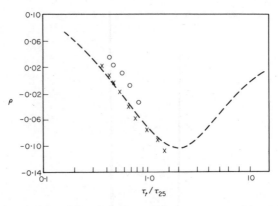

FIG. 13. Comparison of temperature dependence and CS_2 dilution results at 3300 gauss for C_6F_6/TTBP: ×, temperature results $\Delta E = 3.5$ kcal./mole; ○, CS_2 dilution results.

Figure 14 shows the ρ values for the above system obtained at both 3300 and 12,500 gauss upon adding either CS_2 or Cereclor. The results are plotted as a function of $|\tau_t|\tau_{25}$ and it is important to note that there appears to be no serious discontinuity from the assumption that ρ is a function of $\omega_S\tau_t$. Thus since ρ is a function of $\omega_S\tau_t$, changes

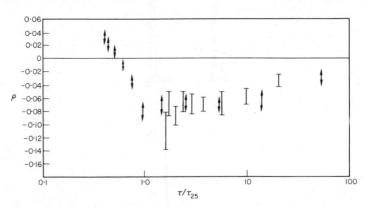

FIG. 14. Plot of enhancement factor ρ versus τ_t/τ_{25} for C_6F_6/TTBP; $\updownarrow$ results at 3300 gauss, $\underline{\mathrm{I}}$ results at 12,500 gauss.

in ω_S and τ_t are equivalent, a point which is useful for obtaining the shape of the ρ versus $\omega_S\tau_t$ curve experimentally.

Quantitative results of temperature and viscosity variation are only available for one other system—CF_3CCl_3/TTBP.[19] However several extensive temperature studies have been carried out by Müller-

Warmuth *et al.*[16] who have measured ρ values and relaxation time data, for several different radicals in fluorocarbon solutions at four different magnetic-field strengths.

It may well be that interpretation of the variable temperature (and viscosity) experiments is more complex than has been assumed. For example, many of the models for the scalar interaction have several parameters, apart from τ_t and there may be cases where it is unjustified to assume that these are unaffected by temperature, as has been done in the past. It is, of course, possible that there may even be a change in the model for the scalar interaction with alteration in temperature! Unlikely though this seems, it does indicate that further quantitative conclusions require far more experimental data than are at present available.

3. *Radical dependence*

When different radicals are employed, there may be a variation in the radical–nucleus interaction due to alteration of the correlation times and changes in the type of interaction.

To illustrate the effects of altering the correlation time only, consider the case of organic free radicals dissolved in benzene, i.e., the case of dipolar interaction modulated by the relative translational diffusion of the radical electron and the hydrogen nucleus. In this case the effect of different radicals is assumed to arise solely from changes in the translational correlation time, τ_t (equation 22). In Table IV are shown the results for series of radicals in benzene solution.[22]

For fluorine nuclei both the correlation time and the type of nuclear–electron interaction will alter with the radical used. To disentangle both these effects it is necessary to study their behaviour over a wide frequency range. This has been done for C_6F_6 and $C_6H_5CF_3$ with the radicals TTBP and Galvinoxyl.[16] The most complete sequence of radicals however has been studied only at low field.[23] In the low-field limit, where $\omega_S\tau_t \ll 1$, the spectral densities $j_{\omega_S} \to 1$ and equation (23) then reduces to the form—

$$\rho = \frac{40-3\xi}{80+3\xi} \tag{30}$$

Thus low-field data can readily give an estimate of the relative proportion of scalar and dipolar coupling for the nucleus–electron interaction. The main drawbacks for making low-field measurements are the poor sensitivity of the n.m.r. experiment, with resulting difficulties in

TABLE IV

Parameters derived for different radicals in benzene solutions

Radical	Translational correlation time, $\tau_t \times 10^{11}$ sec.	dÅ	$\frac{1}{2}(D_I + D_S) \times 10^6$, cm^2/sec.
TTBP	10	3·6	13·0
Galvinoxyl	23	5·7	14·0
Perchlorodiphenylmethyl (PDM)†	24	5·3	12·0
1,3-Bisdiphenylene-2,p-isopropyl-allyl (BDIPA)‡	25	4·5	8·0

†PDM =

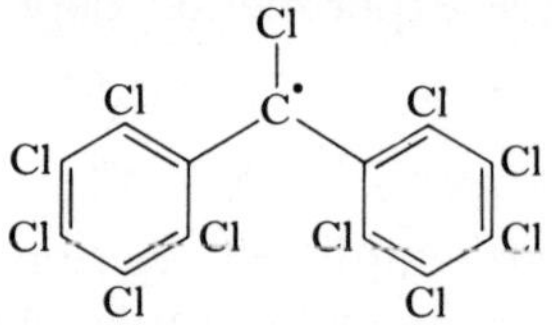

‡BDIPA =

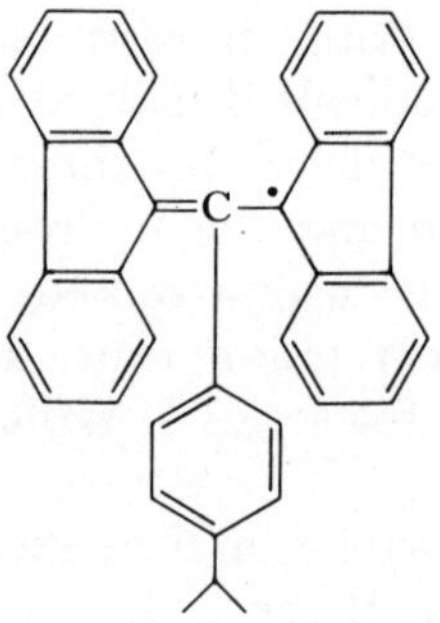

From Cannon.[22]

observing the unenhanced signals (I_0), and also the difficulty in re-
solving chemically shifted nuclei. However, by using molecules with
one type of fluorine present, information can be obtained about the
dependence of the nucleus–electron interaction both on the radical
used and on the chemical environment of the nucleus observed. Thus
the relative amounts of scalar and dipolar coupling for fluorine nuclei
in C_6F_6 and CF_3CCl_3, for a series of organic free radicals, have been
found by experiments performed at 74 gauss.[23] The radicals were
found to form a series that was the same for both the aromatic and
aliphatic fluorine nuclei and which paralleled the extent to which the
unpaired electron density on the free radicals used in the experiments,
is in an exposed position. Table V shows a series of radicals arranged
in order of increasing positive enhancements, i.e., scalar contribution.

TABLE V

**Some free radicals arranged in order of increasing scalar coupling as
determined by ^{19}F Overhauser experiments at 74 gauss**

Radical	Position	Normalized hyperfine splitting, gauss
Galvinoxyl	H_1 central	5·92
	H_4 ring	1·37
	H_{36} butyl	0·05
TTBP	H_2 ring	1·67
	H_9 4-butyl	0·36
	H_{18} 2,6-butyl	0·07
DPPH	N_2	200
WBPC	N_2	97
	H_4 ring	1·97
	H_{12} methyl	6·76

From Poindexter et al.[23]

Figure 15 shows the extrapolated fluorine enhancement for the case
of different fluorobenzenes as a function of the degree of fluorine substitution, for two different radicals DPPH and Galvinoxyl.[24] The
behaviour for the two radicals is markedly different and indicates that
when scalar coupling is present, care must be taken in generalizing
conclusions obtained from measurements with only one radical.

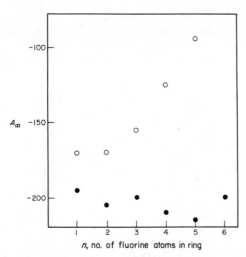

FIG. 15. Extrapolated fluorine enhancement for different fluorobenzenes
$C_6F_nH_{6-n}$: ●, Galvinoxyl; ○, DPPH. (From Stewart et al.[24])

4. Conclusions

The results for ^1H and ^{19}F nuclei show that dipolar coupling can be readily interpreted in terms for a simple model involving translational diffusion. On the other hand, scalar coupling cannot be explained in terms of any one simple model. This is due, in part, to the fact that the dipolar coupling may be treated as a long-range interaction whereas the scalar coupling, which arises from orbital overlap, is a short-range interaction that is extremely sensitive to the local electronic environment both of the molecule containing the nucleus and the radical electron.

V. DEPENDENCE OF THE ENHANCEMENT ON CHEMICAL ENVIRONMENT

To determine the dependence of the radical–nucleus interaction on chemical environment of the nucleus, two types of experiment have been performed. In the low-field experiments, where it is possible to neglect the changes in translational correlation time for different samples, fluorine nuclei in different chemical environments were examined on different molecules. In the high-field experiments (3300 and 12,500 gauss) changes in translational correlation time are important, but their effect can be minimized by comparing different chemically shifted fluorines within the same molecule.

Table VI shows the ^{19}F n.m.r. enhancements for some disubstituted

TABLE VI

^{19}F **Enhancements for disubstituted benzenes/DPPH, measured at 74 gauss**

Compound	A_∞
$o\text{-}C_6H_4F_2$	-170
$m\text{-}C_6H_4F_2$	-160
$p\text{-}C_6H_4F_2$	-180
$o\text{-}C_6H_4FCl$	-180
$m\text{-}C_6H_4FCl$	-145
$p\text{-}C_6H_4FCl$	-150
$o\text{-}C_6H_4FBr$	-180
$m\text{-}C_6H_4FBr$	-140
$p\text{-}C_6H_4FBr$	-150
$o\text{-}C_6H_4FI$	-185
$m\text{-}C_6H_4FI$	-130
$p\text{-}C_6H_4FI$	-130
$o\text{-}C_6H_4F(NO_2)$	-170
$m\text{-}C_6H_4F(NO_2)$	-125
$p\text{-}C_6H_4F(NO_2)$	-130

benzenes with DPPH as radical.[24] The main feature is that fluorine nuclei *ortho* to the substituent are more negatively enhanced, i.e., they show less scalar coupling, which suggests that steric requirements in collisions between the radical and solvent are important.

Experiments at high fields[25] on a series of substituted pentafluorobenzenes with TTBP indicate that, in all cases, the fluorine nuclei *ortho* to the substituent are less positively enhanced even when the substituent is hydrogen. Thus, unlike the low-field results, steric factors alone cannot explain the high-field data. Table VII shows that

TABLE VII

Relative ^{19}F enhancements measured at 12,500 gauss (Q band)

Compound substituent		Position		
	o	*p*	*m*	—CF$_3$
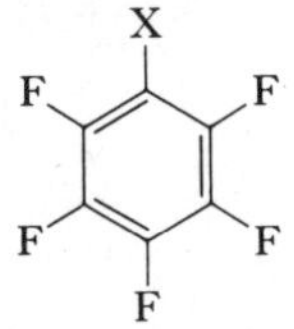 X (pentafluorobenzene) H	1·0	1·31	1·13	..
Cl	1·0	1·26	1·20	..
Br	1·0	1·34	1·16	..
—CH=CH$_2$	1·0	1·58	1·43	..
CF$_3$	1·0	2·70	2·61	0·38
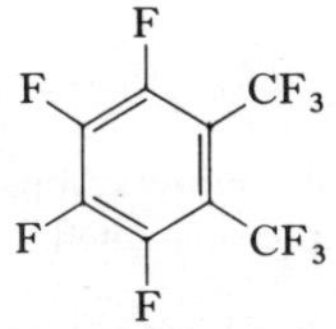 bis-CF$_3$ heptafluorotoluene	1·0	..	2·48	0·52
octafluoronaphthalene	α 1·0	β 4·73		

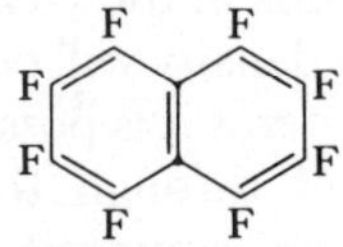

when the fluorine nucleus has two *ortho* fluorine substituents there is substantially more scalar coupling than otherwise. This behaviour parallels the anomalous high-field chemical shifts observed for aromatic fluorines with two *ortho* fluorine neighbours and in both cases may be due to fluorine–fluorine interactions.

VI. MECHANISMS FOR SCALAR INTERACTIONS

So far nothing has been said as to why the presence of a free radical in solution can produce some unpaired electron density at nuclei on other molecules. In principle, there would appear to be at least two mechanisms by which this can occur. It is possible that, when the radical approaches a molecule, a transient bond is formed whereby some unpaired spin density is transferred from the radical to the molecule. If this unpaired electron density which occurs is transferred to an s orbital then, because of the fact that the s orbital has a non-vanishing value at the nucleus there will be a finite electron density at the nucleus and scalar coupling can occur.

A further possible mechanism is provided by the overlap of the charge clouds for the unpaired electron on the radical with the charge clouds for the filled orbitals of the molecule. The operation of the Pauli exclusion principle tends to keep electrons of parallel spin apart, and there will be a contraction of the orbitals containing electrons with spins parallel to the unpaired spin of the radical and a corresponding expansion of the orbital containing the antiparallel spin (Fig. 16).

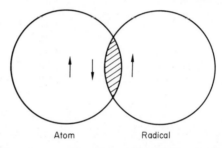

Atom   Radical

FIG. 16. Schematic representation of how the Pauli principle induces unpairing of electron spins. The shaded overlap region is where the principle is violated.

This will lead to a slight unpairing of the electron spins in the vicinity of the nucleus and in the case of s orbitals a finite spin density will occur at the nucleus in question. In the case of π bonded systems it is possible that unpaired electron density may be transmitted through the π system to an s orbital at the nucleus. For example, in the quantitative measurements by Müller-Warmuth et al. on molecules containing fluorine nuclei it was found that the shape of the pulse describing the scalar interaction for aliphatic—CF_3 groups was different from that for benzenoid fluorine nuclei.[16] In the case of —CF_3 groups the pulse describing the interaction is of the shape shown in Fig. 17(a) and may reflect the fact that the radical can only directly interact with the fluorine, whereas for the aromatic fluorine the overall pulse is a super-position of two pulses, one sharp and the other broad (Fig. 17(b)), which may indicate that the radical can interact with the fluorine nucleus either directly or via the π system to which the fluorine is conjugated.

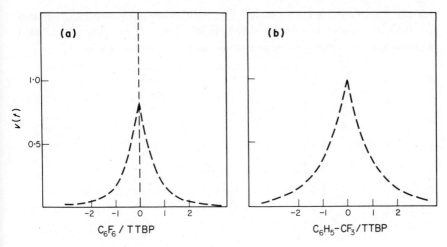

FIG. 17. Pulse shapes used to describe scalar interactions for fluorine nuclei: (a), C_6F_6/TTBP; (b) C_6H_5–CF_3/TTBP. (From Müller-Warmuth et al.[16])

VII. SCALAR SHIFTS

Perhaps the most convincing proof of scalar interaction is afforded by the observation of contact shifts.[17] These arise from the Boltzmann distribution of electron spins in the magnetic field, which tend to align with a small excess of spins antiparallel to the field, resulting in a net magnetic field at a nucleus I. Using the Curie Law,[2] this shift is given by—

$$\frac{\Delta\omega_I}{\omega_I} = -B_{ij}N_S\hbar \frac{\gamma_S}{\gamma_I} \frac{S(S+1)}{3kT} \tag{31}$$

where ω_I is the frequency at which the contact (or scalar) shift is observed, B_{ij} is the coupling constant between the ith nucleus and jth spin and N_S is the number of unpaired electron spins. In order to evaluate $\Delta\omega_I/\omega_I$ and compare this value with the experimental one, B_{ij} must be known. The calculation of B_{ij} depends on the model chosen for the time dependence of the scalar interaction.

The shifts were observed for the fluorine resonances in several solutions of the radical TTBP in hexafluorobenzene, and were measured relative to tetramethylsilane as an internal standard. The experiments were performed in a constant magnetic field of 12,500 gauss by changing from proton to fluorine resonances and vice versa, several times for each solution to eliminate errors in the shifts arising from drifts in the magnetic field. The results are shown in Fig. 18, and the fluorine resonance shifts down field. Thus B_{ij} is positive,[17] and corresponds to a positive spin density at the fluorine nuclei.

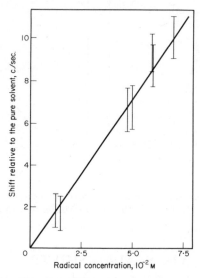

FIG. 18. Plot of the shift of the ^{19}F resonance of solutions of tri-t-butyl phenoxyl radical in C_6F_6 against radical concentration. The shift is towards low-field, and resonance frequency of ^{19}F is 49·8 Mc./sec. (From Dwek et al.[17])

If this shift were caused by scalar interaction of the ^{19}F nuclei with the radical, the shift would collapse when the electron resonance is saturated (i.e., the electron populations are equalized). Figure 19 shows the effect of applying the microwave power to a 10^{-2} M solution of the radical and indeed this is found to be so. Despite the variety of the models, most of them give reasonable calculated values for the shift which are in good agreement with experiment.

VIII. THE THREE-SPIN EFFECT

Originally the three-spin effect was postulated to explain the positive enhancements observed for certain fluorine nuclei in solvents also containing protons.[26] The possibility arose that the fluorine nuclei were being influenced by the proton polarization as well as by the direct coupling to the electron spins. The basic idea behind the three-spin effect can be seen by considering the transitions among the Zeeman energy levels shown in Fig. 20. Since the electron–proton interaction is of the dipolar kind, the predominant coupled transition will be an

FIG. 19. C_6F_6/TTBP solution. Effect of irradiating e.s.r. signal: (a), enhanced low field peak; (b), unenhanced high field peak ($\times 10$).

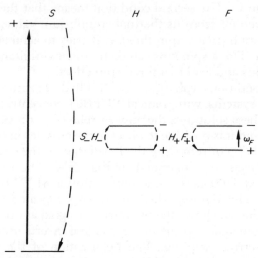

FIG. 20. Zeeman energy levels for electron open S, proton H and fluorine F. The dominant relaxation mechanisms are S_-H_- and H_+F_+.

S_-H_- one, leading to the usual inversion of the proton signal. If the dipolar coupling between the proton and fluorine spins is an appreciable relaxation process for the fluorine nuclei, then when the proton performs an H_+ transition in relaxing towards the thermal equilibrium distribution, there will be a probability that the fluorine spin will perform a simultaneous F_+ transition due to the term H_+F_+ in the fluorine–proton dipolar interaction Hamiltonian. Thus in addition to any fluorine enhancement due to the direct fluorine electron interaction, there will be an additional positive enhancement due to the indirect three-spin interaction.

In order to describe this situation it is possible to consider, in a manner analogous to that for a two-spin system, the set of coupled differential equations describing the rate of change of the populations of the spin Zeeman levels, and full details can be found in Natusch et al.[27] It is possible to show that, for two nuclear spins A and B in the presence of an electron spin C, the conditions for a three-spin effect to occur for the nuclear spin A are that an appreciable fraction of the relaxation of the A spin should be by interaction with nuclear spin B, and that the nuclear spins B should be strongly polarized by interaction with the electron spin C. Since the magnetic moment for an electron spin is about 3 orders of magnitude greater than that of a nuclear spin, the first condition implies that the three-spin effect will only be noticeable in dilute radical solution; otherwise the polarization of spin A would be dominated completely by direct interaction with the electron spin C. The second condition means that the B spin population be driven far from its thermal equilibrium value, thus leading to rapid relaxation (many spin flips) as it tries to achieve its Boltzmann distribution. These spin flips can then induce simultaneous transitions of the A spins and lead to a three-spin effect.

These conditions can often be fulfilled for proton and fluorine containing systems with radical (TTBP) concentrations of 10^{-3} M or less. In these solutions, the nuclear relaxation times are of the order of seconds and it is possible to observe the changes in nuclear polarization on applying or removing the irradiation of the e.s.r. signal. These transient effects are illustrated in Fig. 21A. The experiments were carried out at 3300 gauss on a dilute solution of TTBP in p-difluorobenzene.[27] The Figure, which represents repeated traversals of the ^{19}F n.m.r. signal, shows the unenhanced signal at (a). At (b) the e.s.r. signal is irradiated, and the fluorine signal inverts owing to the direct fluorine–electron coupling. The polarization of the protons, whose relaxation time is considerably longer than that of the fluorine spins, builds up more slowly and then causes the fluorine signal to become less negative till a compromise equilibrium value of the fluorine polarization is reached at (d). When the microwave irradiation is switched off at (e), the fluorine polarization quickly decays and is then driven positive at (f), by interaction with the protons, which, owing to

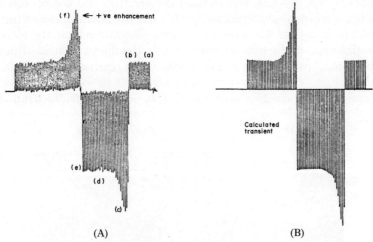

(A)   (B)

FIG. 21. Transient F magnetization in p-$C_6H_4F_2$: A, experiment; B, theory. Time runs from left to right. At (b), microwave radiation is turned on; at (c), it is turned off. (From Natusch *et al.*[27])

their long relaxation time, are still quite strongly polarized, until it finally returns to its original thermal equilibrium value as the proton polarization decays. Figure 22A shows a similar spectrum for *m*-fluorotoluene. In this case the indirect three-spin effect is sufficient to overcome the direct fluorine–electron interaction and a positive enhancement results. The calculated spectra are shown in Figs. 21B and

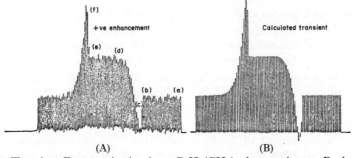

(A)   (B)

FIG. 22. Transient F magnetization in m-$C_6H_4(CH_3)$: A, experiment; B, theory. Time runs from right to left. At (b), microwave radiation is turned on; at (c), it is turned off. (From Natusch *et al.*[27])

22B, and an analysis of these transient effects allows a calculation of the relaxation rate for the fluorine nuclei due to interaction with the protons in solution.

The presence of a three-spin effect can also be revealed by triple irradiation experiments, where both the electron and the proton spin transitions are strongly irradiated. This has the effect of removing the indirect pathway for the transfer of spin polarization from the electron to the fluorine via the proton, leaving only the direct electron–fluorine mechanism. Any additional proton–fluorine Overhauser effect due to the saturation of the proton signal is negligible in solution containing free radicals. Figure 23 shows the results of such a triple-irradiation

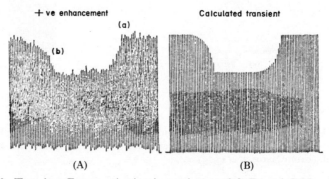

FIG. 23. Transient F magnetization in a mixture of C_6F_6 and C_6H_6 with triple irradiation: A, experiment; B, theory. Time runs from right to left. At (a), proton irradiation is switched on; at (b), it is switched off.

experiment applied to a C_6H_6/C_6F_6 solution containing 10^{-3} M TTBP. The microwave irradiation is being applied continuously. At (a) the proton signal is irradiated and with the removal of the additional positive enhancement, due to the three-spin effect, the fluorine enhancement decreases to the value which arises solely from the direct fluorine–electron spin interaction. At (b) the proton irradiation is removed and the enhanced fluorine signal regains its original value due to both the direct and indirect mechanisms.

It is possible that a signal which is negatively enhanced at high radical concentration may even become positively enhanced at low radical concentration if the three-spin effect outweighs the direct polarization mechanism. One example of this occurring is shown in the ^{13}C spectrum of trichloroethylene.[22] With concentrated TTBP ($\sim 10^{-1}$ M) both the $=CCl_2$ and the $=CHCl$ doublet are negatively enhanced, whereas in dilute TTBP solution, the $=CCl_2$ peak is still negative but the $=CHCl$ doublet is now positive. This is presumably due to the fact that, for carbon directly bonded to hydrogen, the intra-molecular dipole–dipole interaction between the carbon and hydrogen spins is a more efficient relaxation mechanism for the carbon spin than an intermolecular dipolar interaction.

In conclusion, although it has been demonstrated that a three-spin effect exists, it is usually unimportant unless the radical concentration is low. This is readily understandable, since the magnetic moment of the electron is much larger than that of any nucleus so that nuclear–electron interactions are the dominant relaxation terms, except at low concentrations where nuclear–nuclear interactions become im-portant. The presence of a three-spin effect can be revealed most easily either by observation of the transient relaxation behaviour of the nuclear resonance or by triple irradiation experiments. In the latter case, account must be taken of the collapse of any multiplet structure in the interpretation of the results.

IX. SCALAR INTERACTIONS WITH PROTONS

In the earlier Sections we indicated that most measurements of the proton electron Overhauser effect that have been reported may be interpreted in terms of dipolar interactions between the proton and the free-radical electrons; the proton polarization is inverted. On the other hand, the results with ^{19}F nuclei show that there exists a dominant scalar interaction that often results in positive enhancement.

In some special cases, positive proton enhancements have been observed, indicating the presence of a scalar interaction. One of the first systems examined was aqueous solutions of manganese ions.[5] Although a water molecule is in the hydration sphere of the manganese ion, it experiences a scalar interaction with the unpaired manganese electrons. This interaction can be modulated by one of two processes depending on the temperature; either by the rapid relaxation (i.e., flipping) of the electron spins (scalar coupling of the second kind) or by the chemical exchange of the water molecules in the hydration sphere (scalar coupling of the first kind).

A somewhat more unusual case is the positive proton enhancements observed for the t-butyl groups of 2,4,6-tri-t-butylphenol in solutions containing the corresponding phenoxyl radical.[28] In these solutions there is a proton exchange reaction—

In the radical, the protons are subjected to a strong scalar interaction with the electron,[29] and if this interaction is suitably modulated, a positive polarization of these protons will be produced. When the phenoxyl radical accepts a proton and reverts to the original diamagnetic phenol, the positive polarization is transferred, but starts to decay to the negative value expected for dipolar coupling, with the relaxation times of the protons in the diamagnetic molecule. The question then arises as to how the scalar coupling between the unpaired electron and a proton on the radical is modulated. To be an efficient relaxation mechanism and thus to produce sizeable polarization, the dependence of any interaction should be of the order of the electron Larmor frequency. The mechanisms of radical–precursor proton exchange and radical–radical electron exchange were ruled out[28] because they were too slow and because the aromatic protons of the phenol were observed to be negatively enhanced in the normal manner. It has been suggested[28] that in the radical molecule, the scalar coupling to the t-butyl protons occurs at least in part by a hyperconjugative mechanism. This is angular dependent and therefore the coupling is modulated by random rotation of the t-butyl groups. However this mechanism is clearly inapplicable to the aromatic protons. Additional support to this mechanism comes from the positive ^{13}C enhancements observed with t-butyl carbon atoms.[30]

This interpretation has however been questioned by Stehlick and Hausser[31] who have observed the polarization of protons in free radicals by using n.m.r. pulse techniques. They have obtained results for the t-butyl protons in the radicals TTBP, CR and DBNO. Measurement of the ratio of the relaxation times T_1/T_2 and of the magnitude of the polarization, indicates the presence of scalar interaction with the unpaired electrons. In the concentrated radical solutions examined, it was assumed that the radical–radical electron exchange was sufficiently rapid to modulate the scalar interaction. At lower radical concentrations, the dipolar interactions seemed to become dominant in the radicals. At the lower concentrations used by Dwek et al.,[28] the scalar interaction would also be expected to be small, but for their experiments with the radical precursor, this is not the case, and there appears to be a discrepancy which remains unresolved.

Other examples of positive enhancements that have not as yet been extensively studied are the solutions of alkali metals in liquid ammonia or hexamethyl phosphoramide.[32] In these solutions at low metal concentration, it has been found that the metal is completely dissociated into $M^{\oplus}$ and "free electrons". These electrons reside in cavities formed by solvent molecules, and their wave functions extend over their nearest-neighbour solvent molecules, thus leading to a scalar interaction, that can be modulated by electron relaxation or chemical exchange.

X. PHOSPHORUS-31

Most dynamic nuclear polarization experiments performed on ^{31}P systems have been qualitative rather than quantitative.[33, 34] Nevertheless, certain trends have emerged, which prove useful in drawing qualitative conclusions about the nature of the radical–^{31}P interactions in these systems.

Extensive studies have only been carried out at 3300 and 12,500 gauss. Table VIII lists a series of the compounds studied together with the sign of the enhancement observed. At both magnetic fields, the enhancements of all phosphorus resonances in compounds in which the phosphorus is in an oxidation state of three are positive. Since positive

TABLE VIII

Signal enhancement of ^{31}P resonance signals of some phosphorus compounds

	Sign of enhancement at		Oxidation state
Compound	3300 gauss	12,500 gauss	
$(MeO)_3P$	+	+50	III
$(EtO)_3P$	+	+30	III
$(PhO)_3P$	+	+15	III
$(MeO)_3PO$	−	0	V
$(EtO)_3PO$	−	0	V
$(PhO)_3PO$	−	0	V
Ph_3P	+	+20	III
Ph_3PO	−	Not observed	V
Ph_2PCl	+	+15	III
$PhPCl_2$	+	+10	III
$Ph_2P(O)Cl$	±	+1	V
$PhP(O)Cl_2$	+	+1	V
$(EtO)_2P(O)H$	+	+5	V
$(MeO)_2P(O)H$	+	Not studied	V
$(EtO)_2P(O)Cl$	−	+3	V
$(EtO)_2PCl$	+	+1	III
$(EtO)_3PS$	−	+3	V
$(C_4H_9—O—CH_2 \cdot CH_2O)_3PO$	−	0	V
$(Me_3C—C_6H_4O)_3PO$	−	0	V
$(Me_2N)_3PO$	−	0	V

From Atkins *et al.*[34]

enhancements with ^{19}F are indicative of the presence of scalar interactions between the radical electron and the ^{19}F nuclei, the results for
$^{31}P^{III}$ systems have been similarly interpreted.[35] The mechanism that
has been suggested is one of direct contact between the ^{31}P nuclei and
the radical electron. Since ^{31}P nuclei in oxidation state three have a
lone pair of electrons associated with them, which contains largely $3s$
wave function characteristics, a direct mechanism for introducing
some unpaired electron density at the nucleus is thus available from
polarization of these lone pair electrons by the radical electrons.

In contrast to the above behaviour, the enhancements of phosphorus
resonances in P^V compounds are generally negative at 3300 gauss and
zero at 12,500 gauss. Preliminary results have also confirmed this
trend at 74 gauss.[35] This has been interpreted as being due to the
smaller scalar interaction obtained as a consequence of the non-
availability of the lone pair of electrons which are now used in bond
formation. However, when one of the substituents is a hydrogen atom,
there appears to be an increased scalar interaction. This may be because
the radical can then penetrate much closer to the phosphorus and
interact directly with it.

Similarly positive enhancements are observed in compounds of the
type $P^V{=}S$ and P^V—Cl. Both sulphur and chlorine are much larger
than hydrogen, and so the radical cannot approach as close to the P^V
nucleus. Therefore an indirect mechanism via the sulphur or chlorine
atom has been postulated. Two suggestions have been made: (1)
formation of a transient bond between the P=S or P—Cl molecule
and the radical molecule; or (2) direct polarization of the orbitals. Both
these mechanisms will involve mixing in higher orbital energy states.
Although Cl and S have low-lying energy levels available, N and O
do not, and thus more scalar coupling is possible with Cl or S as the
substituents.

^{31}P studies have also been carried out on compounds based on the
P_4 unit,[36] and Table IX shows a list of the compounds studied and
their enhancements. Again the trend shows that when phosphorus is
present as P^{III}, large positive enhancements are obtained. If the
mechanism postulated above is correct, the magnitude of this enhancement can give an indication of the amount of $3s$ wave function character
in the lone pair of electrons. Thus in P_4 and P_4O_6 there would appear
to be a substantial amount of $3s$ wave function in the lone pair—a fact
that has been previously postulated by van Wazer et al.[37] However,
in P_4S_3, there are two chemically shifted phosphorus nuclei which are
differently enhanced. The basal phosphorus nuclei P_β are less enhanced than the apical phosphorus P_α. This would seem to indicate

TABLE IX

Observed ^{31}P enhancements at 12,500 gauss

Compound	Observed enhancement
P_4S_3	$P_\alpha = +60$ $P_\beta = +70$
P_4Se_3	$P_\alpha = +80$ $P_\beta = +80$
P_4O_6	$+60$
P_4 white phosphorus	large $+ve$
P_4S_{10}	$+30$

that there is less $3s$ wave character in the lone pair of the phosphorus nuclei, P_β. On the other hand, with P_4Se_3, no differential enhancements for P_α and P_β are obtained. With P_4S_{10}, a positive enhancement is obtained although the oxidation state of the phosphorus atom is five. Again, this is consistent with mechanism suggested above for scalar interaction with P^V compounds.

Table X shows some preliminary studies of phosphonitrilic ring compounds,[36] where the oxidation state is nominally five. With Cl, or Ph, attached to the phosphorus, the enhancements are positive (at 3300 and 12,500 gauss), whereas with —NMe$_2$ or —OCH$_2$CF$_3$ the enhancements are strongly negative at the lower magnetic field and

TABLE X

^{31}P Enhancement for phosphonitrilic ring compounds

Compound	Observed enhancement	
	X band (3300 gauss)	Q band (12,500 gauss)
$N_3P_3Cl_6$	large $+ve$	$+11$
$N_3P_3Ph_2Cl_4gem$	Ph_2 $+ve$	$+2$
	PCl_2 $+ve$	$+5$
$N_3P_3Ph_4Cl_2gem$	Ph_2 $+ve$	$+0\cdot5$
	PCl_2 $+ve$	$+5$
$N_3P_3(NMe_2)_6$	$-ve$	0
$N_3P_3(OCH_2CF_3)_6$	$-ve$	0

are zero at the higher one. Further studies could well provide information about the bonding around the phosphorus atom in these compounds.

XI. CARBON-13

Preliminary investigations on ^{13}C in natural abundance have, as yet, only been reported in a magnetic field of 3300 gauss.[30] Both negative and positive enhancements have been observed, indicating that scalar interactions between the ^{13}C nucleus and the radical occur. The positive enhancements are observed predominantly in compounds containing sp^3 hybridized carbon atoms bonded to halogen atoms, e.g., $^{13}CCl_4$, $^{13}CHCl_3$ and $^{13}CHBr_3$. As with the ^{31}P results, it has been suggested that the lone pairs of electrons of the halogen atoms participate in the transfer of electron density from the radical to the ^{13}C nucleus. A representative series of enhancements observed for ^{13}C nuclei in solutions containing TTBP is shown in Table XI.

TABLE XI

Variation in ^{13}C enhancements for various halogen methanes

Compound	Enhancement (X band)
CCl_4	
CBr_4	decreasingly
$CHCl_3$	positive
$CHBr_3$	
CH_2Cl_2	
CH_2Br_2	
CH_2I_2	
CH_3Cl	$-ve$

It has been noted[30] that the magnitude of the positive enhancement tends to increase with increasing halogen atom substitution. For example, CH_3Cl shows negative polarization of the carbon nuclei, but $CHCl_3$ shows positive polarization of the carbon nuclei. However it is possible that this effect could arise from an increase in the correlation time of these molecules and is not necessarily indicative of an increase in scalar coupling (see section IV.B.2, Fig. 12). The observation of intramolecular differential ^{13}C enhancements can be used to minimize any correlation time effects in the same way as already discussed for ^{19}F differential enhancements.

A similar series of experiments have been performed on sp^2 hybridized ^{13}C atoms,[22, 38] but all enhancements were found to be negative. However it was found that in $Cl_2C^{(1)}\!\!=\!\!C^{(2)}HCl$, the $C^{(1)}$ is more negatively enhanced that the $C^{(2)}$ doublet, which does not appear to be in accordance with the results of sp^3 hybridized ^{13}C atoms.[30] Since the dipolar correlation time for both the carbon atoms could be expected to be similar, it is argued that the increased scalar interaction with $C^{(2)}$ arises from the ease of approach of the radical (cf. Section X). Thus although the sign of the enhancement with sp^2 hybridized ^{13}C atoms does not immediately indicate the presence of scalar interactions it is possible by differential ^{13}C enhancement experiments to deduce when scalar coupling is present.

Further experiments to investigate the dependence of enhancement with ^{13}C hybridization[22, 38] have shown that for sp, sp^2 and sp^3 carbon in ^{13}C—H bonds, within the same molecule, there is little difference. Perhaps not too much can be concluded from this, since we have already observed that anomalous effects often arise in systems containing ^{13}C and ^{31}P directly bonded to hydrogen.

Attempts to obtain ^{13}C enhancements by the Overhauser effect at magnetic fields greater than 3300 gauss have as yet not been successful. Since the magnitude of the observed enhancement depends on the value of the spectral density function J_{ω_S} (see Section I, Fig. 1) these results suggest that the values of J_{ω_S} in magnetic fields higher than 3300 gauss are too small to cause significant signal enhancement.

XII. APPLICATIONS TO OTHER NUCLEI

Although one of the first double resonance experiments to be performed was on a dispersion of lithium metal,[2] until recently no other experiments have been reported on ^7Li. Although ^7Li possesses a small quadrupole moment, in most cases this does not normally cause very efficient relaxation. Thus in solutions of ^7Li containing free radicals, most of the relaxation of the ^7Li nuclei arises from the pairwise I–S interactions.

Preliminary results for ^7Li salts are shown in Table XII.[39] It is seen that for the neutral radical TTBP the ^7Li enhancement is negative, whereas for the radical anion DBSQ it is positive. Both these radicals have a similar electronic distribution, so the different effects of the radicals may be due to the stronger interaction between the positively charged lithium ion and the negative DBSQ ion in forming a transient ion pair, and thus allowing a transfer of some unpaired electron spin density. Although for WBPC the unpaired electron density resides on the readily approachable methyl groups, the small negative enhancements observed with the lithium can be explained by electrostatic repulsion between both the positively charged ions, thus preventing close approach of the nuclear and electron spins.

TABLE XII

Enhancements obtained at 3300 gauss for various lithium salts with different radicals

Radical	LiCl MeOH	LiOAc MeOH	LiClO$_4$		
			MeOH	Me$_2$CO	EtoAc
Galv.	i.s.	i.s.	i.s.	−	−
TTBP	−	−	−	−	−
DTBQ	+	+	+	..	i.s.
TCSQ	+	+	+	+	i.s.
WBPC	− ?	− ?	0	..	i.s.

i.s. = radical insoluble.

Preliminary studies have also been carried out[39] on solutions of thallium compounds (see Table XIII). In every case studied, the enhancement was positive for both thallus and thallic compounds. However it was found that for thallus compounds the presence of free radical greatly broadened the n.m.r. signal, and that the observed enhancements were much larger than for thallic compounds. A similar explanation to that suggested for phosphorus has been used to explain this behaviour. In the thallus compounds the electron spin density from the free radical can be transmitted to the nucleus via the lone pair of electrons in the $6s$ orbital. In thallic compounds this lone pair is no longer available, and the unpaired electron density is then assumed to be transmitted via an indirect mechanism.

TABLE XIII

Enhancements obtained at 3300 gauss for various thallium salts with different radicals

Radical	TlOAc/MeOH	TlNO$_3$/Ac	Et$_2$TlCl/Py
TTBP	+ 600 v. broad	+ v. large v. broad	+ large
Galv.	+ v. large v. broad	+ v. large v. broad	+ large

v. broad means line width $\sim$ 1 kc./sec.

XIII. CHEMICALLY INDUCED NUCLEAR–ELECTRON OVERHAUSER EXPERIMENTS

In all the experiments mentioned above, the Overhauser effect has been observed by irradiating the e.s.r. signal of the dissolved free radicals. However the essential conditions for production of an Overhauser effect are that the populations of the electron spin Zeeman levels should depart from their thermal equilibrium value and that, as the electron spins relax and attempt to restore the Boltzmann distribution among their levels, they should interact with the nuclear spins present in solution.

When a free radical is produced in a chemical reaction, the orientation of the electron spins with respect to the external magnetic field is random, so that in effect the electron spin states of the newly formed radicals are saturated. Thus if the newly formed radical is sufficiently short-lived, so that any nuclear polarization induced in the radical has not had time to decay before it becomes a diamagnetic molecule, when the n.m.r. signal is observable, an enhanced nuclear signal may be produced. Furthermore the relaxation of the electrons in the newly formed radicals may also induce nuclear spin polarization in other molecules in the solution.

Chemically induced nuclear polarizations have been observed in solutions of reacting organo-metallic substances[40] and in solutions of peroxides and azo compounds undergoing thermal decomposition.[41] Since the chemically induced nuclear polarization depends on the lifetimes of the radicals formed and on the relaxation times of the nuclei, observation of such effects can lead to information about which radicals are formed and their lifetime.

XIV. THE NUCLEAR–NUCLEAR OVERHAUSER EFFECT

If the two mutually relaxing spins are both nuclei, the ratio γ_S/γ_I, where γ_S and γ_I are now the magnetogyric ratios of two nuclear spins, is of the order of unity and therefore very much smaller polarizations are obtainable, so that only fractional changes in the n.m.r. signal intensity may be observed. However several examples of the nuclear Overhauser effect, both intermolecular and intramolecular have been reported. The intramolecular nuclear Overhauser effect is useful in providing conformational and stereochemical information. This arises because the intramolecular dipole–dipole interaction, which is the principal mechanism of relaxation in organic compounds, is of very short range, and varies as the inverse sixth power of the internuclear distance. Thus if intermolecular contributions to the nuclear relaxation processes are minimized by dissolving the compound under study in a magnetically inert solvent (such as carbon disulphide or deutero-benzene) and also by removing all paramagnetic impurities from the solution, the dominant nuclear relaxation process will then be by magnetic dipole–dipole interactions between neighbouring magnetic nuclei within the same molecule. Saturation of the n.m.r. signal from one of the nuclei can lead to intensity changes in the signals of the neighbouring nuclei, the maximum enhancement for dipolar inter-actions being 50% of the integrated signal intensity. Thus in the original example of this effect,[42] the protons H_a and H_b of the half cage acetate shown below are held so close together that the enhance-ments of either proton signal could be observed on irradiation of the other protons.

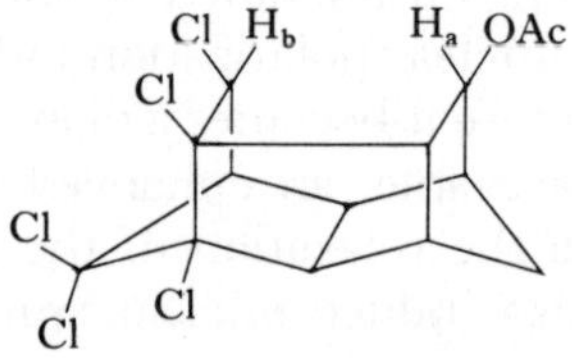

Several other examples have been reported[43,44] in the literature, although in these cases the effect depends on the ordering of the energy levels within the coupled spin systems and is not primarily a relaxation phenomenon.

XV. CONCLUSION

The striking effects observed in the double-resonance experiments, described above, depend on the details of the molecular motion in the system and on the mechanisms of the magnetic interactions between the particles. At the present time, the results can be understood semi-quantitatively in terms of rather simple molecular models, but there is in principle much more detailed information to be obtained.

The increase of the intensity of the nuclear resonance is often quite dramatic and the question arises as to whether the technique has practical application for signal enhancement. Very large enhancements are obtained in mobile liquids at low applied magnetic fields; but un-fortunately at high fields where chemical shifts are large the enhance-ment is all too often small. Furthermore, the enhancement is not always the same for all nuclei in a given molecule, so the valuable information in the intensities of an n.m.r. spectrum may be lost.

The method is not therefore likely to be of routine use for signal enhancement. Nevertheless there *are* many cases of systems where the chemical shifts are very large and still visible at, say, 3300 gauss (0·33 T) and where the Overhauser effect can produce signal enhancements of two orders of magnitude. It has proved valuable already in the study of ^{13}C and ^{31}P resonances. One possibility of overcoming these difficulties involves rapid transfer of a sample from a low-field region in which the nuclear polarization is established by the Overhauser effect to a high-field region where the high resolution n.m.r. spectrum can be obtained. It is easy to visualize several systems that would permit spectra to be recorded continuously in this way.

The different sign of the Overhauser effect for dipolar and scalar coupling provides a very sensitive method for studying these interactions. Although scalar interactions often serve only to reduce the nuclear polarization, they can sometimes be used to great advantage to obtain information on molecular structure as described in the sections on ^{13}C and ^{31}P resonances.

Finally, the nuclear–nuclear Overhauser effect can be used to obtain remarkably subtle details of molecular conformation in favourable systems.

ACKNOWLEDGMENT

We thank the Science Research Council for a Research Fellowship (R.A.D.) and a maintenance grant (D.T.).

REFERENCES

1. I. Solomon, *Phys. Rev.*, 1955, **99**, 559.
2. A. Abragam, "The Principles of Nuclear Magnetism", Clarendon Press, Oxford, 1961.
3. P. S. Hubbard, *Proc. Roy. Soc.*, 1966, **A291**, 537.
4. N. Bloembergen, *J. Chem. Phys.*, 1957, **27**, 595.
5. R. S. Codrington and N. Bloembergen, *J. Chem. Phys.*, 1956, **29**, 600.
6. V. E. Kul'beda, *J.E.T.P.*, 1964, **46**, 106.
7. F. Noack, G. J. Krüger, W. Müller-Warmuth, and R. Van Steenwinkel, *Z. Naturforsch.*, 1967, **22a**, 2102.
8. J. G. Kenworthy, J. A. Ladd and R. E. Richards, *Mol. Phys.*, 1965, **10**, 469.
9. W. Müller-Warmuth, *Z. Naturforsch.*, 1966, **21a**, 153.
10. K. H. Hausser and D. Stehlik, In "Advances in Magnetic Resonance", Vol. III, Academic Press, New York, 1968.
11. R. A. Dwek, H. D. W. Hill, J. G. Kenworthy, D. F. S. Natusch and R. E. Richards, *Mol. Phys.*, 1967, **13**, 27.
12. R. A. Dwek, O. W. Howarth, D. F. S. Natusch and R. E. Richards, *Mol. Phys.*, 1967, **13**, 4517.

13. K. D. Kramer, W. Müller-Warmuth and J. Schindler, *J. Chem. Phys.*, 1965, **43**, 31.
14. K. D. Kramer, W. Müller-Warmuth and N. Roth, *Z. Naturforsch.*, 1965, **20a**, 1391.
15. G. J. Krüger, W. Müller-Warmuth and R. Van Steenwinkel, *Z. Naturforsch.*, 1966, **21a**, 1224.
16. W. Müller-Warmuth, R. Van Steenwinkel and F. Noack, *Z. Naturforsch.*, 1968, **23a**, 506.
17. R. A. Dwek, J. G. Kenworthy, D. F. S. Natusch, R. E. Richards and D. J. Shields, *Proc. Roy. Soc.*, 1966, **A291**, 487.
18. R. A. Dwek, J. G. Kenworthy and R. E. Richards, *Chem. Comm.*, 1966, 74.
19. R. A. Dwek, J. G. Kenworthy, J. A. Ladd and R. E. Richards, *Mol. Phys.*, 1966, **11**, 287.
20. H. S. Gutowsky and J. C. Tai, *J. Chem. Phys.*, 1963, **39**, 208.
21. D. W. McCall, D. C. Douglas and E. Anderson, *J. Chem. Phys.*, 1959, **31**, 1555.
22. T. H. Cannon, D. Phil. Thesis, Oxford, 1968.
23. E. H. Poindexter, J. R. Stewart and P. J. Caplan, *J. Chem. Phys.*, 1967, **47**, 2862.
24. J. R. Stewart, E. H. Poindexter and J. A. Potenza, *J. Amer. Chem. Soc.*, 1967, **89**, 6017.
25. J. S. Hartman and R. E. Richards, unpublished work.
26. R. E. Richards and J. W. White, *Discuss. Faraday Soc.*, 1962, **34**, 96.
27. D. F. S. Natusch, R. E. Richards and D. Taylor, *Mol. Phys.*, 1966, **11**, 421.
28. R. A. Dwek, J. G. Kenworthy and R. E. Richards, *Mol. Phys.*, 1966, **10**, 529.
29. K. H. Hausser, H. Brunner and J. C. Jochims, *Mol. Phys.*, 1966, **10**, 253.
30. D. F. S. Natusch and R. E. Richards, *Chem. Comm.*, 1966, 579.
31. D. Stehlik and K. H. Hausser, *Z. Naturforsch.*, 1967, **22a**, 914.
32. C. Lambert, *J. Chem. Phys.*, 1968, **48**, 2389.
33. R. A. Dwek and R. E. Richards, *Chem. Comm.*, 1966, 581.
34. P. W. Atkins, R. A. Dwek, J. B. Reid and R. E. Richards, *Mol. Phys.*, 1967, **13**, 175.
35. E. H. Poindexter, private communication.
36. R. A. Dwek, R. E. Richards and D. Taylor, unpublished work.
37. J. H. Letcher and J. R. Van Wazer, In "Topics in Phosphorus Chemistry", (M. Grayson and E. J. Griffiths, Eds.), Vol. 5, Chaps. 2 and 3. Interscience, New York, 1967.
38. D. Taylor, D. Phil Thesis, Oxford, 1968.
39. C. W. H. Hirst and R. E. Richards, to be published.
40. H. R. Ward and R. G. Lawler, *J. Amer. Chem. Soc.*, 1967, **89**, 5518.
41. J. Bargon and H. Fischer, *Z. Naturforsch.*, 1967, **22a**, 1551 and 1556.
42. F. A. L. Anet and A. J. R. Bourn, *J. Amer. Chem. Soc.*, 1965, **87**, 5250.
43. W. A. Anderson and R. Freeman, *J. Chem. Phys.*, 1967, **85**, 2053.
44. R. Kaiser, *J. Chem. Phys.*, 1963, **39**, 2435.

Phosphorus-31 Nuclear Magnetic Resonance Spectra of Co-ordination Compounds

J. F. NIXON and A. PIDCOCK

The Chemical Laboratory, University of Sussex, Brighton, Sussex, England

I. INTRODUCTION

PHOSPHORUS-31 n.m.r. spectra have been used to determine the structure of many co-ordination compounds. In addition, the spectral parameters have often been used in discussions of the nature and strength of co-ordinate bonds in which phosphorus is the donor atom. In Section II of this review, we have presented some examples of structure determination involving ^{31}P n.m.r., and we hope that future work of this type will also be assisted by the Tables of shifts and coupling constants given in the later Sections. The Tables contain a selection of the available data for all the main types of compound in which phosphorus is normally considered to behave as an electron-pair donor.

Sections III to VI are concerned with the parameters obtained by analysis of the spectra, and comments on experimental details and methods of analysis have been included where necessary. Because of their intimate connection with the co-ordinate bond, the parameters $^{1}J_{P-M}$, $^{2}J_{PMP'}$, and δ_P are discussed in some detail, but the coupling constants involving the donor phosphorus atom and other nuclei within the ligands receive rather less attention. Although these latter coupling constants are usually different in the free and complexed states of the ligand, they are probably best discussed together with coupling constants of the same type in molecules that may not function as ligands. Also, Mavel[1] has published an excellent review of the n.m.r. parameters of phosphorus compounds other than those obtained from the ^{31}P spectra. We have also limited the scope of this review by excluding from consideration the vast number of known couplings between the donor phosphorus atom and nuclei in other ligands that do not have a phosphorus donor atom. However, we have not confined our attention entirely to those results obtained by ^{31}P n.m.r. Several phosphorus–acceptor atom coupling constants have been measured using the spectrum of the nucleus of the acceptor atom, and one of the most powerful methods of determining the phosphorus–phosphorus coupling constants $^{2}J_{PMP'}$ (Section IV) involves analysis of the spectrum of another nucleus (e.g., ^{19}F) within the ligand.

Experimental techniques of ^{31}P n.m.r. and its applications have been described thoroughly in a recent monograph:[2] the applications discussed in detail concern mainly fields other than co-ordination chemistry.

II. STRUCTURE DETERMINATION

The principles governing the use of n.m.r. to determine the structure of a molecule do not depend on the nucleus studied, but, because proton spectra are usually used to illustrate these principles, we consider it worthwhile to draw attention to the main uses of ³¹P spectra in co-ordination chemistry. In making an assignment of a spectrum, knowledge of the chemical shifts and coupling constants in similar compounds is always helpful, and in most instances structural assignments have to be at least partly based on the magnitudes of the parameters rather than on the multiplicity of the resonances in the spectrum. Another useful aid to the interpretation of phosphorus-containing complexes is the varying widths of the resonances in different ligands. Because phosphorus spectra are often obtained in stationary tubes of up to 15 mm dia., phosphorus–hydrogen coupling involving alkyl or phenyl groups within the ligand is rarely resolved, so that the trialkylphosphines have noticeably broader resonances than such ligands as triphenylphosphine and particularly triphenylphosphite. In complexes of trimethylphosphite, however, the P–O–C–H coupling (ca. 10 c./sec.) is large enough to give observable splitting of the phosphorus resonances when using stationary 8·5 mm tubes. Couplings involving P–H (350 c./sec.) and P–F (1400 c./sec.) bonds are always large enough to be resolved. Phosphorus–phosphorus coupling constants between chemically non-equivalent phosphorus atoms attached to an acceptor atom have magnitudes of about 15 c./sec. and upwards. The smaller couplings, therefore, sometimes do not give observable splittings when the ligands are trialkylphosphines, particularly if the signal-to-noise ratio of the spectrum is not high. We now discuss the two levels of information obtainable from the ³¹P spectra of some representative co-ordination compounds.

A. Symmetry determination

1. *Tris(phosphine)rhodium*(III) *complexes*

The facial isomer of the complex $[RhX_3P_3]$ has equivalent phosphorus atoms, so the spectrum is a doublet due to rhodium–phosphorus coupling, whereas the meridianal isomer has two types of phosphorus atoms, a pair mutually *trans*(b) and one *trans* to X(a) (1).

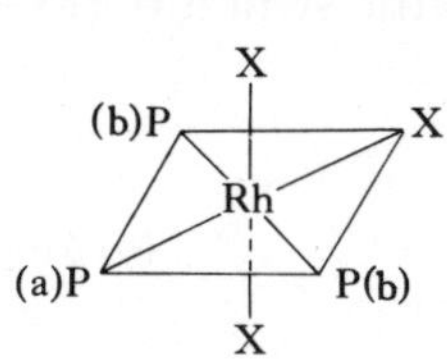

1

The spectrum of $mer\text{-}[RhCl_3(Bu_3P)_3]^3$ is given below (Fig. 1) with the first-order analysis; the coupling $^2J_{P_aRhP_b}$'must cause identical multiplet spacing in the spectra of P_a and P_b, so it is readily distinguished from the rhodium–phosphorus coupling in the spectrum of P_b.

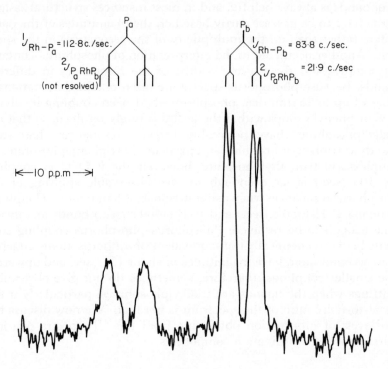

P_a

$^1J_{Rh-P_a} = 112\cdot8\,c./sec.$

$^2J_{P_aRhP_b}$
(not resolved)

P_b

$^1J_{Rh-P_b} = 83\cdot8\ c./sec.$

$^2J_{P_aRhP_b} = 21\cdot9\ c./sec$

$\leftarrow\!10\ p.p.m\longrightarrow$

FIG. 1. ^{31}P n.m.r. spectrum of $mer\text{-}[RhCl_3(Bu_3P)_3]$ in dichloromethane ($8\cdot5$ mm. stationary sample tube at $24\cdot29$ Mc./sec.).

2. A new platinum complex[4]

The binuclear platinum complex (2) reacts with diphenyl phosphonate, $(PhO)_2PHO$, to give a complex with the ^{31}P spectrum shown in Fig. 2, which establishes the structure (3).

Me$_2$PhP, Cl, Cl

Pt, Pt

Cl, Cl, PPhMe$_2$

2

Cl

(b) Me$_2$PhP—Pt—P(OPh)$_2$OH (a)

P(O)(OPh)$_2$ (c)

3

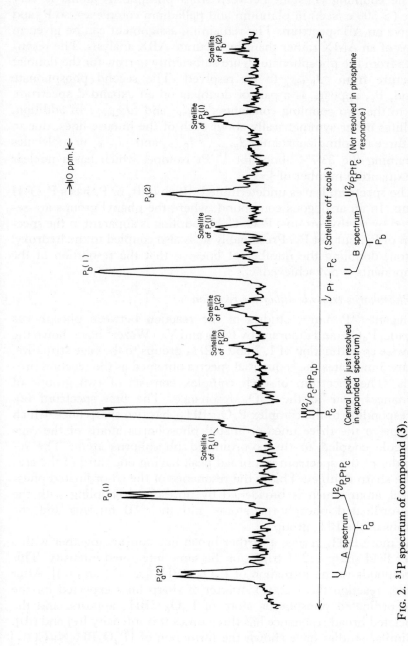

FIG. 2. ^{31}P spectrum of compound (3).
Output of digital memory oscilloscope after accumulation of 366 spectra (8·5 mm. stationary sample tube) at 24·29 Mc./sec. with approximate analysing.

12*

The coupling constant between *trans* phosphorus atoms is very large (> 500 c./sec.) in platinum and palladium complexes, so P_a and P_b give an AB spectrum. The remaining assignment can be given in terms of an AMX rather than the accurate ABX analysis. The resonances from the phosphonate P_a are sufficiently narrow for the doublet structure from $^2J_{P_aPtP_c}$ to be resolved. The second phosphonate ligand, P_c, appears as a pair of doublets on an expanded spectrum, due to the two coupling constants $^2J_{P_cPtP_a}$ and $^2J_{P_cPtP_b}$. In addition, satellites occur symmetrically about each of the intense lines, due to the three coupling constants $^1J_{Pt-P_a}$, $^1J_{Pt-P_b}$ and $^1J_{Pt-P_c}$ in molecules containing the 33·7% abundant ^{195}Pt isotope, which has a nuclear spin quantum number of $\frac{1}{2}$.

The spectrum leaves undetermined which of P_a or P_c has a P–O–H group. In an analogous compound, where the phenyl groups are replaced by methyl groups, P–O–C–H coupling is apparent in the spectrum of P_c, but not P_a. Presumably P_a is also coupled to the hydroxyl proton, doubling the number of lines so that the resolution of the components is not achieved.

3. *Phosphorus trioxide–diborane reaction*

Elegant ^{31}P n.m.r. studies of the reaction between phosphorus trioxide, P_4O_6, and diborane by Riess and Van Wazer[5] have shown the stepwise co-ordination of 1, 2 and 3 BH_3 groups to the cage structure. Figure 3 indicates the sequential spectra obtained as the reaction proceeds. The spectrum of each complex consists of two groups of resonances near to the P_4O_6 resonance. The first spectrum (a), corresponding to the complex $P_4O_6 \cdot BH_3$, has two sharp lines, which are due to the three unco-ordinated phosphorus atoms of the cage molecule coupled to the co-ordinated phosphorus atom. The remainder of the spectrum is a broad peak having one third of the area of the sharp doublet. This is the resonance of the co-ordinated phosphorus atom which is broadened by unresolved coupling with the unco-ordinated phosphorus atoms and the ^{11}B nucleus and the protons of the BH_3 group.

As more B_2H_6 reacts, a further broad line appears together with a lower field sharp 1:2:1 triplet of the same integrated intensity. This corresponds to the formation of $P_4O_6 \cdot 2BH_3$ [see (b) and (c)]. After further reaction the 1:3:3:1 quartet of sharp lines expected for the unco-ordinated phosphorus atom of $P_4O_6 \cdot 3BH_3$ appears, and the associated broad resonance has three times this intensity [(c) and (d)].

Similar studies have shown the formation of $[P_4O_6BH_3Ni(CO)_3]$ (which involves a second-order spectrum analysis), $[P_4O_6\{Ni(CO)_3\}_4]$

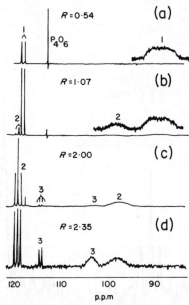

FIG. 3. ^{31}P n.m.r. spectra of a series of compositions made by bubbling diborane through a chloroform solution of phosphorus trioxide. The overall stoicheiometry of each composition is given by the mole ratio, $R = BH_3/P_4O_6$, and the sets of resonances corresponding to individual molecular species are differentiated by the numbers 1, 2 or 3. (From Van Wazer.[5])

and the compounds $[M_n\{P_4(NMe)_6\}]$ $[M = Ni(CO)_3, BH_3; n = 1, 2, 3]$.[6]

B. Information from the magnitudes of shifts and coupling constants

For some molecules, the spectra of the possible different structures would not differ in the number and multiplicities of ^{31}P resonances, but the magnitudes of the shifts and coupling constants may permit an assignment to be made. If the possible structures differ very greatly in the ^{31}P parameters expected from them, then structure determinations on this basis can be virtually unequivocal.

1. *The complex* $[RhCl_3(Bu_3P)_2\{(PhO)_3P\}]^3$

The ^{31}P spectrum (Fig. 4) establishes that the phosphines are equivalent; the low-field resonance from $(PhO)_3P$ (sharp) is split into a doublet by ^{103}Rh ($^1J_{Rh-P} = 202\cdot8$ c./sec.) and triplets by the two phosphines ($^2J_{PRhP'} = 30\cdot3$ c./sec.); the high field resonance from $2Bu_3P$ (somewhat broader resonances) is split by ^{103}Rh ($^1J_{Rh-P} = 79\cdot3$

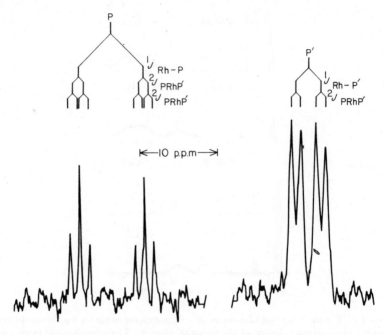

FIG. 4. ^{31}P n.m.r. spectrum of $[\text{RhCl}_3(\text{Bu}_3\text{P})_2\{(\text{PhO})_3\text{P}\}]$ in dichloromethane (8·5 mm. stationary sample tube) at 24·29 Mc./sec.

c./sec.) and the same $^2J_{\text{PRhP}'}$ coupling. Structures (4) and (5) are consistent with these multiplicities, but the meridianal structure (4) is strongly favoured by the similarity of the coupling constant $^1J_{\text{Rh-PBu}_3}$ to that for the mutually *trans* phosphines in *mer*-$[\text{RhCl}_3(\text{Bu}_3\text{P})_3]$, where $^1J_{\text{Rh-P}} = 83·8$ c./sec.[3,7] The coupling in *fac*-$[\text{RhCl}_3(\text{Et}_3\text{P})_3]$ is very different (111·2 c./sec.).[3]

Meridianal
4

Facial
5

Similar considerations of the magnitudes of $^1J_{\text{Pt-P}}$ strongly suggests that for the compounds $[\text{Pt}(\text{Ph}_2\text{MeM})_2(\text{PhMe}_2\text{P})_2]$ (M = Si, Ge), in benzene, the silyl compound is *cis* and the germyl compound *trans*.[8]

2. Mercury dialkylphosphonates

Butcher and co-workers[9] have shown that the ^{31}P chemical shifts in the compounds $[\{(RO)_2PO\}HgX](R=$ alkyl group; $X=Cl,$ Br) are between -60 and -70 p.p.m. A structure based on terco-ordinate phosphorus (6) is expected to have a much lower-field resonance than this [by analogy with $(RO)_3P,$ -138 p.p.m.; $(RO)_2PCl,$ -164 p.p.m.;

$$(RO)_2P\text{—}O\text{—}Hg\text{—}X \qquad\qquad \underset{\displaystyle O}{\overset{\displaystyle RO}{\underset{\|}{\overset{\diagdown}{RO\text{—}P}}}\text{—}Hg\text{—}X}$$

$$\textbf{6} \qquad\qquad\qquad\qquad \textbf{7}$$

$RP(OR)_2,$ -183 p.p.m.]. Compounds analogous to structure (7) have a range of shifts that includes the -60 to -70 p.p.m. region: $(RO)_3PO,$ ~ 0 p.p.m.; $(RO)_2P(O)Cl,$ -3 p.p.m.; $(RO)_2P(O)R,$ -30 p.p.m.; $R_2P(O)(OR),$ -50 p.p.m.; $R_2P(O)Cl,$ -72 p.p.m.

A structure based on (7) is further supported by the observation[4] of extremely large Hg–P coupling constants (7000–13,000 c./sec.) in accumulated spectra of these compounds (Section IIIC.10(c)). This coupling is too large to be anything other than coupling between directly bonded atoms.

3. Aminophosphine complexes

Dialkylaminodifluorophosphines, $R_2NPF_2,$ can in principle give co-ordination compounds in which the donor atom is nitrogen or phosphorus. The observation of a $1:1:1:1$ quartet in the ^{31}P spectrum of $R_2NPF_2BH_3$ with coupling constant $^1J_{P-B}=80$ c./sec. strongly suggests a direct P—B bond.[10] The absence of similar fine structure in the spectrum of the corresponding boron trifluoride adduct in conjunction with other evidence has led to the suggestion that a B—N bond is involved in this compound.[11] On its own, the absence of coupling is only weak evidence for such a structure, because other factors can prevent the observation of phosphorus–boron coupling even in compounds having P—B bond.

Similarly, in a recently described series of complexes,[12] cis-$[Mo(CO)_4P_2]$ $(P=PF_3,$ $CCl_3PF_2,$ $ClCH_2PF_2,$ $R_2NPF_2),$ the P–P coupling constant (obtained from detailed analysis of the ^{19}F spectra) does not vary greatly with the nature of P, so it is very unlikely that the aminophosphine is bonded to the metal by nitrogen.

III. PHOSPHORUS–ACCEPTOR ATOM COUPLING CONSTANTS

The coupling constants $^1J_{P-M}$ are one of the several easily obtainable physical parameters of phosphorus co-ordination compounds, but they are especially important because they are essentially a property of a particular bond of the complex. Other properties, such as the dipole moment or a vibration frequency, often involve substantial contributions from other bonds within the complex, and thus require some estimate of these relative contributions before the property of an individual bond is known. As a means of investigating the nature of P—M bonds, the coupling constants also have an advantage over most other parameters in that an approximate equation for their magnitude can be derived from molecular orbital theory, which principally involves terms associated with the wave function of the P—M bond.

A. Measurement of coupling constants $^1J_{P-M}$

Spin multiplets arising from this coupling have been observed for $M = H,[1, 13, 14]$ $B,[15, 16]$ $Al,[17]$ $Co,[18]$ $Cu,[19]$ $Rh,[3, 7]$ $W,[20-22]$ $Pt[3, 4, 23-26]$ and Hg.[27] The detailed properties of the nuclei concerned are given in Table I. In addition to these, it may also be possible to observe coupling

TABLE I

Isotopes for which $^1J_{P-M}$ has been observed

Nucleus	Natural abundance, %	Magnetic moment (μ), in Bohr magnetons	Spin quantum number (I)	Electric quadrupole moment in multiples of $e \times 10^{-24}$ cm.^{2}
^{1}H	99·98	2·793	$\frac{1}{2}$	0
^{11}B	81·17	2·688	$\frac{3}{2}$	$3·55 \times 10^{-2}$
^{27}Al	100	3·639	$\frac{5}{2}$	0·149
^{59}Co	100	4·639	$\frac{7}{2}$	0·5
^{63}Cu	69·09	2·221	$\frac{3}{2}$	$-0·16$
^{65}Cu	30·91	2·379	$\frac{3}{2}$	$-0·15$
^{103}Rh	100	$-0·0879$	$\frac{1}{2}$	0
^{185}W	14·28	0·115	$\frac{1}{2}$	0
^{195}Pt	33·7	0·6004	$\frac{1}{2}$	0
^{199}Hg	16·86	0·4979	$\frac{1}{2}$	0

Taken from data given by Varian Associates, N.M.R. Table, 4th Edn, 1964.

to the following nuclei, all of which have a nuclear spin quantum number of $\frac{1}{2}$ (isotope, relative abundance): [107]Ag, 51·35; [109]Ag, 48·65; [111]Cd, 12·86; [113]Cd, 12·34; [115]Sn, 0·35; [117]Sn, 7·67; [119]Sn, 8·68; [187]Os, 1·64; [203]Tl, 29·52; [205]Tl, 70·48.

For some complexes of phosphorus ligands, the spectra either do not exhibit the multiplet structure expected from P—M coupling, or the lines of the multiplet are much broader than usual. Some of the possible causes of this behaviour are detailed in the following Sections.

1. Quadrupolar nuclei[28]

If the nucleus of the acceptor atom M has a nuclear spin quantum number greater than $\frac{1}{2}$, the nucleus has an electric quadrupole moment as well as a magnetic dipole moment. The quadrupole interacts with any electric field gradient at the nucleus and, in combination with the molecular motion of the complex, this can provide an important mechanism of relaxation of the M nucleus. At relaxation rates that are slow compared with $^1J_{P-M}$, spin multiplets are observable in the spectra of M and P. As the relaxation rate increases, the multiplets broaden, but the line separations may still be used to derive $^1J_{P-M}$ with good accuracy. At faster relaxation rates the multiplet components of M and P coalesce into a single broadened line, and at high relaxation rates, the phosphorus resonance becomes sharp and the M resonance may become so broad as to be unobservable.

Thus, observations of spin multiplets due to a quadrupolar nucleus are most often successful when the atom M is attached to several identical ligands, because the electric field gradient at the nucleus is thereby made small. As the magnitude of the quadrupole moment becomes large (e.g.,[18] for [59]Co), a symmetrical complex becomes virtually a necessary condition for the observation of coupling.

2. Exchange reactions[28]

By means of the dissociation equilibrium—

$$\text{Ligand} + \text{Acceptor} \rightleftharpoons \text{Complex}$$

a phosphorus donor can exchange between the free state and co-ordinated sites on different acceptor atoms. At slow rates of exchange, multiplet spacings may be used to measure $^1J_{P-M}$, but as the rate of exchange increases, coalescence of the multiplet lines occurs and eventually the spectra of both nuclei collapse to singlets. Analysis of the detailed behaviour may be used to measure the exchange rate in certain circumstances. Such dissociation is probably responsible for the failure to observe P–B coupling in complexes of BMe_3 and BF_3,[15] and the dependence of the doublet separation in the ^{27}Al spectrum on phosphine concentration has been observed in mixtures of aluminium chloride and triphenylphosphine in dichloromethane.[17] It can be anticipated that exchange is also likely to be a difficulty in the observation of couplings involving most of the metals listed on p. 355.

B. Theory of coupling constant $^{1}J_{P-M}$

Coupling constants are usually analysed at present in terms of a MO theory developed by Pople and Santry.[29] They showed that coupling constants involving directly bonded atoms arise almost entirely from the Fermi contact interaction between nuclear moments and electron spins in s orbitals. Using the LCAO approximation and retaining only one-centre integrals, they derived the following expression for $^{1}J_{A-B}$—

$$^{1}J_{A-B} = -\gamma_A\gamma_B \cdot \frac{\hbar}{2\pi} \cdot \frac{256\pi^2}{9}\beta^2|S_A(0)|^2|S_B(0)|^2$$

$$\sum_{i}^{occ} \sum_{j}^{unocc} (^{3}\Delta E_{i \to j})^{-1} c_{iS_A} c_{jS_A} c_{jS_B} c_{iS_B} \quad (1)$$

In this expression, γ_I is the magnetogyric ratio of nucleus I, β is the Bohr magneton, S_A and S_B are the valence state s orbitals of atoms A

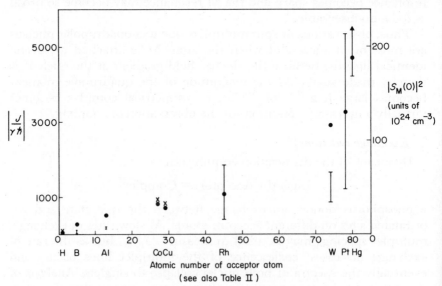

FIG. 5. Variation of atomic number of acceptor atom with

$$|J/\gamma\hbar| \ (\times \text{ and I}) \text{ and } |S_M(0)|^2 \ (\bullet).$$

and B, and the $|S(0)|$ terms are the magnitudes of these orbitals evaluated at the parent nuclei. The summation is carried over all occupied and unoccupied molecular orbitals and involves the triplet excitation energies $^3\Delta E_{i \rightarrow j}$ and the coefficients c of the s atomic orbitals of the coupled atoms in the occupied and unoccupied molecular orbitals.

The term $|S_M(0)|^2$ increases rapidly with increasing atomic number of the acceptor atom,[30] as illustrated in Fig. 5. In this diagram, we have also plotted the range of observed values of $(J/\gamma_M \hbar)$ for the various acceptor atoms (see Table II) and it is evident that the very large couplings observed for the heavier acceptor atoms arise from the large magnitude of $|S_M(0)|^2$ for these atoms.

TABLE II

Phosphorus–metal coupling and reduced coupling constants

Acceptor atom	Atomic number (Z)	$\gamma_M \hbar$†	Observed range of $|^1J_{P-M}|$ c./sec.	Range of $|J/\gamma_M \hbar|$	$|S_M(0)|^2$‡
H	1	5·58	515–525	92·3–94·1	2·16
B	5	1·79	25–180	14·0–100	11·2
Al	13	1·46	240–263	164–100	20·6
Co	27	1·33	1220	917	32·4
Cu	29	1·48	1190–1210	804–818	28·8
Rh	45	−0·1758	69–325	390–1846	43·0
W	74	0·230	200–381	870–1656	116·5
Pt	78	1·201	1460–6400	1217–5329	130·5
Hg	80	0·998	4200–12,970	4208–12,995	188·4

† $\gamma_M \hbar = \mu_M / I$ (see Table I).
‡ From Hartree-Fock calculations[30] (units of 10^{24} cm^{-3}).

1. Complexes of high symmetry

For complexes of type MP$_n$ (P = phosphorus ligand), where the acceptor atom M has an environment with microsymmetry that is T_d or O_h, it is possible to simplify equation (1) considerably, because the only valence shell atomic orbital on the acceptor atom belonging to the totally symmetric representation of the molecular space group is the s orbital. This means that other atomic orbitals on the acceptor atom do not mix with the s orbital and that only totally symmetric ligand combinations need be considered.

Since the ligand has no lone pairs of electrons when bonded to the acceptor, we need not consider the combinations of ligand $3s$ and $3p_\sigma$-orbitals separately, but can work in terms of the hybridized ligand wave functions—

$$\psi_{L_i\sigma} = \alpha\psi_{si} + \sqrt{1-\alpha^2}\,\psi_{p_zi} \qquad (2)$$

($\psi_{L_i\sigma}$ is the wave function on ligand i of the "donor orbital"; ψ_i are the atomic $3s$ and $3p$ orbitals on phosphorus, and α^2 is the s character of the hybrid orbital).

In the approximation that only valence shell molecular orbitals contribute to the bonding, there is then only one term in the sum of equation (1). This derives from the occupied bonding orbital (equation 3) and the corresponding unoccupied antibonding orbital, and also involves the energy of the triplet transition between these orbitals.

$$\psi = c_M\psi_{Ms} + c_L \sum_{i=1}^{n} \psi_{L_i\sigma} \qquad (3)$$

If overlap between atomic orbitals is neglected, the molecular orbitals are given by equations (4) and (5)—

$$\psi = a\psi_{Ms} + \frac{\sqrt{1-a^2}}{\sqrt{n}} \sum_{i=1}^{n} (\alpha\psi_{si} + \sqrt{1-\alpha^2}\,\psi_{pi}) \qquad (4)$$

$$\psi^* = \sqrt{1-a^2}\,\psi_{Ms} - \frac{a}{\sqrt{n}} \sum_{i=1}^{n} (\alpha\psi_{si} + \sqrt{1-\alpha^2}\,\psi_{pi}) \qquad (5)$$

$$(0 < a < 1; \quad 0 < \alpha < 1)$$

We then have—

$$^1J_{P-M} = -\gamma_P\gamma_M \frac{\hbar}{2\pi} \frac{256\pi^2}{9} \beta^2 |S_P(0)|^2 |S_M(0)|^2$$

$$\times \frac{-a^2(1-a^2)}{n}\alpha^2 \times \frac{1}{^3\Delta E_{\psi\psi^*}} \qquad (6)$$

This equation gives reasonable magnitudes of the coupling constants[18] and predicts that the sign of $^1J_{P-M}$ is the same as that of γ_M. This has been verified for Pt–P coupling.[31] Since the acceptor orbital generally has a less favourable energy than the phosphorus lone pair, a^2 will vary from 0 (no bond) to a maximum of 0·5, and the function $a^2(1-a^2)$ increases monotonically in this region (Fig. 6).

Thus, the coupling constant increases as the phosphorus lone pair becomes increasingly of metallic character. The equation further relates $^1J_{P-M}$ directly to α^2, the s character of the phosphorus lone pair orbital (see equation 2), which in simple hybridization theory is related to the X–P–X bond angle, θ, in a ligand PX_3 by the expression—

$$\alpha^2 = \frac{1+2\cos\theta}{\cos\theta - 1} \tag{7}$$

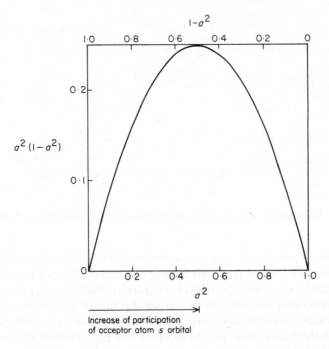

FIG. 6. Relationship between $a^2(1-a^2)$ and a^2 and $1-a^2$.

This function changes in magnitude quite rapidly in the region of 100° (Fig. 7) and α^2 could be an important factor influencing the variation of $^1J_{P-M}$ with the nature of the groups X on phosphorus.

2. Complexes of lower symmetry

Many of the complexes for which $^1J_{P-M}$ data have been collected are those of platinum(II) and rhodium(I) compounds. These are square planar complexes and the highest microsymmetry corresponding to this stereochemistry is D_{4h}. In this symmetry group, the d_{z^2} orbital and the s orbital on the acceptor transform as A_{1g}, so there will be three molecular orbitals involving the s orbital of the metal instead of the two orbitals in the O_h complexes. However, although the d orbitals in rhodium and platinum are more stable than the s orbitals, and are thereby closer in energy to the ligand σ orbitals, the d_{z^2} orbital overlaps the ligand orbitals in the xy plane of the complex far less efficiently than the s orbital. If the mixing of d_{z^2} with s is neglected,

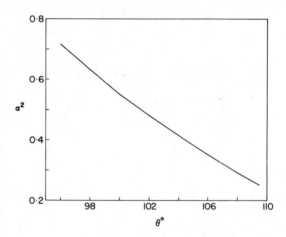

FIG. 7. Dependence of s character of phosphorus lone pair (α^2) on X–P–X bond angle (θ).

the theory is exactly the same as in Section III.B.1 above, and involves only terms associated with one triplet excitation. The effect of the d_{z^2} orbital can be examined by introducing its interaction as a perturbation on the molecular orbitals formed from the ligand plus metal s orbital. Approximate calculations[32] show that the expression for the coupling is only slightly modified, and little error will be introduced by neglecting the d_{z^2} orbital completely.

For complexes of lower symmetry, such as cis-$[MX_4P_2]$, cis-$[MX_2P_2]$, trans-$[MX_2P_2]$ and pseudo-tetrahedral $[MX_3P]$ molecules, the extent and number of orbitals mixing with the acceptor s orbital are greater, so that little progress can be made with the more precise form of the theory, in the absence of reasonably accurate knowledge of the molecular orbitals and their energies. Comparisons between couplings in complexes of the same microsymmetry may, however, still provide useful information.

Alternatively, recourse may be made to the average excitation energy approximation,[29] in which the several triplet excitation energies are replaced by an average value $^3\overline{\Delta E}$. The coupling is then given in terms of $P'_{S_PS_M}$, the total MO bond order between the s

orbitals on the coupled atoms—

$$^1J_{P-M} = \frac{64\pi^2}{9} \beta^2 (^3\Delta E)^{-1} |S_P(0)|^2 \, |S_M(0)|^2 (P'_{S_P S_M})^2 \qquad (8)$$

$$(P'_{S_P S_M} = 2\sum_{i=1}^{n} c_{iS_P} c_{iS_M})$$

Evaluation of P' for a complex of high symmetry leads to equation (6).

It is important to note that, because of the form of the Fermi contact interaction, the coupling constants are given by equations that involve only the σ orbitals and molecular orbital energies of the molecule. Any π-bonding between the ligands and the acceptor atom influences the coupling constant only by modifying the σ-bonding or by altering the screening of the s electrons from the nuclei and thus causing variations in the $|S(0)|^2$ terms.

C. Results for transition metal complexes

1. Application of equations

Apart from the physical constants, the couplings $^1J_{P-M}$ are a function of the rather large number of parameters: a^2, α^2, $|S_P(0)|^2$, $S_M(0)^2$ and $^3\Delta E^{-1}$, but in making comparisons between the coupling constants in different situations, some of these parameters may vary much more than others, and analysis of the results can provide insight into the nature of the bonding in complexes of phosphorus ligands.[24] As an example of the method of interpretation to be applied, and as an introduction to the controversy presently associated with these results, we consider in detail the coupling constants in the complex $[PtCl(Bu_3P)_3]^{\oplus}$ (**8**).[4, 26]

$$\begin{array}{ccc} Cl & & PBu_3 \ (b) \\ & \diagdown \! \diagup & \\ & Pt & \\ & \diagup \! \diagdown & \\ (b) \ Bu_3P & & PBu_3 \ (a) \end{array}$$

8

$J_{P_b-Pt} = 2270$ c./sec. $J_{P_a-Pt} = 3454$ c./sec.

Because the non-equivalent phosphorus atoms are attached to the same immediate neighbours (3 butyl groups and 1 platinum atom), it is reasonable to assume that α^2 and $|S_P(0)|^2$ have closely similar values in the equations for J_{P_a-Pt} and J_{P_b-Pt}.[24] Since also ligands P_a and P_b are attached to a single platinum atom, $|S_{Pt}(0)|^2$ must be the same in both couplings. Now because of the low symmetry of the complex, the metal s orbital contributes to several of the molecular orbitals of the

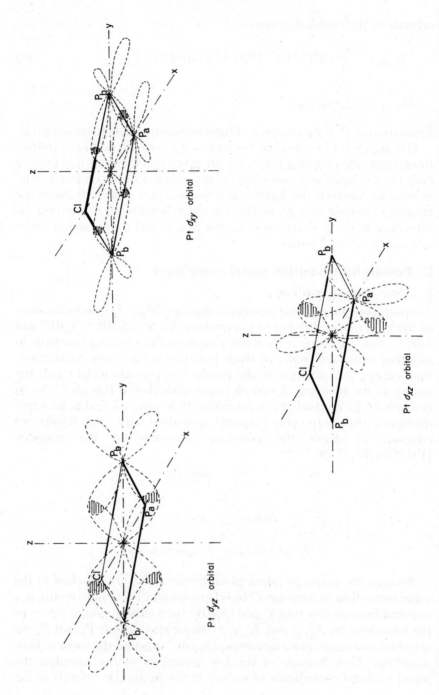

Pt d_{xy} orbital

Pt d_{xz} orbital

Pt d_{yz} orbital

complex and the average excitation energy approximation must be used. The value of $^3\overline{\Delta E}$ will, however, be very similar for two couplings in the same molecule, so the larger coupling to the phosphorus *trans* to chlorine must be due to the greater involvement of the platinum *s* orbital in that bond compared with the bonds to the other phosphorus atoms. This does not necessarily mean that the σ-bond to P_a is more covalent than the σ-bonds to P_b, because the coupling constant reflects only the *s* component of the bonding. The result is, however, consistent with that interpretation.

Different views have been expressed in the literature concerning the origin of these variations in the nature of the phosphorus–metal σ-bonds.[22, 24, 25]

2. π-Bonding hypothesis

Grim *et al.*[7, 20–22, 26, 27] have focused attention on metal–phosphorus π-bonding and its synergic effect on the σ-system, and by use of this approach they have obtained a consistent explanation of their results for complexes of Rh^I and Rh^{III}, W^0, Pt^{II} and Hg^{II}. In the complex $[PtCl(R_3P)_3]^{\oplus}$, (8), the phosphorus atoms mutually *trans* compete with each other for the 4 platinum electrons in the d_{xy} and d_{yz} orbitals. (see facing page). Ligand P_a also competes for the d_{xy} electrons, but its share of the d_{xz} electrons will be large because the other competing ligand, chloride, is a poor π-acceptor. Thus, the back-donation of platinum π-electrons is greater to P_a than to P_b and this leads to P_a being a better σ-donor than P_b and thus to a more covalent σ-bond to P_a. It has been pointed out by Grim *et al.*[21] and by Williams,[33] that removal of metal d_π electrons by phosphines could also affect the coupling constants by another mechanism. Because the *d* electrons of transition-metal complexes have a principal quantum number of one less than the valence state *s* and *p* electrons, removal of the metal d_π electrons reduces the shielding of the *s* and *p* electrons from the parent nucleus and contracts the *s* and *p* orbitals. The π-bonding thereby increases $|S_M(0)|^2$, but in the complex $[PtCl(Bu_3P)_3]^{\oplus}$ this term must be the same for both couplings, so this effect of π-bonding *cannot* explain the difference between the coupling constants in this case.

3. σ-Bonding hypothesis

Although symmetry obviously allows phosphorus–metal π-bonding to occur, its contribution to bond energies and to charge distributions may not be very great in platinum(II) complexes.[24, 25] The underlying assumption of the π-bonding theory is that the large difference between the $Pt–P_a$ and $Pt–P_b$ bonds (as evidenced by the very different coupling constants) would not occur in the absence of platinum–phosphorus π-bonding. For a molecule of this stereochemistry, there is, however, no symmetry requirement that the σ-bonds to P_a and P_b should be equivalent, and indeed, apart from coincidence, they will certainly be nonequivalent even in the absence of π-bonding.

It is now well established in platinum(II) chemistry that Pt—Cl bonds are substantially weaker when *trans* to ligands such as $H^\ominus$ and $CH_3^\ominus$ than when they are *trans* to $Cl^\ominus$. The bonds *cis* to $H^\ominus$ in *trans*-$[PtHCl(EtPh_2P)_2]$ (9)[34] are of very similar length to those *cis* to $Cl^\ominus$ in *trans*-$[PtCl_2(Et_3P)_2]$ (10),[35, 36] so the bond weakening effect of $H^\ominus$ compared with $Cl^\ominus$ is directed specifically at the ligand *trans* to $H^\ominus$. Since neither $H^\ominus$ or $Cl^\ominus$ π-bonds effectively with platinum, this "*trans* influence[24]" of $H^\ominus$ must stem from its effect on the σ-electrons of the complex.

Since it is known[36] that Pt—Cl bonds are also longer when *trans* to Me_3P than *trans* to Cl (see 11), it is very probable that the high *trans* influence of trialkylphosphines also occurs through the σ-electrons. Thus, the σ-bonding of phosphines to platinum is stronger (more covalent) when *trans* to $Cl^\ominus$ than when *trans* to R_3P, and it is to be expected that $J_{P_a–Pt} > J_{P_b–Pt}$ in $[PtCl(Bu_3P)_3]^\oplus$.

$$
\begin{array}{ccc}
\text{PEtPh}_2 & \text{PEt}_3 & \text{PMe}_3 \\
\mid \quad \diagup\,\,2\cdot422\pm0\cdot009\text{ Å} & \mid \quad \diagup\,\,2\cdot294\pm0\cdot009\text{ Å} & \mid \quad \diagup\,\,2\cdot376\pm0\cdot008\text{ Å} \\
\text{H—Pt—Cl} & \text{Cl—Pt—Cl} & \text{Me}_3\text{P—Pt—Cl} \\
\diagup\,\,\text{PEtPh}_2 & \diagup\,\,\text{PEt}_3 & \diagup\,\,\text{Cl} \\
2\cdot268\pm0\cdot008\text{ Å} & 2\cdot298\pm0\cdot018\text{ Å} & 2\cdot247\pm0\cdot007\text{ Å} \\
\mathbf{9} & \mathbf{10} & \mathbf{11}
\end{array}
$$

4. *Summary*

The coupling constants in $[PtCl(Bu_3P)_3]^\oplus$ in conjunction with the approximate MO theory of the Fermi contact interaction leads to the conclusion that the platinum $6s$ orbital is involved to a greater extent with P_a than with P_b in the bonding molecular orbitals of the complex. This result is consistent with the available Pt—P bond length data; Pt—P bonds are significantly longer when *trans* to R_3P than when *trans* to Cl.

The two theories that have been used to explain the differences in the Pt—P bonds are not mutually exclusive. Because of the symmetry of the complex, the $Pt–P_a$ and $Pt–P_b$ bonds are almost certain to differ in both the σ- and the π-components. The theory in Section

III.C.2 above shows that π-bonding to P_a will be stronger than to P_b, and consideration in Section III.C.3 of the bond length changes induced by purely σ-bonding ligands, indicates that the σ-bonding would be stronger for Pt–P_a than Pt–P_b even in the absence of π-bonding. After a discussion of the possible origin of the σ-effects in the next Section, we will consider first those experiments that are designed to determine the relative importance of the σ- and π-effects.

5. *Origin of σ-interactions*

The most important metal orbitals forming the σ-bonds in square planar platinum complexes are, in order of their relative stability, $5d_{x^2-y^2} > 6s > 6p_x, 6p_y$. Syrkin[37] has shown that, if a ligand X is bound to the metal by a strong covalent bond, the orbital used by the metal for that bond will have a high $s + d_{x^2-y^2}$ character, because these atomic orbitals are more stable than the $6p_x$ orbital (Fig. 8). The bond *trans* to X must then have a large metal p_x component and will be less strong. The bonds on the other axis of the molecule could be equivalent and quite strong, or if the ligands are not identical, one bond could be strong $(s - d_{x^2-y^2})$ and the other weak (p_y).

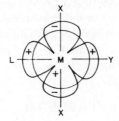

$d_x{}^2{-}_y{}^2$ and s orbitals

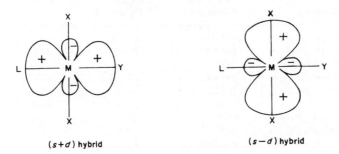

$(s+d)$ hybrid $(s-d)$ hybrid

FIG. 8. Directional properties of hypothetical sd hybrids for square planar platinum(II) complexes. (From Venanzi.[25]).

Thus, in Syrkin's theory, the strongly covalent bonds also have a large metal s component, so provided that other parameters affecting $^1J_{P-M}$ do not vary greatly, large coupling constants can be associated with strong (covalent) P–M bonds.[24]

6. Complexes containing non-equivalent phosphorus atoms

In this Section, we confine our attention to the complexes where the non-equivalence of the phosphorus atoms derives from the stereo-chemistry of the complex, rather than from the groups attached to phosphorus within the ligand. The results for some chloro-complexes are given in Table III. The meridianal form of the rhodium(III) complexes has the structure (12), which is of the same symmetry as the

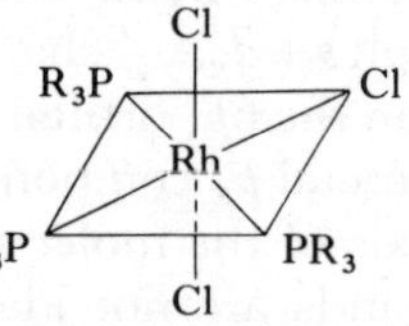

12

complex $[PtCl(R_3P)_3]^\oplus$ discussed previously, so the analysis of these coupling constants involves similar reasoning. The ratio of the coupling constants (r) within a given complex is slightly nearer to unity for the rhodium(III) compounds than for the platinum(II) compounds, suggesting that the directional effects in the bonds are smaller in the rhodium compounds.

TABLE III

Complexes containing non-equivalent phosphorus atoms

Complex	$^1J_{P-M}$, c./sec. P *trans* to Cl	$^1J_{P-M}$, c./sec. P *trans* to P	Ratio, r	Ref.
mer-[RhCl$_3$(Et$_3$P)$_3$]	103 ±8	84 ±5	0·81	3
mer-[RhCl$_3$(Pr$_3$P)$_3$]	103 ±10	81 ±5	0·79	7
mer-[RhCl$_3$(Bu$_3$P)$_3$]	112·8	83·8	0·743	3, 7
mer-[RhCl$_3$(PhEt$_2$P)$_3$]	107 ±12	82 ±12	0·77	7
mer-[RhCl$_3$(PhBu$_2$P)$_3$]	109·7	84·6	0·771	3
[PtCl(Bu$_3$P)$_3$]Cl	3454	2270	0·657	4
[PtCl(PhPr$_2$P)$_3$]Cl	3500	2326	0·665	26
[PtCl(PhBu$_2$P)$_3$]Cl	3490	2305	0·660	26
	P *trans* to Cl	P *trans* to R		
cis-[PtMeCl(Et$_3$P)$_2$]	4179	1719 (R = Me)	0·411	3
cis-[PtPhCl(Et$_3$P)$_2$]	4138	1577 (R = Ph)	0·381	3

A rather different situation exists in the compound *cis*-$[PtMeCl(Et_3P)_2]$ (13), where the non-equivalence of the phosphines

$$\begin{array}{ccc} R & PEt_3 \ (a) & J_{P_a-Pt}=4179 \ \text{c./sec.} \ (R=Me); \ 4138 \ \text{c./sec.} \ (R=Ph) \\ & \diagdown \ \diagup & \\ & Pt & \\ & \diagup \ \diagdown & \\ Cl & PEt_3 \ (b) & J_{P_b-Pt}=1719 \ \text{c./sec.} \ (R=Me); \ 1577 \ \text{c./sec.} \ (R=Ph) \end{array}$$

13

derives from the difference between R and Cl rather than between R_3P and Cl. The application of equation (8) with the same approximations as before, again leads to the conclusion that the difference in the Pt–P coupling constants is due to varying degrees of participation of the platinum 6*s* orbital in the two bonds. Here, however, π-*bonding can be unequivocally excluded* as the origin of the difference in the σ-bonds. Neither the chlorine atom nor the methyl group π-bonds strongly with platinum,[38] so P_a and P_b have equal opportunities to form π-bonds, and if only π-effects were important in determining the magnitude of $^1J_{P-Pt}$, the two coupling constants in the methyl compound would be expected to be closely similar.[3]

The methyl group, compared with chloride, considerably weakens the bond in the *trans* position to itself by an interaction through the σ-electrons of the complex,[38] so the bond Pt—P_b is less covalent and has a smaller *s* component than the bond Pt—P_a. Thus, in this molecule, it is clear that the σ-effects influence the Pt—P bonds very strongly, and it should be pointed out that in this single compound, the coupling constants are the largest and smallest yet found in trialkylphosphine platinum(II) complexes. The σ-effects, therefore, could be large enough on their own to account for the presently known range of couplings. This, however, increases the difficulty of assessing the importance of π-bonding in such systems, because σ-effects are always present in some degree, except in the hypothetical case of ligands bound to a metal by purely π-bonds. The ratio of coupling constants in the phenyl complex is only slightly smaller than that in the methyl complex, so it seems probable that any π-bonding of the phenyl group with platinum has at most only a small effect on the Pt—P σ-bond in the *trans* position.[3]

7. *Comparisons between isomeric complexes*

Because the phosphorus ligands are the same in isomeric complexes, the terms α^2 and $|S_P(0)|^2$ will be closely similar, but $|S_M(0)|^2$, $^3\overline{\Delta E}^{-1}$, and the degree of involvement of the metal *s* orbital may be different.

At first sight, therefore, it appears that little useful information could be gained from comparisons between coupling constants in isomers because there are too many variables.

It is found, however, for platinum[24] and for rhodium complexes, that in a given oxidation state, the coupling constants are much more sensitive to the nature of the *trans* ligand than to the nature of the *cis* ligands (Table IV). This is reasonable if the variations in the coupling are caused principally by variations in the degree of participation of the metal s orbital in the P—M bonds, but the terms $|S_M(0)|^2$ and $^3\overline{\Delta E}^{-1}$ should be affected equally by *cis* of *trans* ligands. Therefore, if the coupling constants in the isomeric complexes are very different, it is reasonable to assume that this is due to differences in the s components of the bonds and that the product of $|S_M(0)|^2$ and $^3\Delta E^{-1}$ is about the same for both isomers.

For tungsten complexes, it has not yet been established that the coupling is more sensitive to the nature of the *trans* than the *cis* groups,

TABLE IV

Effect of *trans* and *cis* ligands on phosphorus–metal coupling constants

Complex	$^1J_{P-M}$, c./sec.	*trans* groups	*cis* groups	Ref.
(1) a: $[PtCl(Bu_3P)_3]^{\oplus}Cl^{\ominus}$	3454	Cl	2P	4
b: $cis\text{-}[PtCl_2(Bu_3P)_2]$	3504	Cl	P,Cl	3, 26
c: $cis\text{-}[PtCl_2(Bu_3P)(PhO)_3P]$	3156	Cl	P',Cl	3
d: $cis\text{-}[PtMeCl(Et_3P)_2]$	4179	Cl	P, CH$_3$	3
e: $cis\text{-}[PtPhCl(Et_3P)_2]$	4138	Cl	P, Ph	3
f: $cis\text{-}[PtCl_2(Bu_3P)(Me_2S)]$	3386	Cl	S,Cl	24
(2) a: $[PtCl(Bu_3P)_3]^{\oplus}Cl^{\ominus}$	2270	P	P, Cl	4
b: $trans\text{-}[PtCl_2(Bu_3P)_2]$	2386	P	2Cl	3, 24, 26
c: $trans\text{-}[PtMeCl(Et_3P)_2]$	2821	P	Me, Cl	3
d: $trans\text{-}[PtPh_2(Et_3P)_2]$	2824	P	2Ph	3
e: $trans\text{-}[Pt(CN)_2(Bu_3P)_2]$	2158	P	2CN	3
(3) a: $cis\text{-}[PtMeCl(Et_3P)_2]$	1719	Me	P, Cl	3
b: $cis\text{-}[PtMe_2(Et_3P)_2]$	1856	Me	Me, P	3
c: $cis\text{-}[PtMe(NCS)(Et_3P)_2]$	1686	Me	NCS, P	3
(4) a: $mer\text{-}[RhCl_3(Bu_3P)_3]$	83·8	P	P, 3Cl	3, 7
b: $mer\text{-}[RhCl_3(Et_3P)_2CO]$	69·2	P	CO, 3Cl	3
c: $mer\text{-}[RhCl_3(Bu_3P)\{(PhO)_3P\}]$	79·3	P	P, 3Cl	3
(5) a: $fac\text{-}[RhCl_3(Et_3P)_3]$	111·2	Cl	2P, 2Cl	3
b: $mer\text{-}[RhCl_3(Bu_3P)_3]$	112·8	Cl	2P, 2Cl	3, 7

The relative independence of J on *cis* groups is illustrated by the constancy of J within the groups 1–5. The dependence of J on *trans* groups is evident from comparing groups 1, 2 and 3 (Pt^{II}) and groups 4 and 5 (Rh^{III}).

but the coupling constant in fac-$[W(CO)_3(Pr_3P)_3]$ (**14**) (P $trans$ to CO)[3] is certainly closer to those in cis-$[W(CO)_4(Bu_3P)_2]$ (**15**) and $[W(CO)_5(Bu_3P)]$ (**17**) (P $trans$ to CO)[21] than that in $trans$-$[W(CO)_4$-$(Bu_3P)_2]$ (**116**) (P $trans$ to P)[22]—

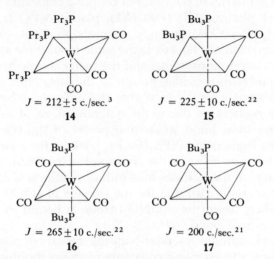

$J = 212 \pm 5$ c./sec.[3]

14

$J = 225 \pm 10$ c./sec.[22]

15

$J = 265 \pm 10$ c./sec.[22]

16

$J = 200$ c./sec.[21]

17

The coupling constants of representative pairs of complexes are given in Table V, together with the ratios of the coupling constants. The ratios of the coupling constants in the isomeric chloro-complexes of rhodium(III) and of platinum(II) are very similar to the ratios within the complexes mer-$[RhCl_3(R_3P)_3]$ and $[PtCl(R_3P)_3]^\oplus$, which were discussed earlier. The platinum(II) compounds, or analogues differing

TABLE V

Some coupling constants in isomeric complexes $[MX_nP_m]$

Molecular formula of complex	$^1J_{P-M}$, c./sec., in isomer with P $trans$ to P	$^1J_{P-M}$, c./sec., in isomer with P $trans$ to X	Ratio r	Ref.
$[RhCl_3(R_3P)_3]$	83·8 (mer)	111·2 (fac)	0·754	3
$[W(CO)_4(Bu_3P)_2]$	265 ± 10	225 ± 10	$1·18 \pm 0·09$	22
$[W(CO)_4(BuPh_2P)_2]$	275 ± 10	230 ± 10	$1·20 \pm 0·1$	22
$[PtCl_2(Bu_3P)_2]$	2386	3504	0·681	3, 24, 26
$[Pt(NO_3)_2(Bu_3P)_2]$	2506	3795	0·660	3
$[Pt(NO_2)_2(Bu_3P)_2]$	2607	2998	0·870	3
$[PtPh_2(Et_3P)_2]$	2824	1705	1·656	3
$[PtCl_4(Bu_3P)_2]$	1474	2065	0·714	3, 24

only in the alkyl groups attached to phosphorus, have been examined by a range of other physical techniques.[24] The results show that the Pt—P bond is appreciably stronger in the *cis*-isomer, and thus supports the interpretation of the coupling constants based on equation (8).[24]

The close similarity of the ratios of coupling constants in the chlorocomplexes of platinum(II) ($r = 0.681$), platinum(IV) ($r = 0.714$) and rhodium(III) ($r = 0.754$) strongly suggests that the mechanism of mutual influence of the ligands is the same in all three systems. Since π-bonding between phosphorus and the metal is expected to decrease rapidly with increasing oxidation state of the metal, this result appears to be inconsistent with the view that the differences between the σ-bonds in the isomers are due to the synergic effects of π-bonding.

The strong *trans* bond weakening power of the phenyl group is evident in the isomers of $[PtPh_2(Et_3P)_2]$, where the coupling is much greater in the *trans* than in the *cis* complex ($r = 1.66$), and the considerable range of magnitudes of σ-inductive effects is apparent from comparing this ratio with that for the isomers of $[Pt(NO_3)_2(Bu_3P)_2]$ ($r = 0.66$), where again the —ONO_2 group is bound to the metal by essentially a pure σ-bond.[3]

Although phosphine—metal π-bonding appears to play a small role in determining the coupling constants in these rhodium(III), platinum(II), and platinum(IV) complexes, its importance could be much greater in the tungsten(0) complexes. Grim *et al*[22] have suggested that the larger coupling in *trans*-$[W(CO)_4P_2]$ compared with the *cis* isomer ($r \sim 1.2$; see Table V) can be accounted for in terms of the greater π-acceptor power of carbon monoxide compared with R_3P. In these compounds, phosphorus competes with carbon monoxide for π-electrons, and the mutually *trans* phosphorus atoms should be more strongly π-bonded than the phosphorus atoms *trans* to carbonyl in *cis* compounds. In complexes of other phosphorus compounds PX_3, where X is an electronegative group, such as fluorine, the π-acceptor strength of the phosphorus atom is larger and approaches that of carbon monoxide. This leads to the prediction that the ratio of coupling constants in isomers of such complexes will approach unity.[22]

The possibility of σ-bond interactions in metal carbonyl derivatives of phosphorus compounds has received little attention in the literature, and experiments with purely σ-bonding ligands are to some extent limited by the difficulty of introducing them into carbonyl complexes. The σ-inductive effect of a ligand L on its neighbours in an octahedral complex $[LM(CO)_5]$ has been assumed[39] to be "isotropic" (that is equal for ligands *cis* and *trans* to L), but there is no symmetry requirement that this should be so. Thus, at present, it is not known whether

σ-effects contribute significantly to the difference between coupling constants in the *cis*- and *trans*-tetracarbonyltungsten complexes.

8. *Comparisons between phosphorus donors*

The coupling constants in complexes of the phosphines $R_nPh_{3-n}P$ have been shown by Grim *et al.*[7, 20-22, 26] to increase with the number of phenyl groups, except when the acceptor is mercury (Table VI).[27] Increasing the number of phenyl groups is considered to reduce the σ-donor power of phosphines, but to increase their π-acceptor power, so the increase in coupling constants in situations where metal π-electrons are available (W^0, Rh^I, Rh^{III} and Pt^{II}) is consistent with the view of Grim *et al.* that the change in π-bonding is more important than the σ-effects. These workers also found a good linear relationship for $PW(CO)_5$ between the coupling constants and the frequencies of the most intense $v(CO)$ band in the infrared spectra.[21*]

The increase in $^1J_{P-M}$ with increasing π-bonding could arise from a synergic effect on the σ-bonds, or from the contraction of the metal $(n)s$ orbitals by reducing the shielding of the $(n-1)d$ electrons.[21] In mercury(II) complexes the $5d$ electrons are too tightly bound to take part in π-bonding,[27] so the weakening of the σ-bonds with increasing number of phenyl groups on the phosphines is likely to be dominant. This interpretation is also consistent with the very large coupling constants found in phosphite and fluorophosphine complexes, since these ligands are considered to be weaker σ-donors, but substantially stronger π-acceptors than the phosphines.

The direct application of equation (8) to results of this kind is not entirely satisfactory, because in comparing the couplings involving only different substituents on phosphorus, many of the variables in the equation could make some contribution. Favourable cases for consideration are those complexes that contain phosphines and phosphites, because the differences in the coupling constants are very large. For the complexes (18 to 24) changing the groups on one phosphorus atom from three butyl groups to three phenoxy groups changes the coupling of that phosphorus to the metal by a factor very close to $1\cdot80$ in all cases. The other P–M coupling constants in the same molecules change by at most only *ca.* 8%, and this implies that $^3\overline{\Delta E}^{-1}|S_M(0)|^2$ varies only slightly with the nature of the groups attached to phosphorus. The greater part of the factor of $1\cdot80$ must therefore derive from changes in $(P'_{S_P S_M})^2$ and $|S_P(0)|^2$. The term $(P'_{S_P S_M})^2$ is directly proportional to the s character of the phosphorus lone pair orbital and involves the degree of participation of the metal s orbital in the P—M bond. This latter variable could well increase as

* Added in proof: See however, S. O. Grim, P. R. McAllister and R. M. Singer, *Chem. Comm.*, 1969, 38.

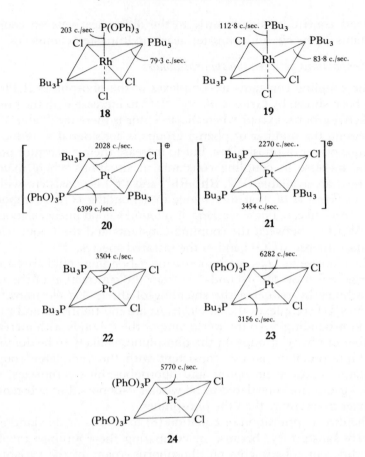

the P—M π-bond order increases, but it would be surprising if $|S_P(0)|^2$ and α_P^2 were unaffected by the substituents on phosphorus. Electronegative substituents contract the phosphorus valence shell orbitals[40] and increase $|S_P(0)|^2$, and if the ideas of Bent,[41] concerning the stereochemistry of carbon compounds, can be applied to phosphorus, electronegative substituents on phosphorus would increase the s character of the phosphorus lone pair. Both of these direct effects of the substituent on the phosphorus atom are expected to affect the magnitude of the coupling constant in the observed direction, and, to a first approximation, they are independent of the acceptor atom. They therefore provide a satisfactory explanation of the constancy of the ratio of phosphite to phosphine coupling constants in otherwise similar complexes. The ratios calculated from the results in Table VI are [complex, ratio] (P' varies): mer-$[RhCl_3P_2P']$, 1·81; $[PtClP_2P']^{\oplus}$, 1·85; cis-$[PtCl_2PP']$, 1·79 and 1·83; and fac-$[W(CO)_3P'_3]$, 1·80.

The slightly larger coupling constants in phenyl phosphine complexes compared with their alkyl phosphine analogues (Table VI) may also be partly due to the effect of the more electronegative phenyl group on $|S_P(0)|^2$ and α^2. The results in Table VI for the mercury complexes have the opposite trend, but complications in the spectra of mercuric halide–phosphine mixtures, thought to be due to exchange processes, have been observed and could possibly be the cause of this anomaly.[4]

TABLE VI

Phosphorus–metal coupling constants, c./sec., in complexes of phosphines $R_nPh_{3-n}P$

P	cis- $[PtCl_2P_2]^{26}$	trans- $[PtCl_2P_2]^{26}$	$[W(CO)_5P]^{21}$	cis- $[W(CO)_4P_2]^{22}$	trans- $[W(CO)_4P_2]^{22}$	$[HgBr_2P_2]^{27}$
Bu_3P	3504	2386	200	225 ± 10	265 ± 10	4777 ± 13
Bu_2PhP	3551	2462	235	220 ± 10	270 ± 10	4629 ± 14
$BuPh_2P$	3641	2531	250	230 ± 10	275 ± 10	4216 ± 6
Ph_3P	3684³	..	280	..	..	..

Other results

1. *Rhodium complexes*

$trans$-$[RhCl(CO)(Bu_3P)_2]^3$	118 ± 1		..	
$trans$-$[RhCl(CO)(Ph_3P)_2]^7$	129 ± 8		..	
mer-$[RhCl_3(Bu_3P)_3]^3$	112·8	$(I=)^*$	83·8	$(I=2)^*$
mer-$[RhCl_3(Bu_2PhP)_3]^3$	110 ± 1	$(I=1)^*$	85 ± 1	$(I=2)^*$
mer-$[RhCl_3(Bu_3P)_2\{(PhO)_3P\}]^3$	203 ± 1	$[(PhO)_3P]$	79·3	$(Bu_3P, I=2)$

2. *Tungsten complexes*

cis-$[W(CO)_4(Me_2NPF_2)_2]^{45}$	370 ± 10	..
cis-$[W(CO)_4(ClCH_2PF_2)_2]^{45}$	370 ± 10	..
fac-$[W(CO)_3(Pr_3P)_3]^3$	212 ± 5	..
fac-$[W(CO)_3\{(MeO)_3P\}_3]^3$	381	..

3. *Platinum complexes*

$[PtCl(Bu_3P)_3]Cl^3$	3454	$(I=1)^*$	2270	$(I=2)^*$
$[PtCl(Bu_2PhP)_3]Cl^{26}$	3490	$(I=1)^*$	2305	$(I=2)^*$
$[PtCl(Bu_3P)_2\{(PhO)_3P\}]Cl^3$	6399	$[(PhO)_3P]$,	2028	$(Bu_3P, I=2)^*$
cis-$[PtCl_2(Bu_3P)\{(PhO)_3P\}]^3$	3156	(Bu_3P)	6282	$[(PhO)_3P]$
cis-$[PtCl_2\{(PhO)_3P\}_2]^3$	5770			
cis-$[PtCl_2\{(EtO)_3P\}_2]^{3,24}$	5698			

* I = relative intensity of resonance.

13

9. *Effect of oxidation state of metal*

Since rhodium(I) and platinum(II) complexes are square planar, and rhodium(III) and platinum(IV) complexes are octahedral, the increase of oxidation state of each metal is accompanied by an increase in the co-ordination number, n, from four to six. Since equation (6) shows that $^1J_{P-M}$ is proportional to n^{-1}, this factor alone should result in the couplings in the higher oxidation state being 0·667 of the coupling in the lower oxidation state. The ratio of couplings found are slightly smaller than 0·67 for chloro-complexes (see Table VII), but are close to this for the methyl complexes (probably because of the tendency of methyl groups to increase coupling to phosphorus in the *cis* position[3]). These results suggest that any increase in $|S_M(0)|^2$ and the covalency of the bonds in the higher oxidation states is nearly cancelled by an increase in $^3\overline{\Delta E}$.

TABLE VII

Variation of some phosphorus–metal coupling constants with oxidation state

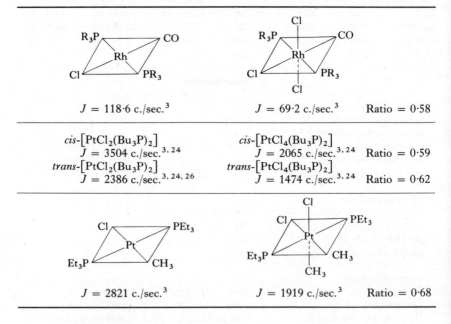

$J = 118\cdot6$ c./sec.[3]	$J = 69\cdot2$ c./sec.[3] Ratio = 0·58
cis-[PtCl₂(Bu₃P)₂] $J = 3504$ c./sec.[3, 24]	*cis*-[PtCl₄(Bu₃P)₂] $J = 2065$ c./sec.[3, 24] Ratio = 0·59
trans-[PtCl₂(Bu₃P)₂] $J = 2386$ c./sec.[3, 24, 26]	*trans*-[PtCl₄(Bu₃P)₂] $J = 1474$ c./sec.[3, 24] Ratio = 0·62
$J = 2821$ c./sec.[3]	$J = 1919$ c./sec.[3] Ratio = 0·68

10. *Other aspects*

(a) *Tungsten complexes.* The coupling constants in the substituted tungsten carbonyls $[W(CO)_{6-m}P_m]$ vary with m and with the stereochemistry of the complexes (Table VI). The larger coupling in the *trans*- than the *cis*-bis(phosphine)tetracarbonyl derivatives is consistent with the π-bonding to phosphorus being greater in the *trans* isomer.[22] That this is likely to be the case can be seen from a simple model in which the relative affinity of CO and R_3P for d_π electrons is assumed to be 2:1. In the *trans* complex the phosphines overlap with two d_π orbitals on tungsten each of the following type (**25**).

25

The total affinity of the ligands for an electron pair in such an orbital is taken as 2×2 (for 2 CO groups) plus 2×1 (for two phosphines), so each phosphorus has a $\frac{1}{6}$ "π-bond order". Because there are two mutually perpendicular d_π orbitals of this type, the π-bond order of each P—W bond is taken to be $\frac{1}{3}$ (70/210). The "π-bond order" in the *cis* isomer is calculated to be somewhat smaller (65/210), and the results for these and other complexes are given in Table VIII.

The coupling constants for complexes of these types are available

TABLE VIII

π-Bond order in phosphorus complexes of tungsten

Complex	P–W "π-bond order"
$[W(CO)_5P]$	60/210
cis-$[W(CO)_4P_2]$	65/210
trans-$W(CO)_4P_2]$	70/210
fac-$[W(CO)_3P_3]$	70/210

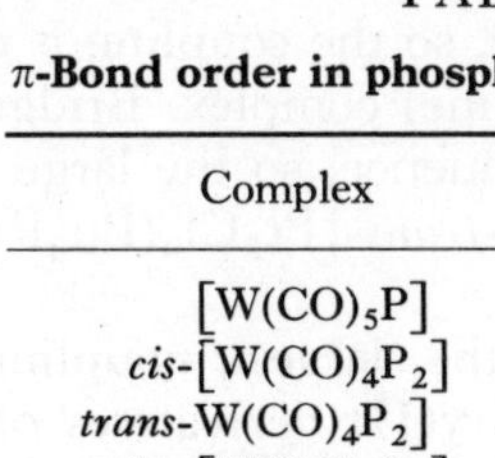

P(a) 72/210
P(b) 77/210

except for *mer*-$[W(CO)_3P_3]$ (Table VI). For $P = Bu_3P$, the coupling constants for $[W(CO)_5P]$ and *cis*- and *trans*-$[W(CO)_4P_2]$ change in the manner expected from Table VIII, but the coupling in *trans*-$[W(CO)_4P_2]$ is expected to be very similar to that in *fac*-$[W(CO)_3P_3]$ (this result is independent of the relative π affinities of P and CO); the experimental results are 265 c./sec. (Bu_3P complex) and 212 c./sec. (Pr_3P complex). Also, it should be noted that for $P = Ph_2BuP$ and $PhBu_2P$ the coupling constants are larger in $[W(CO)_5P]$ than in *cis*-$[W(CO)_4P_2]$. Thus, many of the results suggest that the coupling constants may not be dominated by π-bonding interactions if Table VIII is a reasonable qualitative guide to their magnitude.

More results for *tris*-(phosphine) complexes, particularly for the meridianal isomers, would be a valuable aid to the interpretation of W–P coupling constants. We noted earlier (p. 368) that, for a given ligand, the couplings in these compounds may depend mainly on the *trans* ligand, and if this proves to be correct, the results of Table VIII suggest that in octahedral complexes this is unlikely to arise from the dominance of π-interactions. Until more results are available, it may be best to restrict interpretation to comparisons between complexes of the same microsymmetry (Section IV.C.8).

(b) *Platinum complexes.* Some other results for platinum(II) complexes have been interpreted on the basis that variations in $^3\overline{\Delta E}^{-1}|S_{Pt}(0)|^2$ are not large.[24] The coupling constant in *trans*-$[PtCl_2(Bu_3P)\,(amine)]$ is about 3400 c./sec. and varies only slightly with the nature of the amine. The group *trans* to phosphorus in this molecule has a much lower *trans* influence than phosphine, so the coupling is much larger than in the *trans*-dichlorobis(phosphine) complex. Bridging chlorine atoms also have a very low *trans* influence, so the large coupling of 3800 c./sec. is to be expected for *sym-trans*-$[Pt_2Cl_4(Bu_3P)_2]$.[24]

(c) *Mercury complexes.* Some of the largest coupling constants known have been found[4] for mercury(II) derivatives of the ligand $(EtO)_2P—O^\ominus$, (see also Section II.B.2), so there is little doubt that there is a Hg—P bond in these compounds (Table IX). In solution, the chloro-complex $[\{(EtO)_2PO\}HgCl]$ is found to be dimeric[9] and as the basis of the lowering of v ($P=O$) in the infrared spectrum, the structure (26) has been proposed.[9] Until more is known of the stereochemistry of the mercury in these compounds, detailed discussion of the results is not worthwhile, but it is clear from the smaller coupling in $[\{(EtO)_2PO\}_2Hg]$ compared with the chloro-complex that the mutual influence of phosphorus atoms is strong in mercury(II) com-

TABLE IX

Coupling constants for $[\{(EtO)_2PO\}HgX]$, kc/sec.[4]

X	Cl	Br	I	CH_3CO_2	$(EtO)_2PO$
J	12·63	12·24	11·18	12·97	7·50

plexes as well as in platinum and rhodium complexes. Since π-bonding involving mercury is unlikely to be important, this again points to the operation of strong effects through the σ-electrons of the complexes.

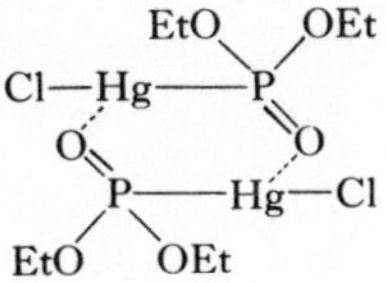

26

(d) *Other metals.* Data included in the construction of Fig. 5, but not discussed here because of the lack of valid comparisons, are [complex, J (c./sec.)]: $[Co(PF_3)_4]^{\ominus}$, 1222 ± 25;[18] $[Cu\{MeO)_3P\}_4]^{\oplus}$, 1190 ± 30;[19] $[Cu\{(EtO)_3P\}_4]$, 1210 ± 30;[19] $[Rh(PF_3)_4]^{\ominus}$, 325.[42]

D. Results for non-transition elements

Very few phosphorus–acceptor atom coupling constants have been reported for complexes of non-transition elements (Table X); even the protonated phosphines appear to have received little attention.[2] The absence of data may be partly explained by the prevalence of very rapid dissociation and recombination reactions for non-transition element compounds (see Section III.A.2), and at present results are available only for the very strong acceptors: $AlCl_3$,[17] $AlBr_3$,[17] BH_3,[15] some other boron hydrides[16] and the proton.[1, 13, 14]

Thus, there is little scope for assessing the relative importance of terms in equation (8) when applied to non-transition elements compounds, so we confine our comment on the results to some very brief comparisons with transition metal complexes.

The coupling $^1J_{P-H}$ in protonated phosphines is larger in $[PhMe_2PH]^{\oplus}$ (525 c./sec.[14]) than in $[Me_3PH]^{\oplus}$ (515 c./sec.[13]), and this is similar to the behaviour found for transition-metal complexes with the exception of mercury(II) (see Section III.B.8). Similarly, phosphites give larger couplings than phosphines in BH_3 complexes, but the ratio of phosphite to phosphine couplings (*ca.* 1·5) is somewhat

TABLE X

Phosphorus coupling constants in complexes of non-transition elements

	Acceptor	$^1J_{P-M}$, c./sec.	Ref.
PH_3	$H^{\oplus}$	550	1
Me_3P	$H^{\oplus}$	515	13
Me_2PhP	$H^{\oplus}$	525	14
PH_3	BH_3	27	43
Me_2PH	BH_3	50	15
Me_3P	BH_3	63·5	15
$(MeO)_3P$	BH_3	97·2	15

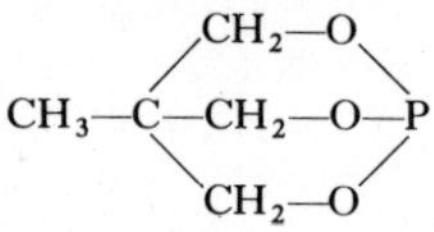

$$CH_3-\overset{\overset{\displaystyle CH_2-O}{\diagup}}{\underset{\underset{\displaystyle CH_2-O}{\diagdown}}{C}}-CH_2-O-P$$ | BH_3 | 96·0 | 15

| 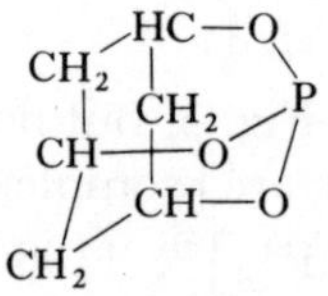 (bicyclic phosphite structure) | BH_3 | 97·6 | 15 |

PHF_2	BH_3	49	43
PF_3	BH_3	39	43
Me_2NPF_2	BH_3	80	10, 11
$(Me_2N)_2PF$	BH_3	80	10, 11
PF_3	B_4H_8	149	16
Me_2NPF_2	B_4H_8	180	11
Me_3P	$AlCl_3$	263	17
Et_3P	$AlCl_3$	262	17
Me_3P	$AlBr_3$	248	17
Et_3P	$AlBr_3$	240	17

smaller than the ratio found for transition-metal complexes (*ca.* 1·8) (Section III.B.8). Fluorinated phosphines give rather smaller coupling constants in BH_3 complexes than expected from analogy with transition-metal compounds, but for the more complex boron hydrides the couplings are much larger.

IV. PHOSPHORUS–PHOSPHORUS COUPLING CONSTANTS IN TRANSITION METAL COMPLEXES

Phosphorus–Phosphorus spin coupling constants through metal atoms have only been obtained recently. There are three distinct situations in which such parameters can be determined from suitable n.m.r. spectra—

(a) By direct observation of the ^{31}P n.m.r. spectrum of complexes containing two or more *different* phosphine ligands co-ordinated to the same metal atom, e.g., in *trans*-$[PdI_2(Me_3P)(Et_3P)]^{44}$ (**27**), where the spectrum is of the AB type (neglecting coupling with protons).

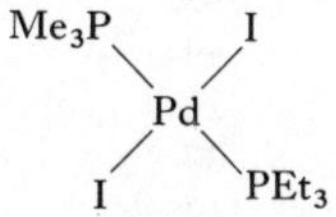

27

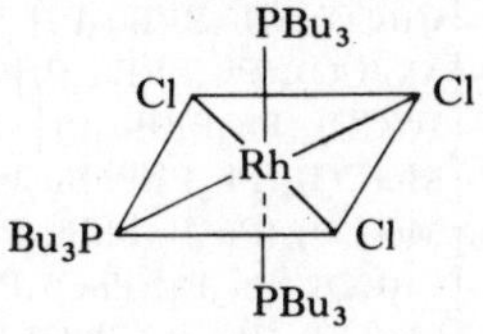

28

(b) By direct observation of the ^{31}P n.m.r. spectrum in systems containing chemically identical phosphine ligands in *different environments* in the complex, e.g., *mer*-$[RhCl_3(Bu_3P)_3]^7$ (**28**) where the spectrum is usually of the AX_2 type (see Section II.A.1).

(c) By detailed analysis of the n.m.r. spectra in favourable cases (see below) of phosphine complexes containing *chemically equivalent* but nevertheless *magnetically non-equivalent* nuclei, e.g., *trans*-$[Cr(CO)_4(PF_3)_2]$ (**29**),[45] *fac*-$[Mo(CO)_3(PF_3)_3]$ (**30**)[46] and *cis*-$[PdCl_2(Me_3P)_2]$ (**31**).[44]

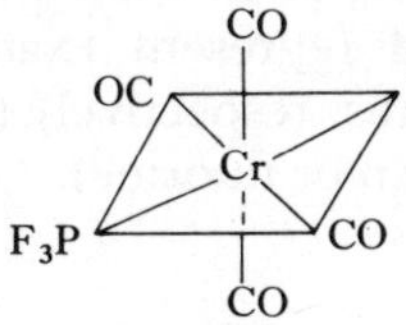

29

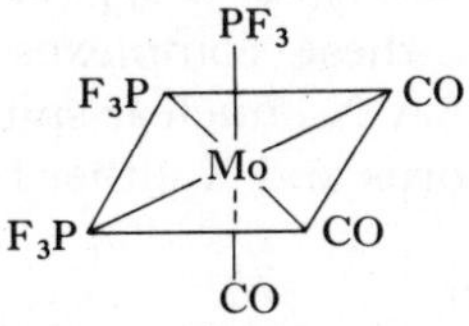

30

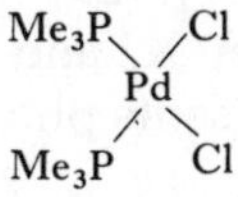

31

Situations (a) and (b) have been illustrated in Section II, and Table XI lists examples of phosphorus–phosphorus coupling constants obtained in this way. In Section (c), however, the situation is more complicated and will be discussed separately below.

TABLE XI

Some coupling constants ($^2J_{PMP'}$) determined by direct observation of the ^{31}P n.m.r. spectra

Complex	$^2J_{PMP'}$, c./sec.	Ref.
mer-$[RhCl_3(Bu_3P)_3]$	21·9	3
mer-$[RhCl_3(Pr_3P)_3]$	22±3	7
mer-$[RhCl_3(PhEt_2P)_3]$	30±8	7
trans-$[Cr(CO)_4(Ph_3P)(Bu_3P)]$	25	47
trans-$[Mo(CO)_4(Ph_3P)(Bu_3P)]$	50	47
trans-$[W(CO)_4(Ph_3P)(Bu_3P)]$	65	47
trans-$[Mo(CO)_4(Ph_3P)(PhBu_2P)]$	49	47
cis-$[Mo(CO)_4(Ph_3P)(PhBu_2P)]$	21	47
trans-$[Cr(CO)_4(Bu_3P)\{(PhO)_3P\}]$	30	47
trans-$[Mo(CO)_4(Bu_3P)\{(PhO)_3P\}]$	112	47
trans-$[W(CO)_4(Bu_3P)\{(PhO)_3P\}]$	120	47
trans-$[W(CO)_4(PhBu_2P)\{(PhO)_3P\}]$	112	47
mer-$[Mo(CO)_3\{(EtO)_3P\}\{Ph_2P(CH_2)_2PPh_2\}]$	104	47
trans-$[PdI_2(Me_3P)(Et_3P)]$	565	44
trans-$[PdI_2(PhMe_2P)\{(PhO)_3P\}]$	829	48
trans-$[PdI_2(PhMe_2P)(Bu_3P)]$	551	48
trans-$[PdI_2(Bu_3P)\{(PhO)_3P\}]$	758	48
cis-$[PtCl_2(Bu_3P)\{(PhO)_3P\}]$	20·0	3
mer-$[RhCl_3(Bu_3P)_2\{(PhO)_3P\}]$	30·3	3

A. Complexes containing magnetically non-equivalent phosphorus atoms

Consider complexes of the general type P_2MZ_n, where M is the metal atom, Z_n represents other ligands in the system and P is the phosphorus ligand in question. If for simplicity P was $(CH_3)_3P$ as in the complex cis-$[PdCl_2(Me_3P)_2]$ (**31**) or PF_3 as in trans-$[Cr(CO)_4-(PF_3)_2]$ (**29**) then these complexes would represent examples of $X_9AA'X_9'$ and $X_3AA'X_3'$ nuclear spin systems, respectively (where A represents phosphorus and X either hydrogen or fluorine).

1. *Detailed analysis*

Detailed analysis of spectra of this type leads in principle to the evaluation of $|J_{AX}|$, $|J_{AX}'|$, $|J_{AA}'|$ and $|J_{XX}'|$. General equations for line positions and intensities of the X part of an $X_nAA'X_n'$ spin system have been presented by Harris[49] for situations where the remote XX' coupling is zero. The appearance of the X part of such a spectrum consists of a doublet of separation $|J_{AX}+J_{AX}'|$ centred at vX, (the chemical shift of the X nucleus), which has relative intensity 2^{2n-1}, together with $2n$ pairs of lines also symmetrically placed about νX of separation S, where—

$$S = [\psi^2 L^2 + J_{AA'}{}^2]^{\frac{1}{2}} \pm [(\psi - 1)^2 L^2 + J_{AA'}{}^2]^{\frac{1}{2}}$$

and $L_{AX} = |J_{AX} - J_{AX'}|$ and ψ is an integer between 1 and n.

(a) Trans *complexes*. In certain *trans*-phosphine metal complexes, e.g., those involving dimethylphenylphosphine, the methyl resonance actually appears as a deceptively simple "triplet" even though the phosphorus nuclei are non-equivalent. This is because the geminal phosphorus–phosphorus coupling constant $^2J_{PMP'}$ is very much larger than L_{PH}, $[L_{PH} = |^2J_{PCH} - {}^4J_{PMCH}|]$, and the $X_n AA'X'_n$ spectrum approximates to an $A_n X_{2n}$ system with the central line of the "triplet" resulting from overlap of lines.

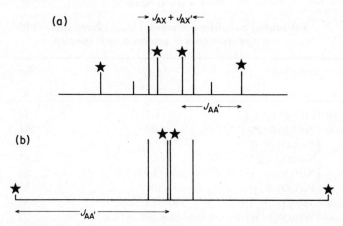

FIG. 9. Variation of the X part of an $X_n AA'X'_n$ spectrum, $(n=2)$, as $|J_{AA'}|$ increases relative to $|J_{AX} - J_{AX'}|$; (a) the starred lines form two AB spectra whose separation is $L_{AX} = |J_{AX} - J_{AX'}|$ where $L_{AX} > J_{AA'}$. (b) $J_{AA'} \gg L_{AX}$.

Figure 9 shows diagrammatically how the appearance of the X part of an $X_n AA'X'_n$ spectrum changes as the magnitude of $J_{AA'}$ increases relative to $|J_{AX} - J_{AX'}|$, for the case where J_{AX} and $J_{AX'}$ are of opposite sign.

For complexed alkyl phosphines $|^2J_{PCH}|$ is usually in the 5–20 c./sec. range, and since $|^4J_{PMPCH}|$ is rather small, $|^2J_{PMP'}|$ is much larger than $|^2J_{PCH} - {}^4J_{PMPCH}|$ in the strongly coupled system, and accordingly the proton spectrum exhibits the triplet pattern. Spectra of this type have been reported by several authors and often discussed in terms of the concept of "virtual" coupling.[50]

13*

(b) cis-*Complexes*. In analogous *cis* complexes, however $|^2 J_{PMP'}|$ and $^4 J_{PMPCH}$ are both small,* and the proton n.m.r. spectrum therefore usually appears as a doublet,[50] (see however ref. 44).

B. Estimated $|^2 J_{PMP'}|$ coupling constants from line-width measurements

Estimates of $^2 J_{PMP'}$ have been made from the width of the central line for certain phosphite complexes of the type $[P_n Ni(CO)_{4-n}]$, $[Fe(CO)_3 P_2]$, and trans-$[P_2 M(CO)_4]$ (M = Cr, Mo, W)[51, 52] where P is $P(OCH_2)_3 CCH_3$; Table XII summarizes some of the published data. The difficulties inherent in the method are reflected in the differing estimates[51, 52] of $|^2 J_{PMP'}|$ made for the complexes of the Group VIa metal carbonyls (see Table XII).

TABLE XII

Estimated coupling constants ($^2 J_{PMP'}$) from line-width measurements of proton n.m.r. spectra

Complex	$^2 J_{PMP'}$, c./sec.	Ref.
cis-$[PtCl_2(Et_3P)_2]$	< 5	44
trans-$[PtCl_2(Me_3P)_2]$	90	31
$[Ni(CO)_2 P_2]$‡	0	51
$[Ni(CO)P_3]$‡	1	51
$[NiP_4]$‡	15	51
$[Fe(CO)_3 P_2]$‡	300	52
trans-$[Mo(CO)_4 P_2]$†‡	210 ± 50	52
trans-$[W(CO)_4 P_2]$†‡	65 ± 10	52
trans-$[Cr(CO)_4 P_2]$†‡	9 ± 2	52

‡ P = $P(OCH_2)_3 CCH_3$.

† These are revised data which had previously been reported in reference 51 as 1, 60 and 80 c./sec. for the Cr, Mo and W complexes, respectively.

Similarly the value of about 90 c./sec. for $|^2 J_{PPtP'}|$ suggested by McFarlane for trans-$[PtCl_2(Et_3P)_2]$,[31] based on intensity measurements in the proton n.m.r. spectrum, appears to be underestimated in view of values in the 550–570 c./sec. range reported in Table XI

* Note added in proof: There have been two very recent reports of transition metal complexes of $P(OCH_2)_3 CR$ where $^2 J_{PMP'}$ is large enough in *cis* compounds to give a "virtually coupled" spectrum (W. E. Stanclift and D. G. Hendricker, *Inorg. Chem.*, 1968, **7**, 1242; P. K. Maples and C. S. Kraihanzel, *Chem. Comm.*, 1968, 922).

for very closely related palladium complexes so values based solely on this method should be treated with some caution.

C. $|^2J_{PMP'}|$ coupling constants in fluorophosphine–transition metal complexes

Fluorophosphines of general formula R_nPF_{3-n} have very large directly bonded phosphorus–fluorine coupling constants $|^1J_{PF}|$[53] (in the 1000–1400 c./sec. range), which change relatively slightly when the ligands are co-ordinated to a wide range of transition-metal atoms.[45, 54–57] As a result, $|^2J_{PMP'}|$ is invariably much smaller than L_{PF}, $|^1J_{PF} - {}^3J_{PMPF}|$, even for the strongly coupled situation. This leads to all the lines in the fluorine or phosphorus n.m.r. spectra being well separated, (spinning 5 mm. tubes required), and enables accurate values for the phosphorus–phosphorus coupling constants to be evaluated. In addition, the magnitude and relative signs of $|^1J_{PF}|$ and $|^3J_{PMPF}|$ are readily obtained.

TABLE XIII

Phosphorus–phosphorus coupling constants ($^2J_{PMP'}$) in octahedral complexes containing fluorophosphine ligands

Complex	$^2J_{PMP'}$, c./sec.	Ref.
cis-$[Cr(CO)_4(PF_3)_2]$	78.5 ± 0.5	45
cis-$[Cr(CO)_4(CCl_3PF_2)_2]$	67.0 ± 1.0	45
cis-$[Cr(CO)_4(Me_2NPF_2)_2]$	62.0 ± 2.0	45
cis-$[Cr(CO)_4\{EtN(PF_2)_2\}]$	78.5 ± 0.5	45
trans-$[Cr(CO)_4(PF_3)_2]$	34.0 ± 0.5	45
cis-$[Mo(CO)_4(PF_3)_2]$	55.5 ± 0.5	12
cis-$[Mo(CO)_4(CF_3PF_2)_2]$	49.0 ± 1.0	12
cis-$[Mo(CO)_4(CCl_3PF_2)_2]$	48.0 ± 0.5	12
cis-$[Mo(CO)_4(ClCH_2PF_2]$	43	12
cis-$[Mo(CO)_4\{EtN(PF_2)_2\}]$	121	45
cis-$[Mo(CO)_4(Me_2NPF_2)_2]$	38.0 ± 1.0	12
cis-$[Mo(CO)_4(Et_2NPF_2)_2]$	38.0 ± 1.0	45
trans-$[Mo(CO)_4(PF_3)_2]$	312	57
cis-$[Mo(CO)_3(PF_3)_3]$	56.4 ± 1.2	46
cis-$[Mo(CO)_3(PhOPF_2)_3]$	55.2	46
cis-$[Mo(CO)_3(C_6H_4O_2PF)_3]$	51.0	46
cis-$[Mo(CO)_3(PhPF_2)_3]$	43.0 ± 1.0	46
cis-$[W(CO)_4(PF_3)_2]$	41	45
cis-$[W(CO)_4(CCl_3PF_2)]$	37.6 ± 0.8	45
cis-$[W(CO)_4(ClCH_2PF_2)_2]$	34.6 ± 0.8	45
cis-$[W(CO)_4(Me_2NPF_2)_2]$	21.1 ± 1.0	45
cis-$[W(CO)_4\{EtN(PF_2)_2\}]$	155.3 ± 0.6	45

Table XIII lists several recently determined $^2J_{PMP'}$ coupling constants in substituted Group VIa metal carbonyl complexes, $[P_nM(CO)_{6-n}]$ $[M = Cr, Mo, W; n = 2, 3]$,[12,45,46] and Fig. 10 illustrates the ^{19}F n.m.r. spectrum of a mixture of *cis*- and *trans*-$[Cr(CO)_4$-$(PF_3)_2]$,[45] which are both $X_3AA'X_3'$ spin systems, where the individual spectra of the two isomers are easily identifiable on account of their different fluorine chemical shifts (about 1·3 p.p.m.).

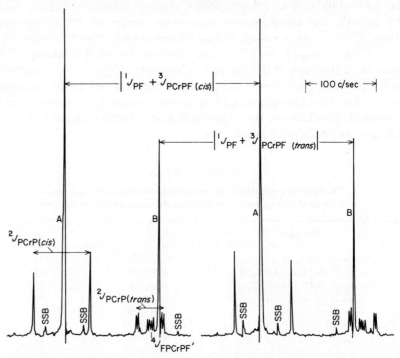

FIG. 10. 94·1 Mc./sec. ^{19}F n.m.r. spectrum of a mixture of *cis*- and *trans*-$[Cr(CO)_4(PF_3)_2]$.[45] A is the *cis* isomer and B is the *trans* isomer. The more extensive fine structure associated with the *trans* isomer result from the larger values of $^3J_{PCrPF}$ and $^4J_{FPCrPF'}$ coupling constants compared with those of the *cis* isomer. SSB = spinning band. (From Johnson *et al.*[45])

A noteworthy feature of the various spin-coupling constants listed in Table XIII is that $|^2J_{PMP'}|$ is always found to be appreciably greater than zero. The two phosphorus–fluorine coupling constants $^1J_{PF}$ and $^3J_{PMPF}$ are always of opposite sign, the latter being rather small (1–5 c./sec.). The *trans* complexes are found to have noticeably larger indirectly bonded phosphorus–fluorine couplings $|^3J_{PMPF}|$ and

$|^4J_{FPMPF'}|$ than their *cis* analogues. In addition, it is believed that $J_{PMP'}$ is *negative* in the *cis*-$[Cr(CO)_4(PF_3)_2]$ and *positive* in the *trans* isomer (see next Section for more discussion).

D. Signs of phosphorus–phosphorus coupling constants

Analysis of the $X_nAA'X_n'$ n.m.r. spectra provides information concerning the relative signs of $^1J_{PF}$ and $^3J_{PMPF}$, but not $^2J_{PMP'}$. Recently, double-resonance experiments[58] on *cis*-$[Mo(CO)_4(CCl_3PF_2)_2]$ and $[Mo(CO)_4\{EtN(PF_2)_2\}]$ (32) have given the following results, based on $K = \frac{1}{2}(^1J_{PF} + {}^3J_{PMPF})$ being *negative*—

Complex	$^2J_{PMP'}$
cis-$[Mo(CO)_4(CCl_3PF_2)_2]$	Negative
cis-$[Mo(CO)_4\{EtN(PF_2)_2\}]$	Positive

Since $^3J_{PMPF}$ is small by comparison with $^1J_{PF}$, and $^1J_{PF}$ has been shown to be negative in unco-ordinated fluorophosphines[59,60] it follows that $^2J_{PMP'}$ is *negative* in the bis-CCl_3PF_2 complex and *positive* in the chelating $EtN(PF_2)_2$ derivative. The reason for this difference

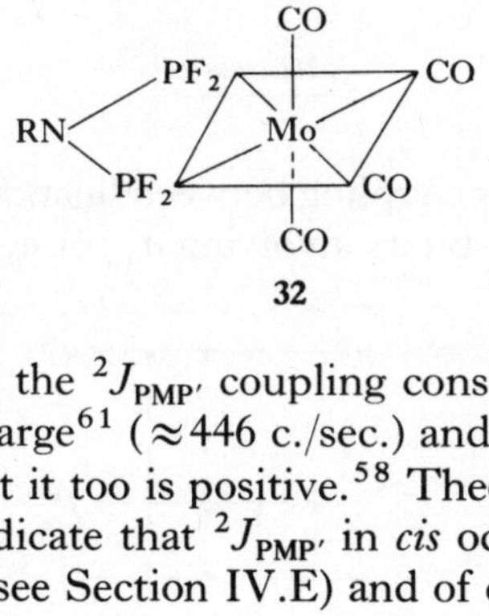

32

is due to the fact that the $^2J_{PMP'}$ coupling constant in the free ligand $[EtN(PF_2)_2]$ is very large[61] (≈ 446 c./sec.) and double-resonance experiments suggest that it too is positive.[58] Theoretical considerations (see Section IV.E) indicate that $^2J_{PMP'}$ in *cis* octahedral complexes is likely to be negative (see Section IV.E) and of opposite sign to $^2J_{PMP'}$ in the *trans* compound.

E. Factors affecting the magnitude of $^2J_{PMP'}$ in octahedral and tetrahedral complexes

1. cis-*Octahedral complexes*

The data for $^2J_{PMP'}$ in *cis*-octahedral complexes presented in Table XIII will be discussed[62] here in relationship mainly to variations firstly in the fluorophosphine ligands, R_nPF_{3-n}, and secondly in the nature of the metal atom. The ligand σ-orbitals which contain s character and therefore contribute to the coupling via the Fermi contact term (see Section III), transform as a_{1_g}, e_g and t_{1_u} representations of the octahedral group. A simplified MO diagram is shown below for the metal d^6 system—

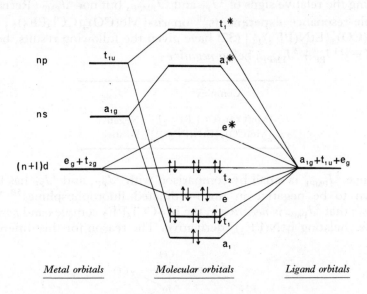

| | Metal orbitals | Molecular orbitals | Ligand orbitals |

Contributions to the *cis* coupling between ligands arise from excitations from filled to empty orbitals involving a_{1g} or e_g orbitals—

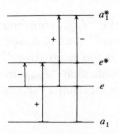

and those excitations involving either $e \rightarrow e^*$ or $a_1 \rightarrow a_1^*$ produce a *negative* contribution to the coupling, whereas $e \rightarrow a_1^*$ or $a_1 \rightarrow e^*$ give *positive* contributions. Now since the magnitude of the contribution of each excitation will be proportional to—

    (i) the inverse of the energy difference ΔE between the states and

(ii) the relative amounts of ligand orbitals in the filled and empty orbitals. If $^2J_{PMP'}$ represents the inter-ligand coupling term, it follows that—

$$^2J_{PMP'} \propto \left\{ -\frac{c_e^2 c_{e*}^2}{\Delta E_{ee*}} + \frac{c_{e*}^2 c_a^2}{\Delta E_{ae*}} + \frac{c_{a*}^2 c_e^2}{\Delta E_{a*e}} - \frac{c_{a*}^2 c_a^2}{\Delta E_{a*a}} \right\}$$

where c_i is the coefficient of the ligand s orbital in the molecular orbital i.

If the numerators are all approximately equal, the coupling will be dominated by the first term in this expression and therefore should be *negative*. The coupling $^2J_{PMP'}$ decreases if the ionic character of the orbitals increases and if the separation of bonding and anti-bonding orbitals increases.

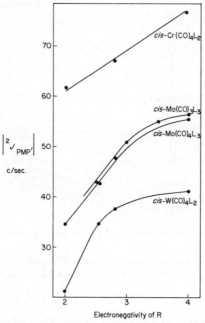

FIG. 11. Relationships between $|^2J_{PMP'}|$ and the electronegativity of R for some R_nPF_{3-n} Group VIa carbonyl complexes. (Data from refs. 12, 45, and 46.)

(a) *Effect on $|^2J_{PMP'}|$ of varying the ligand.* Both the s character of the phosphorus hybrid orbital which is forming the σ-bond to a given transition-metal atom and the amplitude of the phosphorus s orbital at the nucleus, $|S_P(0)|^2$, depend on the electron-withdrawing power of all the substituents attached to the phosphorus atom. Both increase as the electronegativity of the substituents increases. These effects are greater than the effects on the orbital energies, and as a result the trifluorophosphine complexes have the largest magnitude of the $^2J_{PMP'}$ coupling constant for a particular series of complexes of the same stereochemistry, except for the special case of the chelating $EtN(PF_2)_2$ complexes discussed separately. This is illustrated well by Fig. 11 which is a plot of $|^2J_{PMP'}|$ against the electronegativity of the group R for several complexes of general type $[\{R_nPF_{3-n}\}_xM(CO)_{6-x}]$ ($x=2$, 3; M = Cr, Mo and W).[62] It should be noted that the ligand π-orbitals, which transform as $t_{1g} + t_{2g} + t_{1u} + t_{2g}$, will therefore affect the cis coupling constant only in so far as they affect the σ-bonds and $|S_M(0)|^2$ terms.

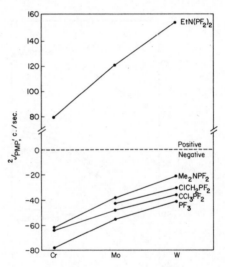

FIG. 12. $^2J_{PMP'}$ coupling constants for Group VIa carbonyl fluorophosphine complexes, cis-$[M(CO)_4P_2]$ (P = PF_3, CCl_3PF_2, $ClCH_2PF_2$, Me_2NPF_2), and $[M(CO)_4\{EtN(PF_2)_2\}]$.[62]

(b) *Variation of* $^2J_{PMP'}$ *with metal atom.* The effect of changing the acceptor atom within the same group of the Periodic Table has been studied for cis-fluorophosphine Group VIa tetracarbonyl complexes (Cr, Mo and W) and the data are plotted in Fig. 12, also taking into account the signs of the coupling constants.[62]

It is interesting to note that in the $EtN(PF_2)_2$ complexes the observed coupling constant can be considered to represent a positive contribution within the ligand, (via nitrogen), and a negative contribution through the metal atom.[58] Now since the magnitude of the negative contribution *decreases* in the order $Cr > Mo > W$ for the normal *cis*-$[M(CO)_4P_2]$ complexes (lower half of graph) the magnitude of $^2J_{PMP'}$ for the special case of the $EtN(PF_2)_2$ complexes should *increase* in the order $W > Mo > Cr$ as is evident from the upper curve.

Very recently Verkade *et al.*[63] have discussed the variation in $^2J_{PMP'}$ in various phosphine complexes of transition metal in terms of the stereochemistry of the complex and the electronegativity of the group attached to phosphorus. They noted that $^2J_{PMP'}$ *trans* was usually greater (in magnitude) than the corresponding $^2J_{PMP'}$ *cis* in $[M(CO)_4P_2]$ complexes except for the $[Cr(CO)_4P_2]$ series. No account was taken of possible variation in sign of the $^2J_{PMP'}$ coupling constants in the different stereochemistries, and it seems likely that differences in the absolute magnitudes $^2J_{PMP'}$ in these complexes simply reflects changes in their position within Fig. 13 relative to the origin.

2. trans *Substituted octahedral complexes*

The simplified MO diagram is shown below—

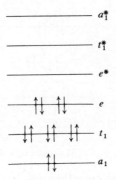

and the coupling arises from excitation between a_1, e and t_1 orbitals with the following numerical weights, relative signs and appropriate coefficients.

Contribution to $^2J_{PMP'}$			
$a_1 \to a_1^*$	$-1/\Delta a_1 a_1^*$	$t_1 \to a_1^*$	$+3/\Delta t_1 a_1^*$
$a_1 \to e^*$	$-2/\Delta a_1 e^*$	$e \to e^*$	$-4/\Delta e e^*$
$a_1 \to t_1^*$	$+3/\Delta a_1 t_1^*$	$e \to t_1^*$	$+6/\Delta e t_1^*$
$t_1 \to e^*$	$+6/\Delta t_1 e^*$	$e \to a_1^*$	$-2/\Delta e a_1^*$
$t_1 \to t_1^*$	$-9/\Delta t_1 t_1^*$		

It follows that the $^2J_{PMP'}$ coupling is almost certainly *positive* on account of the dominant contributions from the positive $t_1 \rightarrow e^*$ and $e \rightarrow t_1^*$ excitations, which have a large numerical weight.

3. Tetrahedral complexes

Recently the phosphorus and fluorine n.m.r. spectra of complexes of general type $[NiP_4]$ and $[Ni(CO)_n P_{4-n}]$[64, 65] (P = fluorophosphine, $R_x PF_{3-x}$) have been studied and expressions for the line positions and intensities in $(AX_n)_4$ spin systems have been tabulated.[64] Table XIV lists some typical values for $^2J_{PMP'}$ in these complexes. A feature of these spectra is the observation of much larger remote $^3J_{PMPF'}$ coupling constants (in the $+20$ to $+35$ c./sec. range) compared with those found in *cis* octahedral complexes.

A similar energy level diagram for $[MP_4]$ complexes may be constructed for zerovalent $[NiP_4]$ complexes (nd^{10} systems)—

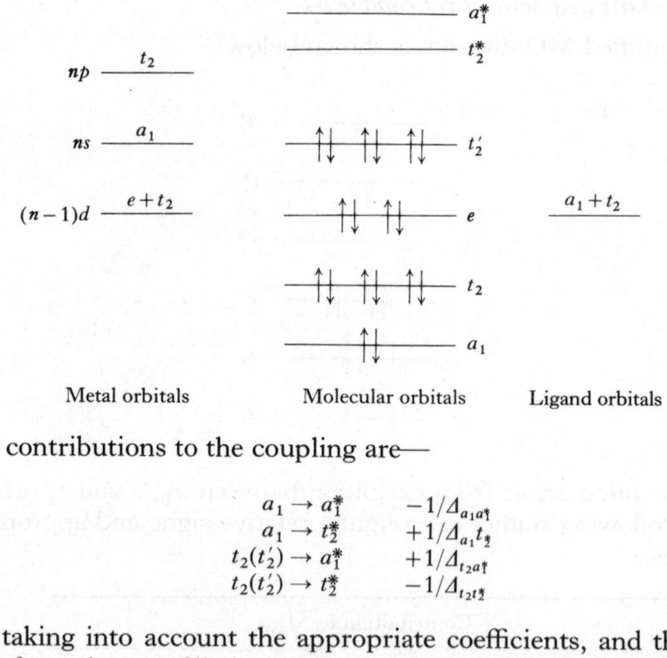

| Metal orbitals | Molecular orbitals | Ligand orbitals |

The contributions to the coupling are—

$$a_1 \rightarrow a_1^* \qquad -1/\Delta_{a_1 a_1^*}$$
$$a_1 \rightarrow t_2^* \qquad +1/\Delta_{a_1 t_2^*}$$
$$t_2(t_2') \rightarrow a_1^* \qquad +1/\Delta_{t_2 a_1^*}$$
$$t_2(t_2') \rightarrow t_2^* \qquad -1/\Delta_{t_2 t_2^*}$$

also taking into account the appropriate coefficients, and the excitations from the two filled sets of t_2 orbitals to a_1^* and t_2^* will dominate the coupling. The resulting sign will in turn depend on the relative order of the unfilled orbitals which are probably rather similar in energy, and the small $^2J_{PMP'}$ couplings sometimes observed in Table XII and Table XIV no doubt reflects such a situation.

TABLE XIV

**Phosphorus–phosphorus coupling constants of some
tetrahedral nickel complexes**

Complex	$^2J_{PMP'}$, c./sec.	Ref.
$[Ni(PF_3)_4]$	<19	65
$[Ni(CCl_3PF_2)_4]$	21 ± 5	65
$[Ni(CO)_2(PF_3)_2]$	39	65
$[Ni(CF_3PF_2)_4]$	<10	65
$[Ni(C_5H_{10}NPF_2)_4]$	~15	65
$[Ni(C_6H_4O_2PF)_4]$	$17\cdot7$	65
$[Ni(ClCH_2PF_2)_4]$	<15	66
$[Ni(CO)_2(Me_2NPF_2)_2]$	very small ~0	65
$[Ni(CO)_2(Et_2NPF_2)_2]$	very small ~0	65
$[Ni(CO)(Me_2NPF_2)_3]$	very small ~0	65
$[Ni(CO)_2\{(Me_2N)_2PF)\}_2]$	very small ~0	65
$[Ni(CO)(Et_2NPF_2)_3]$	very small ~0	65

The accuracy of some of the values for the $[NiP_4]$ complexes is limited in some cases by poorly resolved spectra.

V. INTRA-LIGAND COUPLING CONSTANTS INVOLVING PHOSPHORUS

Changes are usually observed in the magnitude of the coupling constants between phosphorus and other magnetic nuclei within the phosphine ligand when phosphorus becomes co-ordinated to another atom. This Section discusses very briefly some examples of this behaviour, with particular reference to changes in the sign of the coupling constants on co-ordination.

A. Directly bonded nuclei

1. *Phosphorus–hydrogen coupling constants*

Primary or secondary phosphines containing P—H bonds usually exhibit $^1J_{PH}$ coupling constants in the 200 c./sec. range (e.g., PH_3, 182 c./sec.; Me_2PH, 191·6 c./sec.),[2] whereas in co-ordination complexes, for example, with boron acceptor molecules, the directly bonded phosphorus–hydrogen coupling constant lies in the 300–400 c./sec. range (e.g., $PH_3 \cdot BH_3$, 372 c./sec.;[43] $Me_2PH \cdot BH_3$, 350 c./sec.).[67]

Brief reports of the first examples of transition-metal complexes of the parent phosphine PH_3 have recently appeared,[68,69] and $^1J_{PH}$ values are very similar in magnitude to those found in the borane adducts (see Table XV). The larger $^1J_{PH}$ values found in quaternary salts (e.g., $Me_3PH^{\oplus}$, 515 c./sec.,[13] $Me_2PhPH^{\oplus}$, 525 c./sec.)[14] are closer to the 500–700 c./sec. range normally observed in organophosphorous compounds containing quadruply connected phosphorus.[2]

Heteronuclear "tickling" experiments on $PhMe_2PH^{\oplus}$ have indicated that the sign of $^1J_{PH}$ is positive.[14]

TABLE XV

$^1J_{PH}$ **Coupling constants in some PH_3 complexes**

Complex	$^1J_{PH}$, c./sec.	Ref.
$[PH_3 \cdot BH_3]$	372	43
cis-$[Mo(CO)_4(PH_3)_2]$	324	69
cis-$[W(CO)_4(PH_3)_2]$	338	69
$[W(CO)_5(PH_3)]$	341	68
$[Mo(CO)_5(PH_3)]$	327	68
$[Cr(CO)_5(PH_3)]$	337·5	68
$[Fe(CO)_4(PH_3)]$	365	68
$[Mn(\pi-C_5H_5)(CO)_2(PH_3)]$	327	68
$[V(\pi-C_5H_5)(CO)_3(PH_3)]$	324	68

2. Phosphorus–fluorine coupling constants

Very large values for the directly bonded phosphorus–fluorine coupling constants $^1J_{PF}$ have been observed for fluorophosphines of general type R_xPF_{3-x} (e.g., PF_3, 1440 c./sec.; CCl_3PF_2, 1280 c./sec.; $(CF_3)_2PF$, 1003 c./sec.).[53] Cunliffe et al.[59] have shown that the sign of $^1J_{PF}$ in the latter compound is negative and this appears to be a general feature of all directly bonded phosphorus–fluorine coupling constants.[60]

The absolute magnitude of $^1J_{PF}$ is 10–150 c./sec. smaller in fluorophosphine–transition–metal complexes (e.g., $[Ni(CO)_xP_{4-x}]$,[46,62] $[Mo(CO)_3P_3]$,[46] $[HCoP_4]$[42]), although in complexes of the chelating bisdifluorophosphine $RN(PF_2)_2$,[61] $^1J_{PF}$ is larger than in the free ligand. Several literature reports on fluorophosphine–metal complexes give only approximate results for $^1J_{PF}$ (complex) because $^3J_{PMPF}$ has not been estimated (see Section V). Table XVI lists a few examples of accurate $^1J_{PF}$ data for complexes of the type cis-$[M(CO)_4P_2]$ (M = Cr, Mo, W)[45] that were obtained by analysis of spectra of the $X_nAA'X_n'$ type discussed previously (p. 380). There appears to be a small but regular decrease in the magnitude of $^1J_{PF}$ (complex) in the order $Cr > Mo > W$.

TABLE XVI

Directly bonded coupling constants ($^1J_{PF}$) for some fluorophosphines and their co-ordination complexes $cis[M(CO)_4P_2]$

	$^1J_{PF}$ ligand c./sec.	$^1J_{PF}$ (complex), c./sec.		
		M = Cr	M = Mo	M = W
PF$_3$	1440	1311	1308	1282
ClCH$_2$PF$_2$	1196	..	1120	1107
Me$_2$NPF$_2$	1196	1128	1118	1096
EtN(PF$_2$)$_2$	1261	1301	1284	1277

From Johnson et al.[45]

B. Non-bonded nuclei

1. With hydrogen

This type of interaction is typified by coupling constants of the type $^2J_{PCH}$, e.g., in alkyl phosphines and their complexes, and by $^3J_{PXCH}$ for alkyl phosphites (X = O), aminophosphines (X = N) and their derivatives. As already discussed in Section II, the smaller values of the coupling constant between phosphorus and a hydrogen separated by other atoms (0–20 c./sec.) often leads to unresolved line broadening in the phosphorus n.m.r. spectrum. An unusually large value for the indirect coupling constant $^4J_{POCCH}$ (7·2 c./sec.[51, 52]) has been found in the cage phosphite (**33**).

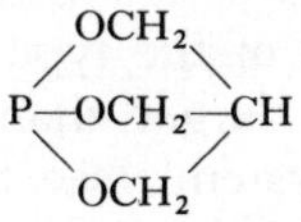

$$P \overbrace{}^{\displaystyle OCH_2} OCH_2 - CH$$

$$\begin{array}{c} \quad\quad OCH_2 \\ \diagup \quad\quad \diagdown \\ P\!-\!OCH_2\!-\!CH \\ \diagdown \quad\quad \diagup \\ \quad\quad OCH_2 \end{array}$$

33

There is considerable evidence to suggest that the coupling constant $^2J_{PCH}$ in alkyl phosphines changes from a small positive value to a larger negative value on complex formation.[1] For example, in MePhPH $^2J_{PCH}$ is $3\cdot0 \pm 0\cdot1$ c./sec., whereas in the corresponding phosphonium bromide $[Me_2PhPH]^{\oplus}Br^{\ominus}$ the value is $-15\cdot5 \pm 0\cdot1$ c./sec.[14] Similarly, Cullingworth et al.[70] have shown that in the Me$_3$P–AlEt$_3$ and related systems, the observed (averaged) $^2J_{PCH}$ coupling constant passes through zero as the aluminium–phosphorus ratio varies, showing that the coupling constants in the free and complexes phosphine are opposite in sign.

In triethylphosphine complexes of the type cis- and trans-$[PtCl_2(Et_3P)_2]$, heteronuclear double-resonance experiments have shown that the signs of the $^2J_{PCH}$ and $^3J_{PCCH}$ coupling constants are negative and positive, respectively.[31]

Verkade et al.[15] have reported that a relationship apparently exists between the magnitude of $^3J_{POCH}$ and the acceptor strength of the Lewis acid for complexes of the type $P.BX_3$, where P represents the cage phosphites (34) and (35). The coupling constants $^2J_{POCH}$

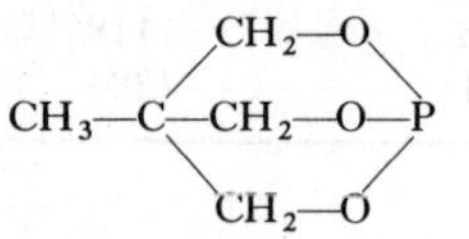

$$CH_3-C(CH_2-O)_3-P$$

$$CH_2(CH-O)(CH_2)(CH-O)(CH_2)(CH-O)P$$

34 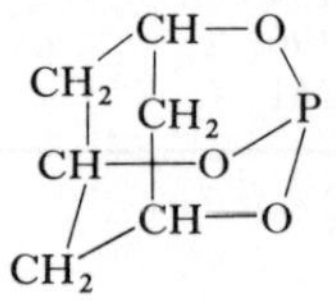   35

were found to decrease in the order $BH_3 > BMe_3 \simeq BF_3$ for both series of complexes.

More recently evidence has been presented[71] that is consistent with a decrease in the absolute magnitude of $^2J_{PCH}$ to zero as the polycyclic phosphine $P(CH_2O)_3CCH_3$ is co-ordinated to iron carbonyl.

2. With fluorine

Perfluoralkyl phosphines $(R_f)_nPX_{3-n}$ ($R_f = CF_3$, C_2F_5, C_3F_7, etc.) usually have $^2J_{PCF}$ values in the 50–80 c./sec. range,[72,73] which increase in absolute magnitude on co-ordination; for example, in transition-metal complexes $^2J_{PCF}$ is typically in the range 90–120 c./sec.[12,55,74] For complexes of the type cis-$[Mo(CO)_4\{(CF_3)_2PX\}_2]$, (X = Cl, Br, I, H), $^2J_{PCF}$ is larger than $^2J_{PMP'}$, and analysis of the resulting $X_6AA'X_6'$ spin system, (see Section V) has recently been achieved,[74] and values of $^2J_{PMP'}$ obtained. Double resonance experiments on $(CF_3)_2PF$ have shown that $^2J_{PCF}$ is positive.[59,60]

VI. PHOSPHORUS CHEMICAL SHIFT MEASUREMENTS

Phosphorus chemical shift data for co-ordination complexes are considerably less well understood than the various coupling constants between phosphorus and other nuclei discussed in Sections III and IV.

In this Section we draw attention to some of the more interesting shift correlations that exist, and in Section VII tabulate chemical shift data for a wider variety of co-ordination compounds.

A. Introduction: theoretical considerations

Before reviewing ³¹P chemical-shift measurements on co-ordination complexes containing phosphorus as the donor atom, it is perhaps useful to outline briefly the various factors that have been considered important in determining the phosphorus chemical shifts of unco-ordinated phosphorus compounds. The reader is referred to previous articles[75–77] and a very recent monograph[2] for full details of some of these aspects.

A general theory of chemical shifts of magnetic nuclei has been given by Ramsey,[78] and the screening constant for a particular nucleus has been conveniently expressed[79] in terms of three main contributions by equation (9)—

$$\sigma = \sigma \text{ (diamagnetic)} + \sigma \text{ (paramagnetic)} + \sigma \text{ (other atoms)} \quad (9)$$

The first term represents the diamagnetic shielding effect on the nucleus in question by the surrounding electron cloud and is usually a major factor for hydrogen atoms in most chemical environments. However, this term is always much less important for other nuclei (e.g., ^{19}F, ^{31}P, ^{59}Co), where the resulting significantly wider spread of observed chemical shifts reflects the dominance of the second term in the expression, σ (paramagnetic) ($\sigma^{(2)}$). This term, which is always negative (i.e., produces a shift to low field), arises from the magnetic-field-induced perturbation of the electronic structure, and is important when low lying excited states are available whose symmetry enables them to be mixed with the ground state. Such a situation is encountered in nuclei other than the isotopes of hydrogen, and for example in the case of phosphorus the contribution from $\sigma^{(2)}$ is roughly about 10^2 as large as the diamagnetic term.[2]

The third term representing the contribution to the chemical shift of neighbouring atoms or groups in the molecule depends on $\Delta\chi . R^{-3}$, where $\Delta\chi$ is the anisotropy in the magnetic susceptibility tensor of the neighbour and R the distance from the nucleus in question. This term is also usually small by comparison with $\sigma^{(2)}$ on account of the rapid falling off of the R^{-3} factor for large values of R.

Following Knight's discovery of ³¹P chemical shifts,[80] attempts have been made to correlate changes in the observed shift parameters with the inductive effects of neighbouring atoms or groups, and the much lower field shifts observed for trivalent phosphorus compounds compared with pentavalent derivatives was originally believed to reflect the presence of fewer valence electrons around the phosphorus atoms. Unexpected ^{31}P chemical shift variations within a series of phosphorus trihalides, PX_3 (X, in order of decreasing shift = F > I > Cl > Br), have been explained in terms of the competing effects of the electro-negativity of the halogen and the partial double-bond character of the P—X bonds.[81, 82, 83]

Empirical additive group contributions to the experimental phosphorus chemical shift, originally suggested by Van Wazer et al.[84] were moderately successful, as were attempts to rationalize the shift data for several tertiary, secondary phosphines.[85] More recently Grim et al. showed[86] that the observed chemical shift for 1209 tertiary and secondary phosphines and quaternary phosphonium salts could be predicted with reasonable certainty using nine empirical group contributions (σ^P) for organic substituents.

In 1956 Muller et al.[87] presented a semi-empirical treatment based on a method suggested by Saika and Slichter for fluorine chemical shifts.[79] This attributed major changes in ^{31}P chemical shifts to variations in the magnitude of the second order paramagnetic term $\sigma^{(2)}$. Since the contribution of s electrons was zero, and that of electrons in closed shells and valence electrons on other atoms could be neglected, the effect on the shielding constant for a single $3p$ electron was expressed as equation (10)—

$$\sigma_P = -\frac{2}{3}\left(\frac{e^2h^2}{m^2c^2}\right)\left(\left\langle\frac{1}{r^3}\right\rangle\text{av}\right)_p \cdot \frac{1}{\Delta E} \qquad (10)$$

where m and c are the mass and charge of the electron, respectively, r is the average distance of a p electron from the phosphorus nucleus and ΔE is an average excitation energy. Unfortunately, the magnitude of ΔE (usually in the 5–8 eV range) is not readily available, and a semi-empirical equation correlating the experimentally observed shift, δ, for PX_3 molecules was developed[87] where—

$$\delta = a - bD$$

a and b were empirical parameters and D was the number of unbalanced p electrons calculated by taking into account the extent of hybridization and the ionicity of the P—X bonds. This equation led to a grossly low value for the chemical shift of trifluorophosphine compared with the other trihalides, and was later modified by Parks[88] to take account of the fact that the wave function asymmetry of the phosphorus atom in PX_3 systems is zero for both p^3 and sp^3 hybridization. The amended equation gave somewhat better agreement between the experimental and calculated values, although the critical dependence of the parameters on the bond angles used in the calculation rather limited its general applicability. Packer has studied the phosphorus chemical shifts of several bistrifluoromethylphosphines, $(CF_3)_2PX$,[73] chosen so that only the substituent (X) was varied, thus minimizing the changes in the phosphorus hybridization. It was found that the chemical-shift variations were qualitatively in agreement with the dominance of the paramagnetic term, but other contributions, such as the anisotropy of the P—X bond and d_π-p_π bonding between phosphorus and X, appeared to be important.

More recently Gutowsky and Larmann[89] and Letcher and Van Wazer[90] have independently presented detailed quantum mechanical interpretations of phosphorus chemical shifts. Somewhat similar general conclusions were reached, although the former treatment was limited to σ-bonding effects, whereas the latter theory was based on the involvement of both σ- and π-orbitals.

Letcher and Van Wazer[90] applying LCAO theory first developed by Pople[91] and Karplus and Das,[92] have expressed the shielding (which was dominated by the magnitude of $\sigma^{(2)}$), in terms of localized bond parameters, e.g., ionic character, hybridization and double bonding. Using expressions for $\sigma^{(2)}$ obtained by Jameson and Gutowsky[93] and taking account of both phosphorus p and d orbital occupation, the phosphorus chemical shift, $\delta - \delta_0$, was related to four parameters ζ_1, ζ_2, B and f by equation (11)—

$$\delta - \delta_0 = \frac{-2e^2\hbar^2}{3m^2c^2\Delta}\left\{\langle r^{-3}\rangle_p\zeta_1 + \langle r^{-3}\rangle_d\zeta_2\right\}$$

$$= B\zeta_1 + Bf\zeta_2 \tag{11}$$

where—

$$B = \left[\frac{-2e^2\hbar^2}{3m^2c^2\Delta}\right]\langle r^{-3}\rangle_p \quad \text{and} \quad f = \frac{\langle r^{-3}\rangle_d}{\langle r^{-3}\rangle_p}$$

and $\delta - \delta_0$ is the phosphorus chemical shift relative to a particular standard. The $\langle r^{-3}\rangle$ term was estimated from the spin-orbit interaction, and it was shown that $\langle r^{-3}\rangle_{np}$ was larger than $\langle r^{-3}\rangle_{nd}$ for the same principal quantum number n. Although B clearly depended on Δ and $\langle r^{-3}\rangle_p$, whose magnitude will vary from one molecule to another, it was nevertheless suggested that within a series of compounds in which the co-ordination number of phosphorus remained unchanged, B should be roughly constant (see below). An important feature of equation (11) was that ζ_1 was determined only by the occupation of the phosphorus p orbitals and ζ_2 similarly depended on the total phosphorus d orbital occupation. If s and p orbitals are essentially involved in σ-bonding and d orbital participation is limited to π-bonding, the total chemical shift $\delta - \delta_0$ could, therefore, be represented as the sum of the two terms δ_σ and δ_π.[90] A value of 11,828·5 p.p.m. has been assigned to δ_σ based on available chemical-shift data on phosphines where π-bonding is unimportant, and similarly d_π can be represented by the expression $\delta_\pi = 2\cdot8\ Bfn_\pi$ where n_π measured the *total* occupation of the d_π orbitals on phosphorus and where B and f were constants that depended only on the co-ordination number of phosphorus and were assigned the values -7719 and $0\cdot0189$, respectively, for terco-ordinate phosphorus compounds. For phosphines of general type PR_3, ζ_1 depended on the electronegativity of R and the RPR bond angle, θ. Figure 13 shows how the effect on ζ_1 decreased

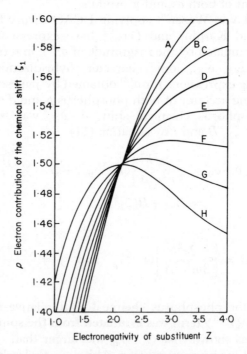

FIG. 13. Contribution of ζ_1 to the theoretical chemical shift for PZ_3 molecules as a function of the electronegativity of Z and the Z–P–Z bond angle, θ (neglecting π-bonding) which varied as follows: A, 111°; B, 108°; C, 105°; D, 102°; E, 99°; F, 96°; G, 93°; H, 90°. (From Letcher and Van Wazer.[90])

for various θ values as the electronegativity of the substituent atom approached that of phosphorus, and the electron distribution in the phosphorus atomic orbitals accordingly became more like that in atomic phosphorus. In Fig. 14 ζ_1 calculated for several phosphines, PZ_3, using appropriate Z–P–Z bond angles and substituent electronegativities has been plotted against the experimental value, and the good agreement found for phosphines containing rather different bond angles and substituent groups supported the suggested constancy of the $\langle r^{-3}\rangle/\varDelta$ term in equation (11).[90]

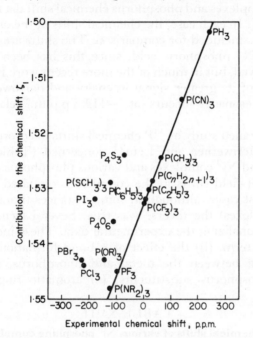

FIG. 14. p Orbital contribution, ζ_1, to the ^{31}P chemical shift as a function of the observed chemical shift for PZ_3 molecules (relative to 85% H_3PO_4). (From Letcher and Van Wazer.[90])

To summarize: phosphorus chemical shifts depend on (a) the imbalance of the σ-bonds caused by electronegativity differences of substituent atoms and the effect of the lone pair of electrons, (b) the extent of occupation of the d orbitals and (c) deviations from geometrical symmetry.

Since the term B in equation (11) is necessarily negative, any increase in ζ_1 should produce a low-field shift, although an increase in the phosphorus σ-orbital occupation would not necessarily produce a larger value for ζ_1. Likewise, a low-field shift was to be expected as ζ_2 increased, i.e., as π-bonding to phosphorus became more important. From these considerations it is clear that chemical-shift relationships should not and do not simply reflect electron-density changes at the particular phosphorus nucleus in question, as is quite often represented in the literature.

B. Co-ordination compounds

Phosphorus n.m.r. spectra have been reported for various co-ordination complexes and phosphorus chemical shift data are tabulated in Section VII. In each case, the chemical shifts of the unco-ordinated phosphines are included for comparison. The shifts are given relative to external 85% phosphoric acid, since this has been the standard usually employed, but in much of the more recent work P_4O_6 has been used because of its greater signal intensity and narrower line width. (The P_4O_6 resonance occurs at $-112\cdot5$ p.p.m. relative to 85% H_3PO_4.)[94]

The first detailed study of ^{31}P chemical shifts in co-ordination compounds by Meriwether and Leto[95] concerned (Tables XVII and XVIII) Ni^{II} and Ni^0 complexes and various phosphorus ligands. They observed lower-field shifts in the complexes compared with the free ligands in most cases, although in some instances (notably PCl_3 and $PhPCl_2$ complexes) the reverse was true. Several factors were considered in rationalizing the experimental data. These included (a) the paramagnetic term, (b) the effect of σ-bond formation, (c) possible d_π–d_π bonding between the metal and phosphorus, (d) inductive effects of phosphorus substituents, (e) aromatic ring currents in

TABLE XVII

^{31}P Chemical shifts of various Ni^0 phosphine complexes, p.p.m. relative to 85% H_3PO_4

Phosphine ligand	δ_P ligand	$\delta_P[Ni(CO)_3P]$	$\delta_P[Ni(CO)_2P_2]$	$\delta_P[Ni(CO)P_3]$	$\delta_P[NiP_4]$
PCl_3	-215	$-185\ (+30)$	$-181\ (+34)$	$-177\ (+38)$	$-170\ (+45)$
PCl_2Ph	-164	..	..	..	$-152\ (+12)$
PF_3	-97	..	..	..	$-127\ (-30)$
$P(OEt)_3$	-140	$-157\ (-17)$	$-160\ (-20)$	$-163\ (-23)$	$-160\ (-20)$
PPh_3	$+6\cdot6$	$-42\cdot9\ (-49\cdot5)$	$-32\cdot6\ (-39\cdot2)$	..	..
PEt_3	$+19\cdot1$	$-47\cdot0\ (-66\cdot1)$	$-20\cdot7\ (-39\cdot8)$	..	..

From Meriwether and Leto.[95]
Figures in parentheses are co-ordination shifts.

phenyl phosphine complexes, (f) bond rehybridization, (g) electro-negativity of atoms joined to phosphorus and (h) steric effects (includ-ing chelation).

For complexes of general type $[Ni(CO)_2(PR_3)_2]$, (R = alkyl, aryl) (see Table XVIII), the constancy of the co-ordination shifts,

TABLE XVIII

[31]P **Chemical shifts of some nickel dicarbonyl di(phosphine) complex** $[Ni(CO)_2P_2]$,[95] **p.p.m. relative to** 85% H_3PO_4

Ligand	δ_P ligand	$\delta_P[Ni(CO)_2P_2]$ complex	Co-ordination shift, Δ, $\delta_{complex} - \delta_{ligand}$
$P(C_6H_5)_3$	+6·6	−32·6	−39·2
$P(C_6H_5)_2Et$	+12·0	−28·7	−40·7
$P(C_6H_5)Et_2$	+16·2	−23·2	−39·4
PEt_3	+19·1	−20·7	−39·8
$P(C_8H_{17})_3$	+31·8	−13·3	−45·1
$P(C_4H_9)_3$	+32·6	−12·1	−44·7
$PEt_2CH_2PEt_2$	+19·3	−21·9	−41·2

($\delta_{complex} - \delta_{ligand}$), for systems where rehybridization effects were approximately constant and steric effects unimportant, was thought to suggest that the low-field shift on co-ordination was mainly due to the strong donor σ-bond from phosphorus to nickel with $d_\pi - d_\pi$ contribu-tions either small or constant. The importance of the paramagnetic term could not be reliably assessed, and the much smaller low-field shifts found for the trialkyl phosphite complexes (and high-field shifts in phosphorus trichloride complexes) had to be accounted for by in-volving weaker σ-bonding between phosphorus and the metal, strong metal→ligand interaction and large rehybridization effects.

Shupack and Wagner[96] have suggested that a correlation exists between the phosphorus chemical shift and the valency of the metal atom in some transition-metal–phosphite complexes. They attributed the low-field shift of the unco-ordinated ligands (see Table XIX), to the effect of the oxygen substituents, and suggested that the high-field shift on co-ordination, e.g., in $P_4O_6.BH_3$,[5] was due to the inductive effect of the BH_3 group. Similar observations had been previously made for borane adducts of trimethyl phosphite and the stereo-chemically interesting "cage" phosphites, 4-methyl-2,6,7-trioxa-phosphabicyclo[2,2,2]octane $P(OCH_2)_3CCH_3$ (34), and 2,8,9-trioxa-1-phospha-adamantane $P(OCH_2)_3CH$ (35).

TABLE XIX

**^{31}P Chemical shifts of some phosphite complexes,
p.p.m. relative to 85% H_3PO_4**

Compounds	$P(OMe)_3$	$P(OEt)_3$	P_4O_6
P †	−141	−138	−113
[Ni(CO)$_3$P]	..	−155 (−17)	−126 (−13)
[NiP$_4$]	..	−157 (−19)	..
[H$_3$B ·P]	−118 (+23)	..	−90·4 (+22·6)
[CuClP]$_4$	−132 (+9)	−128 (+10)	
[CuP$_4$]ClO$_4$	−125 (+16)	−121·5 (+16·5)	
[AgClP]$_4$	−135 (+6)	..	
[AgP$_4$]ClO$_4$	−130 (+11)	−128 (+10)	
[AgP$_4$]NO$_3$	−132 (+9)	..	
[HgCl$_2$P]	..	−115 (+23)	
[NiCl$_2$P$_2$]	..	−118 (+20)	

From Shupack and Wagner.[96]
Figures in parentheses are the complex-free ligand values.
† P = Ligand.

Attention was also drawn[96] to the net increase in shielding for phosphite complexes of Cu^I, Ag^I, Ni^{II} and Hg^{II} as the formal positive charge became larger (see Table XIX), whereas the corresponding zerovalent nickel complex [NiP$_4$] (P = phosphite) showed a downfield shift from the free ligand value. Since Ni^0, Cu^I, Ag^I and Hg^{II} all have d^{10} electronic configurations, it was suggested that the lack of a formal positive charge in the Ni^0 complexes facilitated metal → phosphorus d_π–d_π bonding, which increased the paramagnetic term leading to a downfield shift.

However, Coskran et al.[97] have pointed out several serious limitations to the generality of the above approach, and reported that several phosphite complexes, e.g., [CoP$_5$]NO$_3$, [NiP$_5$](ClO$_4$)$_2$, [AgP$_4$]ClO$_4$, have lower phosphorus chemical shifts than the corresponding free ligand in spite of the formal charge on the metal (see Table XX). They proposed that meaningful shift comparisons should only be attempted within isostructural–isoelectronic systems, where hybridization changes, ligand–ligand repulsions and magnetic anisotropies were minimized. Applying this idea they found that the phosphorus chemical shift of [CuP$_4$]$^\oplus$ and [AgP$_4$]$^\oplus$ were similar and to high field of [NiP$_4$]. Likewise an analogous relationship existed for [AgP$_4$]$^\oplus$ and [NiP$_4$] and [CoP$_5$]$^\oplus$ and [NiP$_5$]$^{2\oplus}$ (see Fig. 15).[97]

TABLE XX

^{31}P Chemical shifts of phosphite complexes of transition metals, p.p.m. relative to 85% H_3PO_4 as external standard

Ligands	$P(OCH_3)_3$	$P(OCH_2)_3CR$	$P(OCH)_3(CH_2)_3$
	−141	−92 [R = Et]	−137
Complex		−93 [R' = n-C$_3$H$_7$]	
[NiP$_5$](ClO$_4$)$_2$	−110	−108	−125
[AgP$_4$]ClO$_4$	−132	..	..
[AgP$_4$]NO$_3$	..	−99	−134
[CuP$_4$]ClO$_4$	−125	..	..
[CoP$_5$]ClO$_4$	..	−138	−157
[CoP$_5$]NO$_3$	−147	..	..
[NiP$_4$]	−163	−128	−153

From Coskran et al.[97]

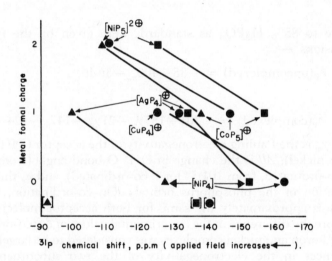

FIG. 15. Plot of ^{31}P chemical shift of complexes of: ▲, $P(OCH_2)_3CR$; ■, $P(OCH)_3$-$(CH_2)_3$; and ●, $P(OCH_3)_3$ versus metal charge on the metal. The points in brackets represent the chemical shifts of the free ligands. (From Coskran et al.[97])

The interpretation of the ^{31}P chemical shifts of the $P_4O_6 \cdot BH_3$ complex and complexes of general type $[\{Ni(CO)_3\}_n(P_4O_6)]$ $(n = 1 - 4)$ by Riess and Van Wazer,[5] which are summarized in Fig. 16, followed directly from the quantum mechanical approach outlined in the introductory Section. Expressions for the chemical shift of uncomplexed and complexed phosphorus atoms in the P_4O_6 complexes, in p.p.m.

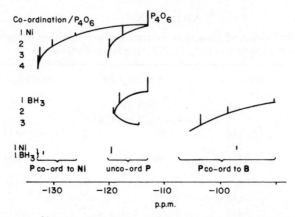

FIG. 16. The ^{31}P chemical shifts of P_4O_6 and its complexes with tricarbonylnickel and with borane. The lengths of the vertical lines denote the relative areas of the complexed and uncomplexed peaks. (From Riess and Van Wazer.[5])

relative to 85% H_3PO_4 as standard, were given by the following expressions[5]—

$$\delta_P(\text{uncomplexed}) = -35 - 400_{n_\pi} - 36\Delta\theta$$

and —

$$\delta_P(\text{complexed}) = -201 + 187\chi_m - 21\chi_m^2 - 147_{n_\pi} - (24 - 8\chi_m)\Delta\theta$$

where χ_m is the Pauling electronegativity of the acceptor (2·0 for BH_3, 1·8 for nickel), $\Delta\theta$ is the change in O–P–O bond angle (from 99° for P unco-ordinated, from 101·5° for P co-ordinated), and n_π the total d_π occupation of the phosphorus orbitals. On co-ordination, this last term was approximately the same for both acceptor molecules, and therefore the difference in the experimental values of δ_P (co-ordinated) for the boron and nickel complexes was considered to be largely due to differences in the electronegativity of the two substituents. The reasons for variations in δ_P (co-ordinated) in the series $[\{Ni(CO)_3\}_nP_4O_6]$ were more difficult to assess, and could equally well be due to small changes in bond angles as to variations in the occupation of the phosphorus d_π orbitals. More recently a somewhat similar low-field shift has been observed for the co-ordinated phosphorus atom in the related complex cis-$[Mo(CO)_4(P_4O_6)_2]$.[98]

Regularities in the phosphorus chemical shifts of several tertiary phosphine complexes of the Group VIa metal carbonyls (Cr, Mo, W) have been discussed by Grim.[21] For a series of complexes $[M(CO)_5(R_nPh_{(3-n)}P)]$ (R=alkyl, M=Cr, Mo and W) the low-field shift on co-ordination becomes progressively smaller in the order $Cr > Mo > W$, and a similar trend has been observed[47] for several Group VIb complexes containing "mixed" ligands of general type $[M(CO)_4PP']$. The observation that the chemical shift in $[Cr(CO)_5(Ph_3P)]$ is $-32·1$ p.p.m. to low-field of $Ph_4P^{\oplus}$, was taken to indicate[21] that the diamagnetic term was certainly not of major importance in determining the chemical shift in these systems, and qualitative support for the importance of the paramagnetic term (which depends on ΔE^{-1} (see equation 10, p. 396) also comes from the observation that nearly all the molybdenum and tungsten complexes were colourless, whereas the chromium derivatives were yellow.[21] The anisotropy of the neighbouring heavy metal atoms could also play an important role in determining δ_P for these complexes, and there was some evidence that steric effects might operate for those phosphines containing bulky groups.[21]

TABLE XXI

^{31}P n.m.r. data for phosphine complexes of group VIa
metals carbonyl, p.p.m. relative to 85% H_3PO_4

Complex	Ligand	Cr	Mo	W	Ref.
$[M(CO)_5P]$	1 Ph_3P	$-55·3$	$-37·5$	$-20·6$	21
	2 Ph_2MeP	$-35·0$	$-15·0$	$+3·8$	21
	3 Ph_2EtP	$-48·3$	$-30·1$	$-12·1$	21
	4 Ph_2iPrP	$-59·5$	$-43·2$	$-26·3$	21
	5 Ph_2BuP	$-45·1$	$-26·5$	$-7·9$	21
	6 Ph_2Bu^tP	$-72·7$	$-57·0$	$-41·7$	21
	7 $PhBu_2P$	$-35·3$	$-17·6$	$+0·8$	21
	8 Bu_3P	$-30·2$	$-12·2$	$+6·4$	21
	9† Ph_2PH	$-31·7$	$-6·5$	..	102
trans- $[M(CO)_4PP']$	10 Ph_3P ⎱ 　　 Bu_3P ⎰	$-74·1$ $-43·3$	$-50·9$ $-22·0$	$-28·4$ $+3·2$	47 47
	Bu_3P ⎱ 11 $(PhO)_3P$ ⎰	$-38·2$ $-185·1$	$-17·2$ -165	$+5·3$ -137	47 47
cis- $[M(CO)_4P_2]$	12 $(CF_3)_2PF$	..	-184	-152	12, 45
	13 Me_2NPF_2	$-203·0$	$-180·5$	$-156·1$	12, 45
	14 CCl_3PF_2	$-211·2$	$-196·5$	$-168·1$	12, 45
	15 $ClCH_2PF_2$	..	-230	$-201·5$	12, 45
	16 PF_3	$-173·3$	-148	$-122·0$	12, 45
	17 $EtN(PF_2)_2$	$-170·7$	$-144·8$	$-114·5$	45

† Data for these complexes was given in c./sec. from P_4O_6 and have been calculated assuming the ^{31}P spectra were measured at 24·3 Mc./sec.

14

More recently, ^{31}P phosphorus chemical-shift measurements have been extended by Nixon *et al.*[12, 45] to include several fluorophosphine complexes of Group VIa metal carbonyl complexes of general type *cis*-$[M(CO)_4P_2]$ [$P=PF_3$, $ClCH_2PF_2$, CCl_3PF_2, R_2NPF_2, $(CF_3)_2$-PF, CF_3PF_2, $RN(PF_2)_2$; $M=Cr$, Mo, W] and data on phosphine complexes *cis*-$[M'(CO)_4(PH_3)_2]$ ($M'=Mo,W$) have also been published.[69] These complexes usually also show the characteristic shift to lower field on co-ordination, the effect being more pronounced for the lighter elements, *viz*, $Cr>Mo>W$. Metal complexes of the bidentate ligand $EtN(PF_2)_2$ are anomalous however, in that only the chromium complex has a lower field shift than the free ligand. Some of the available data for Group VIa metal carbonyl phosphine complexes are summarized in Table XXI and plotted graphically in Fig. 17.

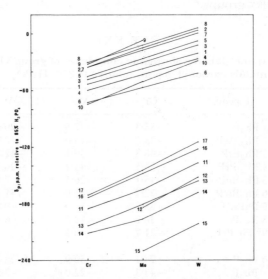

FIG. 17. ^{31}P chemical shifts for phosphine complexes of Group VIa metal carbonyls (see also Table XXI).

Other studies on phosphine complexes of metals within the same group have been made, e.g., for $[M(PF_3)_4]$ (**36**); $M=Ni$, Pd);[56, 66, 100] $[M(CF_3PF_2)_4]$ and $[M\{CF_3)_2PF\}_4]$ ($M=Ni$, Pt);[66, 100] $[M(PF_3)_5]$ (**37**); ($M=Fe$, Ru);[101] $[HM(PF_3)_4]$ and $[M(PF_3)_4]^{\ominus}$ ($M=Co$, Rh, Ir);[42] and $[M(CO)_4(Ph_2PH)_2]$ ($M=Cr,Mo$).[102] In all cases the co-ordination shift is largest for the first member of the particular group. The phosphorus chemical shift of complexes of third row transition

$$
\begin{array}{c}
PF_3 \\
| \\
M \\
\diagup \ | \ \diagdown \\
PF_3 \ \ PF_3 \\
PF_3 \quad (M = Ni, Pd)
\end{array}
\qquad
\begin{array}{c}
PF_3 \\
PF_3 \diagdown \\
\quad\quad M' \text{—} PF_3 \\
PF_3 \diagup \\
PF_3 \quad (M' = Fe, Ru)
\end{array}
$$

| **36** | **37** |

metals usually lie closest to the free ligand valve, and occasionally at slightly higher field. The data for several fluorophosphine–metal complexes which represent the widest range of compounds studied are summarized in Table XXII.

TABLE XXII

^{31}P **Chemical shifts of fluorophosphine complexes of transition metals in the same group, p.p.m. relation to 85% H_3PO_4**

Metal–phosphine complex	Metals	1st row	2nd row	3rd row	Ref.
$[(PF_3)_4MH]$	Co, Rh, Ir	−147·7	−133·4	−93·5	42
$[(PF_3)_4M]^{\ominus}$	Co, Rh, Ir	−159·2	−141·5	−100·9	42
$[(PF_3)_5M]$	Fe, Ru	−163·5	−148·5	..	101
$[(PF_3)_4M]$	Ni, Pd	−140·6	−116	..	56, 66, 99
$[(CF_3PF_2)_4M]$	Ni, Pt	−184·8	..	−155·6	66, 100
$[\{(CF_3)_2PF\}_4M]$	Ni, Pt	−156·7	..	−127·2	66, 100

A downfield phosphorus shift has been observed in all cases in detailed n.m.r. studies of zerovalent nickel and molybdenum complexes of general type $[Ni(CO)_{4-n}P_n]$, and $[Mo(CO)_{6-n}P_n](P = R_xPF_{3-x})$ by Reddy and Schmutzler[56] and independently by Barlow and Nixon.[55] This is also usually accompanied by a lowering of the directly bonded phosphorus–fluorine coupling constant (see Section V.A.). Although the effect on the phosphorus chemical shift of ligand bond angle changes could not be assessed on account of lack of structural data on either the free ligand or the complex, Reddy and Schmutzler[56] have concluded that the paramagnetic term is increased when the phosphine is co-ordinated to the metal, the effect being greater for molybdenum than nickel (see Fig. 18). They proposed that the data provided evidence for an appreciable amount of π-bonding between the metal and phosphorus, the contribution being greater in the case of the nickel. This result suggested that a correlation might exist between the carbonyl stretching frequency v_{CO} and the co-ordination shift ($\delta_{complex} - \delta_{ligand}$) for the $[Ni(CO)_nP_{4-n}]$, $[Mo(CO)_nP_{6-n}]$ complexes, and this seemed to be supported by the available data (Table XXIII). However a more extensive study,[55] using a wider variety of fluorophosphines, has indicated that in general no such simple correlation exists, at least for [Mo(CO)$_4$P$_2$] and [Mo(CO)$_3$P$_3$] complexes (see Table XXIV).

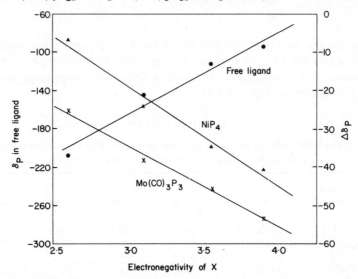

FIG. 18. Plot of ^{31}P chemical shift in free ligands, F$_2$P–X, versus electronegativity of X and versus change in δ_P of ligand on complexation ($\varDelta\delta_P$) in the series [NiP$_4$] and [Mo(CO)$_3$P$_3$]. (From Reddy and Schmutzler.[56])

[31]P chemical-shift measurements on a series of Pt^{II} tertiary phosphine complexes of the type [PtX$_2$P$_2$] (where P = phosphine and X = halogen or pseudohalogen) usually indicated a low-field shift on co-ordination, although some phosphites and trifluorophosphine give higher field shifts on co-ordination. (See Section VII.) For a particular phosphine ligand the observed increase in the chemical shift as the halogen changes from chlorine to bromine to iodine[24] possibly reflects the successive weakening of the platinum—phosphorus σ-bond, since there is a corresponding decrease in the directly bonded platinum–phosphorus spin–spin coupling constant $^1J_{Pt–P}$[24] (see Section III). However changes in the phosphorus chemical shift corresponding to large $^1J_{Pt–P}$ variations are rather less easily rationalized. Similarly, whereas in the [PtCl$_2$P$_2$] series of complexes[26] the chemical shift of the *cis* isomer (for a fixed P) occurred at *higher* field than the corresponding *trans* isomer (see Table XXV) the opposite result was observed during a study of several *mer*-[RhCl$_3$(R$_3$P)$_3$] complexes.[7]

TABLE XXIII

CO stretching frequencies and $\Delta\delta_P$ values in some [Ni(CO)$_2$P$_2$] and [Mo(CO)$_3$P$_3$] complexes

Compound	ν_{CO}, cm^{-1}	$\Delta\delta_P$, p.p.m.
$[Ni(CO)_2(MePFNMe_2)_2]$	2020, 1961	$-15\cdot5$
$[Ni(CO)_2(Et_2N \cdot PF_2)_2]$	2046, 1992	$-24\cdot5$
$[Ni(CO)_2(Me_2N \cdot PF_2)_2]$	2040, 1993	$-25\cdot5$
$[Ni(CO)_2(C_5H_{10}N \cdot PF_2)_2]$	2041, 1993	$-25\cdot5$
$[Ni(CO)_2\{(Me_2N)_2PF\}_2]$	2019, 1961	$-30\cdot2$
$[Mo(CO)_3(PhPF_2)_3]$	2034, 1969	$-25\cdot3$
$[Mo(CO)_3(MePFNMe_2)_3]$	1970, 1882	$-25\cdot7$
$[Mo(CO)_3(PhPFNEt_2)_3$	1960, 1873	$-29\cdot5$
$[Mo(CO)_3\{(Me_2N)_2PF\}_3]$	1969, 1878	$-31\cdot5$
$[Mo(CO)_3(C_5H_{10}N \cdot PF_2)_3]$	1996, 1934	$-38\cdot3$
$[Mo(CO)_3(Et_2N \cdot PF_2)_3]$	1995, 1919	$-38\cdot4$
$[Mo(CO)_3(PhOPF_2)_3]$	2025, 1954	$-40\cdot0$
$[Mo(CO)_3(PrOPF_2)_3]$	2020, 1947	$-46\cdot0$
$\left[Mo(CO)_3\left\{\begin{array}{c}O\\ \\O\end{array}P{-}F\right\}_3\right]$	2041, 1990, 1970	$-48\cdot5$
$[Mo(CO)_3(PF_3)_3]$	2090, 2055	$-53\cdot6$

From Reddy and Schmutzler.[56]

TABLE XXIV

CO stretching frequencies and $\Delta\delta_P$ values for cis-[Mo(CO)$_4$P$_2$] complexes

Complex	ν_{CO}, cm^{-1}				Co-ordination shift, $\Delta\delta_P$, p.p.m.
	A$_1$(2)	A$_1$(1)	B$_1$	B$_2$	
cis-$[Mo(CO)_4(PF_3)_2]$	2091	2022	2022	2003	$-51\cdot5$
cis-$[Mo(CO)_4(CF_3PF_2)_2]$	2094	2036	2036	2013	$-41\cdot0$
cis-$[Mo(CO)_4\{(CF_3)_2PF\}_2]$	2093	2033	2033	2013	$-60\cdot0$
cis-$[Mo(CO)_4(Et_2NPF_2)_2]$	2055	1974	1950	1942	$-32\cdot3$
cis-$[Mo(CO)_4(Me_2NPF_2)_2]$	2057	1978	1993	1945	$-36\cdot5$
cis-$[Mo(CO)_4(ClCH_2PF_2)_2]$	2069	—	1954	1954	$-28\cdot4$
cis-$[Mo(CO)_4(CCl_3PF_2)_2]$	2079	2015	2010	1990	$-66\cdot5$

From Nixon et al.[12, 55, 103]

TABLE XXV

^{31}P co-ordination chemical shifts $\left[\delta_{P(complex)} - \delta_{P(ligand)}\right]$
in $\left[PtCl_2\{R_nPh_{3-n}P\}_2\right]$ **complexes**

Complex	Co-ordination shift, p.p.m.
cis-$\left[PtCl_2(Et_3P)_2\right]$	−30·0
trans-$\left[PtCl_2(Et_3P)_2\right]$	−32·7
cis-$\left[PtCl_2(PhEt_2P)_2\right]$	−20·4
trans-$\left[PtCl_2(PhEt_2P)_2\right]$	−28·4
cis-$\left[PtCl_2(Pr_3P)_2\right]$	−32·8
trans-$\left[PtCl_2(Pr_3P)_2\right]$	−36·8
cis-$\left[PtCl_2(PhPr_2P)_2\right]$	−25·0
trans-$\left[PtCl_2(PhPr_2P)_2\right]$	−34·0
cis-$\left[PtCl_2(Bu_3P)_2\right]$	−33·5
trans-$\left[PtCl_2(Bu_3P)_2\right]$	−37·4
cis-$\left[PtCl_2(PhBu_2P)_2\right]$	−23·9
trans-$\left[PtCl_2(PhBu_2P)_2\right]$	−32·7
cis-$\left[PtCl_2(Ph_2BuP)_2\right]$	−24·1
trans-$\left[PtCl_2(Ph_2BuP)_2\right]$	−29·1

From Grim et al.[26]

A general inspection of the Tables of published phosphorus chemical-shift data on co-ordination complexes (in Section VII) indicates the difficulties in any quantitative understanding. In general it appears that the majority of transition metal—phosphine complexes (particularly those containing the metal in its zerovalent state) have resonances at lower field than the corresponding unco-ordinated phosphine. On the other hand the chemical shifts of all phosphorus trichloride complexes occur at higher field than the free ligand,[95, 111] while the behaviour of phosphite complexes is rather more variable. Phosphine

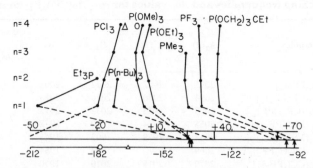

FIG. 19. Variation of the phosphorus chemical shift in complexes of the type [Ni(CO)$_{4-n}$P$_n$], as a function of P and n. (From Poilblanc et al.[111])

complexes with boron acceptors frequently are to high field of the free ligand.

Some very recent chemical shift data for trimethyl phosphite complexes of chromium, molybdenum and tungsten carbonyls, by Poilblanc et al.,[111] are consistent with the conclusions discussed earlier in this section (p. 404–407). These authors have also studied variations in δ_P for nickel carbonyl phosphine complexes, $[Ni(CO)_{4-n}P_n]$, [where $n = 1$ to 4; and P is Me_3P, Et_3P, Bu_3P, PCl_3, PF_3, and $P(OMe)_3$], as a function of the number and nature of the phosphine ligand (see Fig. 19). In addition, the u.v. spectra of several trimethyl phosphite complexes of nickel and Group VIa metal carbonyls have been recorded, to try and assess the importance of the average excitation energy, ΔE, in the paramagnetic term, (equation 10 p. 396), in determining the phosphorus chemical shift of the complex.[111]

VII. TABULATION OF ³¹P CHEMICAL SHIFTS FOR PHOSPHINES AND THEIR COMPLEXES

Compound	Chemical shift, p.p.m. relative to 85% H_3PO_4	Ref.
Tertiary phosphines		
Me_3P	$+62\cdot0$	2
$[Me_3PH]^+$	$+2\cdot8$	85
Et_3P	$+20\cdot4$	2
cis-$[PtCl_2(Et_3P)_2]$	$-9\cdot6$	26
trans-$[PtCl_2(Et_3P)_2]$	$-12\cdot3$	26
trans-$[PtMeCl(Et_3P)_2]$	$-16\cdot2$	3
trans-$[PtMeBr(Et_3P)_2]$	$-13\cdot9$	3
trans-$[PtMeI(Et_3P)_2]$	$-10\cdot8$	3
trans-$[PtMe(NO_3)(Et_3P)_2]$	$-21\cdot0$	3
trans-$[PtMe(N_3)(Et_3P)_2]$	$-17\cdot9$	3
trans-$[PtMe(NCO)(Et_3P)_2]$	$-15\cdot9$	3
trans-$[PtMe(NCS)(Et_3P)_2]$	$-16\cdot9$	3
trans-$[PtMe(NO_2)(Et_3P)_2]$	$-14\cdot7$	3
trans-$[PtMe(CN)(Et_3P)_2]$	$-13\cdot9$	3
cis-$[PtMeCl(Et_3P)_2]$	$-14\cdot6^a$ $-8\cdot7^b$	3
cis-$[PtMeBr(Et_3P)_2]$	$-12\cdot9^a$ $-10\cdot9^b$	3
cis-$[PtMe(N_3)(Et_3P)_2]$	$-16\cdot8^a$ $-6\cdot7^b$	3

^a trans to R in cis-$[PtRX(Et_3P)_2]$
^b trans to X in cis-$[PtRX(Et_3P)_2]$

Compound	Chemical shift, p.p.m. relative to 85% H_3PO_4	Ref.
cis-$[PtMe(NCS)(Et_3P)_2]$	$-15\cdot5^a$	3
	$-4\cdot3^b$	
cis-$[PtMe_2(Et_3P)_2]$	$-9\cdot7$	3
trans-$[PtPhCl(Et_3P)_2]$	$-3\cdot6$	3
trans-$[PtPh_2(Et_3P)_2]$	$-8\cdot0$	3
cis-$[PtPhCl(Et_3P)_2]$†	$-9\cdot2^a$	3
	$-3\cdot1^b$	
cis-$[PtPh_2(Et_3P)_2]$	$-3\cdot5$	3
cis-$[Pt(mes)Br(Et_3P)_2]$†	$-8\cdot3^a$	3
	$-0\cdot8^b$	
$[PtCl_2Me_2(Et_3P)_2]$	$-7\cdot7$	3
$[PtI_2Me_2(Et_3P)_2]$	$+22\cdot8$	3
$[NiCl_2(Et_3P)_2]$	$-15\cdot7\pm1$	104
$[Ni(CO)_2(Et_3P)_2]$	$-20\cdot7$	95
$[Ni(CO)_3(Et_3P)]$	$-47\cdot0$	95
$[Mo(CO)_4(Et_3P)_2]$	$-29\cdot0$	95
$[CuI_4(Et_3P)_3]$	$+26\cdot0$	95
$[BH_3 \cdot Et_3P]$	$-15\cdot5$	105
$[H_2BEt \cdot Et_3P]$	$-14\cdot5$	105
n-Bu_3P	$+32\cdot3$	2
cis-$[PtCl_2(Bu_3P)_2]$	$-1\cdot4, -0\cdot9, -1\cdot2$	24, 3, 26
trans-$[PtCl_2(Bu_3P)_2]$	$-4\cdot9, -4\cdot3, -5\cdot1$	24, 3, 26
cis-$[PtBr_2(Bu_3P)_2]$	$-0\cdot8$	24
trans-$[PtBr_2(Bu_3P)_2]$	~0	24
cis-$[PtI_2(Bu_3P)_2]$	$+1\cdot1$	24
trans-$[PtI_2(Bu_3P)_2]$	$+7\cdot9$	24
cis-$[Pt(CN)_2(Bu_3P)_2]$	$-5\cdot9$	24
trans-$[PtBr_2(EtNH_2)(Bu_3P)]$	$+9\cdot5$	24
trans-$[PtI_2(EtNH_2)(Bu_3P)]$	$+10\cdot5$	24
trans-$[PtCl_2(Et_2NH)(Bu_3P)]$	$+6\cdot2$	24
trans-$[PtBr_2(Et_2NH)(Bu_3P)]$	$+8\cdot7$	24
trans-$[PtCl_2(py)(Bu_3P)]$	$+8\cdot0$	24
trans-$[PtBr_2(py)(Bu_3P)]$	$+11\cdot7$	24
trans-$[PtI_2(py)(Bu_3P)]$	$+14\cdot7$	24
cis-$[PtCl_2(Me_2S)(Bu_3P)]$	$-2\cdot2$	24
$[PtCl(Bu_3)_3]^{\oplus}Cl^{\ominus}$	$-0\cdot7\ (I=1)$‡	3
	$-10\cdot2\ (I=2)$	
trans-$[PtCl_4(Bu_3P)_2]$	~0	24
cis-$[PtCl_4(Bu_3P)_2]$	$-12\cdot5$	24
sym-trans-$[Pt_2Cl_4(Bu_3P)_2]$	$-2\cdot3$	24
$[NiCl_2)Bu_3P)_2]$	$+1\cdot5, 0\pm1$	95, 104

† mes = mesityl
‡ Indicates relative intensities of the two signals.

Compound	Chemical shift, p.p.m. relative to 85% H_3PO_4	Ref.
$[Ni(PhC_2)_2(Bu_3P)_2]$	-15.1	95
$[Ni(CO)_2(Bu_3P)_2]$	-12.1	95
mer-$[RhCl_3(Bu_3P)_3]$	-14.7 ± 0.2 (I=1) $+0.7 \pm 0.2$ (I=2)	7
$[Cr(CO)_5(Bu_3P)]$	-30.2	21
trans-$[Cr(CO)_4(Ph_3P)(Bu_3P)]$	-43.3	47
trans-$[Cr(CO)_4\{(PhO)_3P\}(Bu_3P)]$	-38.2	47
$[Mo(CO)_5(Bu_3P)]$	-12.2	21
trans-$[Mo(CO)_4(Ph_3P)(Bu_3P)]$	-22.0	47
trans-$[Mo(CO)_4\{(PhO)_3P\}(Bu_3P)]$	-17.2	47
$[W(CO)_5(Bu_3P)]$	$+6.4$	21
trans-$[W(CO)_4(BuP)_2]$	$+2.5$	20
trans-$[W(CO)_4(Ph_3P)(Bu_3P)]$	$+3.2$	47
trans-$[W(CO)_4\{(PhO)_3P\}(Bu_3P)]$	$+5.3$	47
Pr_3P	$+33.0$	2
cis-$[PtCl_2(Pr_3P)_2]$	$+0.2$	26
trans-$[PtCl_2(Pr_3P)_2]$	-3.8	26
mer-$[RhCl_3(Pr_3P)_3]$	-14.3 ± 0.4 (I=1) $+0.6 \pm 0.2$ (I=2)	7
Pr_2PhP	$+27.7$	2
cis-$[PtCl_2(Pr_2PhP)_2]$	$+2.7$	26
trans-$[PtCl_2(Pr_2PhP)_2]$	-6.3	26
i-Pr_2PhP	-0.2	2
$[Cr(CO)_5(i-Pr_2PhP)]$	-59.5	21
$[Mo(CO)_5(i-Pr_2PhP)]$	-43.2	21
$[W(CO)_5(i-Pr_2PhP)]$	-26.3	21
Ph_2BuP	$+17.1$	2
cis-$[PtCl_2\{(Ph_2BuP)\}_2]$	-7.0	26
trans-$[PtCl_2(Ph_2BuP)_2]$	-12.0	26
$[Cr(CO)_5(Ph_2BuP)]$	-45.1	21
$[Mo(CO)_5(Ph_2BuP)]$	-26.5	21
$[W(CO)_5(Ph_2BuP)]$	-7.9	21
$Ph_2(t-Bu)P$	-17.1	2
$[Cr(CO)_5\{Ph_2(t-Bu)P\}]$	-72.7	21
$[Mo(CO)_5\{Ph_2(t-Bu)P\}]$	-57.0	21
$[W(CO)_5\{Ph_2(t-Bu)P\}]$	-41.7	21
Ph_3P	$+6.0$	2
$[Ph_3PH]^\oplus$	0	2
$[RhCl(CO)(Ph_3P)_2]$	-29.3 ± 0.4	7
$[NiC_2H_4(Ph_3P)_2]$	-20.3	106
$[Fe(CO)_3(Ph_3P)_2]$	$+9.5$	95
$[Fe(NO)_2(Ph_3P)_2]$	-50.8	95
$[Ni(CO)_3(Ph_3P)]$	-42.9	95
$[Ni(CO)_2(Ph_3P)_2]$	-32.6	95
$[Cr(CO)_5(Ph_3P)_2]$	-55.3	21
trans-$[Cr(CO)_4(Ph_3P)(Bu_3P)]$	-74.1	47

Compound	Chemical shift, p.p.m. relative to 85% H_3PO_4	Ref.
$[Mo(CO)_5(Ph_3P)]$	$-37 \cdot 5$	21
trans-$[Mo(CO)_4(Ph_3P)(Bu_3P)]$	$-50 \cdot 9$	47
trans-$[Mo(CO)_4(Ph_3P)(PhBu_2P)]$	$-51 \cdot 1$	47
cis-$[Mo(CO)_4(Ph_3P)(PhBu_2P)]$	$-38 \cdot 3$	47
$[W(CO)_5(Ph_3P)]$	$-20 \cdot 6$	21
trans-$[W(CO)_4(Ph_3P)(Bu_3P)]$	$-28 \cdot 4$	47
$PhBu_2P$	$+26 \cdot 2$	2
cis-$[PtCl_2(PhBu_2P)_2]$	$+2 \cdot 3$	26
trans-$[PtCl_2(PhBu_2P)_2]$	$-6 \cdot 5$	26
$[Cr(CO)_5(PhBu_2P)]$	$-35 \cdot 3$	21
$[Mo(CO)_5(PhBu_2P)]$	$-17 \cdot 6$	21
trans-$[Mo(CO)_4(PhBu_2P)(Ph_3P)]$	$-27 \cdot 9$	47
cis-$[Mo(CO)_4(PhBu_2P)(Ph_3P)]$	$-12 \cdot 1$	47
trans-$[Mo(CO)_4(PhBu_2P)\{(PhO)_3P\}]$	$-23 \cdot 1$	47
$[W(CO)_5(PhBu_2P)]$	$+0 \cdot 8$	21
Ph_2MeP	$+28 \cdot 0$	2
cis-$[PtCl_2(Ph_2MeP)_2]$	$+1 \cdot 2$	26
$[Cr(CO)_5(Ph_2MeP)]$	$-35 \cdot 0$	21
$[Mo(CO)_5(Ph_2MeP)]$	$-15 \cdot 0$	21
$[W(CO)_5(Ph_2MeP)]$	$+3 \cdot 8$	21
Ph_2EtP	$+12 \cdot 0$	2
cis-$[PtCl_2(Ph_2EtP)_2]$	$-9 \cdot 8$	26
$[Ni(CO)_2(Ph_2EtP)_2]$	$-28 \cdot 7$	95
$[Cr(CO)_5(Ph_2EtP)]$	$-48 \cdot 3$	21
$[Mo(CO)_5(Ph_2EtP)]$	$-30 \cdot 1$	21
$[W(CO)_5(Ph_2EtP)]$	$-12 \cdot 1$	21
Et_2PhP	$+17 \cdot 2$	2
cis-$[PtCl_2(Et_2PhP)_2]$	$-3 \cdot 3$	26
trans-$[PtCl_2(Et_2PhP)_2]$	$-11 \cdot 3$	26
mer-$[RhCl_3(Et_2PhP)_3]$	$-17 \cdot 4 \pm 0 \cdot 5 \ (I=1)$ $-3 \cdot 9 \pm 0 \cdot 5 \ (I=2)$	7
Me_2PPh	$+46 \cdot 9$	2
cis-$[PtCl_2(Me_2PPh)_2]$	$+15 \cdot 2$	26
Phosphites		
$P(OMe)_3$	-141	2
$[H_3B \cdot P(OMe)_3]$	-118	15
$[Me_3B \cdot P(OMe)_3]$	-106	15
$[Ni\{P(OMe)_3\}_5](ClO_4)_2$	-110	97
$[Ni\{P(OMe)_3\}_4]$	$-162 \cdot 3$	97, 111
$[CuCl\{P(OMe)_3\}]_4$	-132	96, 97
$[Cu\{P(OMe)_3\}_4ClO_4$	-125	19
$[Ag\{P(OMe)_3\}_4]ClO_4$	-132	97
$[AgCl\{P(OMe)_3\}]_4$	-135	96
$[Co\{P(OMe)_3\}_5]NO_3$	-147	97
$[Cr(CO)_5\{P(OMe)_3\}]$	$-179 \cdot 6$	111

Compound	Chemical shift, p.p.m. relative to 85% H_3PO_4	Ref.
$[Mo(CO)_5\{P(OMe)_3\}]$	-162	111
$[W(CO)_5\{P(OMe)_3\}]$	$-137\cdot3$	111
cis-$[Mo(CO)_4\{P(OMe)_3\}_2]$	-164	111
trans-$[Mo(CO)_4\{P(OMe)_3\}_2]$	-174	111
cis-$[W(CO)_4\{P(OMe)_3\}_2]$	$-144\cdot1$	111
trans-$[W(CO)_4\{P(OMe)_3\}_2]$	$-148\cdot5$	111
cis-$[Mo(CO)_3\{P(OMe)_3\}_3]$	-166	111
trans-$[Mo(CO)_3\{P(OMe)_3\}_3]$	-165 (I = 1)	111
	-177 (I = 2)	111
cis-$[Mo(CO)_2\{P(OMe)_3\}_4]$	$-166\cdot9$ (P cis)	111
	$-174\cdot5$ (P trans)	111
$[Fe(CO)_4\{P(OMe)_3\}]$	$-178\cdot9$	111
$[Fe(CO)_3\{P(OMe)_3\}_2]$	$-188\cdot5$	111
$[Fe(CO)_2\{P(OMe)_3\}_3]$	$-186\cdot2$	111
$[Ni(CO)_3\{P(OMe)_3\}]$	$-161\cdot4$	111
$[Ni(CO)_2\{P(OMe)_3\}_2]$	$-165\cdot1$	111
$[Ni(CO)\{P(OMe)_3\}_3]$	$-165\cdot8$	111
$P(OEt)_3$	-138	2
$[Ni(CO)_3\{P(OEt)_3\}]$	-157	95
$[Ni(CO)_2\{P(OEt)_2\}]$	-160	95
$[Ni(CO)\{P(OEt)_3\}_3]$	-163	95
$[Ni\{P(OEt)_3\}_4]$	-160	95
$[NiCl_2\{P(OEt)_3\}_2]$	-118	96, 104
$[Cu\{P(OEt)_3\}_4]ClO_4$	$-121\cdot5$	19, 96
$[CuCl\{P(OEt)_3\}]$	-128	96
$[Ag\{P(OEt)_3\}_4]ClO_4$	-128	96
$[HgCl_2\{P(OEt)_3\}_2]$	-115	96
trans-$[Mo(CO)_4\{P(OEt)_3\}_2]$	-171	111
cis-$[Mo(CO)_3\{P(OEt)_3\}_3]$	-162	111
trans-$[Mo(CO)_3\{P(OEt)_3\}_3]$	-164 (I = 1)	111
	-172 (I = 2)	111
$P(OPh)_3$	-128	2
$[Ni(CO)_2\{P(OPh)_3\}_2]$	-146	95
trans-$[Cr(CO)_4(Bu_3P)\{P(OPh)_3\}]$	$-185\cdot1$	47
$[Mo(CO)_4(Bu_3P)\{P(OPh)_3\}]$	-165	47
trans-$[Mo(CO)_4(PhBu_2P)\{P(OPh)_3\}]$	$-165\cdot2$	47
trans-$[W(CO)_4(Bu_3P)\{P(OPh)_3\}]$	$-137\cdot0$	47
cis-$[PtCl_2\{P(OPh)_3\}_2]$	-59	3
cis-$[PtCl_2(Bu_3P)\{P(OPh)_3\}]$	$-52\cdot7$	3
$P(OCH_2)_3CMe$	$-91\cdot5$	2
$[BH_3\cdot P(OCH_2)_3CMe]$	-97	15
$[BMe_3\cdot P(OCH_2)_3CMe]$	-91	15
$[BF_3\cdot P(OCH_2)_3CMe]$	-93	15
$P(OCH_2)_3CEt$	-92	2
$[Ni\{P(OCH_2)_3CEt\}_5](ClO_4)_2$	-108	97
$[Ag\{P(OCH_2)_3CEt\}_4]NO_3$	-99	97

Compound	Chemical shift, p.p.m. relative to 85% H_3PO_4		Ref.
$P(OCH_2)_3CC_3H_7$	-93		2
$[Ni\{P(OCH_2)_3CC_3H_7\}_4]$	-128		97
$[Co\{P(OCH_2)CC_3H_7\}_5]ClO_4$	-138		97
$P(OCH)_3(CH_2)_3$	-137		2
$[BH_3 \cdot P(OCH)_3(CH_2)_3]$	-117		15
$[BMe_3 \cdot P(OCH)_3(CH_2)_3]$	-128		15
$[BF_3 \cdot P(OCH)_3(CH_2)_3]$	-138		15
$[Ni\{P(OCH)_3(CH_2)_3\}_4]$	-153		15
$[Ni\{P(OCH)_3(CH_2)_3\}_5](ClO_4)_2$	-125		15
$[Ag\{P(OCH)_3(CH_2)_3\}_4]NO_3$	-134		97
$[Co\{P(OCH)_3(CH_2)_3\}_5]ClO_4$	-157		97
P_4O_6	$-112\cdot5$		94
	P(coord)	P(uncoord)	
$[Ni(CO)_3(P_4O_6)]$	$-126\cdot3$	$-117\cdot6$	5
$[\{Ni(CO)_3\}_2(P_4O_6)]$	$-130\cdot3$	$-120\cdot0$	5
$[\{Ni(CO)_3\}_3(P_4O_6)]$	$-132\cdot6$	$-120\cdot2$	5
$[\{Ni(CO)_3\}_4(P_4O_6)]$	$-132\cdot9$		5
$[Ni_2(CO)_4(P_4O_6)_3]$		$-117\cdot9$	2
$[Ni(CO)_2(P_4O_6)_2]$		$-117\cdot7$	2
$[Ni_4(CO)_{11}(P_4O_6)_2]$	$-132\cdot0$	-132 ± 1	2
cis-$[Mo(CO)_4(P_4O_6)_2]$	$-135\cdot5$	$-116\cdot4$	98
$[(BH_3)P_4O_6)]$	$-90\cdot4$	$-118\cdot2$	5
$[(BH_3)_2(P_4O_6)]$	$-98\cdot7$	$-119\cdot2$	5
$[(BH_3)_3(P_4O_6)]$	$-103\cdot6$	$-114\cdot6$	5

Fluorophosphines

Compound	Chemical shift	Ref.
PF_3	$-97\cdot0$	2
$[PtCl_2(PF_3)_2]$	$-69\cdot0$	2
$[PtBr_2(PF_3)_2]$	$-68\cdot4$	2
$[PtI_2(PF_3)_2]$	$-68\cdot0$	2
$[Ni(PF_3)_4]$	$-140\cdot6, -137\cdot7$	56, 100, 111
$[Pd(PF_3)_4]$	-116	99
$[Co(PF_3)_4H]$	$-147\cdot7$	42
$[Rh(PF_3)_4H]$	$-133\cdot4$	42
$[Ir(PF_3)_4H]$	$-93\cdot5$	42
$[Co(PF_3)_4]^\ominus$	$-159\cdot2$	42
$[Rh(PF_3)_4]^\ominus$	$-141\cdot5$	42
$[Ir(PF_3)_4]^\ominus$	$-100\cdot9$	42
$[Fe(PF_3)_5]$	$-163\cdot5$	101
$[Ru(PF_3)_5]$	$-148\cdot5$	101
$[Fe(PF_3)_2(NO)_2]$	$-174\cdot3$	42
trans-$[Cr(CO)_4(PF_3)_2]$	$-177\cdot8$	45
cis-$[Cr(CO)_4(PF_3)_2]$	$-173\cdot3$	45
cis-$[Mo(CO)_4(PF_3)_2]$	$-148\cdot0$	12
trans-$[Mo(CO)_3(PF_3)_3]$	$-150\cdot5$	55
cis-$[Mo(CO)_3(PF_3)_3]$	$-150\cdot6$	56

Compound	Chemical shift, p.p.m. relative to 85% H_3PO_4	Ref.
cis-$[W(CO)_4(PF_3)_2]$	$-122 \cdot 0$	45
$[Ni(CO)_3(PF_3)]$	$-136 \cdot 5$	111
$[Ni(CO)_2(PF_3)_2]$	$-136 \cdot 8$	111
$[Ni(CO)(PF_3)_3]$	$-137 \cdot 2$	111
CCl_3PF_2	$-131 \cdot 0$	53
cis-$[Cr(CO)_4(CCl_3PF_2)_2]$	$-211 \cdot 2$	45
cis-$[Mo(CO)_4(CCl_3PF_2)_2]$	$-196 \cdot 5$	12
cis-$[W(CO)_4(CCl_3PF_2)_2]$	$-168 \cdot 1$	45
$[Ni(CCl_3PF_2)_4]$	$-169 \cdot 9$	100
$PhPF_2$	$-208 \cdot 3$	107
$[Ni(PhPF_2)_4]$	$-214 \cdot 8$	107
cis-$[Mo(CO)_3(PhPF_2)_3]$	$-233 \cdot 6$	107
CF_3PF_2	$-158 \cdot 3$	53
cis-$[Mo(CO)_4(CF_3PF_2)_2]$	$-199 \cdot 0$	12
cis-$[W(CO)_4(CF_3PF_2)_2)$	$-170 \cdot 2$	45
$[Ni(CF_3PF_2)_4]$	$-184 \cdot 8$	100
$[Pt(CF_3PF_2)_4]$	$-155 \cdot 6$	66
$(CF_3)_2PF$	$-123 \cdot 9$	43
cis-$[Mo(CO)_4\{(CF_3)_2PF\}_2]$	$-184 \cdot 0$	12
$[Ni\{(CF_3)_2PF\}_4]$	$-156 \cdot 7$	100
$[Pt\{(CF_3)_2PF\}_4]$	$-127 \cdot 2$	66
$ClCH_2PF_2$	$-201 \cdot 6$	53
cis-$[Mo(CO)_4(ClCH_2PF_2)_2]$	$-230 \cdot 0$	12
cis-$[W(CO)_4(ClCH_2PF_2)_2]$	$-201 \cdot 5$	45
$[Ni(ClCH_2PF_2)_4]$	$-211 \cdot 6$	100
PF_2OPF_2	$-114 \cdot 6, -111 \cdot 0$	109
$[H_3B \cdot (PF_2OPF_2)]$	$-105 \cdot 5$ (uncoord) $\left.\vphantom{\begin{array}{c}a\\a\end{array}}\right\}$ $-100 \cdot 7$ (coord)	109
Me_2NPF_2	$-143 \cdot 0$	53
$[H_3B \cdot Me_2NPF_2]$	$-130 \cdot 0$	11
$[BF_3 \cdot Me_2NPF_2]$	$-140 \cdot 0$	11
$[B_4H_8 \cdot Me_2NPF_2]$	$-120 \cdot 0$	11
cis-$[Mo(CO)_4(Me_2NPF_2)_2]$	$-180 \cdot 5$	12
cis-$[W(CO)_4(Me_2NPF_2)_2]$	$-156 \cdot 1$	45
$[Ni(CO)_2(Me_2NPF_2)_2]$	$-168 \cdot 5$	56
cis-$[Cr(CO)_4(Me_2NPF_2)_2]$	$-203 \cdot 0$	45
trans-$[Cr(CO)_4(Me_2NPF_2)_2]$	$-209 \cdot 4$	45
Et_2NPF_2	$-144 \cdot 0$	53
cis-$[Mo(CO)_4(Et_2NPF_2)_2]$	$-179 \cdot 5$	12
cis-$[Mo(CO)_3(Et_2NPF_2)_3]$	$-182 \cdot 4$	56
$[Ni(CO)_2(Et_2NPF_2)_2]$	$-168 \cdot 8$	56
$C_5H_{10}NPF_2$	$-139 \cdot 1$	53
cis-$[Mo(CO)_3(C_5H_{10}NPF_2)_3]$	$-177 \cdot 4$	56
cis-$[Mo(CO)_2(C_5H_{10}NPF_2)_4]$	$-183 \cdot 1$	56
$[Ni(CO)_2(C_5H_{10}NPF_2)_2]$	$-164 \cdot 6$	56
$EtN(PF_2)_2$	$-145 \cdot 3$	61

Compound	Chemical shift, p.p.m. relative to 85% H_3PO_4	Ref.
cis-$[Cr(CO)_4\{EtN(PF_2)_2\}]$	$-170{\cdot}7$	45
cis-$[Mo(CO)_4\{EtN(PF_2)_2\}]$	$-144{\cdot}8$	45
cis-$[W(CO)_4\{EtN(PF_2)_2\}]$	$-114{\cdot}5$	45
$(Me_2N)_2PF$	$-150{\cdot}8$	53
$[H_3B{\cdot}(Me_2N)_2PF]$	$-134{\cdot}0$	11
$[BF_3{\cdot}(Me_2N)_2PF]$	$-138{\cdot}0$	11
cis-$[Mo(CO)_3\{(Me_2N)_2PF\}_3]$	$-182{\cdot}3$	56
$[Ni(CO)_2\{(Me_2N)_2PF\}_2]$	$-181{\cdot}0$	56
$MePF(NMe_2)$	$-168{\cdot}9$	110
cis-$[Mo(CO)_3\{MePF(NMe)\}_3]$	$-194{\cdot}6$	56
$[Ni(CO)_2\{MePF(NMe)\}_2]$	$-184{\cdot}4$	56
$PhPFNMe_2$	$-156{\cdot}0$	110
cis-$[Mo(CO)_3(PhPFNMe_2)]$	$-185{\cdot}5$	56
n-$C_3H_7OPF_2$	$-111{\cdot}5$	53
cis-$[Mo(CO)_3(C_3H_7OPF_2)_3]$	$-157{\cdot}5$	56
$[Ni(C_3H_7OPF_2)_4]$	$-146{\cdot}0$	56
$PhOPF_2$	$-110{\cdot}1$	53
cis-$[Mo(CO)_3(PhOPF_2)_3]$	$-150{\cdot}1$	56
$C_6H_4O_2PF$	$-123{\cdot}1$	56
cis-$[Mo(CO)_3(C_6H_4O_2PF)_3]$	$-171{\cdot}6$	56
$[Ni(C_6H_4O_2PF)_4]$	$-157{\cdot}1$	56

Miscellaneous

PCl_3	$-219{\cdot}0$	2
$[Ni(CO)(PCl_3)_3]$	$-177{\cdot}0, 175{\cdot}7$	95, 111
$[Ni(CO)_2(PCl_3)_2]$	$-181{\cdot}0, 179{\cdot}4$	95, 111
$[Ni(CO)_3(PCl_3)]$	$-185{\cdot}0, 182{\cdot}5$	95, 111
$[Ni(PCl_3)_4]$	$-170{\cdot}0, 172{\cdot}7$	95, 111
$PhPCl_2$	$-162{\cdot}0$	2
$[Ni(PhPCl_2)_4]$	$-152{\cdot}0$	95
$P_4(NMe)_6$	$-82{\cdot}7$	2
$[(H_3B)\{P_4(NMe)_6\}]$	$-80{\cdot}5$ P(coord.) $-103{\cdot}2$ P(uncoord.)	6
$[(H_3B)_2\{P_4(NMe)_6\}]$	$-96{\cdot}7$ P(coord.) $-118{\cdot}1$ P(uncoord)	6
$[(H_3B)_3\{P_4(NMe_6)\}]$	$-110{\cdot}0$ P(coord.) $-112{\cdot}6$ P(uncoord.)	6
$[\{Ni(CO)_3\}\{P_4(NMe)_6\}]$	$-119{\cdot}0$ P(coord.) $-93{\cdot}9$ P(uncoord.)	6
$[\{Ni(CO)_3\}_2\{P_4(NMe)_6\}]$	$-128{\cdot}5$ P(coord.) $-103{\cdot}1$ P(uncoord.)	6
$[\{Ni(CO)_3\}_3\{P_4(NMe)_6\}]$	$-135{\cdot}7$ P(coord.) $-108{\cdot}9$ P(uncoord.)	6
PH_3	$+240{\cdot}0$	2
cis-$[Mo(CO)_4(PH_3)_2]$	$+155{\cdot}0$	69
cis-$[W(CO)_4(PH_3)_2]$	$+175{\cdot}0$	69

Compound	Chemical shift, p.p.m. relative to 85% H_3PO_4	Ref.
$[H_3B\{P(NPr_2)_3\}]$	$-61\cdot6$	2
$[AlEt_3(Ph_2PPPh_2)]$	$+13\cdot0$	108
$[AlEt_3\{EtN(PPh_2)_2\}]$	$-59\cdot0$	108
$[AlEt_3\{MeN(PPh_2)_2\}]$	$-64\cdot0$	108
$[NiCl_2(sec \cdot Bu_3P)_2]$	$-19\cdot3\pm1$	104
$[NiCl_2\{(n\text{-}C_8H_{17})_3P\}_2]$	$+3\cdot6\pm1$	104
$[NiCl_2\{(n\text{-}C_8H_{17})_2PBu\}_2]$	$0\cdot0\pm2\cdot0$	104
$[NiCl_2(\{Me(CH_2)_3CHEtCH_2\}_3P)_2]$	$6\cdot2\pm1$	104
$[NiCl_2\{(CH_2{=}CH{-}CH_2)_3P\}]$	$3\cdot0\pm0\cdot5$	104
$[NiCl_2\{(PhCH_2)_3P\}_2]$	$-1\cdot2\pm1$	104
$[NiCl_2(i\text{-}Bu_2P)_2]$	$10\cdot4\pm1\cdot0$	104
$[NiCl_2(i\text{-}Pr_3P)_2]$	$-44\cdot0\pm2\cdot0$	104
$[Ni(CO)_2\{(CF_3)_3P\}_2]$	$-52\cdot6\pm0\cdot5$	73
$[AlEt_3(Me_2NPMe_2)]$	$+41\cdot0$	108
$[(AlEt_3)_2(Me_2PPMe_2)]$	$+50\cdot0$	108
$[AlEt_2H(Et_2NPPh_2)]$	$-54\cdot0$	108
$mer\text{-}[Mo(CO)_3\{P(OEt)_3\}\{(Ph_2P)_2C_2H_4\}]$	$-53\cdot8$ $\left.\begin{array}{c}\\ \\ \end{array}\right\}$ $-64\cdot5$	47
$[Ni(CO)_2\{(Et_2P)_2C_2H_4\}]$	$-48\cdot6$	95
$[Ni_2(CO)_4\{(Et_2P)_2C_2H_4\}_2]$	$-22\cdot0$	95
$[Ni(CO)_3]_2[(Et_2P)_2C_2H_4]$	$-21\cdot9$	95
$[Ni(CO)_2\{(CH_2CH_2CN)_2P\}_2C_2H_4]$	$-44\cdot9$	95
$[Ni_2(CO)_4[\{CH_2CH_2CN)_2P\}_2C_2H_4]_2]$	$-20\cdot8$	95
$[Mo(CO)_4\{(CH_2CH_2CN)_2P\}_2C_2H_4]$	$-52\cdot6$	95
$[Ni(CO)_2\{o\text{-}C_6H_4(PEt_2)_2\}]$	$-36\cdot6$	95
$[Hg_2Cl_2\{OP(OEt)_2\}_2]$	$-65\cdot0$	9
$[Hg_2Cl_2\{OP(Oi\text{-}C_3H_7)_2\}_2]$	$-61\cdot5$	9
$[Hg_2Cl_2\{OP(OBu)_2\}_2]$	$-66\cdot0$	9
$[Hg_2Br_2\{OP(OBu)_2\}_2]$	$-69\cdot5$	9

ACKNOWLEDGEMENT

We thank Dr. R. M. Lynden-Bell for her assistance particularly with the theoretical sections of this review.

REFERENCES

1. G. Mavel, *In* "Progress in Nuclear Magnetic Resonance Spectroscopy", Vol. 1, Chapter 4. Pergamon Press, London, 1966.
2. M. M. Crutchfield, C. H. Dungan, J. H. Letcher, V. Mark and J. R. Van Wazer, In *Topics Phosphorus Chem.*, 1967, **5**, 19.
3. F. H. Allen and A. Pidcock, unpublished results.

4. A. Pidcock and C. R. Waterhouse, unpublished results.
5. J. G. Riess and J. R. Van Wazer, *J. Amer. Chem. Soc.*, 1966, **88**, 2341; *ibid.*, 1967, **89**, 851; *ibid.*, 1966, **88**, 2166.
6. J. G. Riess and J. R. Van Wazer, *Bull. Soc. chim. France*, 1966, 1846.
7. S. O. Grim and R. A. Ference, *Inorg. Nucl. Chem. Letters*, 1966, **2**, 205.
8. B. T. Heaton and A. Pidcock, *J. Organometal. Chem.*, 1968, **14**, 235.
9. F. K. Butcher, B. E. Deuters, W. Gerrard, E. F. Mooney, R. A. Rothenbury and H. A. Willis, *Spectrochim. Acta*, 1964, **20**, 759.
10. R. Schmutzler, *Adv. Fluorine Chem.*, 1965, **5**, 255.
11. M. A. Fleming, Ph.D. Dissertation, University of Michigan, 1963.
12. G. G. Barlow, J. F. Nixon and J. R. Swain, *J. Chem. Soc. A*, to be published.
13. B. Silver and Z. Luz, *J. Amer. Chem. Soc.*, 1961, **83**, 786.
14. W. McFarlane, *Chem. Comm.*, 1967, 58.
15. J. G. Verkade, R. W. King and C. W. Heitsch, *Inorg. Chem.*, 1964, **3**, 884.
16. A. D. Norman and R. Schaeffer, *J. Amer. Chem. Soc.*, 1966, **88**, 1143.
17. W. H. N. Vriezen and F. Jellinek, *Chem. Phys. Letters*, 1967, **1**, 284.
18. E. A. C. Lucken, K. Noack and D. F. Williams, *J. Chem. Soc. A*, 1967, 148.
19. R. W. King, T. J. Huttemann and J. G. Verkade, *Chem. Comm.*, 1965, 561.
20. S. O. Grim, W. McFarlane and D. A. Wheatland, *Inorg. Nucl. Chem. Letters*, 1966, **2**, 49.
21. S. O. Grim, D. A. Wheatland and W. McFarlane, *J. Amer. Chem. Soc.*, 1967, **89**, 5573.
22. S. O. Grim and D. A. Wheatland, *Inorg. Nucl. Chem. Letters*, 1968, **4**, 187.
23. A. Pidcock, R. E. Richards and L. M. Venanzi, *Proc. Chem. Soc.*, 1962, 184.
24. A. Pidcock, R. E. Richards and L. M. Venanzi, *J. Chem. Soc. A*, 1966, 1707.
25. L. M. Venanzi, *Chem. Brit.*, 1968, 162.
26. S. O. Grim, R. L. Keiter and W. McFarlane, *Inorg. Chem.*, 1967, **6**, 1133.
27. R. L. Keiter and S. O. Grim, *Chem. Comm.*, 1968, 521.
28. J. W. Emsley, J. Feeney and L. H. Sutcliffe, "High Resolution Nuclear Magnetic Resonance Spectroscopy", Chapter 9. Pergamon Press, Oxford, 1966.
29. J. A. Pople and D. P. Santry, *Mol. Phys.*, 1964, **8**, 1.
30. G. W. Smith, Research Publication GMR-444, General Motors Corporation, Warren, Michigan, U.S.A.
31. W. McFarlane, *J. Chem. Soc. A*, 1967, 1922.
32. A. Pidcock, unpublished calculations.
33. R. J. P. Williams, *Chem. Brit.*, 1968, 277.
34. R. Eisenberg and J. A. Ibers, *Inorg. Chem.*, 1965, **4**, 773.
35. G. G. Messmer and E. L. Amma, *Inorg. Chem.*, 1966, **5**, 1775.
36. G. G. Messmer, E. L. Amma and J. A. Ibers, *Inorg. Chem.*, 1967, **6**, 725.
37. Y. K. Syrkin, *Bull. Acad. Sci. U.S.S.R.*, *Classe sci. chim.*, 1948, 69. (See also ref. 25).
38. F. Basolo and R. G. Pearson, "Mechanisms of Inorganic Reactions", 2nd Ed., Chapter 5, Wiley, New York, 1967.
39. W. A. G. Graham, *Inorg. Chem.*, 1968, **7**, 315.
40. D. P. Craig, E. A. Magnusson, *J. Chem. Soc.*, 1956, 4895.
41. H. A. Bent, *Chem. Rev.*, 1961, **61**, 275.
42. W. Lang, Ph.D. Thesis, Technische Hochschule, Munich, 1966.
43. R. W. Rudolph and R. W. Parry, *J. Amer. Chem. Soc.*, 1967, **89**, 1621.
44. R. J. Goodfellow, *Chem. Comm.*, 1968, 114.
45. T. Johnson, R. M. Lynden-Bell and J. F. Nixon, unpublished results.

46. R. K. Harris, personal communication.
47. S. O. Grim, D. A. Wheatland and P. R. McAllister, *Inorg. Chem.*, 1968, **7**, 161.
48. A. Pidcock, *Chem. Comm.*, 1968, 92.
49. R. K. Harris, *Canad. J. Chem.*, 1964, **42**, 2275; *Inorg. Chem.*, 1966, **5**, 701.
50. P. R. Brookes and B. L. Shaw, *J. Chem. Soc. A*, 1967, 1079 and references therein.
51. J. G. Verkade, R. E. McCarley, D. G. Hendricker and R. W. King, *Inorg. Chem.*, 1965, **4**, 228.
52. D. G. Hendricker, R. E. McCarley, R. W. King and J. G. Verkade, *Inorg. Chem.*, 1966, **5**, 639.
53. J. F. Nixon and R. Schmutzler, *Spectrochim. Acta.* 1964, **20**, 1835.
54. J. F. Nixon, *J. Chem. Soc. A*, 1967, 1136.
55. C. G. Barlow and J. F. Nixon, *Inorg. Nucl. Chem. Letters*, 1966, **2**, 323 and unpublished results.
56. G. S. Reddy and R. Schmutzler, *Inorg. Chem.*, 1967, **6**, 823.
57. J. G. Verkade, personal communication.
58. W. McFarlane, R. M. Lynden-Bell, J. F. Nixon and J. Roberts, unpublished results.
59. A. V. Cunliffe, E. G. Finer, R. K. Harris and W. McFarlane, *Mol. Phys.*, 1967, **12**, 497.
60. S. L. Mannatt, D. D. Elleman, A. H. Cowley and A. B. Burg, *J. Amer. Chem. Soc.*, 1967, **89**, 4544.
61. J. F. Nixon, *J. Chem. Soc. A.*, in press.
62. R. M. Lynden-Bell and J. F. Nixon, paper in preparation.
63. F. Ogilvie, J. M. Jenkins, J. G. Verkade and R. J. Clark, 154th A.C.S. Meeting, Chicago, U.S.A., Paper 0.56.
64. R. M. Lynden-Bell, *Mol. Phys.*, 1968, **15**, 523.
65. R. M. Lynden-Bell and J. F. Nixon, unpublished results.
66. J. F. Nixon and M. D. Sexton, *J. Chem. Soc. A.*, in press.
67. J. N. Shoolery, *Discuss. Faraday Soc.*, 1955, **19**, 215.
68. E. O. Fischer, E. Lewis and R. J. J. Schneider, *Angew. Chem. (Int. Edn.)*, 1968, **7**, 136.
69. F. Klanberg and E. L. Muetterties, *J. Amer. Chem. Soc.*, 1968, **90**, 3296.
70. A. R. Cullingworth, A. Pidcock and J. D. Smith, *Chem. Comm.*, 1966, 89.
71. E. J. Boros, R. D. Compton and J. G. Verkade, *Inorg. Chem.*, 1968, **7**, 165.
72. J. F. Nixon, *J. Chem. Soc.*, 1965, 777.
73. K. J. Packer, *J. Chem. Soc.*, 1963, 960.
74. J. F. Nixon and J. R. Swain, unpublished results.
75. R. A. Y. Jones and A. R. Katritsky, *Angew. Chem. (Int. Edn. Engl.)*, 1962, **1**, 32.
76. E. Fluck, "Die Kernmagnetische Resonanz und Ihre Anwendung in der Anorganischen Chemie". Springer Verlag, Berlin, 1963.
77. J. A. Pople, W. C. Schneider and H. J. Bernstein, "High Resolution Nuclear Magnetic Resonance." McGraw Hill, New York, 1959; J. W. Emsley, J. Feeney and L. H. Sutcliffe, "High Resolution Nuclear Magnetic Resonance Spectroscopy", Vols. 1 and 2. Pergamon Press, Oxford, 1966.
78. N. F. Ramsey, *Phys. Rev.*, 1952, **86**, 243.
79. A. Saika and C. P. Slichter, *J. Chem. Phys.*, **22**, 26, 1954.
80. W. D. Knight, *Phys. Rev.*, 1949, **76**, 1259.
81. H. S. Gutowsky, D. W. McCall and C. P. Slichter, *J. Chem. Phys.*, 1953, **21**, 279.
82. W. C. Dickinson, *Phys. Rev.*, 1951, **81**, 717.

83. H. S. Gutowsky and D. W. McCall, *J. Chem. Phys.*, 1954, **22**, 162.
84. J. R. Van Wazer, C. F. Callis, J. N. Shoolery and R. C. Jones, *J. Amer. Chem. Soc.*, 1956, **78**, 5715.
85. L. C. D. Groenweghe, L. Maier and K. Moedritzer, *J. Phys. Chem.*, 1962, **66**, 901, and *J. Chem. Eng. Data*, 1962, **7**, 307.
86. S. O. Grim, W. McFarlane, E. F. Davidoff and T. J. Marks, *J. Phys. Chem.*, 1966, **70**, 581; S. O. Grim and W. McFarlane, *Nature*, 1965, **208**, 995.
87. N. Muller, P. C. Lauterbur and J. Goldenson, *J. Amer. Chem. Soc.*, 1956, **78**, 3557.
88. J. R. Parks, *J. Amer. Chem. Soc.*, 1957, **79**, 757.
89. H. S. Gutowsky and J. P. Larmann, *J. Amer. Chem. Soc.*, 1965, **87**, 3815.
90. J. H. Letcher and J. R. Van Wazer, *J. Chem. Phys.*, 1966, **44**, 815; *ibid.*, **45**, 2916; *ibid.*, 1966, **45**, 2926.
91. J. A. Pople, *Proc. Roy. Soc.*, 1957, **A239**, 541, 550.
92. M. Karplus and T. P. Das, *J. Chem. Phys.*, 1961, **34**, 1683.
93. C. J. Jameson and H. S. Gutowsky, *J. Chem. Phys.*, 1964, **40**, 1714.
94. A. C. Chapman, J. Homer, D. J. Mowthorpe and R. T. Jones, *Chem. Comm.*, 1965, 121.
95. L. S. Meriwether and J. R. Leto, *J. Amer. Chem. Soc.*, 1961, **83**, 3192.
96. S. I. Shupack and B. Wagner, *Chem. Comm.*, 1966, 547.
97. K. J. Coskran, R. D. Bertrand and J. G. Verkade, *J. Amer. Chem. Soc.*, 1967, **89**, 4535.
98. J. F. Nixon and R. Jefferson, unpublished results.
99. G. F. Svatos and E. E. Flagg, *Inorg. Chem.*, 1965, **4**, 422.
100. J. F. Nixon and M. D. Sexton, unpublished results.
101. T. Kruck and W. Lang, *Z. Anorg. Chem.*, 1968, **356**, 118.
102. J. G. Smith and D. T. Thompson, *J. Chem. Soc. A*, 1967, 1694.
103. C. G. Barlow, J. F. Nixon and M. Webster, *J. Chem. Soc. A*, 1968, 2216.
104. E. Fluck and R. Lorentz, *Z. Naturforsch.*, 1967, **22b**, 1095.
105. G. Jugie and J. P. Laurent, *Bull. Soc. chim. France*, 1968, 2010.
106. G. W. Parshall and F. N. Jones, *J. Amer. Chem. Soc.*, 1965, **87**, 5356.
107. R. Schmutzler, *Chem. Ber.*, 1965, **98**, 552.
108. J. G. Riess and J. R. Van Wazer, *J. Amer. Chem. Soc.*, 1966, **88**, 2339.
109. R. Centofani and R. W. Parry, *Inorg. Chem.*, 1968, **5**, 1005.
110. R. Schmutzler, *J. Chem. Soc.*, 1965, 5630.
111. M. Lenzi and R. Poilblanc, *Compt. rend.*, 1966, **263**, 674; R. Mathieu, M. Lenzi and R. Poilblanc, *ibid.*, 1968, **266**, 806; and personal communication.

AUTHOR INDEX

Numbers in parentheses are reference numbers and are included to assist in locating references when the author's names are not mentioned in the text. Numbers in *italics* refer to the page on which the reference is listed.

A

Abdel Rahman, M. M. A., 67(113), 68 (116), *81*

Abel, E. W., 26(196), *32*

Abeler, G., 236(60), *288*

Abragam, A., 301(2), 304(2), 339(2), *343*

Abraham, R. J., 16(128), 17(132), *30, 31,* 36(8), 54(69), 59(87), 62(87), 75 (155), 76(159), *78, 80, 82,* 89(19), 103, *121*

Adam, W., 173(68), *215*

Adams, R., 243, 251, *288*

Agahigian, H., 47(47), *79*, 259(151), 260 (151), 261(151), *290*

Ahluwalia, R., 43(30), *79*

Albano, E., 65(100), *81*

Albrecht, H. P., 47(51), *79*

Alger, T. D., 159, 172(63), 207(63), *214, 215*

Al-Jeboury, F. S., 53(66), *80*

Allen, F. H. 348(3), 351(3), 352(3), 354 (3), 367(3), 368(3), 369(3), 373(3), 374(3), 380(3), 411(3), 412(3), 415 (3), *419*

Allerhand, A., 15(123), 16(125), *30*, 142 (44), *151*

Allinger, N. L. 24(184), *32*, 42(25), *79*

Allingham, Y., 76(161), *82*

Allred, E. L., 20(153), *31*

Altman, J., 18(143), *31*

Altona, C., 17(133), *31*

Amma, E. L., 364(35, 36), *420*

Anderson, C. L., 20(153), *31*

Anderson, E., 318(21), *344*

Anderson, J. E., 20(152), *31*, 75(154), *82*, 101(70), 104(70), *122*

Anderson, W. A., 156(12), *213*, 342(43), *344*

Andrews, T. D., 264(158), 265(158), *290*

Anet, E. F. L., 62(95), 64(97, 98), *81*

Anet, F. A. L., 15, 23(172, 174), *30, 31, 32,* 71(130), *81,* 342(42), *344*

Anet, R., 209(194), *218*

Angyal, S. J., 42(25), 43(30), 48(55), 55 (70), *79, 80*

Anteunis, M., 10(84), *29*, 75, *82*

Aono, K., 12(99), *30*, 138(37), 139(37), 146(53), *151, 152*

Appleton, R. A., 106(99), *122*

ApSimon, J. W., 4(21, 23, 24), *28*, 97, *122*

Armitage, D. A., 26(196), *32*

Armstrong, D. R., 222, *286*

Arnaud, P., 114(132), *123*

Arnett, E. M., 14(108), *30*

Aruldhas, G., 202(176), *217*

Asaki, Y., 136(32), *151*

Ashbaugh, A. L., 103, *122*

Asher, J. D. M., 110(112), *123*

Atkins, P. W., 335, *344*

Attalla, A., 182(110), *216*

Ayres, D. C., 10(86), *29*

B

Baer, F., 5(36), *28*

Baer, H. H., 47(44, 50), 48(50), 69, *79*

Baggett, N., 50(56, 58), 51(56, 61, 62), 52(64), 53(62, 65–67), *79, 80*

Bailey, J. K., 109(104), *123*

Bair, T. I., 114, *123*

Baird, N. C., 158(23), *214*

Baker, B. R., 48(53), *79*

Baker, E. B., 174(71), *215*

Baker, K. M., 100, 101(68), 102, *122*

Baker, M. R., 127(9), *151*

Balasubramaniyan, P., 224(18), 231(43), 235(43), 271(18), 276(43), *287*

423

SUBJECT INDEX

The numbers in **bold** indicate pages on which the topic is discussed in detail.